Mathematical Models with Applications

Mathematics teachers across Texas have said they want a textbook for Mathematical Models with Applications that is at an appropriate level of rigor, has solid examples, and lots of problems. We have created a text that teachers say not only accomplishes these goals, but will also convince students they aren't just learning mathematics, they are learning useful information. This text and its resources are loaded with what you need to help your students be successful in learning the TEKS, preparing them for the TAKS test, Algebra 2, and their futures.

Highlights of *Mathematical Models with Applications*

- Full TEKS coverage
- Variety of activities for different learners:
  - Calculator lessons, Lab exercises, TAKS practice
- Problems in a variety of formats—graphical, numerical, symbolic:
  - TAKS practice workbook, Additional worksheets
- Teacher-friendly resources:
  - TAKS Workbook, Worksheets, Resources in print and on CD, PowerPoint® presentations, Test Bank

How do you coordinate these resources in a coherent way to effectively teach the TEKS, *and* prepare students for the TAKS test and Algebra 2? To answer that question, we have created the Planning Guide and the Pacing Guide.

Planning Guide

- At-a-glance look at TEKS, vocabulary, examples, exercises, and resources for each lesson.
- Example and exercise correlation so that if you break up a lesson, you will know which exercises can be assigned based on which examples were completed.
- Lab exercise correlation to show you when students will have the content base to complete a lab exercise, giving you the freedom to complete the lab at that point, or later in the chapter.
- Other resources are noted, and specify which lesson they complement, including TAKS practice, worksheets, calculator activities, PowerPoint presentations, and assessments.

Pacing Guide

- Suggests daily activities for navigating through chapters in traditional or block schedule.
- Includes assignment guides.
- Includes ideas for ways to use the resources: assessments, group activities, individual learning activities, writing activities, and presentations.

In addition to the text, we have developed a solid ancillary package to support both the teacher and the student:

For the Teacher

- *Teacher's Resource Binder*
  Additional lab activities for each chapter; a Test Bank with five tests per chapter and three final exams; worksheets to accompany each section; solutions to all problems in the text; and a graphing calculator quick reference guide.
- *ExamView® CD*
  Over 800 problems allow you to create your own tests and quizzes.
- *Teacher's Resource CD*
  An electronic version of the Teacher's Resource Binder, as well as PowerPoint lecture slides to accompany each lesson. All electronically available figures from the book are also provided as PowerPoint and JPEG files.

For the Student

- *Student's Workbook*
  Mid point and end-of-chapter practice tests that model the TAKS test.

The ***Mathematical Models with Applications*** text makes the course navigable—it is a small book without distractions, has high relevance to students' lives, and is presented in a non-threatening, accessible writing style. We believe this text will not only help your students learn mathematics, but also help them learn information that will be useful for the rest of their lives.

THOMSON

BROOKS/COLE

Mathematical Models with Applications

Daniel L. Timmons, Catherine W. Johnson, Sonya M. McCook

Acquisitions Editor: John-Paul Ramin

Assistant Editor: Katherine Cook

Editorial Assistant: Dianna Muhammad

Senior Marketing Manager: Tom Ziolkowski

Marketing Assistant: Jennifer Valasquez

Marketing Communications Manager: Darlene-Amidon Brent

Senior Project Manager, Editorial Production: Janet Hill

Senior Art Director: Vernon Boes

Senior Frontlist Buyer: Karen Hunt

Production Service: Sara Dovre Wudali, Buuji, Inc.

Text Designer: Kim Rokusek

Cover Designer: Lisa Delgado

Cover Images: Corbis

Cover Printer: Phoenix Color Corp

Composition: Interactive Composition Corporation

Interior Printer: Quebecor/Taunton

Printed in the United States of America

2 3 4 5 6 7 09 08 07 06

Thomson Higher Education
10 Davis Drive
Belmont, CA 94002-3098
USA

For more information about our products, contact us at:
Thomson Learning Academic Resource Center
1-800-423-0563

For permission to use material from this text or product, submit a request online at **http://www.thomsonrights.com**. Any additional questions about permissions can be submitted by email to **thomsonrights@thomson.com**.

Library of Congress Control Number: 2006922239

Student Edition ISBN 978-0-495-01781-3
Student Edition ISBN 0-495-01781-7

Instructor's Edition ISBN 978-0-495-11332-4
Instructor's Edition ISBN 0-495-11332-8

Supplementary Resources

Teacher's Resource Binder (TRB):
- Practice Worksheets
- Supplemental Lab Exercises
- Chapter Test (5 Forms, A–E)

Teacher's Resource CD-ROM
- PowerPoint Lesson Presentations
- All Teacher's Resource Binder resources

Student Workbook
- TAKS Mid-Chapter 1A
- TAKS Chapter 1B

ExamView CD-ROM

Exercise Correlation	Lesson-Specific Resources	Lab Exercises
	PowerPoint Presentation (CD-ROM)	Lab Exercise 1: What Money? p. 41 Lab Exercise 2: A Hen and a Half? p. 41
Definitions: #1–4 Example 3: #5–6, 11, 13 Example 4: #9–10, 12, 14 Example 5, 6: #7–8, 15–16 Example 7: #17–40	PowerPoint Presentation (CD-ROM) Calculator Mini-Lesson, p. 8 Calculator Mini-Lesson, p. 10 Worksheets, TRB	
Example 8: #1–2, 33–36 Example 9: #3–4, 7–14, 19–20, 37–40 Example 10: #5–6, 15–18, 41–50 Example 11: #21–32	PowerPoint Presentation (CD-ROM) Worksheet, TRB	
Example 12, 13: #1–16 Example 14: #17–22 Example 15, 16: #23–34	PowerPoint Presentation (CD-ROM) Worksheet, TRB TAKS Mid-Chapter 1A (Workbook)	Lab Exercise 5: Max It Out, p. 42 Lab Exercise 6: Batter Up, p. 43
Examples 17, 18: #1–10 Example 19: #11–18 Examples 20, 21: #19–28 Examples 22, 23: #29–45	PowerPoint Presentation (CD-ROM) Worksheet, TRB	
Definition: #1–20 Examples 24, 25: #27–28, 35–36 Example 26: #23–24 Example 27: #21, 22 Example 28: #25–26 Example 29: #29–34, 37	PowerPoint Presentation (CD-ROM) Worksheet, TRB	Lab Exercise 3: Our Solar System, p. 42 Lab Exercise 4: Our Growing Population, p. 42
Examples 30, 31: #1–14, 17–20, 26–40 Example 32: #15–16 Example 33: #21–22 Example 34: #23–24	PowerPoint Presentation (CD-ROM) Worksheet, TRB TAKS Chapter 1B (Workbook)	Supplemental Lab #1: Chop It Up, TRB Supplemental Lab #2: How Many Pets? TRB

Chapter 1—Pacing Guide: 45–50 minute classes

Day	Activities	Assignment Guide
1	Pre-Test (included in TRB)	
2	Lab Activity • Lab Exercise 1: What Money? pp. 41–42 Lesson 1-1: Mathematical Models	Lab Exercise 2: A Hen and a Half? pp. 41–42
3	Lesson 1-2: Real Numbers and Mathematical Operations Calculator Activity • Calculator Mini-Lessons, pp. 8, 10	#2–40 even, pp. 10–11
4	Lesson 1-3: Solving Linear Equations • Examples 8-10	#1–20, p. 16
5	Lesson 1-3: Solving Linear Equations • Example 11, Table 1-2	#21–40, p. 16
6	Lab Activity • Lab Exercise 5: Max It Out, pp. 42–43	#41–50, p. 16
7	Lesson 1-4: Formulas	#1–25, pp. 19–20
8	Lab Activity • Lab Exercise 6: Batter Up, p. 43	#26–34, pp. 19–20, prepare lab report
9	Mid-Chapter Quiz: TAKS Mid-Chapter 1A (Workbook) Lesson 1-5: Ratio and Proportion	#2–44 even, pp. 24–25
10	Lab Activity • Lab Exercise 3, parts a–d: Our Solar System, p. 42	#1–43 odd, pp. 24–25
11	Lesson 1-6: Percents	#2–40 even, pp. 30–31
12	Lab Activity • Lab Exercise 4: Our Growing Population, p. 42	Finish Lab Exercise 3, part e, #1–39 odd, pp. 30–31
13	Lesson 1-7: Word Problem Strategies • Examples 30–31	#1–14, pp. 35–36
14	Lesson 1-7: Word Problem Strategies • Examples 32–34	#15–40, pp. 36–37
15	Lab Activities (choose one, both, or split class) • Supplemental Lab #1: Chop It Up, TRB • Supplemental Lab #2: How Many Pets?, TRB	Prepare lab presentation
16	Lab Presentations Chapter Review	#1–40, pp. 38–39
17	TAKS Chapter 1B (Workbook) in groups	#41–55, pp. 39–40
18	Chapter Test	

Chapter 1—Pacing Guide: Block Scheduling

Day	Activities	Assignment Guide
1	Pre-Test (included in TRB) Lab Activity • Lab Exercise 1: What Money? pp. 41–42 Lesson 1-1: Mathematical Models	Lab Exercise 2: A Hen and a Half? pp. 41–42
2	Lesson 1-2: Real Numbers and Mathematical Operations • Calculator Mini-Lessons, pp. 8, 10	#1–40, p. 10–11
3	Lesson 1-3: Solving Linear Equations	#2–48 even, p. 16
4	Lab Activity • Lab Exercise 5: Max It Out, pp. 42–43 Lesson 1-4: Formulas	#2–34 even, pp. 19–20
5	Mid-Chapter Quiz: TAKS Mid-Chapter 1A (Workbook) Lab Activity (as students finish quiz) • Lab Exercise 6: Batter Up, p. 43 Lesson 1-5: Ratio and Proportion	#2–44 even, pp. 24–25
6	Lesson 1-6: Percents Lab Activity • Lab Exercise 3: Our Solar System, p. 42	#1–40, pp. 30–31
7	Lesson 1-7: Word Problem Strategies	#2–40 even, pp. 35–37
8	Lab Activities (choose one or more, or split class) • Lab Exercise 4: Our Growing Population, p. 42 • Supplemental Lab #1: Chop It Up, TRB • Supplemental Lab #2: How Many Pets? TRB	#1–39 odd, pp. 35–37; prepare lab presentations
9	Lab presentations TAKS Chapter 1B (Workbook) in groups	#1–40, pp. 38–39
10	Chapter Review	#41–55, pp. 39–40
11	Chapter Test Introduction to Chapter 2: • Chapter 2 Supplemental Lab #1: Toto, Are We Still in Kansas? TRB	

Chapter 2—Graphing

Graphs can help us visualize data and their behavior. When ordered-pair solutions of a linear equation are graphed, the result is a straight line. Its slope and direction can be meaningful in interpreting data or predicting future outcomes. In this chapter, we review the topics of graphing lines, interpreting slope, and graphing linear inequalities. We will also use the slope of a given line and a point on that line to write its linear equation.

Chpt/Sec	Lessons	TEKS	Vocabulary
2-1	Rectangular Coordinate System	01.B, 02.A, 02.C	Rectangular coordinate system, origin, quadrants, coordinates, x-coordinate, y-coordinate, p. 46 linear equation, general form, solutions, p. 48
2-2	Graphing Linear Equations	01.B, 02.A, 02.C, 09.A	y-intercept, x-intercept, p. 51 horizontal line, vertical line, p. 53
2-3	Slope	01.B, 02.B, 02.C, 09.A	slope, p. 56 slope-intercept form, p. 61 parallel lines, p. 63 perpendicular lines, p. 64
2-4	Writing Equations of Lines	01.B, 02.B, 02.C, 09.A	
2-5	Linear Inequalities	01.B	linear inequality, p. 73 boundary line, p. 74

Supplementary Resources

Teacher's Resource Binder (TRB):
- Practice Worksheets
- Supplemental Lab Exercises
- Chapter Test (5 Forms, A–E)

Teacher's Resource CD-ROM
- PowerPoint Lesson Presentations
- All Teacher's Resource Binder resources

Student Workbook
- TAKS Mid-Chapter 2A
- TAKS Chapter 2B

ExamView CD-ROM

Exercise Correlation	Lesson-Specific Resources	Lab Exercises
Example 1: #1–12 Example 2: #13–26 Example 3: #27–29 Examples 4, 5: #30–39	PowerPoint Presentation (CD-ROM) Worksheet, TRB	Supplemental Lab #1: Toto, Are We Still in Kansas? TRB
Example 6: #5–12 Example 7: #1–2, 13–22, 27–34, 39–40 Example 8: #3, 23–26 Example 9: #4, #37–38 Example 10: #35–36	PowerPoint Presentation (CD-ROM) Worksheet, TRB	Lab Exercise 2: Linear Equations Practice Activity, p. 80 Lab Exercise 4: Recycling, p. 83 Lab Exercise 5: Mmm, Mmm, Good—Prune Juice, pp. 83–84
Examples 11–15: #1–12 Examples 16–19: #13–25 Example 20: #26–29 Example 21: #31–35 Example 22: #36–40	PowerPoint Presentation (CD-ROM) Worksheet, TRB TAKS Mid-Chapter 2A (Workbook)	Lab Exercise 1: Slope Activity, p. 79
Example 23: #1–2 Example 24: #3–10, 39–40 Example 25: #11–22, 37–38 Example 26: #23–24 Example 27: #25–36	PowerPoint Presentation (CD-ROM) Worksheet, TRB	Lab Exercise 3: Linear Equations of the Graphing Calculator, pp. 80–83 Supplemental Lab #2: Programmin' for Dollars, TRB
Example 28–29: #1-30	PowerPoint Presentation (CD-ROM) Worksheet, TRB TAKS Chapter 2B (Workbook)	

Chapter 2—Pacing Guide: 45–50 minute classes

Day	Activities	Assignment Guide
1	Introduction Lab Activity • Supplemental Lab #1: Toto, Are We Still in Kansas? TRB	
2	Lesson 2-1: Rectangular Coordinate System	#1–40, p. 50
3	Lesson 2-2: Graphing Linear Equations	#1–39 odd, p. 55
4	Lab Activity • Lab Exercise 4: Recycling, p. 83	#2–40 even, p. 55
5	Lesson 2-3: Slope • Examples 11–15	#1–12, p. 66
6	Lab Activity • Lab Exercise 1: Slope Activity, pp. 79–80	Finish lab report
7	Lesson 2-3: Slope • Examples 16–19	#13–25, p. 67
8	Lesson 2-3: Slope • Examples 20–22	#26–40, p. 67
9	Mid-Chapter Quiz: TAKS Chapter 2A (Workbook) Lesson 2-4: Writing Equations of Lines • Examples 23–24	#1–10, p. 72
10	Lesson 2-4: Writing Equations of Lines • Examples 25–26	#11–24, p. 72
11	Lesson 2-4: Writing Equations of Lines • Example 27	#25–40, pp. 72–73
12	Lab Activity • Lab Exercise 3: Linear Equations on the Graphing Calculator, pp. 80–83	Supplemental Lab #2: Programmin' for Dollars, TRB
13	Lesson 2-5: Linear Inequalities	#2–30 even, pp. 76–77
14	Lab Activity • Lab Exercise 2: Linear Equations Practice Activity, p. 80 • Lab Exercise 5: Mmm, Mmm, Good—Prune Juice, pp. 83–84	#1–29 odd, pp. 76–77, prepare lab presentations
15	Lab presentations Chapter Review	#1–29 odd, p. 78
16	TAKS Chapter 2B (Workbook)	#2–30 even, p. 78
17	Chapter Test	

Chapter 2—Pacing Guide: Block Scheduling

Day	Activities	Assignment Guide
1	Introduction Lab Activity Discussion • Supplemental Lab #1: Toto, Are We Still in Kansas? TRB Lesson 2-1: Rectangular Coordinate System	#1–40, p. 50
2	Lesson 2-2: Graphing Linear Equations Lab Activity • Lab Exercise 4: Recycling, p. 83	#1–4, 6–40 even, p. 55
3	Lesson 2-3: Slope • Examples 11–15 Lab Activity • Lab Exercise 1: Slope Activity, pp. 79–80	#1–12, p. 66
4	Lesson 2-3: Slope • Examples 16-22	#13–40, p. 67
5	Mid-Chapter Quiz: TAKS Chapter 2A (Workbook) Lesson 2-4: Writing Equations of Lines	#1–24, p. 72
6	Lab Activity (choose one, both, or split class) • Lab Exercise 3: Linear Equations on the Graphing Calculator, pp. 80–83 • Supplemental Lab #2: Programmin' for Dollars, TRB	#25–40, pp. 72–73
7	Lesson 2-5: Linear Inequalities Lab Activity (choose one, both, or split class) • Lab Exercise 2: Linear Equations Practice Activity, p. 80 • Lab Exercise 5: Mmm, Mmm, Good—Prune Juice, pp. 83–84	#2–30 even, pp. 76–77
8	Finish Labs, prepare lab presentations TAKS Chapter 2B (Workbook)	#1–29 odd, pp. 76–77
9	Chapter Review Lab presentations	#1–30, p. 78
10	Chapter Test Introduction to Chapter 3 • Chapter 3, Lab Exercise 1: Tax Bite 2003, p. 131	

Chapter 3—Functions

There are many quantities in everyday life that are related to one another. In this chapter, we will define and discuss a special kind of relationship between two quantities, called a *function*. We will interpret graphs of functions and examine both linear and non-linear functions. We will also look at application problems involving direct, inverse, and joint variation.

Chpt/Sec	Lessons	TEKS	Vocabulary
3-1	Functions	01.B, 02.A, 02.B	function, independent variable, dependent variable, p. 86 relation, p. 87 domain, range, p. 91 models, p. 92
3-2	Using Function Notation	01.A, 01.B, 01.C, 02.A, 02.B	function notation, p. 96
3-3	Linear Functions	01.B, 05.A, 06.B, 08.C	linear function, p. 102
3-4	Direct and Inverse Variation	01.B, 02.B, 05.A, 08.C	direct variation, directly proportional, varies directly, constant of variation, constant of proportionality, p. 110 inverse variation, p. 111 joint variation, combined variation, p. 112
3-5	Nonlinear Functions	01.B, 02.D	quadratic function, p. 117 roots, p. 119 power function, p. 122 exponential function, p. 123

Supplementary Resources

Teacher's Resource Binder (TRB):
- Practice Worksheets
- Supplemental Lab Exercises
- Chapter Test (5 Forms, A–E)

Teacher's Resource CD-ROM
- PowerPoint Lesson Presentations
- All Teacher's Resource Binder resources

Student Workbook
- TAKS Mid-Chapter 3A
- TAKS Chapter 3B

ExamView CD-ROM

Exercise Correlation	Lesson-Specific Resources	Lab Exercises
Examples 1–2: #15–19 Example 3: #1, 3–4, 7–14, 21–29 Example 4: #2, 5, 6, 20, 30	PowerPoint Presentation (CD-ROM) Worksheet, TRB	Lab Exercise 1: Tax Bite 2003, p. 131 Lab Exercise 5: Name That Function!, p. 133 Lab Exercise 6: Do You Want Pizza for Lunch?, p. 134 Supplemental Lab #1: Recreation, TRB
Examples 5–7: #5–10 Example 8, 9: #1–4 Example 10: #11–22 Example 11: #23–26 Example 12: #27–30	PowerPoint Presentation (CD-ROM) Worksheet, TRB	
Example 13–15: #1–8, 13–16, 19–20 Example 16: #9–12, 17–18	PowerPoint Presentation (CD-ROM) Worksheet, TRB TAKS Mid-Chapter 3A (Workbook)	Lab Exercise 2: The Growth of Burger King, pp. 131–132 Lab Exercise 3: Using a Graphing Calculator for Linear Equations, pp. 132–133
Examples 17–19: #1–6 Example 20: #7–14 Example 21: #15–24 Examples 22–23: #25–40	PowerPoint Presentation (CD-ROM) Worksheet, TRB	Supplemental Activity #2: Hooke's Law, TRB Supplemental Lab #3: Let's Go Surfing, TRB
Example 24–26: #1–6 Example 27: #17–20 Example 28: #7–10, 21–22 Example 29: #11–16 Example 30: #23–24	Calculator Mini-Lesson, p. 119 PowerPoint Presentation (CD-ROM) Worksheet, TRB TAKS Chapter 3B (Workbook)	Lab Exercise 4:Rebound Height and Variation, p. 133 Lab Exercise 8: Patterns in Exponential Functions, p. 136 Lab Exercise 7: Transformations of Nonlinear Functions, pp. 134–136

Chapter 3—Pacing Guide: 45–50 minute classes

Day	Activities	Assignment Guide
1	Introduction Lab Activity • Lab Exercise 1: Tax Bite 2003, p. 131	
2	Lesson 3-1: Functions	#1–30, pp. 92–95
3	Lab Activity (choose one, both, or split class) • Lab Exercise 5: Name That Function, p. 133 • Supplemental Lab #1: Recreation, TRB	Finish lab/complete other lab
4	Lesson 3-2: Using Function Notation • Examples 5–9	#1–10, p. 100
5	Lesson 3-2: Using Function Notation • Examples 10–12	#11–30, pp. 100–102
6	Lesson 3-3: Linear Functions • Examples 13–15	#1–8, 13–16, 19–20, pp. 107–109
7	Lesson 3-3: Linear Functions • Example 16 Lab Activity • Lab Exercise 3: Using a Graphing Calculator for Linear Functions, pp. 132–133	#9–12, 17–18, pp. 108–109
8	Mid-Chapter Quiz: TAKS Chapter 3A (Workbook) Lesson 3-4: Direct and Inverse Variation • Examples 17–20	#1–14, pp. 115–116
9	Lesson 3-4: Direct and Inverse Variation • Examples 21–23	#15–40, pp. 116–117
10	Lab Activity • Supplemental Activity #2: Hooke's Law, TRB	
11	Lesson 3-5: Nonlinear Functions • Examples 24–26 • Calculator Mini-Lesson, p. 119	#1–6, p. 125
12	Lab Activity • Lab Exercise 7: Transformations of Nonlinear Functions, pp. 134–136	
13	Lesson 3-5: Nonlinear Functions • Examples 27–30	#7–19, pp. 125–126
14	Lab Activity • Lab Exercise 8: Patterns in Exponential Functions, p. 136	
15	Lab Activity • Lab Exercise 4: Rebound Height and Variation, p. 133	#20–24, p. 126
16	Chapter Review TAKS Chapter 3B (Workbook)	#1–40, pp. 127–129
17	Chapter Test	
18	Transition to Chapter 4: • Lab Exercise 2: The Growth of Burger King, pp. 131–132	Finish Lab Exercise 2

Chapter 3—Pacing Guide: Block Scheduling

Day	Activities	Assignment Guide
1	Introduction Lab Activity Discussion • Lab Exercise 1: Tax Bite 2003, p. 131 Lesson 3-1: Functions Lab Activity • Supplemental Lab #1: Recreation	#2–30 even, pp. 92–95
2	Lesson 3-2: Using Function Notation Lab Activity • Lab Exercise 5: Name That Function, p. 133	#2–30 even, pp. 100–102
3	Lesson 3-3: Linear Functions Lab Activity • Lab Exercise 3: Using a Graphing Calculator for Linear Functions, pp. 132–133	#2–20 even, pp. 107–109
4	Mid-Chapter Quiz: TAKS Chapter 3A (Workbook) Lesson 3-4: Direct and Inverse Variation	#1–20, pp. 115–117
5	Lab Activity • Supplemental Activity #2: Hooke's Law	#20–40, pp. 115–117
6	Lesson 3-5: Nonlinear Functions • Calculator Mini-Lesson, p. 119	#1–12, pp. 125–126
7	Lab Activity • Lab Exercise 7: Transformations of Nonlinear Functions, p. 134	#13–24, pp. 125–126
8	Lab Activities: • Lab Exercise 4: Rebound Height and Variation, p. 133 • Lab Exercise 8: Patterns in Exponential Functions, p. 136	Prepare lab presentations
9	Lab presentations Chapter Review TAKS Chapter 3B (Workbook)	#1–40, pp. 127–129
10	Chapter Test Transition to Chapter 4: • Lab Exercise 2: The Growth of Burger King, pp. 131–132	Finish Lab Exercise 2

Chapter 4—Mathematical Models in Personal Finance

As we have seen in previous chapters, a function relates two variables to each other. A rule or relationship exists between two sets of data that connects values in one set with values in the other set. Many times, this rule is in the form of an algebraic equation or formula also known as a mathematical model. In this chapter, we will look at various mathematical models in making decisions about personal finances. We will examine options for purchasing a home, purchasing an automobile, investments, and insurance.

Chpt/Sec	Lessons	TEKS	Vocabulary
4-1	Mathematical Models in the Business World	01.B, 02.A	retail sales tax, p. 138 depreciation, straight-line method of depreciation, residual value, p. 139 markup, p. 141
4-2	Mathematical Models in Personal Income	01.B, 05.A, 05.B	straight commission, p. 144
4-3	Mathematical Models in Banking	01.B, 05.A, 05.B, 05.C, 06.B, 07.A	interest, principal, rate, simple interest, maturity value, p. 152 compound interest, p. 154 Banker's rule, ordinary interest, p. 155 continuous compounding, p. 159
4-4	Mathematical Models in Consumer Credit	01.B, 05.A, 05.C, 06.A, 06.B, 07.A, 08.A	installment buying, closed-end credit, open-end credit, p. 161 unpaid balance method, average daily balance method, p. 162 Truth-in-Lending Act, annual percentage rate (APR), p. 163
4-5	Mathematical Models in Purchasing an Automobile	01.B, 05.A, 06.A, 06.B, 07.A	Lease, p. 170
4-6	Mathematical Models in Purchasing a Home	01.B, 02.D, 05.A, 06.A, 06.B, 07.A, 08.A, 08.B	mortgage, closing, closing costs, p. 175 amortization table, p. 176 fixed-rate mortgage, p. 178 adjustable-rate mortgages, p. 179
4-7	Mathematical Models in Insurance Options and Annuities	01.B, 02.D, 06.A, 08.A, 08.B	premium, insurance policy, face value, insurer, underwriter, insured, policy holder, indemnity, p. 182 liability insurance, p. 183 uninsured motorist insurance, p. 185
4-8	Mathematical Models in Stocks, Mutual Funds, and Bonds	01.C, 06.C	stock, share, shareholder, p. 189 dividends, p. 190 mutual fund, bonds, face value, p. 191

Supplementary Resources

Teacher's Resource Binder (TRB):
- Practice Worksheets
- Supplemental Lab Exercises
- Chapter Test (5 Forms, A–E)

Teacher's Resource CD-ROM
- PowerPoint Lesson Presentations
- All Teacher's Resource Binder resources

Student Workbook
- TAKS Mid-Chapter 4A
- TAKS Chapter 4B

ExamView CD-ROM

Exercise Correlation	Lesson-Specific Resources	Lab Exercises
Example 1: #1–4 Example 2: #5–8 Example 3: #9–14 Example 4: #15–26 Example 5: #27–30	PowerPoint Presentation (CD-ROM) Worksheet, TRB	Lab Exercise 2: Depreciation, p. 199
Example 6: #1–14, 21–22 Example 7: #15–20 Example 8: #23–28	PowerPoint Presentation (CD-ROM) Worksheet, TRB	Lab Exercise 3: Phone 'Em Up, p. 200
Examples 9–10: #1–8, 13–16 Example 11: #9–12 Examples 12–14: #17–26 Example 15: #27–30	PowerPoint Presentation (CD-ROM) Calculator Mini-Lesson, p. 157 Worksheet, TRB	Lab Exercise 1: Saving for College Expenses, p. 199
Example 16: #1–10 Example 17: #11–16 Example 18: #17–24 Example 19: #25–30	PowerPoint Presentation (CD-ROM) Worksheet, TRB TAKS Mid-Chapter 4A (Workbook)	Lab Exercise 4: Purchasing Furniture, p. 200
Example 20: #7–12 Example 21: #1–2, 13–26 Example 22: #27–30 Examples 23–24: #3–6, 31–36	PowerPoint Presentation (CD-ROM) Worksheet, TRB	
Example 25: #1–3, 6–17 Example 26: #30–35 Example 27: #5, 40–41 Examples 28–29: #4, 18–29, 36–39	PowerPoint Presentation (CD-ROM) Worksheet, TRB	
Examples 30–31: #1–7, 10–15, 22, 24 Examples 32–33: #8–9, 16–21, 23, 25	PowerPoint Presentation (CD-ROM) Worksheet, TRB	
Example 34: #1–8 Example 35: #13–16 Example 36: #9–12, 17–20	PowerPoint Presentation (CD-ROM) Worksheet, TRB TAKS Chapter 4B (Workbook)	Lab Exercise 5: Creating a Stock Portfolio, p. 202

Chapter 4—Pacing Guide: 45–50 minute classes

Day	Activities	Assignment Guide
1	Lesson 4-1: Mathematical Models in the Business World • Examples 1–3 Lab Exercise 2: Depreciation, p. 199	#1–14, pp. 142–143
2	Lesson 4-1: Mathematical Models in the Business World • Examples 4–5	#15–30, pp. 143–144
3	Lesson 4-2: Mathematical Models in Personal Income	#1–28, pp. 149–151
4	Lab Exercise 3: Phone 'Em Up, p. 200 Lesson 4-3: Mathematical Models in Banking • Examples 9–11	#1–16, pp. 160
5	Lesson 4-3: Mathematical Models in Banking • Examples 12–15 • Calculator Mini-Lesson, p. 157	#17–30, pp. 160–161
6	Lab Activity • Lab Exercise 1: Saving Money for College, p. 199 Lesson 4-4: Mathematical Models in Consumer Credit • Examples 16–17	#1–16, pp. 165–167
7	Lesson 4-4: Mathematical Models in Consumer Credit • Examples 18–19	#17–30, pp. 165–167
8	Mid-Chapter Quiz: TAKS 4A (Workbook) Lab Activity • Lab Exercise 4: Purchasing Furniture, p. 200	Finish lab exercise
9	Lesson 4-5: Mathematical Models in Purchasing an Automobile • Examples 20–22	#1–2, 7–30, pp. 173–174
10	Lesson 4-5: Mathematical Models in Purchasing an Automobile • Examples 23–24	#3–6, 31–36, pp. 173–174
11	Lesson 4-6: Mathematical Models in Purchasing a Home • Examples 25–27	#1–3,5–17, 30–35, pp. 180–181
12	Lesson 4-6: Mathematical Models in Purchasing a Home • Examples 28–29	#4, 18–29, 36–41, pp. 180–182
13	Lesson 4-7: Mathematical Models in Insurance Options and Annuities	#1–25, pp. 187–188
14	Lesson 4-8: Mathematical Models in Stocks, Mutual Funds, and Bonds	#1–20, pp. 193–194
15	Chapter Review	#1–37, pp. 196–197
16	TAKS 4B (Workbook) Lab Activity preview and get students organized • Lab Exercise 5: Creating a Stock Portfolio, p. 202	
17	Chapter Test	

Chapter 4—Pacing Guide: Block Scheduling

Day	Activities	Assignment Guide
1	Lesson 4-1 Lab Exercise 2: Depreciation, p. 199	#2–30 even, pp. 142–144
2	Lesson 4-2: Mathematical Models in Personal Income Lab Activity • Lab Exercise 3: Phone 'Em Up, p. 200	#2–28 even, pp. 149–151
3	Lesson 4-3: Mathematical Models in Banking • Calculator Mini-Lesson, p. 157 Lab Activity • Lab Exercise 1: Saving Money for College, p. 199	#2–30 even, pp. 160–161
4	Lesson 4-4: Mathematical Models in Consumer Credit	#2–30 even, pp. 165–167
5	Mid-Chapter Quiz: TAKS 4A (Workbook) Lab Activity • Lab Exercise 4: Purchasing Furniture, p. 200	#1–29 odd, pp. 165–167, finish lab exercise
6	Lesson 4-5: Mathematical Models in Purchasing an Automobile	#1–6, 8–30 even, 31–33, pp. 173–174
7	Lesson 4-6: Mathematical Models in Purchasing a Home	#1–5, 6–40 even, 41, pp. 180–182
8	Lesson 4-7: Mathematical Models in Insurance Options and Annuities	#1–25, pp. 187–188
9	Lesson 4-8: Mathematical Models in Stocks, Mutual Funds, and Bonds	#1–20, pp. 193–194
10	Chapter Review Lab Activity preview and get students organized: • Lab Exercise 5: Creating a Stock Portfolio, p. 202	#1–37, pp. 196–197
11	Chapter Test TAKS Chapter 4B (Workbook)	

Chapter 5—Systems of Equations

Some problems or situations involve the interaction of two or more variables. Business profit, for example, is based on the cost of production and the income from selling a product. A break-even point can be determined using a system of equations so that the business will be sure to make a profit. Several methods for solving systems of equations such as these will be explored in this chapter.

Chpt/Sec	Lessons	TEKS	Vocabulary
5-1	Solving Systems by Graphing	01.B, 02.A, 02.C, 06.B	system of equations, solutions, p. 204 consistent, inconsistent, dependent, p. 206
5-2	Solving Systems Algebraically	01.B, 06.B	substitution, linear combination, p. 210 dependent equations, infinitely many solutions, p. 215
5-3	Solving Systems with Cramer's Rule	06.B	Cramer's rule, determinant, elements, p. 217
5-4	Applications of Linear Systems	07.B	supply, demand, equilibrium point p. 222 break-even analysis, p. 223
5-5	Systems of Nonlinear Functions	01.B, 01.C, 02.A, 02.C, 07.B, 07.C	nonlinear system of equations, p. 226

Chapter 5—Pacing Guide: 45–50 minute classes

Day	Activities	Assignment Guide
1	Lesson 5-1: Solving Systems by Graphing	#1–31 odd, pp. 209–210
2	Lab Activity • Lab Exercise 1: Which Salary Option? p. 233 • Lab Exercise 3: Applying to Medical School, p. 234	#2–32 even, pp. 209–210
3	Lesson 5-2: Solving Systems Algebraically	#1–35 odd, p. 216
4	Lab Activity (repeat using algebraic solutions, compare) • Lab Exercise 1: Which Salary Option? p. 233 • Lab Exercise 3: Applying to Medical School, p. 234	#2–36 even, p. 216
5	Lesson 5-3: Solving Systems with Cramer's Rule	#1–29 odd, pp. 219–220
6	Lab Activity • Supplemental Lab #2: Matrix Practice, TRB Mid-chapter Quiz: TAKS 5A (Workbook)	#2–30 even, pp. 219–220
7	Lesson 5-4: Applications of Linear Systems	#1–29 odd, pp. 224–226
8	Lab Activity (choose one or both) • Supplemental Lab #3: Salt Water, TRB • Supplemental Lab #4: It's the Law (Of Supply and Demand), TRB	#2–30 even, pp. 224–226
9	Lesson 5-5: Systems of Nonlinear Functions	#2–22 even, pp. 229–230
10	Lab Activity • Supplemental Lab #1: Let's Go Buy a House, TRB	Prepare lab report/presentation
11	Lab Presentations TAKS Chapter 5B (Workbook)	#1–21 odd (Lesson 5–5) pp. 229–230
12	Chapter Review	#1–35, pp. 231–232
13	Chapter Test	

Supplementary Resources

Teacher's Resource Binder (TRB):
- Practice Worksheets
- Supplemental Lab Exercises
- Chapter Test (5 Forms, A– E)

Teacher's Suite CD-ROM
- PowerPoint Lesson Presentations
- All Teacher's Resource Binder resources
- Solutions

Student Workbook
- TAKS Mid-Chapter 5A
- TAKS Chapter 5B

ExamView CD-ROM

Exercise Correlation	Lesson-Specific Resources	Lab Exercises
Examples 1, 3–4: #7–24 Example 2: #1–6 Example 5: #26–31	PowerPoint Presentation (CD-ROM) Worksheet, TRB	Lab Exercise 3: Applying to Medical School, p. 234 Lab Exercise 1: Which Salary Option? p. 233
Examples 6–7: #1–5 Examples 8–9: #7–11, 14–15, 17–22, 24–36 Examples 10–11: #6, 12, 13, 16, 23	PowerPoint Presentation (CD-ROM) Worksheet, TRB	
Example 12: #1–6 Examples 13–14: #7–30	PowerPoint Presentation (CD-ROM) Worksheet, TRB TAKS Mid-Chapter 5A (Workbook)	Supplemental Lab #1: Let's Go Buy a House, TRB Supplemental Lab #2: Matrix Practice, TRB
Example 15: #3–4, 7, 24 Example 16: #1–2, 9–10, 18, 26–27 Example 17: #5–6, 14 Example 18: #20–21 General exercises: 8, 11–13, 15–17, 19, 22–23, 25	PowerPoint Presentation (CD-ROM) Worksheet, TRB	Lab Exercise 2: Catering Business, p. 233 Supplemental Lab #3: Salt Water, TRB Supplemental Lab #4: It's the Law (Of Supply and Demand), TRB
Example 19–20: #1–12 Example 21: #13-22	PowerPoint Presentation (CD-ROM) Worksheet, TRB TAKS Chapter 5B Workbook	

Chapter 5—Pacing Guide: Block Scheduling

Day	Activities	Assignment Guide
1	Lesson 5-1: Solving Systems by Graphing Lab Activity • Lab Exercise 3: Applying to Medical School, p. 234	#2–32 even, pp. 209–210
2	Lesson 5-2: Solving Systems Algebraically Lab Activity • Lab Exercise 1: Which Salary Option? p. 233	#2–36 odd, p. 216
3	Lesson 5-3: Solving Systems with Cramer's Rule Lab Activity • Supplemental Lab #2: Matrix Practice, TRB	#1–29 odd, pp. 219–220
4	Mid-Chapter Quiz: TAKS 5A (Workbook) Lesson 5-4: Applications of Linear Systems	#1–29 odd, pp. 224–226
5	Lab Activity (choose one or both) • Supplemental Lab#3: Salt Water, TRB • Supplemental Lab #4: It's the Law (Of Supply and Demand), TRB	#2–30 even, pp. 224–226
6	Lesson 5-5: Systems of Nonlinear Functions Lab Activity • Supplemental Lab #1: Let's Go Buy a House, TRB	#2–20 even, pp. 229–230
7	TAKS Chapter 5B (Workbook) Chapter Review	#1–35, pp. 231–232
8	Chapter Test Introduction to Chapter 6: (choose one, both, or split class) • Supplemental Activity #1: Pair 'Em Up, TRB • Supplemental Activity #2: Flip 'Em Over, TRB	

Chapter 6—Probability Models

The first formal theories of probability were proposed by Blaise Pascal and Pierre Fermat from France. Their theories applied primarily to games of chance. However, in our time, many things in business, the sciences, and other areas are described in terms of probabilities. This chapter will give a brief introduction to the laws of probability and how they are used to assist in decision making.

Chpt/Sec	Lessons	TEKS	Vocabulary
6-1	What Is Probability?	03.C, 04.A, 04.B, 07.C	probability, random, experiment, outcomes, event, p. 236 empirical probability, theoretical probability, p. 237 law of large numbers, conditional probability, p. 238
6-2	Theoretical Probability	03.C, 04.A, 04.B, 07.C	equally likely outcomes, sample space, p. 242 laws of probability, p. 244
6-3	Odds	07.C	odds, p. 249
6-4	Counting Principle and Tree Diagrams		counting principle, p. 252 tree diagram, p. 253
6-5	Or and And Problems		mutually exclusive events, independent events, p. 257 addition rule, pp. 257–258 multiplication rule, p 260
6-6	Permutations and Combinations		factorial, p. 263 permutation, combination, p. 265
6-7	Applied Probability Problems	01.C	

Supplementary Resources

Teacher's Resource Binder (TRB):
- Practice Worksheets
- Supplemental Lab Exercises
- Chapter Test (5 Forms, A–E)

Teacher's Resource CD-ROM
- PowerPoint Lesson Presentations
- All Teacher's Resource Binder resources

Student Workbook
- TAKS Mid-Chapter 6A
- TAKS Chapter 6B

ExamView CD-ROM

Exercise Correlation	Lesson-Specific Resources	Lab Exercises
Examples 1–2: #1–17 Example 3: #18–25	PowerPoint Presentation (CD-ROM) Worksheet, TRB	Lab Exercise 1: A Simple Survey, p. 276 Lab Exercise 3: A "Tacky" Lab, p. 276 Lab Exercise 5: Walk On By, p. 277 Supplemental Lab #1: Pair 'Em Up, TRB Supplemental Lab #2: Flip 'Em Over, TRB
Examples 4–6: #1–11, 22–27, 40–44 Examples 7–8: #13–21, 31–39, 45–48 Example 9: #12, 28–30	PowerPoint Presentation (CD-ROM) Worksheet, TRB	Lab Exercise 2: Devising a Game, p. 276
Examples 10–11: #1–13, 16–17 Example 12: #18–29 Example 13: #14–15	PowerPoint Presentation (CD-ROM) Worksheet, TRB	
Examples 14–16: #1–6, 29–32 Examples 17–19: #7–28	PowerPoint Presentation (CD-ROM) Worksheet, TRB TAKS Mid-Chapter 6A (Workbook)	
Examples 20–21: #1–10 Examples 22–23: #11–12 Example 24: #13–25	PowerPoint Presentation (CD-ROM) Worksheet, TRB	Lab Exercise 4: Don't Lose Your Marbles, p. 277
Example 25: #13–14, 17, 20 Examples 26–27: #6–8 Examples 28, 30: #1–2, 10–12, 15–16, 26, 28–30 Examples 29, 31:#3–4, 9, 18–19, 21–24, 27	PowerPoint Presentation (CD-ROM) Calculator Mini-Lesson, p. 260 Calculator Mini-Lesson, p. 261 Worksheet, TRB	
Examples 32–34: #1-24	PowerPoint Presentation (CD-ROM) Worksheet, TRB TAKS Chapter 6B (Workbook)	Supplemental Lab #3: Triangulating a Probability, TRB Supplemental Lab #4: Yahtzee, TRB

Chapter 6—Pacing Guide: 45–50 minute classes

Day	Activities	Assignment Guide
1	Introduction to Chapter 6 (choose one, both, or split class) • Supplemental Activity #1: Pair 'Em Up, TRB • Supplemental Activity #2: Flip 'Em Over, TRB Lesson 6-1: What Is Probability? • Examples 1–2	#1–17, pp. 239–240
2	Lab Activity • Discuss and assign Lab Exercise 1: A Simple Survey, p. 276 • How can class efficiently gather all the data? Lesson 6-1: What Is Probability? • Example 3	#18–25, pp. 240–241
3	Lesson 6-2: Theoretical Probability • Examples 4–6	#1–11, p. 247
4	Lesson 6-2: Theoretical Probability • Examples 7–9	#12–30, pp. 247–248
5	Lab Activity • Lab Exercise 2: Devising a Game, p. 276 • Finish Lab Exercise 1: A Simple Survey, p. 276	#31–52, pp. 248–249
6	Lesson 6-3: Odds	#1–29, pp. 251
7	Lesson 6-4: Counting Principle and Tree Diagrams	#1–32, pp. 255–256
8	Mid-Chapter Quiz: TAKS 6A (Workbook) Lesson 6-5: Or and And Problems • Examples 20–21	#1–10, pp. 261–262
9	Lab Activity • Lab Exercise 4: Don't Lose Your Marbles, p. 277	
10	Lesson 6-5: Or and And Problems • Examples 22–24	#11–25, p. 262
11	Lesson 6-6: Permutations and Combinations • Examples 25–28, 30 • Calculator Mini-Lesson, p. 264 • Calculator Mini-Lesson, p. 265	#1–2, 6–8, 10–12, pp. 267–268
12	Lesson 6-6: Permutations and Combinations • Examples 29, 31	#3–5, 9, 13–30, pp. 267–268
13	Lesson 6-7: Applied Probability Problems	#1–12, pp. 270–271
14	Lab Activity • Supplemental Lab #3: Triangulating Probabilities, TRB	#13–24, pp. 270–271
15	Lab Activity • Supplemental Lab #4: Yahtzee, TRB	Prepare lab presentation
16	Lab presentations Chapter Review	#1–31 odd, pp. 273–274
17	TAKS 6B (Workbook)	#2–30 even, pp. 273–274
18	Chapter Test	

Chapter 6—Pacing Guide: Block Scheduling

Day	Activities	Assignment Guide
1	Discuss Introduction to Chapter 6 Lab Activities • Supplemental Activity #1: Pair 'Em Up, TRB • Supplemental Activity #2: Flip 'Em Over, TRB Lesson 6-1: What Is Probability?	#1–3, 4–24 even, pp. 239–241
2	Lab Activity • Discuss and assign Lab Exercise 1: A Simple Survey, p. 276 • How can class efficiently gather all the data? Lesson 6-2: Theoretical Probability	#1–4, 6–52 even, pp. 247–249
3	Lab Activity • Lab Exercise 2: Devising a Game, p. 276 Lesson 6-3: Odds	#1–29, p. 251
4	Lab Activity • Finish Lab Exercise 1: A Simple Survey, p. 276 • Lab Exercise 3: A "Tacky" Lab, p. 276 Lesson 6-4: Counting Principle and Tree Diagrams	#1–32, pp. 255–256
5	Mid-Chapter Quiz: TAKS 6A(Workbook) Lesson 6-5: Or and And Problems	#1–25, pp. 261–262
6	Lab Activity • Lab Exercise 4: Don't Lose Your Marbles, p. 277 Lesson 6-6: Permutations and Combinations • Calculator Mini-Lesson, p. 264 • Calculator Mini-Lesson, p. 265	#1–30, pp. 267–268
7	Lesson 6-7: Applied Probability Problems Lab Activity • Supplemental Lab #3: Triangulating Probabilities, TRB	#1–12, pp. 270–271
8	Lab Activity • Supplemental Lab #4: Yahtzee, TRB	#13–24, pp. 270–271, prepare lab presentation
9	Lab presentations Chapter Review	#1–31, pp. 273–274
10	Chapter Test TAKS 6B (Workbook)	

Chapter 7—Modeling with Statistics

Collecting, classifying, and summarizing quantitative information or facts and then using this information to make *informed* decisions is the basic aim of the area of mathematics called *statistics*. In this chapter, your students will be introduced to the fundamentals of this topic. They will learn from this chapter how to recognize when statistical procedures have been misused by some group, business, organization, or government agency.

Chpt/Sec	Lessons	TEKS	Vocabulary
7-1	Introduction to Statistics	03.A, 03.B, 03.C	descriptive statistics, inferential statistics, data, qualitative data, quantitative data, p. 280 population, sample, bias, random sampling, p. 281 strata, stratified sampling, systematic sampling, cluster sampling, convenience sampling, p. 282
7-2	Descriptive Statistics	02.B, 03.A, 03.B	average, measures of central tendency, p. 284 mode, median, p. 285 mean average, p. 287 weighted mean, p. 289
7-3	Organizing and Displaying Data	02.A, 03.A, 03.B	circle graph, pie graph, p. 291 stem-and-leaf display, p. 294 frequency distribution, p. 295 modal class, midpoint of the class, p. 297
7-4	Variation	02.B, 03.A	variation, dispersion, range, p. 301 standard deviation, p. 302
7-5	Normal Curve	03.A, 03.B,	normal curve, bell curve, p. 306 normally distributed, p. 307 empirical rule, area under the normal curve, symmetrical, probability, table of areas, standard scores, p. 308 z-scores, p. 309 probability of events, p. 311 percentile rank, p. 313
7-6	Scatter Diagrams and Linear Regression	01.C, 02.A, 02.B, 02.D, 03.A, 03.B, 03.C, 08.C	scatter diagram, p. 317 negative correlation, p. 318 best-fit line, linear regression analysis, least-squares line, prediction equations, p. 319 correlation coefficient, p. 321

Supplementary Resources

Teacher's Resource Binder (TRB):
- Practice Worksheets
- Supplemental Lab Exercises
- Chapter Test (5 Forms, A–E)

Teacher's Resource CD-ROM
- PowerPoint Lesson Presentations
- All Teacher's Resource Binder resources

Student Workbook
- TAKS Mid-Chapter 7A
- TAKS Chapter 7B

ExamView CD-ROM

Exercise Correlation	Lesson-Specific Resources	Lab Exercises
Definitions: #1–10 Example 1: #11–20 Example 2: #21–30	PowerPoint Presentation (CD-ROM) Worksheet, TRB	
Examples 3–9: #1–13, 15–26 Example 10: #14 (save example 10 & do with lab 5)	PowerPoint Presentation (CD-ROM) Worksheet, TRB	Lab Exercise 2: College Placement Test Statistics, p. 327 Lab Exercise 5: GPA Mania, p. 328 Supplemental Lab #1: Start Your Engines! TRB
Example 12: #4 Example 13: #5 Example 14: #1, 8a, 10a Examples 15–16: #2–3, 6–12	PowerPoint Presentation (CD-ROM) Worksheet, TRB TAKS Mid-Chapter 7A (Workbook)	Lab Exercise 7: Graphing Calculator Histograms, p. 330
Examples 17–19: #1–22	PowerPoint Presentation (CD-ROM) Calculator Mini-Lesson, p. 304 Worksheet, TRB	Lab Exercise 3: Radio Advertisements, p. 327
Definitions/Theorems: #1–7 Example 20: #27–30, 36 Examples 21–22: #8–22, 26, 31–38 Example 23: #23–25	PowerPoint Presentation (CD-ROM) Worksheet, TRB	Lab Exercise 1: A Statistical Analysis of M&Ms, p. 327 Supplemental Lab #2: Let's Get Our Terminology Straight, TRB Supplemental Lab #3: How Tall's That Girl/Guy? TRB
Example 24: #1–4, 11, 15 Example 25: #7–10 Example 26: #5–6, 12–14, 16	PowerPoint Presentation (CD-ROM) Worksheet, TRB TAKS Chapter 7B (Workbook)	Lab Exercise 4: Predicting Sales at Burger King, p. 327 Lab Exercise 6: Cookie Monster, p. 329 Lab Exercise 8: Deriving an Exponential Function from Data, p. 330 Supplemental Lab #4: It's All in the Swing, TRB

Chapter 7—Pacing Guide: 45–50 minute classes

Day	Activities	Assignment Guide
1	Lesson 7-1: Introduction to Statistics Lab Activity • Preview Lab Exercise 3: Radio Advertisement, p. 327, and assign data collection	#1–30, pp. 283–284
2	Lesson 7-2: Descriptive Statistics • Examples 3–9	#1–13, p. 290
3	Lab Activity • Supplemental Lab #1: Start Your Engines!, TRB	#15–26, pp. 290–291
4	Lesson 7-2: Descriptive Statistics • Example 10 Lab Activity • Lab Exercise 5: GPA Mania, p. 328	#14, p. 290, finish lab exercise
5	Lesson 7-3: Organizing and Displaying Data • Examples 11–14	#1, 4, 5, 8a, 10a, pp. 299–300
6	Lesson 7-3: Organizing and Displaying Data • Examples 15–16 Lab Activity • Lab Exercise 7: Graphing Calculator Histograms, p. 330	#2–3, 6–12, pp. 299–301
7	Mid-Chapter Quiz: TAKS 7A (Workbook) Lesson 7–4: Variation	#1–2, 4–22 even, pp. 305–306
8	Lab Activity • Lab Exercise 3: Radio Advertisements, p. 327	3–21 odd, pp. 305–306
9	Lesson 7-5: Normal Curve	#1–19, p. 314
10	Lab Activity Lab Exercise 1: A Statistical Analysis of M&Ms, p. 327 • Preview and assign data collection for Supplemental Lab #3: How Tall's That Girl/Guy? TRB	#20–38, p. 315
11	Lab Activity • Supplemental Lab #3: How Tall's That Girl/Guy? TRB	Finish lab exercises
12	Lesson 7-6: Scatter Diagrams and Linear Regression	#1–10, pp. 321–322
13-14	Lab Activities (choose two or more, or split class) • Lab Exercise 4: Predicting Sales at Burger King, p. 327 • Lab Exercise 6: Cookie Monster, p. 329 • Lab Exercise 8: Deriving an Exponential Function from Data, p. 330 • Supplemental Lab #4: It's All in the Swing, TRB	#11–16, pp. 322–323, prepare lab presentations
15	Lab Presentations TAKS 7B (Workbook)	#1–10, pp. 324–325
16	Chapter Review	#11–22, pp. 325
17	Chapter Test	

Chapter 7—Pacing Guide: Block Scheduling

Day	Activities	Assignment Guide
1	Lesson 7-1: Introduction to Statistics Lab Activity • Preview Lab Exercise 3: Radio Advertisement, p. 327 and assign data collection	#1–30, pp. 283–284
2	Lesson 7-2: Descriptive Statistics Lab Activity (choose one, both, or split class) • Supplemental Lab #1: Start Your Engines! TRB • Lab Exercise 5: GPA Mania, p. 328	#1–26, pp. 290–291
3	Lesson 7-3: Organizing and Displaying Data Lab Activity • Lab Exercise 7: Graphing Calculator Histograms, p. 330	#1–12, pp. 299–301
4	Mid-Chapter Quiz: TAKS 7A (Workbook) Lesson 7-4: Variation	#1–2, 4–22 even, pp. 305–306
5	Lab Activity • Lab Exercise 3: Radio Advertisements, p. 327 Lesson 7-5: Normal Curve Lab Activity • Preview and assign data collection for Supplemental Lab #3: How Tall's That Girl/Guy? TRB	#1–17, p. 314
6	Lab Activity • Lab Exercise 1: A Statistical Analysis of M&Ms, p. 327 • Supplemental Lab #3: How Tall's That Girl/Guy?, TRB	#18–38, p. 315
7	Lesson 7-6: Scatter Diagrams and Linear Regression Lab Activity • Lab Exercise 4: Predicting Sales at Burger King, p. 327	#1–10, pp. 321–322
8	Lab Activities (choose one, both, or split class) • Lab Exercise 6: Cookie Monster, p. 329 • Lab Exercise 8: Deriving an Exponential Function from Data, p. 330 Supplemental Lab #4: It's All in the Swing, TRB	#11–16, pp. 322–323, prepare lab presentations
9	Lab presentations Chapter Review	#1–22, pp. 324–325
10	Chapter Test TAKS 7B (Workbook)	

Chapter 8—Additional Applications of Algebraic Modeling

This chapter will give students a brief taste of many areas where mathematical modeling is used every day. Several of the areas, such as music, may surprise them at first. Don't let the fact that mathematics is involved ruin their enjoyment of music and the arts.

Chpt/Sec	Lessons	TEKS	Vocabulary
8-1	Models and Patterns in Plane Geometry		perimeter, p. 334 circumference, pi, p. 335 area, p. 336
8-2	Models and Patterns in Right Triangles		right triangles, Pythagorean Theorem, p. 341 hypotenuse, legs, p. 342
8-3	Models and Patterns in Art and Architecture—Perspective and Symmetry	09.A	perspective, principal vanishing point, horizon line, eye level, p. 347 symmetry, reflection symmetry, p. 350 rotation symmetry, p. 351
8-4	Models and Patterns in Art, Architecture, and Nature—Proportion		proportion, scale drawings, p. 354 Golden ratio, p. 357 Fibonacci numbers, p. 359
8-5	Models and Patterns in Music	09.B	frequency, Hertz, pitch, octave, p. 363
8-6	Models and Patterns in Science and Technology	08.A	exponential function, p. 366 exponential growth, p. 367 quadratic formula, p. 370

Supplementary Resources

Teacher's Resource Binder (TRB):
- Practice Worksheets
- Supplemental Lab Exercises
- Chapter Test (5 Forms, A–E)

Teacher's Resource CD-ROM
- PowerPoint Lesson Presentations
- All Teacher's Resource Binder resources

Student Workbook
- TAKS Mid-Chapter 8A
- TAKS Chapter 8B

ExamView CD-ROM

Exercise Correlation	Lesson-Specific Resources	Lab Exercises
Examples 1–3: #2, 9–10, 25 Examples 4–6: #1, 3–8, 11–24	PowerPoint Presentation (CD-ROM) Worksheet, TRB	Lab Exercise 1: Room Areas, p. 377 Lab Exercise 2: A Comparison of Calculated and Measured Volumes, p. 377
Example 7: #1–8 Example 8: #9–15 Examples 9–10: #16–27	PowerPoint Presentation (CD-ROM) Worksheet, TRB	
Example 11: #1–4, 12, 14–15, 26–28 Examples 12–13: #5–11, 13, 16–25	PowerPoint Presentation (CD-ROM) Worksheet, TRB TAKS Mid-Chapter 8A (Workbook)	
Examples 14–16: #1–13 Example 17–18: #14–24	PowerPoint Presentation (CD-ROM) Worksheet, TRB	Lab Exercise 4: Are Golden Rectangles Really Cute? p. 378 Lab Exercise 5: The Golden Belly Button Project, p. 378 Lab Exercise 6: Fibonacci Flowers, p. 378
Example 19: #1–20	PowerPoint Presentation (CD-ROM) Worksheet, TRB	Lab Exercise 3: Musicians and Mathematics, p. 378 Lab Exercise 7: Mozart Sonatas and the Golden Ratio, p. 378
Examples 20–21:#1–6 Examples 22–23: #7–10 Example 24: #11–16 Example 25: #17–23	PowerPoint Presentation (CD-ROM) Calculator Mini-Lesson, p. 367 Worksheet, TRB TAKS Chapter 8B (Workbook)	Lab Exercise 8: Examining Exponential Decay, pp. 378–379

Day	Activities	Assignment Guide
1	Lesson 8-1: Models and Patterns in Plane Geometry • Examples 1–3	#2, 9–10, 25, pp. 339–341
2	Lesson 8-1: Models and Patterns in Plane Geometry • Examples 4–6	#1, 3–8, 11–24, pp. 339–341
3	Lab Activity • Lab Exercise 2: A Comparison of Calculated and Measured Volumes, p. 377	Lab Exercise 1: Room Areas, p. 377
4	Lesson 8-2: Models and Patterns in Right Triangles	#1–2, 4–26 even, pp. 345–347
5	Lesson 8-3: Models and Patterns in Art and Architecture	#1–28, pp. 352–353
6	Mid-Chapter Quiz: TAKS 8A (Workbook) Lesson 8-4 Models and Patterns in Art, Architecture, and Nature • Examples 14–16	#1–13, pp. 360–361
7	Lesson 8-4 Models and Patterns in Art, Architecture, and Nature • Examples 17–18	#14–24, p. 361
8	Lab Activities: (one or more, or split class) • Lab Exercise 4: Are Golden Rectangles Really Cute? p. 378 • Lab Exercise 5: The Golden Belly Button Project, p. 378 • Lab Exercise 6: Fibonacci Flowers, p. 378	Finish lab(s)
9	Lesson 8-5: Models and Patterns in Music	#1–20, pp. 365–366
10	Lesson 8-6: Models and Patterns in Science and Technology • Calculator Mini-Lesson, p. 367 • Examples 20–21	#1–6, p. 372
11	Lab Activity • Lab Exercise 8: Examining Exponential Decay, pp. 378–379	Finish lab activity.
12	Lesson 8-6: Models and Patterns in Science and Technology • Examples 22–25	#7–23, pp. 372–373
13	Lab Activity • Choose from remaining lab activities	Prepare lab presentations
14	Lab presentations TAKS Chapter 8B	Finish TAKS Chapter 8B
15	Chapter Review.	#1–25, pp. 375–376
16	Chapter Test	

Chapter 8—Pacing Guide: Block Scheduling

Day	Activities	Assignment Guide
1	Lesson 8-1: Models and Patterns in Plane Geometry	#1–25, pp. 339–341
2	Lab Activity (choose one, both, or split class) • Lab Exercise 2: A Comparison of Calculated and Measured Volumes, p. 377 • Lab Exercise 1: Room Areas, p. 377 Lesson 8-2: Models and Patterns in Right Triangles	#1–2, 4–26 even, pp. 345–347
3	Lesson 8-3: Models and Patterns in Art and Architecture	#1–28, pp. 352–353
4	Mid-Chapter Quiz: TAKS 8A (Workbook) Lesson 8-4 Models and Patterns in Art, Architecture, and Nature	#1–12, pp. 360–361
5	Lab Activities (choose one or more, or split class) • Lab Exercise 4: Are Golden Rectangles Really Cute? p. 378 • Lab Exercise 5: The Golden Belly Button Project, p. 378 • Lab Exercise 6: Fibonacci Flowers, p. 378	#13–24, p. 361
6	Lesson 8-5: Models and Patterns in Music Lab Activity • Lab Exercise 7: Mozart Sonatas and the Golden Ratio, p. 378	#1–20, pp. 365–360
7	Lesson 8-6: Models and Patterns in Science and Technology • Calculator Mini-Lesson, p. 367 Lab Activity • Lab Exercise 8: Examining Exponential Decay, pp. 378–379	#1–23, pp. 372–373
8	TAKS Chapter 8B Chapter Review	#1–25, pp. 375–376
9	Chapter Test	

Mathematical Models with Applications

DANIEL L. TIMMONS
Alamance Community College

CATHERINE W. JOHNSON
Alamance Community College

SONYA M. McCOOK
Alamance Community College

THOMSON
™
BROOKS/COLE

Australia • Brazil • Canada • Mexico • Singapore
Spain • United Kingdom • United States

THOMSON
™
BROOKS/COLE

Mathematical Models with Applications
Daniel L. Timmons, Catherine W. Johnson, Sonya M. McCook

Acquisitions Editor: John-Paul Ramin

Assistant Editor: Katherine Cook

Editorial Assistant: Dianna Muhammad

Senior Marketing Manager: Tom Ziolkowski

Marketing Assistant: Jennifer Valasquez

Marketing Communications Manager: Darlene-Amidon Brent

Senior Project Manager, Editorial Production: Janet Hill

Senior Art Director: Vernon Boes

Senior Frontlist Buyer: Karen Hunt

Production Service: Sara Dovre Wudali, Buuji, Inc.

Text Designer: Kim Rokusek

Cover Designer: Lisa Delgado

Cover Images: Corbis

Cover Printer: Phoenix Color Corp

Composition: Interactive Composition Corporation

Interior Printer: Quebecor/Taunton

Library of Congress Control Number: 2006922239

Student Edition ISBN 0-495-01781-7

Instructor's Edition ISBN 0-495-11332-8

Thomson Higher Education
10 Davis Drive
Belmont, CA 94002-3098
USA

For more information about our products, contact us at:
Thomson Learning Academic Resource Center
1-800-423-0563

For permission to use material from this text or product, submit a request online at **http://www.thomsonrights.com**. Any additional questions about permissions can be submitted by email to **thomsonrights@thomson.com**.

Contents

Preface

The longer mathematics lives, the more abstract—and therefore, possibly also the more practical—it becomes. – Eric Temple Bell (1883–1960)

TO THE STUDENT

Why take math courses? You may have asked yourself or your teacher this very question. Perhaps you asked because you don't see a need for math in your future. Perhaps you asked because you have always feared mathematics. Well, no matter what your math history has been, your math future can be better. As you start this new course, try to cultivate a positive attitude and look at the tips we offer for success.

Math can be thought of as a tool. It does have a practical value in your daily life as well as in most professions. In some fields, such as engineering, accounting, business, drafting, welding, carpentry, and nursing, the connection to mathematics is obvious. In others, such as music, art, history, criminal justice, and early childhood education, the connection is not as clear. But, we assure you, there is one. The logic developed by solving mathematical problems can be useful in all professions. For example, those in the criminal justice field must put together facts in a logical way and come to a solution for the crimes they investigate. This involves mathematical process.

Mathematical modeling is the process of examining a given situation or "real-world" problem and then developing an equation, formula, table, or graph that correctly represents the main feature of the situation. This is the application of mathematics to life situations—wallpapering your room, budgeting your money, using a credit card, predicting future outcomes from current data. In this course, you will derive algebraic equations, use formulas, draw and interpret graphs, and analyze many situations mathematically.

If you have struggled with mathematics in past courses, we have some tips for you about success in math. Try to develop a positive attitude, improve your study habits, and make a commitment to yourself to succeed. Do this on the first day of class. Don't wait until you've done poorly on two or three tests to change your habits. If you have some math anxiety, try these tips for success:

- Learn from your mistakes by reworking all the problems that you missed on a test or homework assignment.
- Take advantage of all available help after school from tutor centers or from your teacher.
- Form a study group to study outside of class time.

- Be well prepared for tests. Practice "taking tests" at home with a timer if you usually get nervous during a test.
- Write down memory cues before beginning a test. Scribble down a formula that you are worried about forgetting at the top of the test before you begin working. Then your mind will relax so you can think through each problem.
- Begin a test by doing the easiest problems first. You do not always have to begin with the first problem on the test.
- Skip problems on a test that you don't understand and come back to them later. Don't spend too much time on any one problem.

You *can* choose to be successful by paying attention in class, doing your homework, and using these tips. As this course progresses, you will quickly come to realize that mathematics is everywhere around us, affecting our lives each day.

FEATURES OF THE BOOK

Laboratory Exercises

The National Council of Teachers of Mathematics (NCTM), in its publication *Principles and Standards for School Mathematics,* states: "Students must learn mathematics with understanding, actively building new knowledge from experience and prior knowledge." This book reinforces the mathematical principles that are learned in Algebra I and uses them to model real-life situations that involve mathematics. We have included laboratory exercises at the end of each chapter and a wide variety of other activities in the ancillary materials available with this text. Some are designed to be completed as individual assignments and others require group work. There are assignments that require access to a computer lab and several that require online work. We have tried to make the labs versatile so the teacher can use any technology available. However, teachers are not required to have technology in order to teach a successful course using this book.

Calculator Mini-Lessons

NCTM also states in *Principles and Standards for School Mathematics:* "Technology is essential in teaching and learning mathematics; it influences the mathematics that is taught and enhances students' learning." We have created calculator mini-lessons throughout the book to aid students who are unfamiliar with calculators in becoming more proficient. Instructions for both a standard scientific calculator and a graphing calculator are provided. The use of graphing calculators is recommended in several areas such as graphing nonlinear functions, science and technology applications, and linear regression. However, the use of a graphing calculator is not essential to the successful completion of a course using this book.

Chapter Summaries

At the end of each chapter is a chapter summary listing key terms and formulas and points to remember.

Examples

We have included clear step-by-step examples in each section to illustrate the concepts and skills being introduced. More examples have been added to the material in several sections based on suggestions by other instructors.

Answer Key

The answer key provides odd-numbered answers to the practice sets. The focus of this book is understanding the modeling process involved in solving a problem. Having answers available helps students know if their thinking process has been correct. All answers are provided for the chapter reviews and chapter tests.

ACKNOWLEDGMENTS

There have been many whose efforts have brought us to this point and we are grateful to them for their suggestions and encouragement. Students at Alamance Community College who used the original manuscript offered many helpful ideas and we are grateful to them for their assistance.

We would particularly like to thank those who reviewed this manuscript for us:

Connie Koehn	Elsik High School—Alief, TX
Diana Ochoa	Conroe High School—Conroe, TX
Paul Shaklovitz	Pasadena High School—Pasadena, TX
Sandra Kay Westbrook	Keller High School—Keller, TX

We also wish to give our special thanks to the following persons who aided and encouraged us throughout this process: Ray Harclerode, Wendy Weisner, Valerie Rechtin, and all those involved in the production of this edition, including John-Paul Ramin, mathematics editor at Thomson Brooks/Cole, Janet Hill, project production manager at Thomson Brooks/Cole, Katherine Cook, assistant editor at Thomson Brooks/Cole and Sara Dovre Wudali at Buuji, Inc.

Daniel Timmons
Catherine Johnson
Sonya McCook

Keys to Success

BEFORE CLASS STARTS

✓ Find a quiet, comfortable place to work outside of class.
✓ Make both short-term and long-term study schedules.
✓ Discourage interruptions.
✓ Take short breaks occasionally.
✓ Do not procrastinate.
✓ Give yourself some warm-up time by working simple problems.

IN CLASS

✓ Ask questions early in the term.
✓ Listen for critical points.
✓ Lost? Mark your location in your notes and see your teacher at the end of class, or at another convenient time.
✓ Review your notes from the previous class before going to class again.
✓ Be sure to read the text sections that correspond to your lecture notes.
✓ Form a study group with some of your classmates.

ABOUT THOSE CLASS NOTES

✓ Your notes are your links between your class and your textbook.
✓ Never write at the expense of listening.
✓ Forget about correct grammar while taking notes.
✓ Use a lot of abbreviations.
✓ Be sure to copy down class examples.
✓ You may even want to rewrite your class notes to make them clearer and neater for future reference.
✓ Compare your notes with those of some of your classmates; they may have gotten some points that you missed and vice versa.

PROPERLY USE THIS TEXTBOOK

✓ Read the section due for lecture before class.
✓ Read each section twice, first quickly and then slowly while referring to your class notes.
✓ Writing down a concept or idea is definitely linked to your thinking processes, so write things down as they occur to you in your reading.
✓ Look up the definition of unfamiliar terms.

LOVE THOSE WORD PROBLEMS

✓ Think about the problem before jumping into a solution.
✓ Be sure to clearly delineate the questions to be answered.
✓ Break long, complicated problems into parts.
✓ Work with your study group but remember that you must be able to solve problems on your own at test time.
✓ Ask for help (from your teacher, a tutor, or classmates) when you need it.

TEST PREPARATION

✓ Be sure you know what topics are to be covered.
✓ You and your study group members should make up reasonable questions for each other to practice.
✓ Review old quizzes or tests if you can.
✓ Reread the notes you took in class, particularly those that indicate weakness.
✓ Honestly admit your weaknesses and work on strengthening them.

chapter one

A Review of Algebra Fundamentals

IN THIS CHAPTER

"The mathematical sciences particularly exhibit order, symmetry, and limitation; and these are the greatest forms of the beautiful." – Aristotle

This chapter is intended as a brief summary of some of the major topics of an introductory algebra course. It is not intended to replace such a course. A review of algebraic properties, rules for solving equations in one variable, ratios and proportions, percents, and strategies for solving word problems are included in this chapter. Students should be familiar with these topics because these skills will be necessary for success in subsequent chapters.

A model of an object is not the object itself but is a scaled-down version of the actual object. We are all familiar with model airplanes and cars. Architects and engineers build model buildings or bridges before constructing the actual structure. Machine parts are modeled by draftspersons, and nurses learn anatomy from models of the human body before working on the real thing. All models have two important features. The first is that a model will contain many features of the real object. The second is that a model can be manipulated fairly easily and studied so that we can better understand the real object. In a similar way, a **mathematical model** is a mathematical *structure* that approximates the important aspects of a given situation. A mathematical model may be an equation or a set of equations, a graph, table, chart, or any of several other similar mathematical structures.

The process of examining a given situation or "real-world" problem and then developing an equation, formula, table, or graph that correctly represents the main features of the situation is called *mathematical modeling*. The thing that makes "real-life" problems so difficult for most people to solve is that they appear to be simple on the surface, but are often complicated with many possible variables. You have to study the problem and then try to connect the information given in the problem to your mathematical knowledge and to your problem-solving skills. To do this, you have to build a mental picture of just what is going on in a given situation. This mental picture is your *model* of the problem. In the real world, construction and interpretation of mathematical models is one of the more important uses of mathematics. As you work through this book, you will have many chances to construct your own mathematical models and then work with them to solve problems, make predictions, and carry out any number of other tasks.

Definition

Mathematical Model
A mathematical structure that approximates the important features of a situation. This model may be in the form of an equation, graph, table, or any other mathematical tool applicable to the situation.

When the attempt is made to construct a model that duplicates what is observed in the real world, the results may not be perfect. The more complicated the system or situation, the greater the amount of information that must be collected and analyzed. It can be very difficult to account for all possible variables or causes in real situations. For example, when you turn on your television set tonight to get the weather forecast for tomorrow, the forecaster uses a very complicated model to help predict future events in the atmosphere. The model being used is a *causal model*. No causal model is ever a perfect representation of a physical situation because it is very difficult, if not impossible, to account for all possible causes of the results observed.

Causal models are based on the best information and theory currently available. Many models used in business, industry, and laboratory environments are not able to give definitive answers. Causal models allow predictions or "educated guesses" to be made that are often close to the actual results observed. As more information is gained, the model can be refined to give better results. If this were a meteorology class, a psychology class, or similar study, then many models would be of this type.

Some things can be described precisely if there are just a few simple variables that can be easily measured. The models used to describe these situations are called *descriptive models*. The formula for the area of a rectangle, $A = lw$, models the area of a rectangle and can be used to calculate the area of a rectangular figure precisely. It may be of some comfort to you to know that most of the models that you study in this book will be of the descriptive type.

It is important to note that even the most commonly used formulas were not always so certain. The various formulas, procedures, or concepts that we use in our workplaces and around our homes were all developed over a period of time by trial-and-error methods. As *experiments* were done and the results gathered, the formulas have been refined until they can be used to predict events with a high degree of accuracy. In this textbook, you will learn to do some of the same kinds of things to develop models and procedures to solve specific problems.

EXAMPLE 1   A Price-Demand Model

Suppose a grocery store sells small bunches of flowers to its customers. The owner of the store gathers data over the course of a month comparing the demand for the flowers (based on the number of bunches sold) to the prices being charged for the flowers. If he sells 15 bunches of flowers when the price is $2 per bunch but only 10 bunches when the price is $4 a bunch, he can graph this information to model the price-demand relationship.

The graph in Figure 1-1 shows us that, as the price increases, the demand for flowers decreases. This model can help the store owner set a reasonable price so that he will make a profit but also sell his flowers before they wilt!

Figure 1-1
Price-demand model.

EXAMPLE 2   Formulas as Models

Financial planning involves putting money into sound investments that will pay dividends and interest over time. Compound interest helps our investments grow more quickly because interest is paid on interest plus the original principal.

■ TABLE 1-1

Example 2

Number of Years	Compounded Yearly ($)
0	1,000.00
1	1,100.00
2	1,210.00
5	1,610.51
10	2,593.74
20	6,727.50
30	17,449.40
40	45,259.26
50	117,390.85

The formula $M = P(1 + i)^n$, where P = principal, n = years, and i = interest rate per period, can be used to calculate the value of an investment at a given interest rate after a designated number of years. Table 1-1 shows the value of a $1000 investment compounded yearly at 10% for 50 years. As you can see, the growth is phenomenal between the 20th and 50th year of the investment. This is an example of exponential growth calculated using a formula.

These examples illustrate two of the types of problems that we will examine throughout this book. We will use graphs, charts, and formulas to model our problems. It may be difficult to predict the future, but analyzing trends through mathematical modeling can give us insight into our world and how it works. Through modeling we can make educated guesses about the future, and, it is hoped, use these models to give us some control over our fates.

Section 1-2   REAL NUMBERS AND MATHEMATICAL OPERATIONS

Real Numbers

In algebra, the set of numbers commonly encountered in solving various equations and formulas and in graphing is called the **real numbers**. The set of real numbers can be broken down into several subsets:

1. The **rational numbers**
    (a) The **natural** or **counting numbers** = {1, 2, 3, 4, 5, . . .}
    (b) The **whole numbers** = {0, 1, 2, 3, 4, 5, . . .}
    (c) The **integers** = {. . . , −2, −1, 0, 1, 2, . . .}
    (d) The **rational numbers** = numbers that can be expressed as a ratio of two integers, such as $\frac{1}{2}$, $-\frac{5}{3}$, 0, 6 (as $\frac{6}{1}$), $\frac{-8}{-5}$, and so forth.
2. The **irrational numbers** = numbers that cannot be expressed as the ratio of two integers, such as $\sqrt{2}$ or π (pi) or similar numbers that are nonterminating, nonrepeating decimal numbers.

The set of real numbers is an infinite set of numbers, so it is impossible to write them all down. Thus, a **number line** is often used to picture the real numbers. The number line shown in Figure 1-2 is a *picture* of all the real numbers.

The symbol $\sqrt{}$ is called a radical sign and indicates the **square root** of the number under the symbol. Finding a square root is the inverse of squaring a number. The square root of every number is either positive or 0, so negative numbers do not have square roots in the set of real numbers. Some square roots result in whole-number answers. For example, $\sqrt{25} = 5$, because $5^2 = 25$. Other square

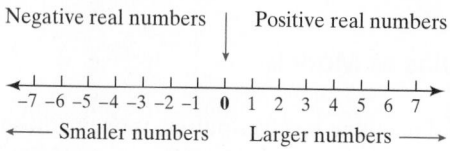

Negative real numbers | Positive real numbers

−7 −6 −5 −4 −3 −2 −1 **0** 1 2 3 4 5 6 7

← Smaller numbers   Larger numbers →

Figure 1-2
Number line.

Figure 1-3
Locating real numbers on a number line.

roots have inexact decimal equivalents and are classified as irrational numbers. The number $\sqrt{3}$ is an irrational number. If you use your calculator to derive a decimal representation for this number, it must be rounded. If we round it to hundredths place, $\sqrt{3} = 1.73$.

All numbers, whether rational or irrational, can be located at some position on the number line. In comparing two real numbers, the number located farther to the right on the number line is the larger of the two numbers. Finding the decimal equivalent of square roots will help us locate them easily on the number line. (See Figure 1-3.)

Operations with Real Numbers

When performing computations using algebra, both positive and negative numbers are used. In this section, we will *briefly* review addition, subtraction, multiplication, and division of real numbers.

Absolute Value   Look at the number line in Figure 1-4. Notice that the line *begins* at 0, has positive numbers to the right of 0, and negative numbers to the left. The **absolute value** of a number is its distance from 0. Distances are always measured with positive numbers, so the absolute value of a number is never negative. For example, the numbers 3 and -3 are both the same distance from 0. The $+3$ is three units to the right of 0 and the -3 is three units to the left of 0.

Because they are both the same distance from 0, they both have the same absolute value, 3. The symbol for the absolute value of 3, or any other number, is a pair of vertical lines with the number in between them: $|3|$. Using this symbol, we would write the absolute values discussed previously as

$$|3| = 3$$

$$|-3| = 3$$

Here are a few more examples:

$$|0| = 0$$

$$-|-8| = -8$$

$$|-0.45| = 0.45$$

$$\left|\frac{1}{2}\right| = \frac{1}{2}$$

Equal distances

Figure 1-4
Absolute value is the distance from 0. $|3| = |-3| = 3$.

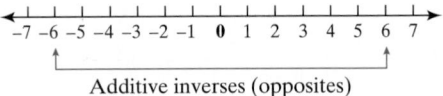

Figure 1-5
Additive inverses.

Additive Inverses or Opposites   Two numbers that are the same distance from 0 but on opposite sides of 0 on the number line are said to be **additive inverses** of each other. For example, both 6 and −6 have the same absolute value, so they are the same distance from 0. However, 6 is to the right of 0 and −6 is to the left of 0. Thus, 6 and −6 are additive inverses. (See Figure 1-5.)

Here are some other additive inverses or opposites:

$$10, -10$$

$$0.34, -0.34$$

$$\frac{1}{2}, -\frac{1}{2}$$

An important fact about additive inverses is that the sum of any number and its additive inverse is always equal to 0 [i.e., $2 + (-2) = 0$]. Because $0 + 0 = 0$, 0 is its own additive inverse.

Rule

Addition of Real Numbers

1. If all numbers are positive, then add as usual. The answer is positive.
2. If all numbers are negative, then add as usual. The answer is negative.
3. If one number is positive and the other negative, then
   (a) Find the absolute values of both numbers.
   (b) Find the difference between the absolute values.
   (c) Give the answer the sign of the original number with the largest absolute value.

■ EXAMPLE 3   **Addition of Real Numbers**

$$5 + 2 = 7 \qquad -2.6 + 6.8 = 4.2$$

$$-5 + (-2) = -7 \qquad -\frac{7}{8} + \frac{3}{4} = -\frac{1}{8}$$

$$-5 + 2 = -3 \qquad 5 + (-2) = 3$$

Rule

Subtraction of Real Numbers

1. Change the number to be subtracted to its additive inverse or opposite.
2. Change the sign indicating subtraction to an addition sign.
3. Now follow the rules given for addition.

This rule gives students more trouble than any other rule in fundamental algebra. Often this rule is written as follows: "Change the sign of the number to be subtracted and then add."

EXAMPLE 4   **Subtraction of Real Numbers**

$$5 - 2 = 5 + (-2) = 3 \qquad -8 - (-6) = -8 + 6 = -2$$
$$8 - 15 = 8 + (-15) = -7 \qquad 5.4 - 9.2 = 5.4 + (-9.2) = -3.8$$

Rule

Multiplication and Division of Real Numbers

1. Multiply or divide the numbers as usual.
2. If both numbers have the same sign, then the answer is positive.
3. If the signs of the numbers are different, then the answer is negative.

EXAMPLE 5   **Multiplication of Real Numbers**

$$2(4) = 8 \qquad -\frac{1}{2}\left(\frac{1}{4}\right) = -\frac{1}{8}$$
$$-2(-4) = 8 \qquad -4.5(2) = -9$$
$$2(-4) = -8 \qquad 0(2) = 0$$
$$0(-5) = 0$$

Remember that 0 is neither positive nor negative.

Calculator Mini-Lesson

Operations with Real Numbers

Your calculator knows all of the rules for adding, subtracting, multiplying, and dividing real numbers. It even knows the rule about division by 0. An important thing to remember is that the calculator will speed up your calculations, but it cannot read the problem. If you properly enter the operations, then the calculator will give you a correct answer. If you enter the numbers and operations improperly, then all the calculator will do is give you a wrong answer quickly.

When doing operations with signed numbers on your calculator, be sure to distinguish between the subtraction sign and the negative sign. On most scientific calculators, you must enter the number and then the sign into the calculator. For example, to do the problem $-4 - (-5)$, use the following keystrokes: 4 $\boxed{+/-}$ $\boxed{-}$ 5 $\boxed{+/-}$ $\boxed{=}$.

The second sign in the keystroke list is the subtraction key. All others are negative signs. Some calculators are direct entry, so enter the signs in the order given in the problem. A graphing calculator is a direct-entry calculator and has the negative key labeled $(-)$. Read your manual to be sure about operations with real numbers.

EXAMPLE 6   Division of Real Numbers

$$-8 \div 2 = -4 \qquad\qquad 0 \div 5 = 0$$

$$-8 \div (-2) = 4 \qquad\qquad 0 \div (-8) = 0$$

$$-\frac{1}{2} \div \left(-\frac{1}{2}\right) = 1 \qquad\qquad 6 \div 0 = \text{undefined}$$

$$8.2 \div (-2) = -4.1 \qquad\qquad -7.8 \div 0 = \text{undefined}$$

Remember that division by 0 cannot be done in the real number system.

Evaluation of Expressions   Suppose that you had to find the numerical value of the following expression:

$$5 + 2(3)$$

There are two possible results, depending on which operation, addition or multiplication, is performed first. If the addition is done first, then the result will be as follows:

$$5 + 2(3) = 7(3) = 21$$

If the multiplication is done first, the result will be different:

$$5 + 2(3) = 5 + 6 = 11$$

The order in which operations are performed does make a difference. So, which is correct? We can easily find out if we first study the rules for **order of operations**.

Rule

The Order of Operations

1. If any operations are enclosed in parentheses, do those operations first.
2. If any numbers have exponents (or are raised to some power), do those next.
3. Perform all multiplication and division in order, from left to right.
4. Perform all addition and subtraction in order, from left to right.

Referring to the problem $5 + 2(3)$, you see that it contains two operations, addition and multiplication. If we follow the order of operations, the multiplication would be performed first, followed by the addition. Therefore, the correct result is 11.

With a little practice, this rule becomes very easy to remember. It will be an important part of many algebra problems, so it is worth your time to practice it. As an aid to remembering the rule, a "silly" statement is often used as a mnemonic device.

For example:

"Please Entertain My Dear Aunt Sally"

The first letter of each word (PEMDAS) corresponds to part of the rule for the order of operations. P stands for parentheses, E for exponents, MD for multiplication/division, and AS for addition/subtraction.

EXAMPLE 7   Order of Operations

Find the value of each of the following expressions by following the order of operations.

1. $2(3 + 5) =$ (parentheses)
   $2(8) =$ (multiply)
   16

2. $3^2 + 5 - 7 =$ (exponents)
   $9 + 5 - 7 =$
   $14 - 7 =$ (add and subtract, from left to right)
   7

3. $-2[4 + (-5 + 2)] =$ (parentheses)
   $-2[4 + (-3)] =$ (brackets)
   $-2[1] =$ (multiply)
   -2

4. $14 \div 2 \cdot 7 + 6 =$
   $7 \cdot 7 + 6 =$ (divide/multiply, left to right)
   $49 + 6 =$ (add)
   55

Calculator Mini-Lesson

The Order of Operations

Your calculator will perform several operations at once and is able to follow the order of operations automatically. Just be careful to enter all of the operations, numbers, and symbols in the same order as they are written in the problem.

Some helpful hints:

1. If you use a graphing calculator, you must use the parentheses key when raising a negative number to an exponent. For example, if you enter $(-3)^2$ into a graphing calculator without the parentheses, the answer will be -9. The calculator will not assume that you are including the sign in the squaring process if you do not use grouping symbols. On most regular scientific calculators, entering 3 $\boxed{+/-}$ $\boxed{x^2}$ will tell the calculator to square the sign also.

2. When entering a problem like $\frac{25 + 31}{2}$ into your calculator, be sure to enter 25 $\boxed{+}$ 31 $\boxed{=}$ $\boxed{\div}$ 2. If you do not enter the equal sign, the calculator will only divide 31 by 2 and then add 25. It is following the order of operations!

If the expression contains a complicated fraction with several operations in the numerator, the denominator, or both, then you must evaluate the numerator and denominator as if they were two separate little expressions and then divide last. For example:

$$\frac{2(4 - 5)}{2(2) + 1}$$

To evaluate this expression, start with the numerator and follow the order of operations until you arrive at one number. Next, do the same for the denominator. Finally, divide the two numbers to arrive at the correct answer.

$$\frac{2(-1)}{2(2) + 1} = \frac{-2}{4 + 1} = \frac{-2}{5} = -0.4$$

Practice Set 1-2

1. List the following set of numbers in numerical order from lowest to highest.

$$\left\{ -\sqrt{5}, 4, 3\frac{1}{2}, -1, 0, -2.6, \frac{7}{13} \right\}$$

2. List the following set of numbers in numerical order from lowest to highest.

$$\left\{ -3.5, |-2|, \sqrt{5}, -1, \frac{1}{2}, 1\frac{3}{8}, -1.625 \right\}$$

3. Use $<$, $>$, or $=$ to complete each of the following.

(a) $\sqrt{7} \, ? \, 3$ (b) $-5 \, ? \, -5\frac{1}{4}$ (c) $\pi \, ? \, 0.3$

4. Use $<$, $>$, or $=$ to complete each of the following.

(a) $\frac{8}{5} \, ? \, 2.3$ (b) $-3.1 \, ? \, -3.8$ (c) $4.5 \, ? \, \sqrt{15}$

Evaluate each of the following by applying the appropriate rule for basic operations with signed numbers.

5. $5 + (-3)$

6. $-6 + (-5)$

7. $60 \div 0$

8. $-567 \div 0$

9. $|6 - 8|$

10. $-|-2 - 10|$

11. $-1\frac{1}{3} + \frac{7}{8}$

12. $\frac{3}{4} - 2\frac{4}{5}$

13. $-(-2) + 10$

14. $7 - (-2) + 6$

15. $-\frac{8}{9} \div \frac{4}{21}$

16. $-\frac{5}{8} \div \frac{15}{24}$

Evaluate each of the following expressions, being careful to follow the order of operations.

17. $7 \cdot 3 - 2 \cdot 13$

18. $(-3)(5) - (-8)(2)$

19. $\frac{15}{[-16 - (-11)]}$

20. $\frac{27}{(-24 + 21)}$

21. $8 - (-6)(4 - 7)$

22. $40 + (-2)(8 - 3)$

23. $\frac{2(-6 + 6)}{23 - 97}$

24. $\frac{2(5) - 10}{-7 - (-2)}$

25. $(-8)^2 - 7(8) + 5$

26. $(-3)^3 - 5(-2) + 3$

27. $\frac{2^2 + 4^2}{5^2 - 3^2}$

28. $\frac{12^2 - 10^2}{5^2 + 1^2}$

29. $\frac{3(-5 + 1)}{12(3) + (-5 + 2)(-3 - 1)}$

30. $\frac{5(-8 + 3)}{13(-2) + (-6 - 1)(-4 + 1)}$

31. $\frac{5}{8} - 5\left(\frac{1}{8}\right)$

32. $\frac{5}{6} - 3\left(\frac{1}{6}\right)$

33. $1.25 + \frac{6.5}{0.5} + (0.25)^2$

34. $2.5 + \frac{7.5}{0.3} + (0.5)^2$

35. $\frac{3^3 - 2^3}{-4(-3 + 1)}$

36. $\frac{2^3 - 4^3}{-8(-3 + 2)}$

37. $-4[(-2)(6) - 7]$

38. $-6[(7)(-2) - 3]$

39. $(3 - 8)(-2) - 10$

40. $-20 - (-1)(-7 - 11)$

Section 1-3   **SOLVING LINEAR EQUATIONS**

In our review of equation-solving procedures, extensive use of the properties of real numbers will be required. The principles used are designed to result in what are called **equivalent equations**. For example, are $x + 3 = 5$ and $x = 2$ equivalent equations? If x is replaced with the number 2 in both equations, then both equations can be seen to be true mathematical statements. Because of this, they are equivalent equations.

The properties of equality that we study in algebra are very important in the process of solving equations. These properties are briefly reviewed in this section.

Rule

The Addition Property of Equality
For any real numbers a, b, and c,

$$\text{if } a = b, \text{ then } a + c = b + c$$

This property simply says that the same number may be added to (or subtracted from) both sides of an equation and the new equation will be equivalent to the original equation.

EXAMPLE 8

Solving a Linear Equation Using the Addition Property of Equality

Solve the equation $x + 6 = 13$ for the value of x.

To solve this, or any, equation you must isolate the variable on one side of the equal sign. To do this, the 6 must be removed. Because it is added, we can remove it by adding its additive inverse. The additive inverse of 6 is -6, so add -6 to both sides.

$$x + 6 + (-6) = 13 + (-6)$$
$$x + 0 = 7$$
$$x = 7$$

and the equation is solved.

Check this answer by substituting 7 for x in the original equation.

$$\text{Check:} \quad x + 6 = 13$$
$$7 + 6 = 13$$
$$13 = 13$$

In solving equations, you will often be adding additive inverses to both sides.

Rule

The Multiplication Property of Equality
For any real numbers a, b, and c $(c \neq 0)$, if $a = b$, then $ac = bc$.

This property says if we multiply both sides of an equation by the same number, the new equation will be equivalent to the original one. The object of this property is to change the coefficient of the variable to a 1.

EXAMPLE 9

Solving a Linear Equation Using the Multiplication Property of Equality

Solve $2h = 26$ for the value of h.

The coefficient of the variable in this equation is 2, not 1. If we multiply by the reciprocal of 2, then by the inverse property of multiplication the result will equal 1. So, using the multiplication property of equality, we multiply both sides of the equation as follows:

$$\frac{1}{2}(2h) = \frac{1}{2}(26)$$

$$h = 13$$

Check your answer by substituting 13 for h in the original equation.

$$2h = 26$$

$$2(13) = 26$$

$$26 = 26$$

Often several steps will be required to solve a particular equation. Several properties may be used. Remember that parentheses must be removed first in the solving process if at all possible.

One of the properties of real numbers that is quite useful in algebra is the **distributive property**. This property allows us to remove parentheses in an equation so the properties of equality can be applied to find the solution. The distributive property states that $a(b + c) = ab + ac$ for all real numbers a, b, and c.

▪ EXAMPLE 10   Solving a Linear Equation Using the Distributive Property

Solve $2(x + 4) = 18$ for the value of x.

$$2(x + 4) = 18$$

Remove the parentheses with the distributive property.

$$2x + 8 = 18$$

Remove the 8 by adding its inverse, -8.

$$2x + 8 + (-8) = 18 + (-8)$$

$$2x + 0 = 10$$

$$2x = 10$$

Make the coefficient of the variable x a 1 by multiplying by the reciprocal of 2 (this is equivalent to dividing both sides by 2).

$$\frac{1}{2}(2x) = \frac{1}{2}(10)$$

$$x = 5$$

Check your answer by substituting 5 for x in the original equation.

$$2(x + 4) = 18$$

$$2(5 + 4) = 18$$

Now follow the order of operations to evaluate this expression.

$$2(9) = 18$$

$$18 = 18$$

So, x does equal 5.

EXAMPLE 11   Solving a Linear Equation Containing Fractions

Solve the equation $\frac{1}{2}x - 3 = \frac{2}{3} + 3x$.

The easiest way to solve an algebraic equation containing fractions is to first multiply the entire equation by the least common denominator (LCD) of the fractions in the equation. This will result in an equivalent equation with only integer coefficients. The LCD of this equation is 6, so we will multiply all terms by 6.

$$\frac{1}{2}x - 3 = \frac{2}{3} + 3x$$

$$6\left(\frac{1}{2}x\right) - 6(3) = 6\left(\frac{2}{3}\right) + 6(3x) \qquad \text{(multiply each term by 6)}$$

$$3x - 18 = 4 + 18x \qquad \text{(simplify)}$$

$$3x - 18 + (-18x) = 4 + 18x + (-18x) \qquad \text{(add } -18x \text{ to each side)}$$

$$-15x - 18 = 4 \qquad \text{(simplify)}$$

$$-15x - 18 + 18 = 4 + 18 \qquad \text{(add 18 to each side)}$$

$$-15x = 22 \qquad \text{(simplify)}$$

$$x = -\frac{22}{15} \qquad \text{(divide both sides by } -15)$$

A summary of the steps needed to solve any linear equation is given in Table 1-2.

■ **TABLE 1-2   Solving Linear Equations**

To Solve Linear Equations:	**Solve:** $\dfrac{1}{2}(x + 5) = 2(x - 1) + 5$
Step 1 Clear the equation of all fractions by multiplying all terms on each side of the equation by the lowest common denominator of all the fractions present.	$2\left[\dfrac{1}{2}(x + 5) = 2(x - 1) + 5\right]$ $2\left(\dfrac{1}{2}\right)(x + 5) = 2(2)(x - 1) + 2(5)$ $(x + 5) = 4(x - 1) + 10$
Step 2 Remove any grouping symbols, such as parentheses, using the distributive property.	$x + 5 = 4x - 4 + 10$
Step 3 Simplify each side of the equation by combining any like terms.	$x + 5 = 4x + 6$
Step 4 Using the addition property of equality, gather all terms containing the specified variable on one side of the equation and place all other terms on the other side of the equation.	$x - x + 5 = 4x - x + 6$ $5 = 3x + 6$ $5 - 6 = 3x + 6 - 6$ $-1 = 3x$
Step 5 Using the multiplication property of equality, find the value of the variable in question.	$-\dfrac{1}{3} = \dfrac{3x}{3}$ $-\dfrac{1}{3} = x$
Step 6 Check your answer for correctness.	$\dfrac{1}{2}\left(-\dfrac{1}{3} + 5\right) = 2\left(-\dfrac{1}{3} - 1\right) + 5$ $\dfrac{1}{2}\left(-\dfrac{1}{3} + \dfrac{15}{3}\right) = 2\left(-\dfrac{1}{3} - \dfrac{3}{3}\right) + \dfrac{15}{3}$ $\dfrac{1}{2}\left(\dfrac{14}{3}\right) = 2\left(-\dfrac{4}{3}\right) + \dfrac{15}{3}$ $\dfrac{7}{3} = -\dfrac{8}{3} + \dfrac{15}{3}$ $\dfrac{7}{3} = \dfrac{7}{3}$ So, $x = -\dfrac{1}{3}$ is correct

Practice Set 1-3

Solve each of the following linear equations.

1. $x + 6 = -4$

2. $x - 5 = -2$

3. $3x + 7 = x$

4. $2x + 3 = 5x$

5. $2(x - 8) = 4$

6. $-3(x + 3) = 12$

7. $35 - 3x = 5$

8. $24 + 2x = -8$

9. $-4x + 5 = -54 + 41$

10. $3x + 2 = -20 + 31$

11. $7 - 3x = 2 - 5x$

12. $10 - 2x = 3 + 4x$

13. $3x + 9 = 42$

14. $5x - 8 = 17$

15. $-7(2x + 3) = -7$

16. $-3(5x + 1) = -6$

17. $3(x - 2) + 2 = 11$

18. $4(x + 1) + 8 = 16$

19. $3x + 5 = -5x - 8 + 1$

20. $2x - 6 = -3x + 6 - 2$

21. $-\dfrac{3x}{8} = -\dfrac{15}{32}$

22. $\dfrac{2x}{5} = -\dfrac{7}{8}$

23. $\dfrac{x}{5} - 12 = 7$

24. $2 - f = \dfrac{f}{5}$

25. $w + \dfrac{3}{4} = \dfrac{5}{8}$

26. $2x + \dfrac{1}{3} = -\dfrac{2}{5}$

27. $\dfrac{2}{3}x + 8 = \dfrac{1}{2}$

28. $\dfrac{5}{8}x - \dfrac{1}{2} = 4$

29. $\dfrac{1}{3} + \dfrac{1}{6}x - 2 = \dfrac{2}{3}x + \dfrac{1}{2}$

30. $\dfrac{3}{4} + \dfrac{1}{2}x + 6 = -\dfrac{5}{8}x - \dfrac{1}{4}$

31. $\dfrac{3}{4}(4 - x) = 3 - x$

32. $3(x - 5) + 1 = \dfrac{1}{4}(2x - 8)$

33. $k - 76.98 = 43.56$

34. $m + 36.28 = 1.5$

35. $x - 0.5x = 12$

36. $x + 0.07x = 2.14$

37. $3.5x + 3 = x - 1.75$

38. $6 - 1.75x = 4.25 + x$

39. $-4y + 3 = 12 - 4y$

40. $2x + 1 = 6x - 5 - 4x$

41. $7a - (a - 5) = -10$

42. $3s + 5(s - 3) + 8 = 0$

43. $3(x - 5) - 5x = 2x + 9$

44. $5x - 3(1 - 2x) = 4(2x - 1)$

45. $6x - 2(3 - 4x) = 6(3x + 2)$

46. $2p + 4(p - 3) = 5p - 1$

47. $4(3 - x) + 2x = -12$

48. $3 - 2(x - 4) = 3(3 - x)$

49. $3(x - 2) + 7 = 5 - 2(x + 3)$

50. $4(2x - 8) + 1 = 3 - 4(x - 1)$

Section 1-4   FORMULAS

A formula is an equation that contains more than one variable. It can be thought of as a "recipe" for solving a particular type of problem. There are many standard formulas that we can access to help us solve problems. A formula can be used as a model for problems in the areas of geometry, banking and finance, and science.

The formula $d = rt$ relates distance (d) to rate (r) and time (t). This is the formula that you use every day when you decide what time to leave to arrive at a particular destination on time (or how fast to drive to get there!). It is also the formula patrol officers use to catch you speeding on the highway.

EXAMPLE 12   Distance Formula

1. The Shearin family is traveling across the country to California for their summer vacation. If they plan to drive about 8 hours per day and can average 60 mph, how far can they travel per day?

$$d = rt \qquad \text{(distance formula)}$$
$$d = (60\,\text{mph})(8\,\text{hr}) \qquad \text{(substitute given values)}$$
$$d = 480\,\text{mi}$$

2. If they decide to travel at least 600 miles per day, how long will they be traveling each day if they can average 60 mph on the highway?

$$d = rt \qquad \text{(distance formula)}$$
$$600 = (60\,\text{mph})(t) \qquad \text{(substitute given values)}$$
$$\frac{600}{60} = \frac{60t}{60} \qquad \text{(divide both sides by 60)}$$
$$10\,\text{hr} = t$$

EXAMPLE 13   The Perimeter of a Dog Pen

The perimeter of a rectangular dog pen is 40 feet. If the width is 6 feet, find the length of the pen.

$$2L + 2W = P \qquad \text{(perimeter formula)}$$
$$2L + 2(6\,\text{ft}) = 40\,\text{ft} \qquad \text{(substitute given values)}$$
$$2L + 12 = 40 \qquad \text{(simplify)}$$
$$2L = 28 \qquad \text{(add } -12 \text{ to both sides)}$$
$$L = 14\,\text{ft} \qquad \text{(divide both sides by 2)}$$

Therefore, the length of the dog pen is 14 feet.

Some formulas are complicated and require the use of a scientific calculator or computer to simplify computations. Therefore, it is important that you become proficient at using your calculator. Look at the following example and use your calculator to follow the steps in calculating the correct answer.

■ EXAMPLE 14   **The Compound-Interest Formula**

Lucero deposits $2500 into a savings account that pays 4.5% interest compounded monthly. Find the value of her account after 5 years.

Let M = the maturity value of the account, P = $2500, r = 4.5% or 0.045, n = 12 months, and t = 5 years and substitute these values into the compound-interest formula.

$$M = P\left(1 + \frac{r}{n}\right)^{nt} \qquad \text{(compound-interest formula)}$$

$$M = 2500\left(1 + \frac{0.045}{12}\right)^{12 \cdot 5} \qquad \text{(substitute values)}$$

$$M = 2500(1 + 0.00375)^{60} \qquad \text{(simplify fraction and exponent)}$$

$$M = \$3129.49 \qquad \text{(round answer to the nearest penny)}$$

Note: For exact results, *do not* round any part of the answer until you have completed the problem. Then round the final answer to the nearest penny.

As you can see from these examples, we may often need to rearrange the problem to answer the question asked. One way to do this is to rewrite the given formula by solving for a specified variable. For example, in the formula $d = rt$, we can rewrite this formula solving for r ($r = \frac{d}{t}$) or solving for t ($t = \frac{d}{r}$).

To solve a formula for a given variable, we must isolate that variable on either side of the equal sign. All other variables will be on the other side. To do this, we follow the same algebraic rules and principles that we have used to solve equations in the past. Look at the following example.

■ EXAMPLE 15   **Rewriting a Formula**

Solve the formula for the area of a triangle for the variable h.

$$A = \frac{1}{2}bh \qquad \text{(formula for the area of a triangle)}$$

$$2(A) = 2\left(\frac{1}{2}bh\right) \qquad \text{(multiply both sides by 2)}$$

$$2A = bh$$

$$\frac{2A}{b} = \frac{bh}{b} \qquad \text{(divide both sides by } b\text{)}$$

$$\frac{2A}{b} = h$$

The same relationship is maintained among the variables, but the formula has been rewritten to solve for the value of h.

EXAMPLE 16   **Rewriting an Equation**

Solve $h = vt + 16t^2$ for v.

$$h = vt + 16t^2 \qquad \text{(given equation)}$$

$$h - 16t^2 = vt + 16t^2 - 16t^2 \qquad \text{(subtract } 16t^2 \text{ from both sides)}$$

$$h - 16t^2 = vt$$

$$\frac{h - 16t^2}{t} = \frac{vt}{t} \qquad \text{(divide both sides by } t)$$

$$\frac{h - 16t^2}{t} = v \qquad \text{(rewritten equation solved for } v)$$

Practice Set 1-4

Evaluate each formula using the given values of the variables.

1. Distance formula: $d = rt$, if $r = 50$ mph and $d = 125$ mi

2. Distance formula: $d = rt$, if $d = 170$ mi and $t = 2.5$ hr

3. Simple interest: $I = Prt$, if $P = \$5000$, $r = 5\%$, and $t = 2$ years

4. Simple interest: $I = Prt$, if $I = \$616$, $P = \$2800$, and $t = 4$ years

5. Area of a circle: $A = \pi r^2$, if $r = 3$ in. (use 3.14 for π)

6. Area of a circle: $A = \pi r^2$, if $A = 12.56$ ft^2 (use 3.14 for π)

7. Area of a triangle: $A = \frac{1}{2}bh$, if $A = 36$ in.^{2} and $b = 8$ in.

8. Area of a triangle: $A = \frac{1}{2}bh$, if $A = 150$ cm^2 and $h = 40$ cm

9. Hero's formula for the area of a triangle: $A = \sqrt{s(s-a)(s-b)(s-c)}$, if $a = 5$ in., $b = 12$ in., $c = 13$ in., and $s = 15$ in.

10. Hero's formula for the area of a triangle: $A = \sqrt{s(s-a)(s-b)(s-c)}$, if $a = 3$ in., $b = 4$ in., $c = 5$ in., and $s = 6$ in.

11. Conversion of Fahrenheit to Celsius: $C = \frac{5}{9}(F - 32)$, if $F = 68°$

12. Conversion of Fahrenheit to Celsius: $C = \frac{5}{9}(F - 32)$, if $F = -4°$

13. Conversion of Celsius to Fahrenheit: $F = \frac{9}{5}C + 32$, if $C = -10°$

14. Conversion of Celsius to Fahrenheit: $F = \frac{9}{5}C + 32$, if $C = 100°$

15. Slope of a line: $m = \frac{y_2 - y_1}{x_2 - x_1}$, if $(x_1, y_1) = (2, -4)$ and $(x_2, y_2) = (-1, -3)$

16. Slope of a line: $m = \frac{y_2 - y_1}{x_2 - x_1}$, if $(x_1, y_1) = (-1, 0)$ and $(x_2, y_2) = (-3, -2)$

17. Compound interest: $M = P\left(1 + \frac{r}{n}\right)^{nt}$, if $P = \$5000$, $r = 4.5\%$, $n = 12$, and $t = 10$

18. Compound interest: $M = P\left(1 + \frac{r}{n}\right)^{nt}$, if $P = \$12{,}000$, $r = 3.25\%$, $n = 12$, and $t = 5$

19. Quadratic formula: $x = \dfrac{-b \pm \sqrt{b^2 - 4ac}}{2a}$,

if $a = 1$, $b = 5$, and $c = -6$

20. Quadratic formula: $x = \dfrac{-b \pm \sqrt{b^2 - 4ac}}{2a}$,

if $a = 2$, $b = -9$, and $c = -5$

21. Exponential growth: $y = Ae^{rn}$, if $A = 1,500,000$ bacteria, $r = 5.5\%$ per hour, $n = 7$ hr

22. Exponential growth: $y = Ae^{rn}$, if $A = 45,000$ people, $r = 1.5\%$ per year, $n = 10$ years

Solve each formula or equation for the designated letter.

23. $I = Prt$ for r (simple interest)

24. $P = 2L + 2W$ for L (perimeter of a rectangle)

25. $A = \dfrac{1}{2}bh$ for b (area of a triangle)

26. $F = ma$ for m (force)

27. $A = \dfrac{x + y}{2}$ for x (average of two numbers)

28. $2x + 3y = 6$ for y (linear equation)

29. $V = lwh$ for w (volume of a rectangular solid)

30. $A = \dfrac{1}{2}(B + b)h$ for B (area of a trapezoid)

31. $S = 2\pi rh + 2\pi r^2$ for h (surface area of a right circular cylinder)

32. $F = \dfrac{9}{5}C + 32$ for C (Celsius to Fahrenheit)

33. $V = \dfrac{1}{3}bh$ for b (volume of a right pyramid)

34. $d = 16t^2$ for t (distance in feet an object falls in t seconds)

Section 1-5   RATIO AND PROPORTION

The distance from the Earth to the Moon is approximately 240,000 miles. The distance from Jupiter to one of its moons is approximately 260,000 miles. Although these distances differ by 20,000 miles, they are approximately the same. This relationship is indicated by the quotient, or ratio, of the distances.

$$\frac{240,000}{260,000} = \frac{12}{13}$$

The **ratio** of one number to another number is the quotient of the first number divided by the second. We can express the ratio of 7 to 8 in the following ways:

1. Use a ratio sign $7{:}8$ (7 to 8)
2. Use a division symbol $7 \div 8$ (7 divided by 8)
3. Write as a fraction $\frac{7}{8}$ (seven-eighths)
4. Write as a decimal 0.875 (eight hundred seventy-five thousandths)

When working with ratios, be sure that all distances, masses, and other measurements are expressed in the same units. For example, to find the ratio of the height of a tree that is 4 feet high to the height of a tree that is 50 inches high, you must first express the heights in the same unit. Remember that 1 foot = 12 inches, so 4 feet = 4(12) = 48 inches. Therefore, the ratio will be $\frac{48}{50}$, which reduces to $\frac{24}{25}$ or 24:25.

Rule

Finding Ratios

1. Express the measurements in the same unit.
2. Divide the two measurements by writing them as a fraction.
3. Reduce the fraction.
4. Express the fraction using a ratio sign.

■ EXAMPLE 17   **Simplifying Ratios**

Express the following ratios in simplest form.

(a) $5:15$
(b) $18:24$
(c) $20x:35x$

(a) Remember that another way to write $5:15$ is as a fraction, $\frac{5}{15}$. Because 5 is the greatest number that will divide evenly into the numerator and denominator, the fraction can be reduced to $\frac{1}{3}$. So the ratio $5:15$ simplifies to $1:3$.
(b) The greatest common factor for 18 and 24 is 6. $18:24$ will simplify to $3:4$.
(c) The greatest common factor for $20x$ and $35x$ is $5x$. $20x:35x$ will simplify to $4:7$.

■ EXAMPLE 18   **Simplifying the Ratios of Two Measured Amounts**

State each ratio in simplest form.

(a) 20 min : 2 hr
(b) 6 ft : 120 in.
(c) 6 weeks : 3 days

(a) Remember that to find the ratio, the measurements must be in the same unit. Because 1 hr = 60 min, then 2 hr = 2(60) = 120 min. Divide each by 20 min.

$$20 \text{ min} : 120 \text{ min} = 1:6$$

(b) 1 ft = 12 in., so 6 ft = 6(12) = 72 in. Divide each by 24 in.

$$72 \text{ in.} : 120 \text{ in.} = 3:5$$

(c) 1 week = 7 days, so 6 weeks = 6(7) = 42 days. Divide each by 3 days.

$$42 \text{ days} : 3 \text{ days} = 14:1$$

A ratio is a comparison of two numbers having the same units of measure. These like units will cancel, leaving all ratios as pure fractions. A **rate** is similar to a ratio, but the units of measure are different. Because the units are different, they will not cancel but are usually reduced to a **unit rate** having a denominator of 1. For example, 55 mph is a rate that can be written as 55 mi:1 hr.

EXAMPLE 19   **Calculating Unit Rates**

Find each unit rate.

(a) $4.35 for 3 lb of cheese
(b) 549 mi in 18 hr
(c) 337.5 mi on 13.5 gal of gas

(a) Write the rate as a fraction.

$$\frac{\$4.35 \div 3}{3 \text{ lb} \div 3} = \frac{\$1.45}{1 \text{ lb}} = \$1.45/\text{lb}$$

The unit rate is $1.45/pound.

(b) Write the rate as a fraction.

$$\frac{549 \text{ mi} \div 18}{18 \text{ hr} \div 18} = \frac{30.5 \text{ mi}}{1 \text{ hr}} = 30.5 \text{ mi/hr}$$

The unit rate is 30.5 miles/hour.

(c) Write the rate as a fraction.

$$\frac{337.5 \text{ mi} \div 13.5}{13.5 \text{ gal} \div 13.5} = \frac{25 \text{ mi}}{1 \text{ gal}} = 25 \text{ mi/gal}$$

The unit rate is 25 miles/gallon.

An equation that states that two ratios or rates are equal is called a **proportion**. Proportions can be written in different ways. For instance,

$$\frac{4}{6} = \frac{2}{3} \text{ (equal ratios)} \qquad 18{:}20 :: 9{:}10 \text{ (equal ratios)}$$

The first of these proportions is read "4 is to 6 as 2 is to 3." The next proportion is read "18 is to 20 as 9 is to 10." As you can see, another way to express a proportion is to write it using colons. For example, the proportion $\frac{a}{b} = \frac{c}{d}$ can be written as $a{:}b :: c{:}d$. Both forms of the proportions are read "a is to b as c is to d."

The four quantities of a proportion are called its *terms*. So the terms of $a{:}b :: c{:}d$ are a, b, c, and d. The first and last terms of a proportion are called the **extremes**, and the second and third terms are called the **means**. Therefore, in the proportion $a{:}b :: c{:}d$, a and d are the extremes and b and c are the means.

We can use the multiplication property of equality to show that in any proportion the product of the extremes is equal to the product of the means. This property is known as the cross-multiplication property. By applying this property to the proportion $a:b :: c:d$, we get the equation $ad = bc$. This fact can be used to solve proportions.

Rule

Cross-Multiplication Property

1. $a:b :: c:d$ is equivalent to $ad = bc$.

2. $\dfrac{a}{b} = \dfrac{c}{d}$ is equivalent to $ad = bc$.

■ EXAMPLE 20   **Using the Cross-Multiplication Property to Solve a Proportion**

Solve the following equation for x: $\dfrac{3}{x} = \dfrac{5}{4}$

$$\dfrac{3}{x} = \dfrac{5}{4} \qquad \text{(original equation)}$$

$$3(4) = 5(x) \qquad \text{(cross-multiplication property)}$$

$$12 = 5x \qquad \text{(simplify)}$$

$$\dfrac{12}{5} = x \qquad \text{(divide both sides by 5)}$$

■ EXAMPLE 21   **Using the Cross-Multiplication Property to Solve a Proportion**

Solve the following equation for x: $\dfrac{2x-3}{5} = \dfrac{x+2}{6}$

$$\dfrac{2x-3}{5} = \dfrac{x+2}{6} \qquad \text{(original equation)}$$

$$6(2x-3) = 5(x+2) \qquad \text{(cross-multiplication property)}$$

$$12x - 18 = 5x + 10 \qquad \text{(distributive property)}$$

$$7x = 28 \qquad \text{(subtract } 5x \text{ and add 18)}$$

$$x = 4 \qquad \text{(divide by 7)}$$

Proportions can also be used to solve application problems that involve ratios or rates.

EXAMPLE 22   Solving a Word Problem Using a Proportion

Mr. Cook had a yield of 1155 bushels of corn last year in a 35-acre field. If he plants corn in a 42-acre field this year, how many bushels of corn should he expect?

Let x = the number of bushels of corn.

35 acres yields 1155 bushels of corn.

42 acres yields x bushels of corn.

Because we have two pairs of corresponding quantities, use a proportion to solve the problem.

$$\frac{35 \text{ acres}}{1155 \text{ bushels}} = \frac{42 \text{ acres}}{x \text{ bushels}}$$

$$35x = 42(1155)$$

$$35x = 48{,}510$$

$$x = 1386 \text{ bushels}$$

EXAMPLE 23   Solving a Word Problem Using a Proportion

Five tickets to a Texas Tech football game cost $137.50. What is the cost of eight tickets?

$$\frac{5 \text{ tickets}}{\$137.50} = \frac{8 \text{ tickets}}{x}$$

$$5x = 8(137.50)$$

$$5x = 1100.00$$

$$x = \$220.00$$

Practice Set 1-5

Express the following ratios in simplest form.

1. 45 min:2 hr
2. 1 hr:35 min
3. 4 in.:4 ft
4. 3 ft:60 in.
5. 6 ft:3 yd
6. 2 yd:12 ft
7. 8 weeks:16 days
8. 5 days:1 week
9. 25 mL:1 L
10. 2400 mL:2 L

Find the unit rate for each of the following.

11. 304 mi on 9.5 gal of gas
12. 450 mi on 20 gal of gas
13. $3.50 for 10-min phone call
14. $86.40 for 720 kWh of electricity
15. $850 in 5 days

16. $270 for 40 hr of work

17. 24 lb turkey for 15 people

18. 5.5 lb hamburger for 12 people

Solve the following proportions for *x*.

19. $\dfrac{x}{5} = \dfrac{3}{4}$

20. $\dfrac{9}{2x} = \dfrac{6}{4}$

21. $\dfrac{30}{126} = \dfrac{5}{3x}$

22. $\dfrac{2x}{7} = \dfrac{8}{14}$

23. $\dfrac{3x + 6}{35} = \dfrac{2x - 18}{5}$

24. $\dfrac{x - 2}{7} = \dfrac{2x + 2}{28}$

25. $\dfrac{15}{18} = \dfrac{x - 1}{x}$

26. $\dfrac{3}{x + 4} = \dfrac{5}{2x + 3}$

27. $\dfrac{3}{x + 1} = \dfrac{18}{9x - 3}$

28. $\dfrac{x + 8}{6} = \dfrac{2x - 8}{3}$

Solve the following word problems using proportions.

29. Three cans of tuna cost $3.51. How much will five cans cost?

30. Six cans of baked beans are on special for $7.14. How much will four cans cost?

31. A plane can fly 1800 km in 2 h. How far can it fly in 3 h?

32. The train travels 96 mi in 2.75 hr. At this rate, how long will it take to make a 480-mi trip?

33. Jewell's recipe for $2\frac{1}{2}$ dozen blueberry muffins calls for $1\frac{1}{4}$ cups of flour. How many muffins can be made with 3 cups of flour?

34. A sugar cookie recipe that makes 3 dozen cookies requires $2\frac{1}{2}$ cups of powdered sugar. If you want to make enough cookies so that each of 30 students in your child's class gets exactly two cookies, how much powdered sugar will you need?

35. Everett is 5 ft 10 in. tall and casts a shadow 8 ft 9 in. long. A flag pole next to him casts a shadow of 14 ft. How tall is the flag pole?

36. Olivia needs to determine the approximate height of a tree in her yard. She measures the length of the shadow of the tree to be 20 ft. At the same time, standing beside the tree, her shadow is 10.5 ft long and her height is 5 ft 4 in. Approximately how tall is the tree?

37. In an electric circuit, the current increases with the voltage. If the current is 1.8 A when the voltage is 18 V, what is the voltage when the current is 5.4 A?

38. When an electric current is 10 A, the electromotive force is 50 V. Find the force when the current is 25 A if the force is proportional to the current.

39. Hook's law says that the force required to stretch a spring is proportional to the distance stretched. If a force of 12 lb is required to stretch a spring 6 in., how much force is required to stretch the spring 10 in.?

40. Refer to Hook's law in problem 39 and calculate the force needed to stretch a spring $2\frac{1}{2}$ in. if a force of 30 lb is needed to stretch the spring 12 in.

41. The amount of money paid by *JTM Magazine* for an article is based on the number of words in the article. If the magazine pays $240 for a 1200-word article, how much will it pay for an article of 1500 words?

42. An automatic doughnut machine can produce 1500 doughnuts in 9 hours. How long would it take the machine to make 300 doughnuts?

43. A certain type of car consumes 60 L of gasoline in 3 h. If the rate of consumption is constant, how much gasoline will be used on a 35-h trip?

44. A new RV gets 9.2 mpg. How much gas will be required for a 460-mi trip to the beach?

45. At the local university, the female students outnumber the male students 5 to 4. If there are 2120 male students enrolled at the university, how many female students are enrolled?

Section 1-6   PERCENTS

A **percent** is a ratio whose second term is 100. Percent means parts per hundred. The word percent comes from the Latin phrase *per centum*, which means per hundred. In mathematics, we use the symbol % for percent. For example, 5% means

5 parts per 100 parts, which can also be written 5/100, or 0.05. In working with problems involving percents, some conversions of percents to decimals or fractions may be needed. Review the following rules.

Changing a Percent to a Fraction   Remove the percent sign and multiply the number by 1/100. Reduce the fraction.

$$6\% = 6 \cdot \frac{1}{100} = \frac{6}{100} = \frac{3}{50}$$

$$150\% = 150 \cdot \frac{1}{100} = \frac{150}{100} = \frac{3}{2}$$

Changing a Percent to a Decimal   Remove the percent sign and multiply the number by 0.01. (This is the same as moving the decimal two places to the left.)

$$6\% = 6 \cdot 0.01 = 0.06$$

$$150\% = 150 \cdot 0.01 = 1.5$$

Changing a Fraction or Decimal to a Percent   Multiply the fraction or decimal by 100 and add a percent sign.

Changing a fraction to a percent: $\frac{3}{50} = \frac{3}{50} \cdot 100 = \frac{300}{50} = 6\%$

Changing a decimal to a percent: $0.06 = 0.06 \cdot 100 = 6\%$

Note: It is often easier to change a fraction to a percent by first changing it to a decimal number and then multiplying it by 100. This is especially true when using a calculator for these conversions.

Changing a fraction to a percent on the calculator: $\frac{3}{4} = 3 \div 4 = 0.75$ $0.75 \cdot 100 = 75\%$

Remember that the percent sign is very important in determining the value of the number. The percent symbol means "out of one hundred."

$$0.05 = 5\% = \frac{5}{100} \qquad \text{(5 out of 100)}$$

$$0.05\% = \frac{0.05}{100} = \frac{5}{10,000} \qquad \text{(0.05 out of 100 or 5 out of 10,000)}$$

In the previous section, we discussed ratios and proportions. A percent is a ratio with a denominator of 100. Expressing the given percent as a ratio and using the cross-multiplication property to complete the problem can easily solve many percent problems. The basic model for a percent problem is as follows.

Important Equations

$$\frac{P}{B} = \frac{r}{100}$$

where r is the rate (percent written as a ratio), P is the percentage, and B is the base.

EXAMPLE 24   Finding a Percent Using a Proportion

Frances Cosgrove receives $1850 per month as salary. Her rent is $555 per month. What percent of her salary is spent for rent?

Percent = r = ?   Salary = B = $1850   Rent = P = $555

$$\frac{P}{B} = \frac{r}{100} \qquad \text{(formula)}$$

$$\frac{\$555}{\$1850} = \frac{r}{100} \qquad \text{(substitute values)}$$

$$(\$555)(100) = \$1850r \qquad \text{(cross-multiplication property)}$$

$$\$55,500 = \$1850r \qquad \text{(simplify)}$$

$$30 = r \qquad \text{(divide both sides by \$1850)}$$

Therefore, her rent is 30% of her monthly income.

EXAMPLE 25   Using a Proportion to Solve a Percent Problem

When the Band Boosters finished their fall fundraiser, they had $819 in the bank. If this is 65% of their goal for the year, what is the fundraising goal for this year?

Percent = r = 65   Money raised = P = $819   Goal = B = ?

$$\frac{P}{B} = \frac{r}{100} \qquad \text{(formula)}$$

$$\frac{\$819}{B} = \frac{65}{100} \qquad \text{(substitute values)}$$

$$(\$819)(100) = 65B \qquad \text{(cross-multiplication property)}$$

$$\$81,900 = 65B \qquad \text{(simplify)}$$

$$\$1260 = B \qquad \text{(divide both sides by 65)}$$

Therefore, the fundraising goal for the year is $1260.

Another method of solving percent problems is to translate the problem into an algebraic equation and solve it using your algebra skills. These problems can be fairly easy to solve, if you remember a few key words in mathematics. Two commonly used words that you may encounter in percent problems are

of, which means "multiply"

is, which means "equal to"

To find the percent of a number using an equation, the percent is changed to a decimal and then multiplied times the original quantity, which is called the *base*. The answer to this problem is called a *percentage*. For example, 20% of 55 is solved by the computation $0.20 \times 55 = 11$. In this problem, the 0.20 is the rate (the percent), the 55 is the base (the original total quantity), and the 11 is the percentage (the answer to the percent problem). The basic equation is

Rate (percent as a decimal) $\cdot$ Base (original total amount) $=$ Percentage (answer)

If you know any two of the three parts of this equation, you can easily solve for the third variable. Look at the following example demonstrating this process.

EXAMPLE 26   Finding a Number if the Percent Is Known

12% *of* what number *is equal to* 6?

    Our goal is to "translate" this sentence into an algebraic equation. To do this, we convert the 12% to its decimal equivalent, 0.12, locate the words "of" and "is equal to," and rewrite the sentence algebraically.

$$0.12 \cdot x = 6 \qquad \text{(write the equation)}$$

$$x = \frac{6}{0.12} \qquad \text{(divide both sides by 0.12)}$$

$$x = 50 \qquad \text{(simplify)}$$

Check: To check your answer, calculate 12% of 50 to see if the answer is 6.

$$12\% \text{ of } 50 = 0.12 \cdot 50 = 6$$

EXAMPLE 27   Finding a Percentage

75% of $300 is how many dollars?

    Translate the problem into an equation and solve. Remember to change the percent to the equivalent decimal number.

$$0.75 \cdot \$300 = x \qquad \text{(write the equation)}$$

$$\$225 = x \qquad \text{(simplify)}$$

    The method demonstrated in Example 27 is very useful to us in our daily lives. It is used to calculate sales tax (tax rate times cost of items purchased), tips (15%–20% times the cost of the meal), amount saved at a sale (percent savings times purchase amount), and simple interest earned on investments (interest rate times investment times number of years).

EXAMPLE 28   Finding a Missing Percent

What percent of 200 is 13?

$$x \cdot 200 = 13 \qquad \text{(write the equation)}$$

$$x = \frac{13}{200} \qquad \text{(divide both sides by 200)}$$

$$x = 0.065 \qquad \text{(simplify)}$$

Now multiply the decimal number by 100 to change it into the equivalent percent.

$$x = 0.065 \cdot 100 = 6.5\%$$

We are often interested in the percent increase or decrease of two quantities that have changed over time. For example, if I make $6.50 an hour and receive a $0.13 per hour increase, I can calculate the percent raise that I have received using the following formula.

Important Equations

Percent Increase/Decrease

$$\text{Percent increase/decrease} = \frac{\text{new value} - \text{original value}}{\text{original value}} \cdot 100$$

If my new salary is $6.63 per hour and my original salary is $6.50 per hour, I can calculate the percent increase of my raise as follows:

$$\text{Percent increase/decrease} = \frac{\text{new value} - \text{original value}}{\text{original value}} \cdot 100$$

$$\text{Percent increase/decrease} = \frac{6.63 - 6.50}{6.50} = \frac{0.13}{6.5} \cdot 100 = 2\%$$

Therefore, I have received a 2% increase in my salary. This formula can be used to calculate percent gains and losses in the stock market, percent increases and decreases in the prices of goods and services, and so forth.

EXAMPLE 29   Calculating Percent Loss

Joanna purchased Lucent stock at $45 per share 5 years ago. Today, the stock sells for $4.65 per share. Calculate her percent loss on this purchase.

$$\text{Percent loss} = \frac{\text{new value} - \text{original value}}{\text{original value}} \cdot 100$$

$$\text{Percent loss} = \frac{4.65 - 45}{45} \cdot 100 = \frac{-40.35}{45} \cdot 100$$

$$-0.8966 \cdot 100 = -89.66\% = -90\%$$

Therefore, Joanna has sustained a loss of 90% on her original investment in Lucent.

Practice Set 1-6

Change each percent to a fraction. Reduce it to its lowest terms.

1. 8%
2. 15%
3. 180%

4. 150%
5. $33\frac{1}{3}\%$
6. $64\frac{1}{2}\%$

Change each percent to a decimal.

7. 5%
8. 8%
9. 0.05%

10. 0.125%
11. 1.5%
12. 4.9%

13. 125%
14. 200%

Change each fraction or decimal to a percent.

15. 0.005
16. 0.25
17. $\frac{2}{3}$

18. $\frac{7}{2}$
19. 1.5
20. 2.55

Solve the following word problems.

21. Find 15% of 75.

22. Find 27% of 250.

23. 2.5% of what number is 33.5?

24. 42% of what number is 25.2?

25. 306 is what percent of 450?

26. 33.5 is what percent of 150?

27. A high school football team has played 3 out of 12 regular-season games and its record is 2 wins and 1 loss. The coach estimates that, to make it to the state playoff games, his team must win about 85% of its remaining games. How many more regular-season games must the team win in order to be in the playoffs?

28. Elijah's free throw percentage this season is 65%. Based on this statistic, if he shoots 12 free throws during a basketball game, how many do you expect him to complete?

29. Eat at Joe's Restaurant just increased the price of its Mega Burger by 12%. If the Mega Burger cost $1.75 before the increase, how much does it cost now?

30. Your hourly rate of pay is $7.75/hour. If you receive a 4% increase in your hourly rate, what is the new rate?

31. The cost of a large can of vegetable soup went down from $1.17 to $1.07. By what percent did the price decrease?

32. Gasoline prices increased from $2.35^9 to $2.41^9 overnight. By what percent did the price increase?

33. The price of one share of ABC stock rose from $55.20 per share to $57.96. What was the percent increase shown by the stock?

34. The population of Swan Quarter was 550 in 1995. Ten years later, it had decreased to 536. By what percent did the population decrease?

35. The 2002 American Community Survey sponsored by the U.S. Census Bureau projects the population of North Carolina as 8,063,874, with 21.2% representing African Americans. What is the best estimate of the African American population of North Carolina using these statistics?

36. Raleigh is the capital of North Carolina and, according to the 2002 American Community Survey sponsored by the U.S. Census Bureau, has a projected population of 289,551 people. If 8.5% of this total represents the Hispanic population, how many Hispanics live in Raleigh?

37. The advertisement for a deskjet printer gives a sale price of $149.99. The regular price of the printer is $169.99. What is the percent discount on this printer?

38. The list price for a used 2005 Honda Odyssey with low mileage is $22,465. If the dealer advertises a $1250 reduction in price for the Independence Day sale, what is the percent discount that he is offering?

39. A copper alloy contains 75% copper by weight. How much copper is in 2.00 kg of the alloy?

40. A brass rod has a length of 2.675 m when measured at room temperature. If this rod expands 0.35% due to heating, what will its length be then?

Section 1-7   WORD PROBLEM STRATEGIES

To be successful in solving word problems, you must have a firm knowledge of the fundamental rules of algebra and be able to exercise some common sense. *Common sense* is a way of saying that it takes experience to become adept at solving word problems. How do you acquire that needed experience? There's only one way. Practice solving word problems. There will be lots of practice problems in this book. You should look at the homework and practice assignments as a chance to improve your skills. Use the five steps to solving word problems listed in Table 1-3.

Table 1-4 provides a list of key words to look for in solving word problems. These words indicate mathematical operations that are part of the problem. This is not a complete list, so space is left for you to write in any other words you discover while solving problems in this book.

Another word commonly found in word problems is the word *and*. The word *and* is not one of those listed in the table because it generally serves another purpose. It usually shows the *location of an operation*. In each of the following examples, note that the indicated operation is placed where the word *and* is located.

The sum of 7 *and* 5 is $7 + 5$

The difference between 7 *and* 5 is $7 - 5$

■ **TABLE 1-3**   **Five Steps to Solving Word Problems**

Step 1 Read the problem. Put down your pencil and read the problem all the way through. Decide what quantity the problem is asking you to find. Remember that mathematics has a special language of its own. Pay special attention to key words.

Step 2 Select a variable to represent the quantities in the problem. It may be good to start with a list of the key words representing the quantities in the problem and then assign each of them a variable. The statement immediately preceding the question mark is usually the key statement. Read it carefully.

Step 3 Translate the word problem into a mathematical statement (equation/model) that describes the conditions of the problem. It may be helpful to start with a "word" equation and then substitute the variables and given values in place of the words they represent. This is the tough step. Look for patterns or try to match a new problem to a similar one that you have already worked. Guessing is allowed here.

Step 4 Using algebra, solve the equation you have written for the value(s) that is (are) required.

Step 5 Check your solution in the *original wording* of the problem, not in your derived equation. Is your answer reasonable?

▨ **TABLE 1-4**   Indicator Words

Addition	Subtraction	Multiplication	Division
plus	less	product	divided by
more	minus	double	goes into
more than	take away	triple	quotient
sum	subtract	of	divide
total	subtracted from	twice	per
increased by	difference	times	
added to	less than		**Equals**
sum of	fewer	**Equals**	
increase of	decreased by		is
	loss of	gives	the same as
		are	equals
			yields

There are many other key words in problems that will tell you what the problem expects you to do. For example, *compute*, *draw*, *write*, *show*, *identify*, *graph*, and *state*. Can you think of any others?

▉ EXAMPLE 30   Solving a Simple Word Problem

Step 1   Read the problem.

One number is 12 more than another number. The sum of the two numbers is 156. What are the two numbers?

Step 2   List quantities and assign variables.

Let one number be represented by "x." If this is the first number, then the other number will be $x + 12$. Also note that the word *sum* means that the two numbers are to be added.

Steps 3 and 4   Translate into an algebraic equation and solve.

One number plus another number = 156.

$$x + (x + 12) = 156$$
$$x + x + 12 = 156 \quad \text{(remove parentheses)}$$
$$2x + 12 = 156 \quad \text{(combine like terms)}$$
$$2x = 144 \quad \text{(add } -12 \text{ to both sides)}$$
$$x = 72 \quad \text{(divide both sides by 2)}$$
$$x + 12 = 84 \quad \text{(add 12 to 72 to calculate the second number)}$$

So, the two numbers are 72 and 84.

Step 5   Check the answer.

Do our two numbers fulfill the requirements of the problem? Is one number 12 more than the other?

$$84 - 72 = 12$$

So, the answer is "yes."
    Do the two numbers add up to 156?

$$72 + 84 = 156$$

Yes, they do.

EXAMPLE 31   Problem Solving

Step 1   Read the problem.

The number of students enrolled in English 101 classes is four more than twice as many as are enrolled in Psychology 101 classes. The total enrollment for the classes combined is 160 students. How many are enrolled in each subject?

Step 2   List quantities and assign variables.

Number of students in Psychology 101 $= x$

Number in English 101 $= 2x + 4$ (four more than twice Psychology 101)

Steps 3 and 4   Translate into an algebraic equation and solve.

Now we write the equation for the total number of students.

Number of psychology students + English students $= 160$

$$x + 2x + 4 = 160$$
$$3x + 4 = 160 \quad \text{(combine like terms)}$$
$$3x = 156 \quad \text{(add } -4 \text{ to both sides)}$$
$$x = 52 \quad \text{(divide both sides by 3)}$$

Therefore, there are 52 students in Psychology 101 classes and

$$2x + 4 = 2(52) + 4 = 108 \text{ students in English 101 classes.}$$

Step 5   Check the answer.

Does the number of students match the requirements of the problem? Yes.

$$108 + 52 = 160 \quad \text{(total students enrolled)}$$

EXAMPLE 32   Calculating Averages

Mary scored 88, 98, 82, and 75 on her first four of five math tests. What must she score on the fifth test to average a score of 85 for all five tests?

The desired average of 85 is obtained by dividing the sum of the scores by 5. So, we can multiply 85 by 5 to get the total that all five grades must add up to.

$$5(85) = 425$$

The sum of all five grades, including the unknown one, must be 425.

$$88 + 98 + 82 + 75 + x = 425$$

$$343 + x = 425 \qquad \text{(combine like terms)}$$

$$x = 82 \qquad \text{(subtract 343 from both sides)}$$

Mary must score an 82 on the fifth test to have an average score of 85.

EXAMPLE 33   Consecutive Integers

The sum of four consecutive integers is -2. What are the integers?

First, be sure you understand what *consecutive integers* are. *Consecutive* means one directly after the other. For example, 5, 6, and 7 are consecutive integers and so are -11, -10, and -9. From this brief example, you should see that to get from one integer to the next you just add 1.

Let x be the first of the four integers. The second would be $x + 1$, and the third $x + 2$, and the fourth $x + 3$.

The problem states that the sum of the four integers is -2, so we write this equation to represent the relationship

$$x + (x + 1) + (x + 2) + (x + 3) = -2$$

$$4x + 6 = -2 \qquad \text{(combine like terms)}$$

$$4x = -8 \qquad \text{(add } -6 \text{ to both sides)}$$

$$x = -2 \qquad \text{(divide both sides by 4)}$$

Answer:

First: $x = -2$

Second: $x + 1 = -2 + 1 = -1$

Third: $x + 2 = -2 + 2 = 0$

Fourth: $x + 3 = -2 + 3 = 1$

Check:

$$-2 + (-1) + 0 + 1 = -2$$

EXAMPLE 34

Consecutive Odd or Even Integers

Find three consecutive odd integers such that the sum of the first, 2 times the second, and 3 times the third is 82.

When we consider odd or even integers, if we assign x to the first number, the second must be designated $x + 2$. This allows us to skip the number immediately next to our number. For example, if the first number is odd, the next odd number is 2 steps away $(x + 2)$. If the first number is even, the next even number is also 2 steps away $(x + 2)$.

Three consecutive odd integers:

First: x

Second: $x + 2$

Third: $x + 4$

The first plus 2 *times the second* plus 3 *times the third* is 82:

$$x + 2(x + 2) + 3(x + 4) = 82$$

$$x + 2x + 4 + 3x + 12 = 82 \qquad \text{(distributive property)}$$

$$6x + 16 = 82 \qquad \text{(simplify)}$$

$$6x + 16 + (-16) = 82 + (-16) \qquad \text{(add } -16 \text{ to both sides)}$$

$$6x = 66 \qquad \text{(divide both sides by 6)}$$

$$x = 11$$

Answer:

First: $x = 11$

Second: $x + 2 = 11 + 2 = 13$

Third: $x + 4 = 11 + 4 = 15$

Check:

$$11 + 2(13) + 3(15) = 11 + 26 + 45 = 82$$

Practice Set 1-7

Write an algebraic expression for each statement given below. Let x represent the unknown quantity in each one.

1. Twice a number increased by 6

2. Three less than twice a number

3. The product of a number and 7 decreased by 2

4. The sum of 3 and 4 times a number

5. Triple the sum of 4 and a number

6. Twice the difference of a number and 6

7. Five less than one-third of a number

8. A number decreased by three-fourths of itself

Two quantities are being compared in each of the following problems. Write an algebraic expression for each quantity.

9. Ann earns $5000 more per year than Bill.
   Ann's salary =
   Bill's salary =

10. Friday's class attendance was 3 more than half of Monday's attendance.
    Friday's attendance =
    Monday's attendance =

11. The length of a rectangle is 5 m more than twice the width of the rectangle.
    Length =
    Width =

12. A rod is cut into three segments and each is 1 in. longer than the previous one.
    Short rod =
    Middle-sized rod =
    Long rod =

Write an equation that properly models each problem below. Then solve the problem.

13. A piece of rope 60 m long is cut into two pieces so that the longest piece is twice the length of the shorter. How long are the two pieces?

14. Mario is 18 years older than Joshua. If the sum of their ages is 46 years, how old is each?

15. Jeff wants to make an A in his math course this semester. To do so, he must have an average of 90 or above. If his test scores this semester are 88, 91, and 95, what is the score that he would need on his final test to attain an average of exactly 90?

16. In an introductory algebra course, the lowest average a student can have to earn a B is 84. If Michelle hopes to earn a B in the course and her grades are 60, 92, 78, and 89, what must she score on the last test to attain this average? Will she make a B in the course?

17. Frank's electric bill for the month of March was $85.78. The electric company charges a flat monthly fee of $20.00 for service plus $0.14 per kilowatt-hour of electricity used. Approximately how many kilowatt-hours of electricity did Frank use in March?

18. Michelle's cell phone bill last month was $69.90. Her basic monthly charge for unlimited minutes in her calling area is $29.95. Miscellaneous fees and taxes this month totaled $9.95. She is charged $0.40 per minute when she is out of her service area. How many "out of area" minutes was she charged for this month?

19. The Mighty Mites scored 39 points in their basketball game on Saturday. This was one point less than twice what their opponent scored. Find the number of points scored by their opponent.

20. The Perry brothers, Jim and Gaylord, were natives of North Carolina and were outstanding pitchers in the major leagues during the 1960s and 1970s. Together they won 529 games. Gaylord won 99 more games than Jim. How many games did each brother win?

21. The sum of three consecutive integers is 87. What are the three integers?

22. Are there three consecutive integers whose sum is 100? Explain your answer.

23. The sum of three consecutive odd integers is −273. What are the numbers?

24. The sum of three consecutive odd integers is 1503. What are the integers?

25. Which is the best buy: Brand X green beans costing $1.49 for 8 oz or Brand Z which costs $2.12 for 12 oz?

26. Which is the best deal: five 2-L colas for $4.95 or three 2-L colas for $2.99?

27. A real estate agent estimates the value of a certain house and lot to be $175,000. If the house is worth approximately 6.5 times the value of the lot, how much is each worth separately?

28. A house costs 7 times as much as the lot it stands on, and together the house and lot cost $164,000. What is the cost of the lot?

29. You are vacationing in Japan and want to buy a steak for dinner. The steak costs 949 yen. If the exchange rate is 146 yen to the dollar, how many dollars will the steak cost you?

30. The exchange rate for the British pound is approximately 0.549 pounds = 1 U.S. dollar. If you return from Great Britain with 65 pounds, at that exchange rate how many U.S. dollars will you receive when you exchange your pounds for dollars?

31. In the 2000 presidential election, there were 537 electoral votes cast. George Bush received five more electoral votes than Al Gore. Find the number of electoral votes received by each candidate.

32. In the Senate, after the 2002 election, there was one senator who was registered Independent, and there were three more Republicans than Democrats. Of the 100 senators, how many were Republicans and how many were Democrats?

33. A piece of pipe is 40 in. long. It is cut into three pieces. The longest piece is 3 times as long as the middle-sized piece, and the shortest piece is 23 in. shorter than the longer piece. Find the lengths of the three pieces of pipe.

34. A 56-cm piece of tubing is cut into three pieces. The shortest piece is 16 cm shorter than the middle-sized piece and the longest piece is 12 cm shorter than the middle-sized piece. Find the lengths of the three pieces.

35. In 2003, Gil de Ferran won the Indianapolis 500 with an average speed of 156.291 mph. Calculate the total time of the race.

36. In 1911, Ray Harroun won the first Indianapolis 500 with an average speed of 74.602 mph. Calculate the total time of the race.

37. Michael Dell, chairman and CEO of Dell Computers, Inc., earns $3.56 million less than Samuel Palmisano, chairman and CEO of IBM, Inc. Together their annual salaries total $10.44 million. Find the salary of each executive.

38. The September 2003 quarterly statement for Ford Motor Company showed that its gross profit for that quarter was $17,000 less than the gross profit reported by General Motors during the same quarter. Together their gross profits totaled $17,809,000. Find the quarterly profit reported by each company.

39. During the 2002 football season, the average home attendance at Washington Redskins games was 8992 more than the average home attendance at the Carolina Panther games. If the sum of these averages is 151,994, find the average home attendance for each team.

40. Dickie Hemric of Wake Forest University (1952–1955) leads the Atlantic Coast Conference in total career points in basketball. His total is 31 points higher than that of the second leading scorer, Johnny Dawkins of Duke University (1983–1986). Together they scored a career total of 5143 points. Find the point totals for each.

Chapter Summary

Key Terms, Properties, and Formulas

absolute value $|x|$
additive inverse (opposite)
distributive property
equivalent equations
extremes
integers
irrational numbers
mathematical model

means
natural numbers
  (counting numbers)
number line
order of operations
percent
proportion
rate

ratio
rational numbers
real numbers
square root
unit rate
whole numbers

Points to Remember

Rules for addition of signed numbers: If all numbers are positive or negative, then add as usual and keep the same sign. If one number is positive and the other negative, then find the difference of the absolute values of both numbers and give the answer the sign of the original number with the largest absolute value.

Rules for subtraction of signed numbers: Change the number to be subtracted to its additive inverse or opposite and follow the rules for addition.

Rules for multiplication and division of signed numbers: Multiply or divide the numbers as usual. If both numbers have the same sign, then the answer is positive. If the signs of the numbers are different, then the answer is negative.

Order of operations:

1. Parentheses
2. Exponents
3. Multiplication and division in order from left to right
4. Addition and subtraction in order from left to right

Addition property of equality:

$$\text{If } a = b, \text{ then } a + c = b + c$$

Multiplication property of equality:

$$\text{If } a = b, \text{ then } ac = bc \qquad (c \neq 0)$$

Distributive property:

$$a(b + c) = ab + ac$$

Cross-multiplication property:

$$\text{If } \frac{a}{b} = \frac{c}{d}, \text{ then } ad = bc$$

$$\text{Percent increase/decrease} = \frac{\text{new value} - \text{original value}}{\text{original value}} \cdot 100$$

Chapter Review Problems

1. What is the additive inverse of $\frac{2}{3}$?

2. What is the opposite of -9?

Evaluate each of the following (remember the order of operations).

3. $-|-3 + 5|$

4. $-7^2 + 9$

5. $6 - 3(4 - 7) \div 4$

6. $23.89 \div -3.48$

7. $3^2 + |-28| - (6^2 - 8)$

Solve each of the following equations.

8. $2x - 9 = -5x + 7$

9. $2x - 7x = 15$

10. $3 = \frac{1}{3} - 2x$

11. $-5(n - 2) = 8 - 4n$

12. $\frac{2x}{3} - 5 = 7$

13. $2x + 3(x - 5) = 15$

14. $-2(x - 1) - 3x = 8 - 4x$

15. $7(x - 2) - 6(x + 1) = -20$

Solve each formula or equation for the indicated variable.

16. $I = Prt$ for t (simple interest)

17. $2x + 3y = 9$ for y (linear equation in slope-intercept form)

18. $C = \pi d$ for d (circumference of a circle)

19. $a + b + c = P$ for c (perimeter of a triangle)

Express the following ratios in simplest form.

20. 27 min:3 hr

21. 4 weeks:21 days

22. 6 in.:5 ft

Find each unit rate.

23. $60 in 5 hr

24. 44 bushels from 8 trees

25. $74.25 for 9 hr

Solve the following proportions for *x*.

26. $\dfrac{x}{3} = \dfrac{4}{7}$

27. $\dfrac{2}{3} = \dfrac{8}{2x}$

28. $\dfrac{x-3}{8} = \dfrac{3}{4}$

29. $\dfrac{4x-3}{7} = \dfrac{2x-1}{3}$

Solve the following percent problems.

30. What is 12.5% of 150?

31. What percent of 80 is 10?

32. 4% of what number is 64?

Solve each of the following word problems.

33. Juan is buying a 2-year certificate of deposit that pays simple interest at a rate of 8% per year. He is investing $2000. How much interest will he earn at the end of 2 years? ($I = Prt$)

34. The area of a triangle can be calculated with the formula $A = \frac{1}{2}bh$. Find the area of a triangle whose base is 3 in. and whose height is 4 in.

35. A car that sold for $7200 had a sales tax of $240. How much is the tax on a car that sells for $9000?

36. A pump can fill a 2400-L water tank in 50 min. How much water can it pump in half an hour?

37. An advertisement claims that, in a recent poll, three out of four dentists recommended brushing with Wenderoth toothpaste. If there were 92 dentists polled, how many favored Wenderoth toothpaste?

38. If 160 lb of an alloy contains 76.8 lb of copper, what percent of the alloy is copper?

39. Jerry's monthly salary is $1800. After he received a 1.5% raise, what was his new monthly salary?

40. A copper alloy contains 80% copper by weight. How much copper is in 2.00 kg of this alloy?

41. A brass rod has a length of 1.5671 m when measured at room temperature. If this rod expands 0.45% due to heating, what will its length be then?

42. A 50-L volume of oxygen is placed under pressure so that the volume is decreased to 46.1 L. By what percent was the volume decreased?

43. The price of a gallon of gasoline increased from $2.54^9 to $2.64^9 in the week before Memorial Day. What percent increase was this?

44. A telephone company charges for long-distance calls as follows: $1.24 for the first 4 minutes plus $0.28 for each additional minute or fraction thereof. If you make a long-distance call and the charges are $3.76, how many minutes long was your call?

45. A local cellular phone company charges Elaine $50 per month and $0.36 per minute of phone use in her usage category. If Elaine was charged $99.68 for a month's cellular phone use, determine the number of whole minutes of phone use.

46. A plumber charged $115 to install a water heater. This charge included $40 for materials and $30 per hour labor charge. How long did it take for the plumber to make this installation?

47. Find the temperature after a rise of 22°F from an initial temperature of −37°F.

48. The daily temperature readings for three consecutive days in January in Saskatoon, Saskatchewan, Canada, were −7°C, 9°C, and −11°C. What was the average temperature for these three days?

49. Dave has a board that is 33 in. long. He wishes to cut it into two pieces so that one is 3 in. longer than the other. How long must each piece be?

50. A piece of rope is 79 cm long. It is cut into three pieces. The longest piece is 3 times as long as the shortest piece, and the middle-sized piece is 14 cm longer than the shortest piece. Find the lengths of all three pieces.

51. Fred bought a cassette player and a calculator for a total cost of $208. If the cassette player cost $140

more than the calculator, how much did the calculator cost?

52. A child's piggy bank contains only dimes and nickels. There are 52 coins in the bank, and the number of dimes is 2 less than twice the number of nickels. How much money is in the bank?

53. To find the total cost of production of an item, an economist uses the formula $T = UN + F$, where T is the total cost, U is the cost per unit, N is the number of units produced, and F is fixed costs (e.g., heat, electricity, etc.). If it costs $15 per unit

to make the product, fixed costs are $2500, and the total cost of production for the last week was $16,750, how many units were produced?

54. Explain why the following simplification is incorrect. Then correctly simplify the initial expression.
$$2 + 3(2x + 4) = 5(2x + 4) = 10x + 20$$

55. It is 182 mi over the river and through the woods to Grandma's house. If you were to travel country roads and average only 52 mph, how long would it take you to get to Grandma's house?

Chapter Test

1. $|8| = |-8| = 8$. Explain what this means.

2. What is the "additive inverse" of a number?

Simplify each of the following:

3. $2(5 - 7)^3$

4. $|3^2 - 2(6 - 5)|$

5. $\dfrac{6(-5)}{2} + 3(6 - 9) - 7$

Solve each of the following equations.

6. $3(y + 7) = 2y - 5$

7. $\dfrac{5x}{6} = 2x - 7$

8. $6x + x - 0.9 = 6x + 0.9$

9. $4y - 6(y + 4) = 1 - y$

10. $7 - (3x - 1) = 5x$

Solve each formula for the indicated variable.

11. $V = lwh$ for w — (volume of a rectangular solid)

12. $h = vt - 16t^2$ for v — (height above ground of projectile)

Express the following ratios in simplest form.

13. 4 hr:1 day

14. 10 ft:160 in.

Find each unit rate.

15. $413.20 for 4 days

16. 7.5 lb for six people

17. 50 eggs from 10 chickens

Solve the following proportions for x.

18. $\dfrac{7}{12} = \dfrac{3x}{10}$

19. $\dfrac{x - 4}{8} = \dfrac{2x + 3}{9}$

Solve the following percent problems.

20. Find 15% of 85.

21. What percent of 150 is 33.5?

22. 2.5% of what number is 16.25?

Solve the following word problems.

23. If the sales tax rate in the county is 6%, find the sales tax on a purchase of $29.95.

24. It is customary to leave a waitress a 15% tip. If the total cost of a meal is $45.80, how much should you leave as a tip?

25. In a sample of 85 fluorescent lightbulbs, three were found to be defective. At this rate, how many defective bulbs should be found in 510 bulbs?

26. A machine can process 300 parts in 20 min. How many parts can be processed in 45 min?

27. To purchase a wallpaper border for the living room, Jose needs to find the perimeter of the room to know how long the border should be. If the room is rectangular, with a length of 20 ft and width of 12 ft, how many feet of border will he need to complete the job? ($P = 2L + 2W$)

28. Car rental company A rents cars for $20 plus $0.10 per mile driven. Company B rents cars for $10 plus $0.30 per mile. For what number of miles driven would the cost of renting a car from company A equal that of company B?

29. Maria invested $15,000 in a technology company in early 2006. By January of 2007, her investment was only worth $6500. What is the percent decrease in Maria's investment?

30. You are scheduling passengers for cruise ships. One ship holds twice as many passengers as a second ship. Together they can hold 2250 passengers. How many passengers will the smaller ship accommodate?

31. Michelle's age is 10 years less than 5 times Sarah's age. If the sum of their ages is 44 years, find their ages.

32. Boats can be rented at Lake Michael for $14.50 for the first 3 hours plus $4.50 for each additional hour. How much would it cost to rent a boat for 6.5 hours?

33. A voltmeter consistently reads 6% too high. What is the actual voltage of a certain source if this meter reads 120 volts?

34. The distance between two plates is measured to be 0.453 cm. If the measuring instrument has an error range (tolerance) of ±0.15%, what are the largest and smallest possible actual distances between these two plates?

35. A 21-ft board is cut into a long piece and a short piece. The long piece is 1 ft more than 3 times the short piece. Find the length of each piece.

Suggested Laboratory Exercises

These are some problems that are good for group discussion and collaborative work. Work with your chosen group to set up and solve these "fun" problems.

LAB EXERCISE 1

What Money?

You approach a co-worker, Alice, to get some change for the drink machine. You ask Alice to change a dollar for you. She replies that she does have some change in her pocket but can't change a dollar. Then you ask if she can change a half-dollar (I guess you have one of those old Kennedy halves on you). Alice says that she can't change a half-dollar either. At this point, you ask how much change she has. Alice replies that she has $1.15 in change. What coins (any valid U.S. coins less than $1 are possible) does Alice actually have in her pocket? How did you arrive at this answer?

LAB EXERCISE 2

A Hen and a Half?

If a hen and a half lay an egg and a half in a day and a half, how many eggs will six hens lay in seven days?

LAB EXERCISE 3

Our Solar System

The closer a planet is to the Sun, the shorter the length of time it takes that planet to make one orbit around the Sun. Go to your school library or the Internet and research the length of time it takes each of the nine known planets in our solar system to orbit the Sun and the mass of each planet. Fill in the following table. Round off the times and masses to the nearest whole number for each planet.

Name	Year (days)	Mass (kg)
Mercury		
Venus		
Earth		
Mars		
Jupiter		
Saturn		
Uranus		
Neptune		
Pluto		

(a) How many Earth years = one Pluto year?
(b) How many Earth years = one Venus year?
(c) If you compare the time it takes the Earth to make one orbit of the Sun with that of Jupiter, how long will it take the Earth to gain one full orbit on Jupiter?
(d) How many Earth masses = one Saturn mass?
(e) What percentage of the mass of all planets in the solar system is Jupiter's mass?

LAB EXERCISE 4

Our Growing Population

The most recent census was taken in the year 2000. The goal of the census is to gather statistical data about the population of the United States as a whole and statistics about each individual state in the union. The data concerning population numbers for each state and many other interesting statistics can be obtained at www.census.gov.

For this lab, go to the Web site www.census.gov/dmd/www/schoollessons.html. Choose "the state of your state" worksheet and use the data available at this Web site to complete the worksheet. You will learn how your state has changed in population, its percent increase or decrease in population, and what percentage of the entire United States your state's population represents. You will also be able to compare data about your state with that of other states in the United States.

LAB EXERCISE 5

Max It Out

Your instructor will give you 12 equal-length items (straws, toothpicks, etc.). Assume that each item represents a length of fence 10 ft long. You are to use these pieces of fence to construct a rectangle. You may not bend or break the individual pieces of fence. Start forming rectangles with a width of 10 ft, then a width of 20 ft, and so forth (fill in the following table). What is the largest area that may be enclosed using all of the pieces of fencing? What happens to the perimeter as the areas of the various rectangles change? Did you have any trouble completing the chart? If so, what was the problem?

Width (ft)	Length (ft)	Area (ft²)	Perimeter (ft)
10			
20			
30			
40			
50			
60			

LAB EXERCISE 6   ## Batter Up

Baseball fanatics love to keep all kinds of statistics about players and teams. The sports pages of the newspaper are full of them during every baseball season. One odd statistic is called the *slugging percentage*. It is calculated by taking the total number of bases that the player got per hit and then dividing by the total number of times the player batted, whether he got a hit or not.

1. Let S = a single (one base per hit), D = a double (two bases per), T = a triple (three bases per), H = a home run (four bases per), and A = the total number of at bats. Write an equation for calculating a player's slugging percentage.
2. Get a baseball statistics or record book from the school library or gather statistics from a Web site such as www.mlb.com and calculate the slugging percentage for a current player (e.g., Sammy Sosa) and a retired player (e.g., Ty Cobb).
3. Compare your results with published statistics (either from a book or perhaps from the previous Web site) to see if your model is a good one.

chapter two

Graphing

IN THIS CHAPTER

"Mathematics is a game played according to certain simple rules with meaningless marks on paper." – David Hilbert

Graphs can help us visualize data and their behavior. When ordered-pair solutions of a linear equation are graphed, the result is a straight line. Its slope and direction can be meaningful in interpreting data or predicting future outcomes. In this chapter, we review the topics of graphing lines, interpreting slope, and graphing linear inequalities. We will also use the slope of a given line and a point on that line to write its linear equation.

Section 2-1   RECTANGULAR COORDINATE SYSTEM

You know how to graph a number as a point on a number line. Ordered pairs are graphed as points in a plane on what is called the **rectangular coordinate system**. The rectangular coordinate system consists of a horizontal axis called the *x*-**axis** and a vertical axis called the *y*-**axis**. The *x*- and *y*-axes intersect in a right angle. The point of intersection of the two axes is called the **origin**, and the coordinate plane is separated into four regions called **quadrants**. (See Figure 2-1.)

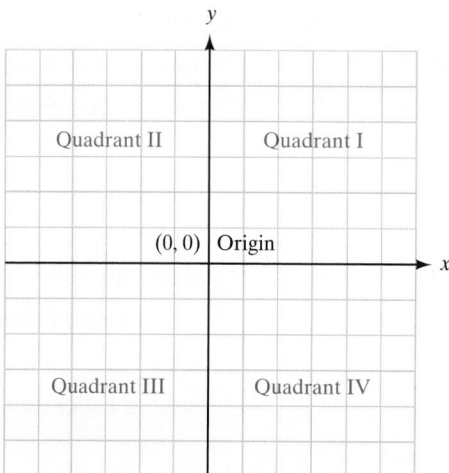

Figure 2-1
Rectangular coordinate system.

Each point in the plane corresponds to an ordered pair (x, y) of real numbers. The x and y values are called the **coordinates** of the point. The first number in the ordered pair is the *x*-**coordinate** and it tells you how many units to the left or right the point is from the origin. If x is positive you will move to the right of $(0, 0)$ and if x is negative you will move to the left of $(0, 0)$. The second number in the ordered pair is the *y*-**coordinate** and it tells you how many units up or down the point is from the *x*-axis. If y is positive, you will move up from the *x*-axis and if y is negative you will move down from the *x*-axis. The coordinates for the origin are $(0, 0)$.

Locating a point in a plane is called *plotting* the point. We will look at several examples of plotting points in the rectangular coordinate system in Example 1.

EXAMPLE 1   Plotting Points on the Rectangular Coordinate System

Plot the points $(-1, 3)$, $(4, -2)$, $(0, -3)$, $(2, 5)$, $(-2, -4)$ on a rectangular coordinate system.

The point $(-1, 3)$ is one unit to the left of the vertical axis and three units up from the horizontal axis. The other four points are plotted in the same fashion. (See Figure 2-2.)

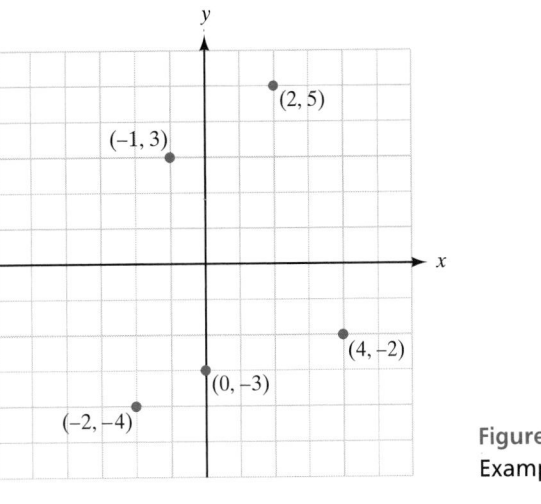

Figure 2-2
Example 1.

In the next example, we will determine the coordinates of the point by looking at the rectangular coordinate system.

EXAMPLE 2

Identifying the Coordinates of Points in a Rectangular Coordinate System

Determine the coordinates of the points shown in Figure 2-3.

Point A lies three units to the right of the vertical axis and two units below the horizontal axis. So point A is the ordered pair $(3, -2)$. The coordinates for the other four points can be determined in the same manner. The coordinate for point B is $(1, 4)$, point C is $(-5, 0)$, point D is $(-2, -2)$, and point E is $(-1, 3)$.

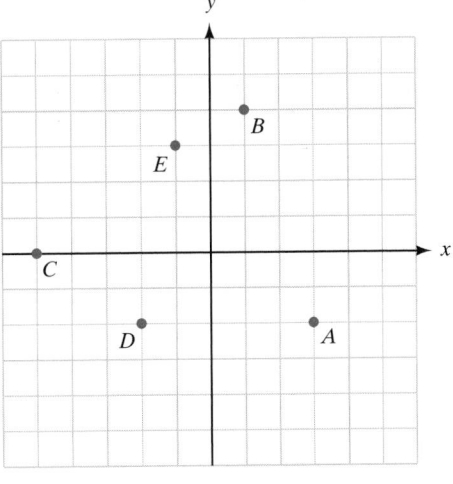

Figure 2-3
Example 2.

The rectangular coordinate system allows us to visualize relationships between two variables. In mathematics, relationships between variables are written as an equation. From the equation, we can construct a table of values that satisfies the given equation. In this chapter, we will be looking at a specific type of equation called a **linear equation**. The graph of a linear equation is a line. The **general form** for a linear equation is $Ax + By = C$. (Note that A and B are not both 0.) The **solutions** of a linear equation are the ordered pairs (x, y) that make the equation true. We can determine if an ordered pair is a solution of a linear equation by substituting those coordinates into the equation to verify that they give a true equality.

EXAMPLE 3   Verifying the Solutions of a Linear Equation

Are the ordered pairs $(3, 2)$ and $(7, 9)$ solutions of the linear equation $2x - y = 5$?

(a) We will verify the solution $(3, 2)$ by substituting it into the equation.

$$2x - y = 5$$
$$2(3) - (2) = 5$$
$$6 - 2 = 5$$
$$4 = 5 \quad \text{(false statement)}$$

Because the ordered pair $(3, 2)$ produces a false equality, this ordered pair is not a solution of this equation.

(b) We will verify the solution $(7, 9)$ by substituting it into the equation.

$$2x - y = 5$$
$$2(7) - (9) = 5$$
$$14 - 9 = 5$$
$$5 = 5 \quad \text{(true statement)}$$

Because the ordered pair $(7, 9)$ produces a true equality, this ordered pair is a solution of this equation.

You can find solutions of a linear equation by giving a value to one variable and solving the resulting equation for the other variable. It is often easier to solve the equation for one of the variables such as y and substitute values of x to generate a set of solutions.

EXAMPLE 4   Finding Solutions to a Linear Equation

Find five solutions to the linear equation $2x + y = 6$.

First, solve the equation for x or y. In this case, solving for y will be easier because y has a coefficient of 1.

◼ **TABLE 2-1   Example 4**

x	$y = -2x + 6$	y	Solution
3	$y = -2(3) + 6$	0	$(3, 0)$
4	$y = -2(4) + 6$	-2	$(4, -2)$
0	$y = -2(0) + 6$	6	$(0, 6)$
1	$y = -2(1) + 6$	4	$(1, 4)$
2	$y = -2(2) + 6$	2	$(2, 2)$

$$2x + y = 6$$

$$y = -2x + 6 \qquad \text{(subtract } 2x \text{ from both sides)}$$

Choose five values for x and then replace x with its value, and solve each equation for y. (See Table 2-1.)

◼

EXAMPLE 5   **Finding Solutions to a Linear Equation**

Find the indicated ordered-pair solutions to the linear equation

$$x - 6y = 18$$

$$(0, \underline{\quad}), (-2, \underline{\quad}), (\underline{\quad}, 1)$$

Because we are given the values of both x- and y-coordinates and asked to calculate the value of the missing coordinates, we will substitute the values into the equation as given.

(a) Find the ordered-pair solution $(0, \underline{\quad})$.

$$x - 6y = 18$$

$$0 - 6y = 18 \qquad \text{(replace } x \text{ with the value } 0)$$

$$-6y = 18$$

$$y = -3$$

This solution is $(0, -3)$.

(b) Find the ordered-pair solution $(-2, \underline{\quad})$.

$$x - 6y = 18$$

$$-2 - 6y = 18 \qquad \text{(replace } x \text{ with the value } -2)$$

$$-6y = 20$$

$$y = \frac{20}{-6} = -\frac{10}{3}$$

This solution is $(-2, -\frac{10}{3})$.

(c) Find the ordered-pair solution (___, 1)

$$x - 6y = 18$$

$$x - 6(1) = 18 \qquad \text{(replace } y \text{ with the value 1)}$$

$$x - 6 = 18$$

$$x = 24$$

This solution is $(24, 1)$.

Practice Set 2-1

Graph the following points on the same set of axes.

1. $(5, 3)$
2. $(1, 2)$
3. $(-3, -5)$
4. $(-5, -2)$
5. $(-4, 0)$
6. $(0, -2)$
7. $(-3, 3)$
8. $(-4, -5)$
9. $(0, 0)$
10. $(-3, 1)$
11. $(4, -3)$
12. $(5, -4)$

Problems 13 to 26 refer to the following diagram.

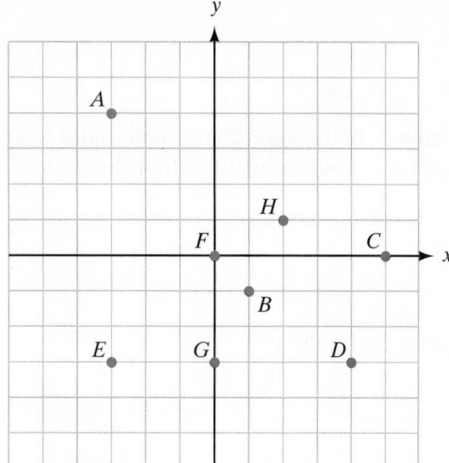

Give the coordinates and the quadrant or axis where each point is located.

13. F
14. H
15. A
16. B
17. E
18. C
19. G
20. D

Refer to the previous diagram and name the point(s) described.

21. The point is on the positive x-axis.
22. The x-coordinate is 0.
23. The y-coordinate is 0.
24. The point is on the negative y-axis.
25. The x-coordinate is the opposite of the y-coordinate.
26. The point in quadrant IV that is nearest the x-axis.
27. Is the ordered pair $(3, 4)$ a solution of the equation $2x - 5y = 26$? Show work to support your answer.
28. Is the ordered pair $(32, 0)$ a solution of the equation $\frac{3}{4}x + 8y = 24$? Show work to support your answer.
29. Is the ordered pair $(3, -2)$ a solution of the equation $3x + 2y = 5$? Show work to support your answer.

Use the following table to find ordered-pair solutions for the equations in problems 30 to 40.

x	y
0	
3	
	-2
	0

30. $x - y = 6$
31. $x + y = 8$
32. $2x + y = 6$
33. $x - 3y = 12$
34. $2x + 5y = 10$
35. $x + 4y = 0$
36. $3x - 4y = 8$
37. $y = x$
38. $4x - y = 3$
39. $-x - 2y = 6$
40. $x + y = 0$

Section 2-2   GRAPHING LINEAR EQUATIONS

In the previous section, we saw that the solutions to a linear equation can be represented by points on a rectangular coordinate system. The set of all solution points of a linear equation is called its graph. In this section, we will discuss graphing linear equations by finding points for x and y and by finding two specific points called the *x-intercept* and *y-intercept*.

EXAMPLE 6   Graphing a Line by Plotting Points

Sketch the graph of $2x - y = 4$.

First, let us solve the equation for y.

$$2x - y = 4$$

$$-y = -2x + 4 \qquad \text{(subtract } 2x \text{ from both sides)}$$

$$y = 2x - 4 \qquad \text{(divide both sides by } -1\text{)}$$

Second, choose arbitrary values for x and create a table of values. Because two distinct points determine a line, we need to find at least two solutions of the equation. Choosing more than two points allows us to see a pattern developing between the x and y coordinates. (See Table 2-2.)

Third, plot the points and draw a line connecting the five points. (See Figure 2-4.)

TABLE 2-2   Example 6

x	$y = 2x - 4$	Solution Point
3	$2(3) - 4 = 2$	$(3, 2)$
4	$2(4) - 4 = 4$	$(4, 4)$
0	$2(0) - 4 = -4$	$(0, -4)$
1	$2(1) - 4 = -2$	$(1, -2)$
2	$2(2) - 4 = 0$	$(2, 0)$

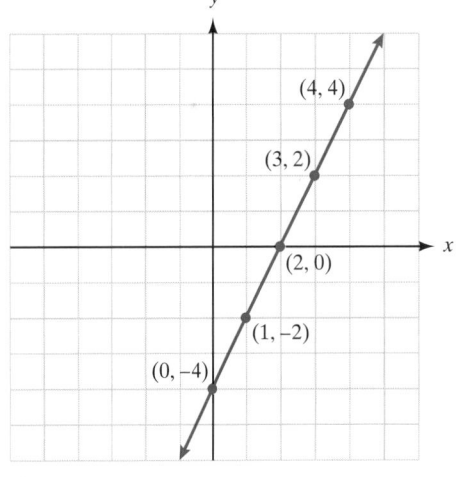

Figure 2-4
Example 6.

Notice that if we let x have the value 0 and find the y value that makes the equation true, we have found where the line crosses the y-axis. This y value is called the **y-intercept**. Similarly, the **x-intercept** is the x value where the line crosses the x-axis. You can find the x-intercept by giving y the value 0 and solving for x.

Rule

Finding the Intercepts of a Line

1. To find the *x*-intercept, replace *y* with 0 and solve the equation for *x*.
2. To find the *y*-intercept, replace *x* with 0 and solve the equation for *y*.

EXAMPLE 7   Graphing a Line Using Intercepts

Draw the graph of $4x + y = 3$.

To find the *x*-intercept, substitute 0 for *y* and solve for *x*.

$$4x + 0 = 3$$

$$4x = 3$$

$$x = \frac{3}{4} \qquad \text{x-intercept } \left(\frac{3}{4}, 0\right)$$

To find the *y*-intercept, substitute 0 for *x* and solve for *y*.

$$4(0) + y = 3$$

$$y = 3 \qquad \text{y-intercept } (0, 3)$$

To find another point on the line, choose any value for *x* and solve for *y*. Let $x = 1$.

$$4(1) + y = 3$$

$$4 + y = 3$$

$$y = -1 \qquad \text{point } (1, -1)$$

Graph the points $(\frac{3}{4}, 0)$, $(0, 3)$, and $(1, -1)$. Draw the graph of $4x + y = 3$. (See Figure 2-5.)

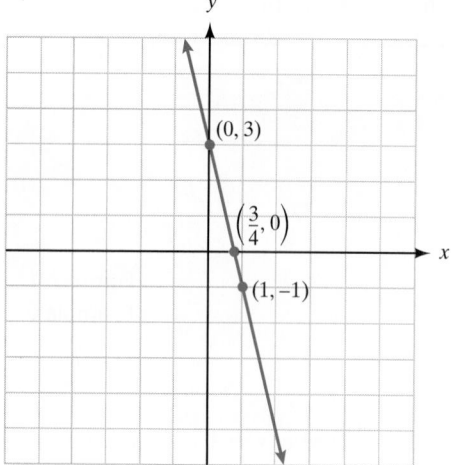

Figure 2-5
Example 7.

EXAMPLE 8   **Graphing a Line That Passes through the Origin**

Draw the graph of $x + 3y = 0$.

To find the x-intercept, substitute 0 for y and solve for x.

$$x + 3(0) = 0$$

$$x = 0 \qquad x\text{-intercept } (0, 0)$$

To find the y-intercept, substitute 0 for x and solve for y.

$$0 + 3y = 0$$

$$3y = 0$$

$$y = 0 \qquad y\text{-intercept } (0, 0)$$

Notice that the x- and y-intercepts are the same. This is a case when you *must* find another point to draw the graph, because two *different* points are needed to determine a line.

To find another point on the line, choose a value for y and solve for x. Let $y = 1$.

$$x + 3(1) = 0$$

$$x + 3 = 0$$

$$x = -3 \qquad \text{point } (-3, 1)$$

Graph the points $(0, 0)$ and $(-3, 1)$. Draw the graph of $x + 3y = 0$. (See Figure 2-6.)

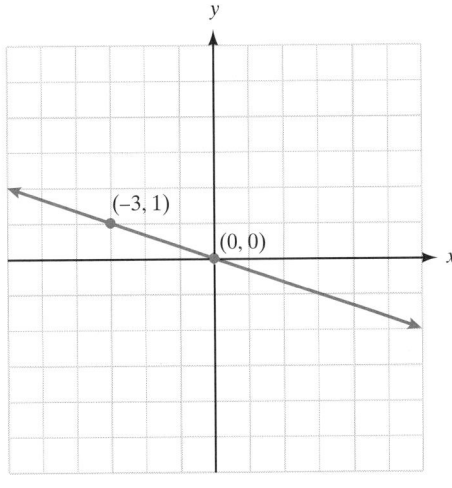

Figure 2-6
Example 8.

All of the graphs that we have looked at up to this point have been diagonal lines. There are two special types of lines called **horizontal** and **vertical lines**.

EXAMPLE 9   The Graph of a Horizontal Line

Draw the graph of $y = -2$.

    We can write this equation in standard form as $0x + y = -2$. Clearly, this equation is satisfied if y has a value of -2 and x has any value. If we choose the ordered pairs $(3, -2)$ and $(-4, -2)$, we see that the equation $y = -2$ is true in both cases. By plotting these points and drawing the graph, we have a horizontal line that has a y-intercept of -2. (See Figure 2-7.)

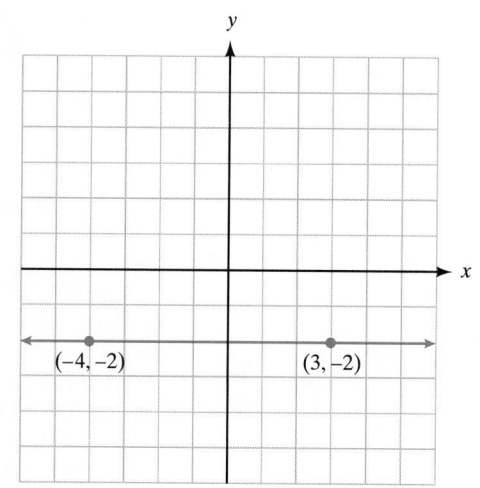

Figure 2-7
Example 9.

EXAMPLE 10   The Graph of a Vertical Line

Draw the graph of $x = 3$.

    We can write this equation in standard form as $x + 0y = 3$. Again, this equation will be satisfied if x is 3 and any value for y is chosen. If we choose ordered pairs $(3, -1)$ and $(3, 4)$, we see that the equation $x = 3$ is true for both cases. By plotting these points and drawing the graph, we have a vertical line with an x-intercept of 3. (See Figure 2-8.)

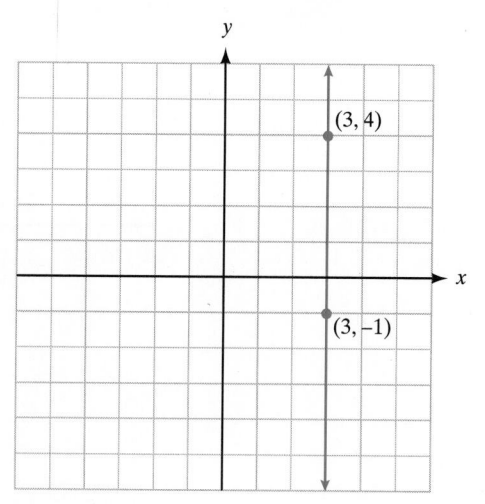

Figure 2-8
Example 10.

Important Equations

Equations for Horizontal and Vertical Lines

The equation of a vertical line is $x = a$, where a is the x-intercept of the line.
The equation of a horizontal line is $y = b$, where b is the y-intercept of the line.

A good way to remember the difference in the equations of horizontal and vertical lines is to note that if an equation has only an x variable, then that equation only intersects the x-axis and does not intersect the y-axis. Similarly, if the equation only has a y variable, it intersects the y-axis and does not intersect the x-axis. The only exceptions to this rule are the two axes themselves, $x = 0$ and $y = 0$.

Practice Set 2-2

1. Explain how to find the x-intercept of a linear equation.

2. Explain how to find the y-intercept of a linear equation.

3. If you calculate the x- and y-intercepts of an equation passing through the origin, what additional information will you need before you can graph the line?

4. Which one of these equations has its graph as a horizontal line?
   (a) $2x = 6$
   (b) $2y + 6 = 0$
   (c) $x + 6y = 0$
   (d) $x - 6 = 0$

Find the missing coordinate in each of the following solutions to the given equations.

5. $x - y = 6$ (__, 0)   (0, __)   (__, −2)

6. $x + y = 8$ (__, 0)   (0, __)   (__, −2)

7. $2x + y = 6$ (__, 0)   (0, __)   (__, −2)

8. $x - 3y = 12$ (__, 0)   (0, __)   (__, −2)

9. $y = -2$ (3, __)   (0, __)   (__, −2)

10. $x = 3$ (__, 0)   (3, __)   (__, −2)

11. $2x + 5y = 10$ (__, 0)   (0, __)   (__, −2)

12. $x + 4y = 0$ (__, 0)   (0, __)   (__, −2)

Find the x- and y-intercepts of each equation and use them to sketch the graphs.

13. $-x - 2y = 4$

14. $x - 5y = 10$

15. $-x - 2y = 5$

16. $x + 3y = 6$

17. $2x + 3y = 6$

18. $-3x - 2y = 12$

19. $3x - 5y = 15$

20. $4x - 3y = 12$

21. $4x - y = 3$

22. $2x - 5y = 8$

23. $3x = 2y$

24. $4x = -2y$

25. $x + y = 0$

26. $x - y = 0$

27. $2x + 8 = -4y$

28. $2x - y - 1 = 0$

29. $x = 2y + 2$

30. $3x - 6 = -y$

31. $y = 0.2x - 4$

32. $y = -0.25x + 3$

33. $x + \dfrac{1}{2}y = 3$

34. $\dfrac{3}{4}x + y = -2$

35. $x = -3$

36. $5x - 3 = 0$

37. $3y = 2$

38. $y - 6 = 0$

39. $3y + x = 4$

40. $5y - x = 8$

Section 2-3   **SLOPE**

The **slope** of a line can be defined as the steepness of the line. To describe the steepness, or slope, of an airplane's flight path shortly after takeoff, you would estimate the vertical rise for every 100 meters of horizontal run and compute the ratio. Slope can also be defined as a rate of change. In this example, the slope number indicates a rate of change in the airplane's altitude. (See Figure 2-9.)

$$\frac{\text{Rise}}{\text{Run}} = \frac{15}{100} = \frac{3}{20}$$

Figure 2-9
Slope of an airplane's flight path.

If you want to find the slope of a straight line, choose any two points on the line and count the number of units in the rise (up or down) and the run (right or left) from one point to the other. The slope is the ratio of the rise to the run.

EXAMPLE 11   **Calculating the Slope of a Line from a Graph**

Calculate the slope of the line shown in Figure 2-10.
    The line passes through the points $A(-2, 1)$ and $B(5, 4)$. Start at point A and count up three units. Then turn right and count seven units to reach point B. The rise, or vertical change, in moving from point A to point B is $+3$. The run, or horizontal change, in moving from point A to point B is $+7$. Because slope is the ratio of the rise to the run, the slope of this line is $\frac{3}{7}$. Notice that the line rises to the *right* when the slope is *positive*.

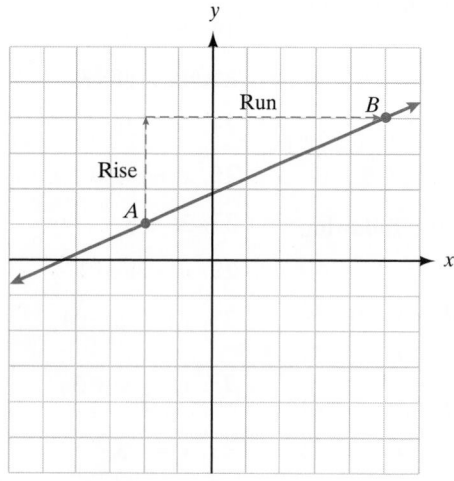

$$\frac{\text{Rise}}{\text{Run}} = \frac{\text{up } 3}{\text{right } 7} = \frac{3}{7}$$

Figure 2-10
Example 11.

EXAMPLE 12   Calculating the Slope of a Line from a Graph

Calculate the slope of the line in Figure 2-11.

The line passes through the points $A(-3, 5)$ and $B(1, 2)$. This time we calculate the slope by beginning at point B and moving to point A. The rise is three units up $(+3)$ and the run is four units left (-4).

The slope $= \frac{\text{rise}}{\text{run}} = \frac{3}{-4} = -\frac{3}{4}$. Notice that the line falls as it moves from *left* to *right* when the slope is *negative*.

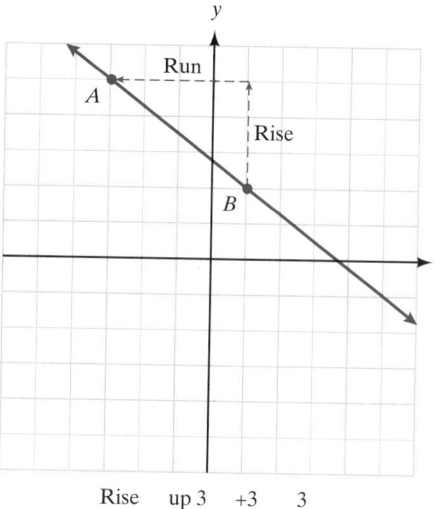

$$\frac{\text{Rise}}{\text{Run}} = \frac{\text{up } 3}{\text{left } 4} = \frac{+3}{-4} = -\frac{3}{4}$$

Figure 2-11
Example 12.

In general, we evaluate the behavior of a line as it moves from left to right. Therefore, lines with positive slopes are increasing as they move from left to right, and lines with negative slopes are decreasing as they move from left to right. (See Figure 2-12.)

We can now make a general definition for slope that can be used to calculate the slope of a line when given two points on the line. Given two points (x_1, y_1) and (x_2, y_2), to find the slope, subtract the y-coordinates and divide that by the difference in the x-coordinates. The variable m is generally used to represent the slope number.

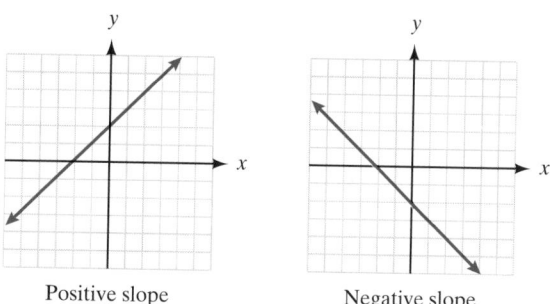

Positive slope   Negative slope

Figure 2-12

Important Equations

Slope of a Line

$$m = \frac{\text{rise}}{\text{run}} = \frac{\text{change in } y}{\text{change in } x} = \frac{\Delta y}{\Delta x} = \frac{y_2 - y_1}{x_2 - x_1}$$

where (x_1, y_1) and (x_2, y_2) are points on the given line.

When the formula for slope is used, the *order* of subtraction is important. You must compute the numerator and denominator using the *same order* of subtraction.

$$\text{Slope} = \frac{y_2 - y_1}{x_2 - x_1} = \frac{y_1 - y_2}{x_1 - x_2} \neq \frac{y_2 - y_1}{x_1 - x_2}$$

■ EXAMPLE 13   **Calculating the Slope of a Line Given Two Points on the Line**

Determine the slope of the line that passes through the points $(0, -5)$ and $(1, -3)$.

$$\text{Slope} = \frac{y_2 - y_1}{x_2 - x_1}$$

$$\text{Slope} = \frac{-3 - (-5)}{1 - 0}$$

$$\text{Slope} = \frac{2}{1} = 2$$

The slope of the line is 2.

■ EXAMPLE 14   **Calculating the Slope of a Line Given Two Points on the Line**

Find the slope of a line that passes through the points $(2, 3)$ and $(2, -1)$.

$$\text{Slope} = \frac{y_2 - y_1}{x_2 - x_1}$$

$$\text{Slope} = \frac{-1 - 3}{2 - 2}$$

$$\text{Slope} = \frac{-4}{0} \qquad \text{(division by 0 is undefined)}$$

Therefore, the slope of this line is undefined and if graphed will be a vertical line. (See Figure 2-13.)

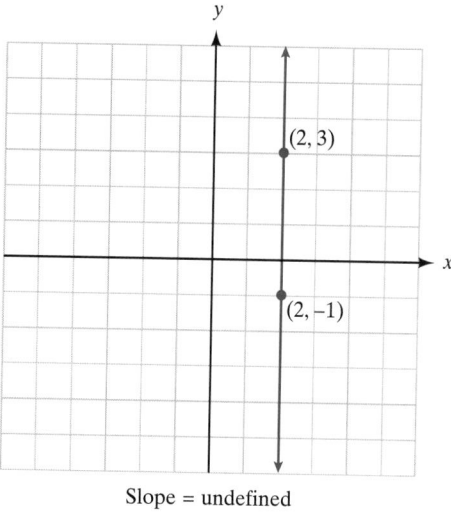

Slope = undefined

Figure 2-13
Example 14.

■ EXAMPLE 15   **Calculating the Slope of a Line Given Two Points on the Line**

Find the slope of a line that passes through the points $(-2, 4)$ and $(3, 4)$.

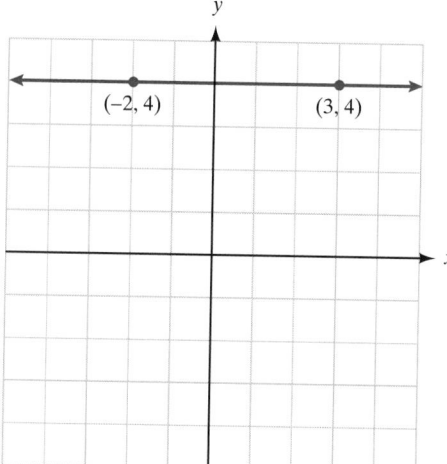

$$\text{Slope} = \frac{y_2 - y_1}{x_2 - x_1}$$

$$\text{Slope} = \frac{4 - 4}{3 - (-2)}$$

$$\text{Slope} = \frac{0}{5}$$

$$\text{Slope} = 0$$

If you graph the points $(-2, 4)$ and $(3, 4)$, you will see that the line is a horizontal line. (See Figure 2-14.)

Slope = 0

Figure 2-14
Example 15.

Rule

Slopes of Vertical and Horizontal Lines
The slope of a vertical line is undefined.
The slope of a horizontal line is 0.

We have discussed graphing linear equations by finding x- and y-intercepts and by finding additional points on the line. Another method that can be used to graph a linear equation is plotting a point on the line and applying the slope to find another point on the line. If we know one point on the line and the direction the line is taking (slope), then it is easy to graph it.

EXAMPLE 16   Graphing Lines Using the Slope

Graph the line that passes through the point $(1, -2)$ and has a slope of -1.

(a) First, we must plot the point $(1, -2)$.
(b) Second, we will apply the slope to find another point. Recall that, for graphing purposes, slope $= \frac{\text{rise}}{\text{run}}$. Because the slope is -1, we can rewrite this as $\frac{-1}{1}$. This tells us that the rise is -1 and the run is 1. Notice that any time the slope is an integer, the run will always equal 1. To apply the slope, we will start at $(1, -2)$ and then we will move down one unit and to the right one unit to locate another point on the line. Because the slope is negative, we must go in a negative direction one time. This means that we could also move up one and to the left one to find another point on the line. (See Figure 2-15.)

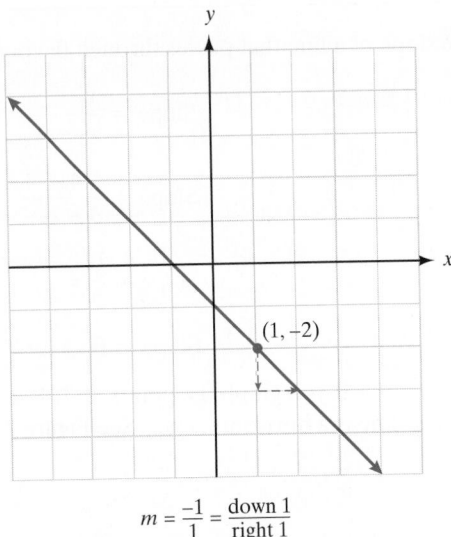

$$m = \frac{-1}{1} = \frac{\text{down } 1}{\text{right } 1}$$

Figure 2-15
Example 16.

EXAMPLE 17   Graphing Lines Using the Slope

Graph the line that passes through the point $(-1, -1)$ and has a slope of $\frac{2}{3}$.

Plot the point $(-1, -1)$. Apply the slope by starting at $(-1, -1)$ and moving up two units and right three units. Notice that because the slope is positive, we could also move down two units and to the left three units. (See Figure 2-16.)

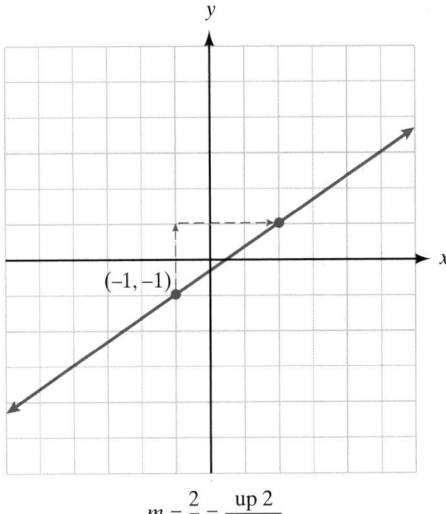

$$m = \frac{2}{3} = \frac{up\ 2}{right\ 3}$$

Figure 2-16
Example 17.

Recall from Section 2-1 that we discussed the general form for a linear equation. A second form for an equation of a line is called the **slope-intercept form**. This form of the equation is derived from the general form by solving it for y.

Important Equations

Linear Equations

General form:

$$Ax + By = C$$

Slope-intercept form:

$$y = mx + b$$

where m = slope and b = y-intercept.

We can easily graph a line by changing the general equation of the line into its slope-intercept form. Once we have written the equation in this form, the slope number (m) is the coefficient of x, and the y-intercept is the constant (b). Always start graphing from the location of the y-intercept. Then use the slope number to help you locate another point on the line.

EXAMPLE 18   **Graphing Lines Using the Slope-Intercept Form of the Equation**

Find the slope and y-intercept of the following linear equation and then graph the line.

$$3x + 2y = 3 \qquad \text{(original equation)}$$

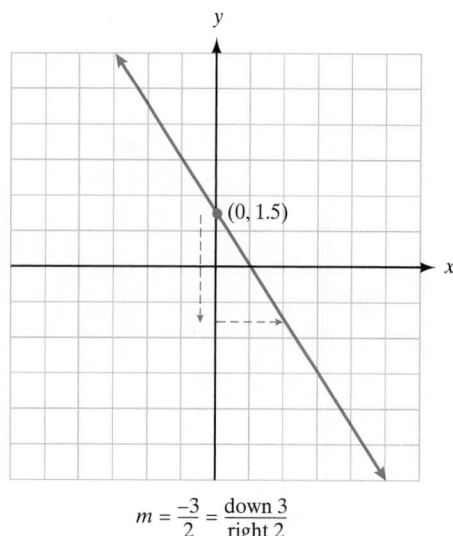

$$m = \frac{-3}{2} = \frac{\text{down } 3}{\text{right } 2}$$

Figure 2-17
Example 18.

Put the equation into slope-intercept form by solving the equation for y.

$$2y = -3x + 3 \qquad \text{(subtract } 3x \text{ from both sides)}$$

$$\frac{2y}{2} = \frac{-3x}{2} + \frac{3}{2} \qquad \text{(divide both sides by 2)}$$

$$y = \frac{-3x}{2} + \frac{3}{2} \qquad \text{(simplify)}$$

$$\text{Slope} = -\frac{3}{2} \qquad y\text{-intercept} = \frac{3}{2} = 1.5$$

Plot the y-intercept on the graph. Remember that the y-intercept is the point where the line crosses the y-axis, in this case $(0, 1.5)$. Next, apply the slope to find another point on the line. Start at $(0, 1.5)$ and move down three units and to the right two units. (See Figure 2-17.)

EXAMPLE 19   Graphing Lines Using the Slope-Intercept Form of the Equation

Find the slope and y-intercept of $-\frac{1}{3}x + \frac{1}{6}y = \frac{1}{2}$ and graph the line.

$$-\frac{1}{3}x + \frac{1}{6}y = \frac{1}{2} \qquad \text{(original equation)}$$

It will be easier to put this equation into slope-intercept form if the fractions are eliminated from the equation. This can be done by multiplying all terms of the equation by the lowest common denominator (LCD) of the fractions, which in this case is 6.

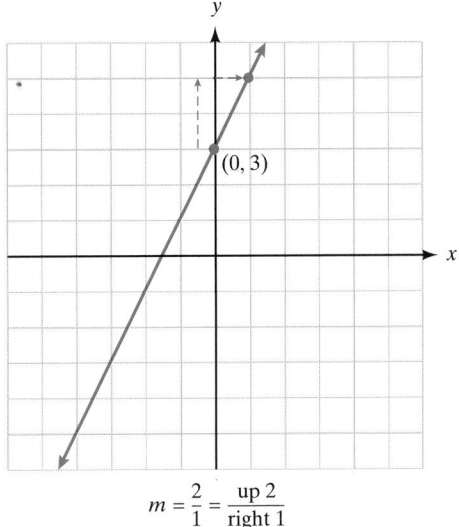

$$m = \frac{2}{1} = \frac{\text{up } 2}{\text{right } 1}$$

Figure 2-18
Example 19.

$$6\left(-\frac{1}{3}x\right) + 6\left(\frac{1}{6}y\right) = 6\left(\frac{1}{2}\right) \qquad \text{(multiply the equation by 6)}$$

$$-2x + y = 3$$

$$y = 2x + 3 \qquad \text{(add } 2x \text{ to both sides)}$$

$$\text{Slope} = \frac{2}{1} \qquad y\text{-intercept} = 3$$

Now graph the line. (See Figure 2-18.)

Parallel and Perpendicular Lines

We have been discussing the graphs of linear equations. Two lines that lie in the same plane and do not intersect are called **parallel lines**. The graphs of $y = 2x + 1$ and $y = 2x - 3$ are shown in Figure 2-19.

What do you notice about these lines? Because they do not intersect, they are parallel lines. Look carefully at the equations of these lines. The slope of $y = 2x + 1$ is 2 and the slope of $y = 2x - 3$ is also 2. This illustrates the relationship between slope and parallel lines.

Rule

The Slopes of Parallel Lines
If two lines are parallel, then they have the same slope.
If two lines have the same slope, then they are parallel.

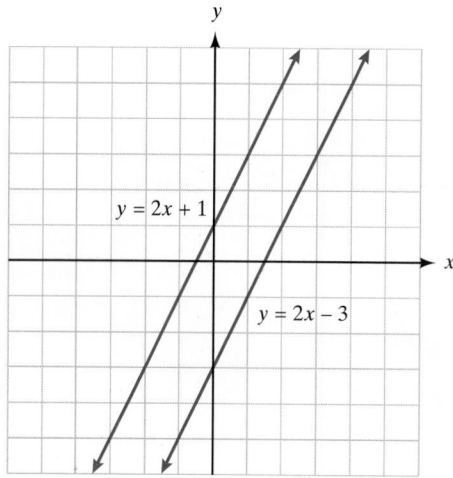

Figure 2-19
Two parallel lines.

Note that, although vertical lines have slopes that are undefined, they are parallel.

EXAMPLE 20   Finding the Slopes of Parallel Lines

Find the slope of a line parallel to the line whose equation is $-6x + 3y = 15$.

Because parallel lines have the same slope, the first step is to find the slope of $-6x + 3y = 15$. Recall that, to find the slope of a line, we put the equation into slope-intercept form ($y = mx + b$).

$$-6x + 3y = 15$$

$$3y = 6x + 15$$

$$y = 2x + 5 \qquad \text{slope is 2}$$

Therefore, the slope of any line parallel to $-6x + 3y = 15$ is 2.

The slopes of perpendicular lines also have a special relationship. **Perpendicular lines** are two lines that intersect to form right angles. The graphs of $y = -3x - 2$ and $y = \frac{1}{3}x + 1$ are shown in Figure 2-20.

Look carefully at the slopes of these two lines. The slope of $y = -3x - 2$ is -3. The slope of $y = \frac{1}{3}x + 1$ is $\frac{1}{3}$. What do you notice about the relationship of their slopes? One thing to note is that one line has a positive slope and the other has a negative slope. If they both had positive slopes or both had negative slopes, the lines would not form right angles. The directions of the lines are also reversed, and

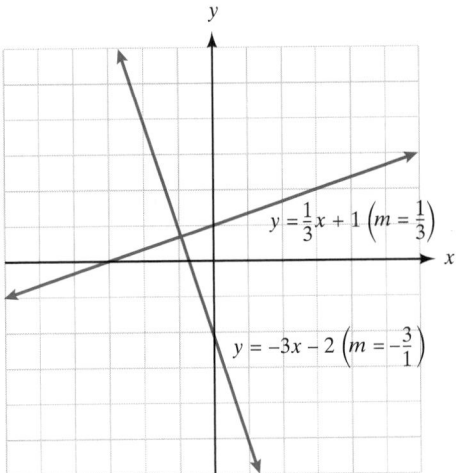

Figure 2-20
Two perpendicular lines.

that is illustrated by the change in the slope ratio. The ratio of numbers representing the rise over the run in the given line is reversed in the perpendicular line.

Rule

The Slopes of Perpendicular Lines
The slopes of nonvertical perpendicular lines are negative reciprocals of each other. The product of their slopes is -1.
Lines are also perpendicular if one of them is vertical and the other is horizontal.

The rule about negative reciprocals does not apply to vertical or horizontal lines because the slope of a vertical line is undefined and the reciprocal of the slope of a horizontal line would also be undefined. However, it is easy for us to see that a horizontal line would be perpendicular to a vertical line and vice versa.

■ EXAMPLE 21   **Finding the Slopes of Perpendicular Lines**

Find the slope of a line perpendicular to the line whose equation is $x - 2y = 2$.
Because the slopes of perpendicular lines are negative reciprocals of each other, we first find the slope of $x - 2y = 2$.

$$x - 2y = 2$$
$$-2y = -x + 2$$
$$y = \frac{1}{2}x - 1 \qquad \text{slope is } \frac{1}{2}$$

Therefore, the slope of any line perpendicular to $x - 2y = 2$ is the negative reciprocal of $\frac{1}{2}$ or $-\frac{2}{1} = -2$.

EXAMPLE 22   Slopes of Parallel and Perpendicular Lines

Determine if the graphs of $x = 3$ and $x = 5$ are parallel, perpendicular, or neither.

Because $x = 3$ is a vertical line going through the point $(3, 0)$ and $x = 5$ is a vertical line going through the point $(5, 0)$, their slopes are both undefined. Because the slopes are the same, the lines are parallel. Notice also that if you look at the graphs of the lines $x = 3$ and $x = 5$ you will see that the lines are parallel. (See Figure 2-21.)

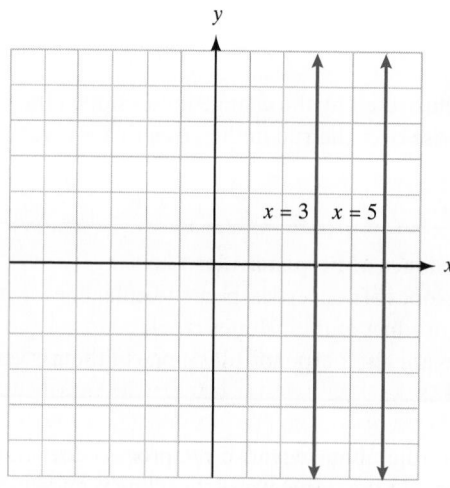

Figure 2-21
Example 22.

Practice Set 2-3

Determine the slopes of the lines passing through each pair of points.

1. $(6, 1)$ and $(8, -4)$ 2. $(5, 7)$ and $(4, -6)$

3. $(-3, 0)$ and $(8, 2)$ 4. $(-6, -3)$ and $(4, 1)$

5. $(-8, -2)$ and $(-4, 8)$ 6. $(6, 1)$ and $(6, 7)$

7. $(2.5, 3)$ and $(1, -9)$ 8. $\left(1\frac{3}{4}, \frac{1}{3}\right)$ and $\left(2, \frac{1}{6}\right)$

A line has a slope of 7. For each pair of points in problems 9 to 12 that are on the line, use the slope formula to find the missing coordinate.

9. $(x, 8)$ and $(4, 1)$

10. $(6, y)$ and $(2, -13)$

11. $(3, -6)$ and $(7, y)$

12. $(x, -2)$ and $(-6, -3)$

Find the slope and y-intercept and graph the following linear equations.

13. $y = -4x + 1$ **14.** $y = -4$

15. $3x + 2y = 6$ **16.** $x + 3y = 12$

17. $2x - 3y = 4$ **18.** $4x = 11$

19. $4y - x = 10$ **20.** $2x - y = 2$

21. $\dfrac{3}{4}x - \dfrac{1}{2}y = \dfrac{5}{8}$ **22.** $\dfrac{2}{3}x + 2y = 2$

23. $y = -x$ **24.** $3x - 2y = 7$

25. $4y = 12 + x$

Find the slope of a line parallel to lines with the following equations.

26. $y = -4x + 1$ **27.** $3x - 8y = 11$

28. $x = 3$ **29.** $-x + 6y = 2$

30. $y = 2$

Find the slope of a line perpendicular to lines with the following equations.

31. $x + y = 3$ **32.** $3x - 2y = 8$

33. $x = 2$ **34.** $-2x + 5y = 10$

35. $y = 2$

Determine whether the graphs of the following equations are parallel, perpendicular, or neither.

36. $x + y = 7$
   $x + y = -10$

37. $x + y = 5$
   $x - y = -5$

38. $3x + 2y = 6$
   $-2x + 3y = 4$

39. $y = 2x$
   $y = x$

40. $y = 3$
   $x = 3$

Section 2-4   **WRITING EQUATIONS OF LINES**

In previous sections, we looked at two forms of the linear equation. One we called the general form and it was written $Ax + By = C$. The second form was called the slope-intercept form and it was written $y = mx + b$. We used the slope-intercept form of the equation to help us graph lines. In this section, we will use this form of the equation to help us write the equation of a line if we are given specific information about the line.

In the equation $y = mx + b$, recall that m represents the slope of the line, b represents the y-intercept (where the line crosses the y-axis), and x and y represent points on the line. To write the equation of a line using $y = mx + b$, we need to find the values of m and b. Then, if necessary, we can rewrite this equation in general form $Ax + By = C$.

EXAMPLE 23   **Writing the Equation of a Line Using the Slope-Intercept Form**

Find an equation of a line in general form with a slope of -2 and a y-intercept of 4.

Look at the given information. Because we know the slope is -2 and the y-intercept is 4, we will substitute these values into the slope-intercept form of a linear equation.

$$y = mx + b \quad \text{(slope-intercept form)}$$
$$y = -2x + 4 \quad \text{(substitute } -2 \text{ for the slope and 4 for the } y\text{-intercept)}$$

Next, we rewrite the equation in general form.

$$2x + y = 4 \quad \text{(add } 2x \text{ to both sides)}$$

EXAMPLE 24   Writing the Equation of a Line Given One Point and the Slope

Find an equation of a line that passes through the point $(-2, 1)$ and has a slope of 3.

Given that the slope is 3 and the line passes through the point $(-2, 1)$, we will substitute these values into the slope-intercept form of the equation.

$$y = mx + b \quad \text{(slope-intercept form)}$$
$$1 = 3(-2) + b \quad \text{(substitute } m = 3, x = -2, y = 1)$$
$$1 = -6 + b \quad \text{(simplify)}$$
$$7 = b \quad \text{(add 6 to both sides to solve for } b)$$

Now write the equation of this line using the slope-intercept form by substituting the value of m and calculated value of b.

$$y = mx + b$$
$$y = 3x + 7 \quad \text{or} \quad 3x - y = -7 \quad \text{(general form)}$$

For every equation that we write, we need a minimum of two pieces of information: the slope and a point on the line. If the slope is not told to us directly, then there must be a way to calculate the slope from the information given. If we are given two points on the line, then we can use the formula $m = \frac{y_2 - y_1}{x_2 - x_1}$ to calculate the needed slope. If we are given the equation of another line and asked to write the equation of a line parallel to it or perpendicular to it, we can find our needed slope by using the slope-intercept form, $y = mx + b$, to find the slope of the given line for use in completing the problem.

EXAMPLE 25   Writing the Equation of a Line Given Two Points on the Line

Find an equation of a line that passes through the points $(3, 2)$ and $(-1, 5)$.

First, we must find the slope of the line. Let $(x_1, y_1) = (3, 2)$ and $(x_2, y_2) = (-1, 5)$. Remember the slope formula is

$$m = \frac{y_2 - y_1}{x_2 - x_1} = \frac{5 - 2}{-1 - 3} = \frac{3}{-4} = -\frac{3}{4}$$

Second, we will substitute one point and the slope into the slope-intercept form for a linear equation.

$$y = mx + b \qquad \text{(slope-intercept form)}$$

$$2 = -\frac{3}{4}(3) + b \qquad \left(\text{substitute } m = -\frac{3}{4}, x = 3, y = 2\right)$$

$$2 = -\frac{9}{4} + b \qquad \text{(simplify)}$$

$$2 + \frac{9}{4} = -\frac{9}{4} + \frac{9}{4} + b \qquad \left(\text{add } \frac{9}{4} \text{ to both sides}\right)$$

$$\frac{8}{4} + \frac{9}{4} = b \qquad \text{(common denominator)}$$

$$\frac{17}{4} = b$$

Now write the equation of the line using the slope and y-intercept that you have calculated.

$$y = mx + b$$

$$y = -\frac{3}{4}x + \frac{17}{4}$$

To check your work, substitute the x values of the original ordered pairs into this equation to determine if the y value calculated matches the original points.

Original point: $(3, 2)$ Let $x = 3$.   Then $y = -\frac{3}{4}(3) + \frac{17}{4}$

$$= -\frac{9}{4} + \frac{17}{4} = \frac{8}{4} = 2$$

Original point: $(-1, 5)$ Let $x = -1$.   Then $y = -\frac{3}{4}(-1) + \frac{17}{4}$

$$= \frac{3}{4} + \frac{17}{4} = \frac{20}{4} = 5$$

The points check, so this is the correct equation of the line that passes through these two points.

In Example 25, it does not matter which of the two points is labeled (x_1, y_1) and which is labeled (x_2, y_2). Try switching the labels to $(x_1, y_1) = (-1, 5)$ and $(x_2, y_2) = (3, 2)$ and reworking the problem to see that you obtain the same equation.

Horizontal and Vertical Lines

From the slope-intercept form of the equation of a line, you can see that a horizontal line has an equation of the form:

$$y = (0)x + b \qquad \text{(horizontal line has a slope of 0)}$$

$$y = b \qquad \text{(equation for a horizontal line)}$$

The Point-Slope Form

Another form of the line that can be used to find an equation of a line given the slope and a point on the line is the **point-slope form.**

$$y - y_1 = m(x - x_1)$$

$m = $ the slope of the line

(x_1, y_1) is a point on the line

Often it is convenient to use this form by filling in the missing numbers and simplifying the equation. Using the information in Example 24,

$$y - 1 = 3(x - (-2))$$

$$y - 1 = 3(x + 2)$$

$$y - 1 = 3x + 6$$

$$y = 3x + 7$$

or

$$3x - y = -7$$

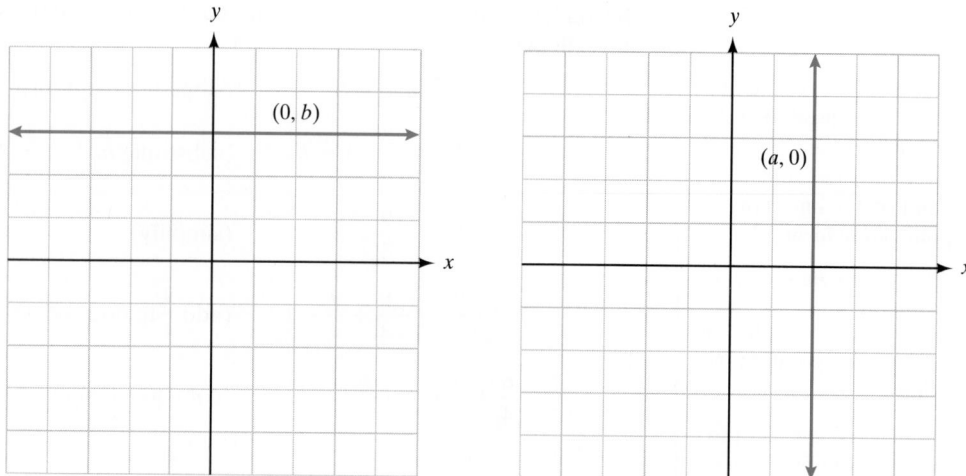

Figure 2-22
Graph of a horizontal line: $y = b$.

Figure 2-23
Graph of a vertical line: $x = a$.

This is consistent with the fact that each point on a horizontal line through $(0, b)$ has a y-coordinate of b. (See Figure 2-22.)

Similarly, each point on a vertical line through $(a, 0)$ has an x-coordinate of a. (See Figure 2-23.)

Therefore, a vertical line has an equation of the form $x = a$.

EXAMPLE 26   Writing the Equations of Horizontal and Vertical Lines

Write an equation for each of the following lines.

(a) Vertical line through $(-1, 4)$
(b) Line passing through $(-4, 6)$ and $(2, 6)$
(c) Line passing through $(3, 7)$ and $(3, -9)$

(a) Because the line is vertical and passes through the point $(-1, 4)$, we know that every point on the line has an x-coordinate of -1.
    Therefore, the equation is $x = -1$.
(b) The line through $(-4, 6)$ and $(2, 6)$ is horizontal, and every point on the line has a y-coordinate of 6.
    Therefore, the equation is $y = 6$.
(c) The line through $(3, 7)$ and $(3, -9)$ is vertical, and every point on the line has an x-coordinate of 3.
    Therefore, the equation is $x = 3$.

Parallel and Perpendicular Lines

Recall from the previous section the following facts about parallel and perpendicular lines:

Rule

The Slopes of Parallel and Perpendicular Lines
Parallel lines have the same slopes.
The slopes of nonvertical perpendicular lines are negative reciprocals of each other.

EXAMPLE 27

Writing the Equations of Lines Parallel and Perpendicular to a Given Line

Find the equations of the lines that pass through the point $(2, -4)$ and are (a) parallel and (b) perpendicular to the line $x - 2y = 7$.

Write the given equation in slope-intercept form in order to determine its slope.

$$x - 2y = 7$$

$$-2y = -x + 7 \qquad \text{(subtract } x \text{ from both sides of the equation)}$$

$$y = \frac{1}{2}x - \frac{7}{2} \qquad \text{(divide all terms by } -2\text{)}$$

Therefore, the line has a slope of $\frac{1}{2}$.

(a) Any line parallel to the given line must have the same slope. Therefore, the slope of our new line is $\frac{1}{2}$, and it passes through the point $(2, -4)$.

$$y - y_1 = m(x - x_1) \qquad \text{(point-slope form)}$$

$$y - (-4) = \frac{1}{2}(x - 2) \qquad \text{(substitute } m = \frac{1}{2}, x = 2, y = -4\text{)}$$

$$y + 4 = \frac{1}{2}(x - 2) \qquad \text{(simplify)}$$

$$y + 4 = \frac{1}{2}x - 1 \qquad \text{(distributive property)}$$

$$y = \frac{1}{2}x - 5 \qquad \text{(slope-intercept form)}$$

or

$$x - 2y = 10 \qquad \text{(general form)}$$

Notice that this equation and the original equation written in slope-intercept form ($y = \frac{1}{2}x - \frac{7}{2}$) are identical except for the values of b. All parallel lines will have identical slopes but different y-intercepts.

(b) Any line perpendicular to the given line must have a slope that is the negative reciprocal of $\frac{1}{2}$. Therefore, the slope of our second line is -2, and it passes through the point $(2, -4)$.

$$y = mx + b \qquad \text{(slope-intercept form)}$$

$$-4 = (-2)2 + b \qquad \text{(substitute } m = -2, x = 2, y = -4\text{)}$$

$$-4 = -4 + b \qquad \text{(simplify)}$$

$$0 = b \qquad \text{(solve for } b\text{)}$$

Write the equation: $y = -2x + 0$ or $y = -2x$.

Important Equations

Summary of Equations of Lines

1. General form of equation of a line: $Ax + By = C$
2. Slope-intercept form of equation of a line: $y = mx + b$
3. Point-slope form of the equation: $y - y_1 = m(x - x_1)$
4. Slope of line through (x_1, y_1) and (x_2, y_2): $m = \dfrac{y_2 - y_1}{x_2 - x_1}$
5. Parallel lines have the same slope.
6. Perpendicular lines have slopes that are negative reciprocals of each other (with the exception of vertical and horizontal lines).
7. Equation of a vertical line: $x = a$
8. Equation of a horizontal line: $y = b$

Practice Set 2-4

Find an equation of a line given the following information. Final answers should be left in slope-intercept form.

1. Slope $= -2$ y-intercept $= 8$

2. Slope $= 5$ y-intercept $= -3$

3. Passes through the point $(6, -2)$ slope $= \dfrac{1}{2}$

4. Passes through the point $(8, 1)$ slope $= -\dfrac{3}{4}$

5. Passes through the point $(-8, -9)$ slope $= -2$

6. Passes through the point $(2, 5)$ slope $= -1$

7. Passes through the point $(-1, 4)$ slope $= \dfrac{5}{2}$

8. Passes through the point $(-3, 1)$ slope $= -\dfrac{1}{3}$

9. Slope $= -\dfrac{1}{3}$ x-intercept $= 5$

10. Slope $= -\dfrac{2}{5}$ x-intercept $= -5$

11. Passes through the points $(4, 3)$ and $(7, 9)$

12. Passes through the points $(1, 3)$ and $(6, 10)$

13. Passes through the points $(5, -2)$ and $(8, -2)$

14. Passes through the points $(6, 1)$ and $(-2, 1)$

15. Passes through the points $(-1, 4)$ and $(1, 2)$

16. Passes through the points $(6, -3)$ and $(8, -9)$

17. Passes through the points $\left(7, 1\dfrac{1}{3}\right)$ and $\left(5, \dfrac{1}{3}\right)$

18. Passes through the points $\left(5\dfrac{2}{3}, 5\right)$ and $\left(2\dfrac{2}{3}, -4\right)$

19. Passes through the points $(-4, 3)$ and $(-1, -4.5)$

20. Passes through the points $(5, -2)$ and $(3, 1.5)$

21. Passes through the points $(3, -5)$ and $\left(3, 1\dfrac{1}{3}\right)$

22. Passes through the points $\left(5, 2\dfrac{3}{5}\right)$ and $(5, 2)$

23. Slope $=$ undefined   passes through $(1, 4)$

24. Slope $=$ undefined   passes through $(-3, 5)$

25. Passes through the point $(1, -7)$ and is parallel to the line $2x + y = 6$

26. Passes through the point $(-6, 5)$ and is parallel to the line $x - 2y = 8$

27. Passes through the point $(3, 10)$ and is perpendicular to the line $x - 3y = -4$

28. Passes through the point $(-2, 6)$ and is perpendicular to the line $2x - y = 4$

29. Passes through the point $(-2, 9)$ and is parallel to the line through $(2, 8)$ and $(-1, 11)$

30. Passes through the point $(-1, -4)$ and is parallel to the line through $(0, 1)$ and $(5, -1)$

31. Passes through the point $(-5, 2)$ and is perpendicular to the line through the points $(-4, 1)$ and $(1, 3)$

32. Passes through the point $(3, 6)$ and is perpendicular to the line through the points $(5, 2)$ and $(6, -1)$

33. Passes through the point $(3, 2)$ and is parallel to the line $x = 4$

34. Passes through the point $(-6, 1)$ and is parallel to the line $y = 8$

35. Passes through the point $(-1, 3)$ and is perpendicular to the line $x = 4$

36. Passes through the point $(-2, 0)$ and is perpendicular to the line $y = -9$

37. x-intercept of 3 and y-intercept of -1

38. x-intercept of -5 and y-intercept of -6

39. Passes through the origin and has a slope of -1

40. Passes through the origin and has a slope of $\dfrac{2}{3}$

Section 2-5   LINEAR INEQUALITIES

In the previous sections, we discussed how to graph a linear equation. We will now look at the graph of a **linear inequality**.

The graph of an inequality in two variables consists of all ordered pairs that make the statement of the inequality true. Inequalities in two variables are graphed similarly to equations in two variables. The graph of $y = -2x + 3$ is a line with a slope of -2 and a y-intercept of 3. This line separates the coordinate plane into two regions. (See Figure 2-24.)

Similarly, the graph of $y \geq -2x + 3$ is a region or half plane bordered by a line with a slope of -2 and a y-intercept of 3. The "greater than" symbol tells us to shade the region above the line. In that region, the value of y is greater than $-2x + 3$. Look at Figure 2-25.

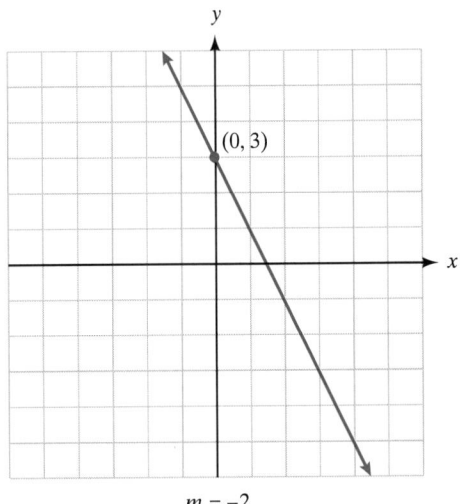

$m = -2$

Figure 2-24
Graph of $y = -2x + 3$.

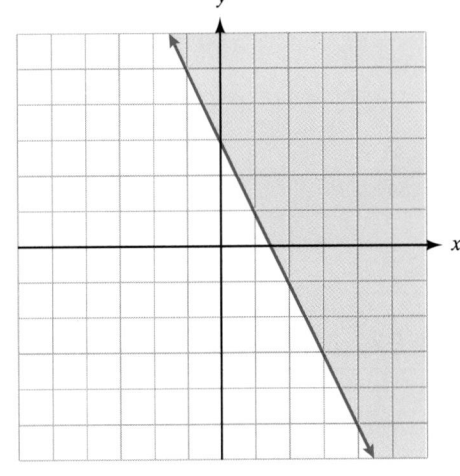

Figure 2-25
Graph of $y \geq -2x + 3$.

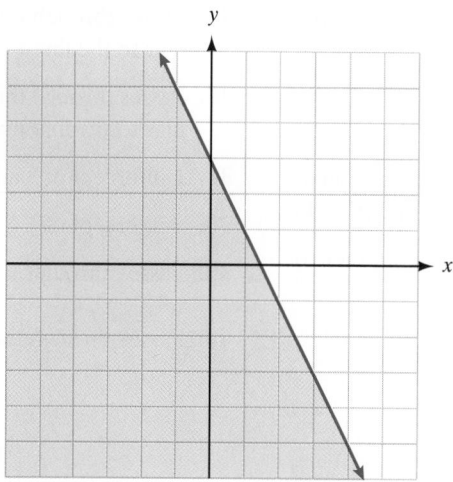

Figure 2-26
Graph of $y \leq -2x + 3$.

The graph of $y \leq -2x + 3$ is also a region or half plane bordered by a line with a slope of -2 and a y-intercept of 3. The "less than" symbol tells us to shade the region below the line. In that region, the value of y is less than $-2x + 3$. (See Figure 2-26.)

The line described by $y = -2x + 3$ is called the **boundary line**. It divides the plane into two regions. If the boundary line is part of the graph ($\leq$ or $\geq$), it is drawn as a solid line. If the boundary line is not part of the graph ($<$ or $>$), it is drawn as a broken line.

Rule

Steps for Graphing Linear Inequalities

1. Graph the boundary line.
   (a) Solve the inequality for y.
   (b) Identify the slope and the y-intercept.
2. Draw a solid line if the equality is included ($\leq$ or $\geq$).
   Draw a broken line if the equality is not included ($<$ or $>$).
3. If the equation is in the form $y >$ or $y \geq$, then shade above the line. If the equation is in the form $y <$ or $y \leq$, then shade below the line.

■ EXAMPLE 28   **Graphing a Linear Inequality**

Graph $3x + y \leq 2$.

$$3x + y \leq 2 \qquad \text{(solve for } y\text{)}$$

$$y \leq -3x + 2 \qquad \text{(subtract } 3x \text{ from both sides)}$$

$$\text{Slope} = -3 \qquad y\text{-intercept} = 2 \qquad \text{(identify the slope and } y\text{-intercept)}$$

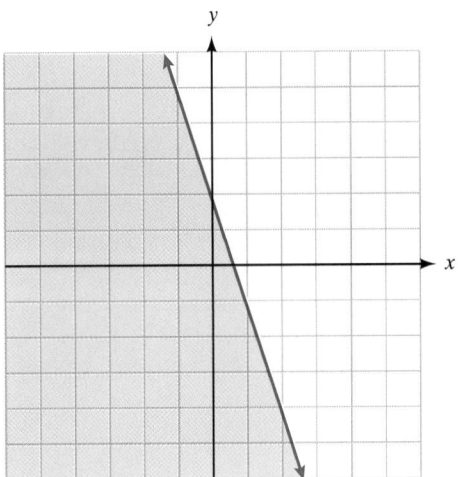

Figure 2-27
Example 28.

Draw the line using a solid line because the equality is included. Our inequality is of the form "$y \leq$," so our rules tell us to shade below the boundary line. (See Figure 2-27.)

When solving inequalities for y, there is one important rule to remember: If you divide or multiply an inequality by a negative number, the direction of the inequality must be reversed. So if we are solving $-2y > 4$, our final answer would be $y < -2$. If we do not reverse the inequality sign, the answer includes values of y greater than -2, and these values will not check in the original inequality.

EXAMPLE 29   **Graphing a Linear Inequality**

Graph $x - 2y < 2$.

$x - 2y < 2$	(solve for y)
$-2y < -x + 2$	(subtract x from both sides)
$y > \dfrac{1}{2}x - 1$	(divide both sides by -2; change the direction of the inequality)
Slope $= \dfrac{1}{2}$ y-intercept $= -1$	(identify the slope and y-intercept)

Draw the line using a broken line because the equality is not included. Shade the portion of the graph that satisfies the inequality. Because this in-

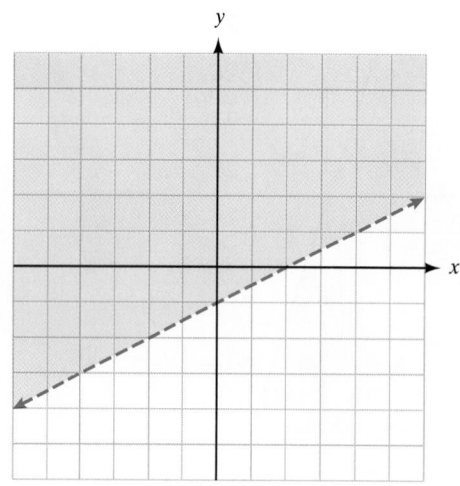

Figure 2-28
Example 29.

equality is of the form "$y >$," our rule tells us to shade above the boundary line. (See Figure 2-28.)

If you are unsure about your shading, you can determine which region to shade by testing one point from inside each region. If a point makes the inequality true, then that point lies on the side of the boundary line that should be shaded. For example, if we test the point $(0, 0)$ for the inequality in Example 29, we will discover that it satisfies the equation, and therefore the shading should be on the same side as the point $(0, 0)$.

$$x - 2y < 2$$

$$0 - 2(0) < 2 \qquad \text{(substitute into the inequality)}$$

$$0 < 2 \qquad \text{(true statement)}$$

Practice Set 2-5

Graph the following linear inequalities.

1. $y \leq x + 4$	2. $y \leq x - 2$	9. $x - y < -1$
3. $y > x - 3$	4. $y > x + 1$	11. $y \geq -3$
5. $y \geq 2x$	6. $y \geq -3x$	13. $2x + 5y \leq -10$
7. $x + y \geq 2$	8. $x + y \geq 1$	15. $3x - 2y \leq 5$

9. $x - y < -1$ 10. $x - y < -5$

11. $y \geq -3$ 12. $y \geq 2$

13. $2x + 5y \leq -10$ 14. $3x + 4y \leq -12$

15. $3x - 2y \leq 5$ 16. $5x - 2y \leq 8$

17. $4 - 3y > 2x$ 18. $6 - 2y > 4x$

19. $y < x - 1$

20. $y < 2x + 1$

21. $x < 2y + 4$

22. $x < 3y + 2$

23. $5x + 4y > 20$

24. $5x - 2y < -10$

25. $x + 2 \leq -3$

26. $x < 3$

27. $y > x$

28. $-2x - 0.5y > -1$

29. $x - 2y > 4$

30. $3x + 4y < 1$

Chapter Summary

Key Terms, Properties, and Formulas

boundary line	parallel lines	vertical line
coordinate	perpendicular lines	x-axis
general form	quadrant	y-axis
horizontal line	rectangular coordinate system	x-coordinate
linear equation	slope	y-coordinate
linear inequality	slope-intercept form	x-intercept
origin	solutions	y-intercept

Points to Remember

The slope of a line can be found by using two points on the line or by putting the equation of a line into slope-intercept form.

The x-intercept of a line is found by substituting a 0 for y and solving for x. The y-intercept of a line is found by substituting a 0 for x and solving for y.

Lines that have the same slope are parallel.

Lines that are perpendicular (except for vertical and horizontal lines) have slopes that are negative reciprocals of each other.

The slope of a horizontal line is 0. The slope of a vertical line is undefined.

An equation of a line can be found from the slope and the y-intercept, the slope and any point on the line, or from two points on the line.

$$\text{Slope of a line} = \frac{\text{rise}}{\text{run}} = \frac{y_2 - y_1}{x_2 - x_1}$$

General form (linear equation):

$$Ax + By = C$$

where A, B, and C are integers and $A > 0$.

Slope-intercept form (linear equation):

$$y = mx + b$$

where m is the slope and b is the y-intercept.

Point-slope form (linear equation):

$$y - y_1 = m(x - x_1)$$

where m is the slope and (x_1, y_1) is a point on the line.

Chapter Review Problems

Graph each ordered pair in problems 1 to 4 and name the quadrant or axis on which it lies.

1. $(2, 4)$
2. $(-3, 4)$
3. $(-2, -1)$
4. $(0, 6)$

5. Is the point $(1, -4)$ a solution to the equation $2x - y = 6$? Show work to support your answer.

Determine the missing coordinate that satisfies the linear equation.

6. $2x - y = 8$ $(-2, \_\_\_)$
7. $y = -7x + 2$ $(6, \_\_\_)$
8. $3x + 2y = 8$ $(\_\_\_, 4)$
9. $y = 7$ $(\_\_\_, 7)$
10. $5x - 3y = 11$ $(0, \_\_\_)$

Find the x- and y-intercepts and the slope of the following linear equations. Sketch the graph for each equation.

11. $y = \dfrac{1}{3}x - 1$
12. $x = -4$
13. $2x + y = 5$
14. $-3x + 2y = 6$
15. $x - 3y = -3$
16. $y = 3$

Determine the slope of the line passing through each pair of points.

17. $(1, 4)$ $(2, 7)$
18. $(-2, 4)$ $(5, -10)$
19. $(-3, 6)$ $(-3, 8)$
20. $(-4, 6)$ $(-6, -1)$

Write an equation of a line given the following information.

21. Slope $= 2$ y-intercept $= -3$
22. Passes through the points $(-2, 6)$ and $(-3, -4)$
23. Slope $= -2$ passes through the point $(3, 4)$
24. Passes through the point $(-2, 5)$ and is perpendicular to the line $y = 2x - 5$
25. y-intercept $= 4$ parallel to the line $3x - 4y = 9$

Graph the following linear inequalities.

26. $y > -2x + 3$
27. $2x - 2y \leq 6$
28. $-y < -x$
29. $x \leq 5$
30. $4x + 3y \geq 6$

Chapter Test

Graph each ordered pair in problems 1 to 3 and name the quadrant in which it lies.

1. $(-2, 3)$
2. $(3, -1)$
3. $(-3, -4)$

4. Is the ordered pair $(-3, 5)$ a solution of the equation $3x + 2y = -1$? Show work to support your answer.

Graph each linear equation. State the x- and y-intercepts and the slope.

5. $-4x + y = -4$
6. $2x + y = -4$
7. $x = 5$
8. $x + y = 3$
9. $y = -2$

Find the slope of the following lines.

10. A line through the points $(2, -1)$ and $(-3, -2)$
11. A line perpendicular to a line whose slope is -3
12. A vertical line
13. The line with the equation $y = x$

Write the equation of a line given the following information.

14. Slope $= -3$ passes through $(-1, 6)$

15. Slope $= \frac{1}{2}$ passes through $(-6, 1)$

16. Passes through $(0, -4)$ and $(1, 2)$

17. y-intercept $= 4$ and is perpendicular to the line $2x - y = 3$

18. Passes through the point $(2, -3)$ and is parallel to the line $x = 5$

Graph the following linear inequalities.

19. $y < -2x - 3$

20. $2x - 3y \leq -6$

Suggested Laboratory Exercises

LAB EXERCISE 1

Slope Activity

Purpose: Slope refers to the steepness of a line or an incline. In this exercise, you will measure the rise and run of several staircases and calculate their slopes. The values that you obtain will then be compared to building code guidelines to determine if the stairs in question meet the building code safety standards.

Procedure: Choose several different stairways in your classroom building or nearby buildings or at home. If all of the individual steps are of equal height and width, carefully measure the height (rise) of one step and the width (run) of one step. The choice of units should not affect the value of the slope, because slope is a simple ratio of the amount of rise to the amount of run. To confirm this, measure the values of rise and run in both English (USCS) and metric (SI) units. Record these data in a table similar to the one that follows. Calculate the slope using both sets of units.

Note: If individual steps are of different heights or widths, you will have to measure all the heights and add them to get the total rise for the stairs, and then measure all the widths and add them to get the total run for the stairs.

Data:

Staircase #1: Location: _____.

Units	Rise	Run	Slope Fraction	Decimal
Metric (SI)				
USCS				

Staircase #2: Location: _____.

Units	Rise	Run	Slope Fraction	Decimal
Metric (SI)				
USCS				

Analysis: Now you must find out the local building code for the type of building in which the stairs are located. Call the office of the local building inspector for your city or county to get this value. Some information may be available on local municipal Web sites. Or use this value as a general guide: Staircases for general use by the public should have a slope of 0.545 or less. Do the staircases you measured meet the building code?

LAB EXERCISE 2   ## Linear Equations Practice Activity

Do each of the following on graph paper. Answer all questions posed on this lab sheet.

1. Using graph paper and a ruler, plot the points $(-6, 2)$ and $(6, 10)$.
2. Sketch the line that goes through these two points. Be sure that the line extends past both points and intersects both the x- and y-axes.
3. Based on the graph alone, should the slope of this line be positive or negative?
4. Using the coordinates of the two points given in question 1, use the slope formula to calculate the slope of this line.
5. By counting blocks vertically and horizontally on your graph, verify the slope you calculated in question 4.
6. What are the x- and y-intercepts of this line? Look at your graph.
7. Find the slope and y-intercept of the line $2x - 3y = -18$. Is this consistent with the line you have drawn on your graph?
8. Using the equation in question 7, complete the following ordered pairs:
   $(12, \_\_)$ $(-3, \_\_)$ $(3, \_\_)$ $(9, \_\_)$.
9. Plot the ordered pair solutions you calculated in question 8 on the graph. They should lie on your line.

LAB EXERCISE 3   ## Linear Equations on the TI-83 Plus® Graphing Calculator

The purpose of this lab activity is to help you to become familiar with a graphing calculator. There are several different brands of graphing calculators in use today, and they all have similar functions. This exercise is written for the TI-83 Plus, but is adaptable to other brands. The main point is to learn to graph using the calculator. Other functions of the calculator will be covered if necessary or useful.

All equations *must* be written in slope-intercept form ($y = mx + b$) before entering them into the calculator. Be sure that you have reviewed Section 2-3 of this chapter before you begin this exercise.

Now get your calculator and begin:

1. Turn the calculator on and check to see if the screen is dark enough to easily see the blinking cursor in the upper left-hand corner of the screen. If not, press the 2nd key and then hold down the up ▲ or down ▼ arrow to darken or lighten the screen. Now press the WINDOW key. If the list shown does not look like the following list, then use the down arrow ▼ arrow key followed by the CLEAR key to remove the numbers and then enter the ones shown below. This sets the size of the graph to run from 10 to −10 on both axes.

   $X_{min} = -10$ $X_{max} = 10$ $X_{scl} = 1$ $Y_{min} = -10$ $Y_{max} = 10$ $Y_{scl} = 1$

2. Press the $\boxed{Y=}$ button. You should see a list that goes from Y_1 to Y_8. This screen will allow you to enter up to eight equations or functions to graph on one screen.

3. Type in "x" using the $\boxed{X,T,\Theta}$ key so that $Y_1 = x$ is shown. If you type this incorrectly, press $\boxed{DEL}$ to erase it and start over. Once you have the equation typed in, press $\boxed{GRAPH}$. Record the graph as seen on your calculator in the space given here. Call this line number 1 on your drawing. Now hit the $\boxed{Y=}$ key again, followed by the down arrow key and type in $5x$ so that $Y_2 = 5x$. Press the $\boxed{GRAPH}$ key and you should see both lines graphed. Record the second line on this paper as line number 2. Now go back to the $\boxed{Y=}$ screen as before and let $Y_3 = 0.2x$. Remember that $0.2 = \frac{1}{5}$. $\boxed{GRAPH}$ and record this line as number 3. *If you use a fractional coefficient, you must use parentheses around the fraction for the calculator to interpret it correctly: $Y = (1/5)x$.*

Based on the lines shown on your calculator screen, you should have three lines drawn in Figure 2-29 that represent these equations.

1. $Y_1 = x$
2. $Y_2 = 5x$
3. $Y_3 = 0.2x$

    or

    $Y_3 = \frac{1}{5}x$

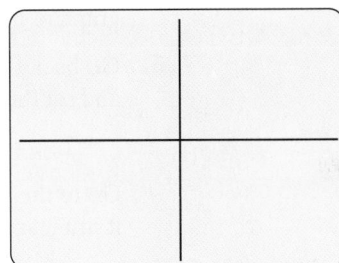

Figure 2-29

Use the graphs of these three lines to answer each of the following questions.

(a) Which line is the steepest?
(b) How does the coefficient of x in the equation $Y = mx + b$ affect the graphs?
(c) What do these three lines have in common?

4. Go back to the $\boxed{Y=}$ screen and press $\boxed{CLEAR}$ to erase each equation. Now enter each of the following equations. $\boxed{GRAPH}$ them and record them in Figure 2-30.

1. $Y_1 = 2x + 5$
2. $Y_2 = 2x - 5$
3. $Y_3 = 2x$

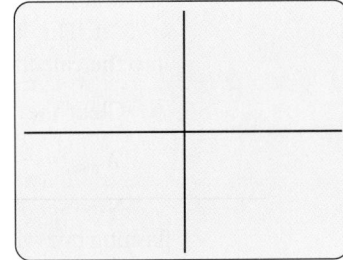

Figure 2-30

Answer the following questions about these graphs.

(a) What do these three graphs have in common?
(b) How do the graphs differ from each other?
(c) Explain how the value of b in $Y = mx + b$ affects each graph.
(d) What do you know about the slopes of these lines?

5. Go back to the $\boxed{Y=}$ screen, clear all the equations, and enter equations $Y_1 = 2x - 5$ and $Y_2 = -2x - 5$. Then $\boxed{GRAPH}$ and draw them in Figure 2-31.

Figure 2-31

Answer each of the following questions about these graphs.

(a) What do these two graphs have in common?
(b) Which graph is steeper or are they both of the same steepness?
(c) How does the sign of the coefficient of x in the equation $Y = mx + b$ affect the graph of a line?

6. Go back to the $\boxed{Y=}$ screen and clear all equations. Press the $\boxed{WINDOW}$ key and set the values as follows:

$$X_{min} = -6 \quad X_{max} = 6 \quad X_{scl} = 1 \quad Y_{min} = 4 \quad Y_{max} = 4 \quad Y_{scl} = 1$$

Go to the $\boxed{Y=}$ screen and set $Y_1 = \frac{2}{3}x + 1$. $\boxed{GRAPH}$ the equation and record it in Figure 2-32.

Figure 2-32

Using the rules about the slopes of perpendicular lines, find the equation of a line that has the same y-intercept as the given line ($y = \frac{2}{3}x + 1$) but is *perpendicular* to it. This is line Y_2. Write it here: $Y_2 =$ _____. Now enter the equation into the calculator and $\boxed{GRAPH}$ it. Does Y_2 look perpendicular to Y_1?

7. Clear the $\boxed{Y=}$ screen and reset the $\boxed{WINDOW}$ as below:

$$X_{min} = -10 \quad X_{max} = 10 \quad X_{scl} = 1 \quad Y_{min} = -10 \quad Y_{max} = 10 \quad Y_{scl} = 1$$

Now set $Y_1 = 3x - 6$ and $\boxed{GRAPH}$ it. Now press the $\boxed{TRACE}$ key. A small flashing box will appear on the line and values of X and Y will be shown at the bottom of the screen. If you now press the left $\boxed{\blacktriangleleft}$ and right $\boxed{\blacktriangleright}$ arrow keys, you will see the little box move along the line and the values of X and Y at the bottom of the screen will change. By moving the box, locate the x- and y-intercepts of this line. What are they shown to be on the calculator screen? According to the $\boxed{TRACE}$ function:

(a) the x-intercept is _____.
(b) the y-intercept is _____.

Are these exact values or are they just approximations? _____
Find the x- and y-intercepts algebraically:

(a) x-intercept = _____.
(b) y-intercept = _____.

8. Return to the $\boxed{Y=}$ screen and enter each of the following equations. Then $\boxed{\text{GRAPH}}$ these equations and record them in Figure 2-33.

   1. $Y_1 = 3$
   2. $Y_2 = 7$
   3. $Y_3 = -3$
   4. $Y_4 = -7$

Figure 2-33

Now find a single equation that is perpendicular to all of these lines (do not use the y-axis). Write its equation here and graph it as Y_5. $Y_5 = $ _____.

LAB EXERCISE 4

Recycling

According to recycling records kept by the Environmental Protection Agency (found at www.epa.gov on the Web), 38% of postconsumer newsprint was recycled in 1990, 45% in 1992, 47% in 1994, and 60% in 2001 (the last year for which the EPA currently has data). The least-squares-fit equation for these data (this will be covered in Chapter 7) written in slope-intercept form is

$$y = 2.1x + 37$$

where y = percent recycled and x = the year number coded as 1990 = 1, 1992 = 3, 1994 = 5, and 2001 = 12.

(a) Graph these data (percent recycled vs. year number code), leaving room at both ends of your graph for past and future years.
(b) Is the slope positive or negative? What does the slope tell us about the rate of postconsumer newsprint recycling?
(c) Calculate the x-intercept year. What is it and what is the meaning of this point for these data? Plot this point on your graph.
(d) During what year will recycling theoretically reach 75% according to this model? Plot this point on your graph.
(e) Theoretically, will recycling ever reach 100%? Practically speaking, is that really possible?

LAB EXERCISE 5

Mmm, Mmm, Good—Prune Juice

A local supermarket has been tracking the sales of a popular new product, frozen prune juice. The supermarket manager let C be the number of cans sold and P the price per can (in dollars) and came up with the following linear equation to model the expected sales of frozen prune juice as a function of the price per can:

$$C(P) = -3500P + 14,000$$

1. Draw a graph of this function in the first quadrant only.
2. What is the x-intercept of this function and what does it mean in this situation?

chapter three

Functions

3

IN THIS CHAPTER

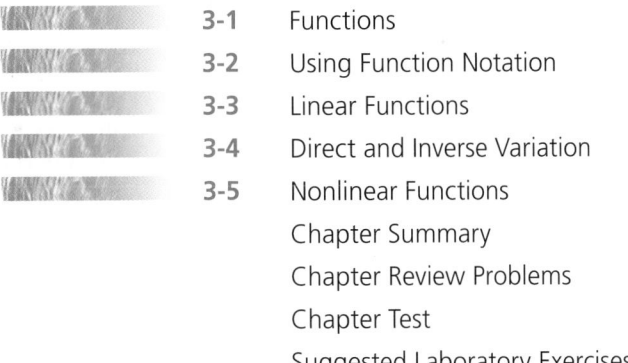

"Our federal income tax law defines the tax y to be paid in terms of the income x; it does so in a clumsy enough way by pasting several linear functions together, each valid in another interval or bracket of income. An archeologist who, five thousand years from now, shall unearth some of our income tax returns together with relics of engineering works and mathematical books, will probably date them a couple of centuries earlier, certainly before Galileo and Vieta." — **Hermann Weyl**

There are many quantities in everyday life that are related to one another. In this chapter, we will define and discuss a special kind of relationship between two quantities called a function. We will interpret graphs of functions and examine both linear and nonlinear functions. We will also look at application problems involving direct, inverse, and joint variation.

Section 3-1   FUNCTIONS

Many quantities in everyday life are related to one another or depend on one another. A fundamental idea in mathematics and its applications is that of a **function**, which tells how one thing *depends* on another. For example, the amount of bacteria in a growing culture is dependent on the amount of time that passes. The amount of sales tax owed on a purchase is dependent on the total cost of the items purchased. As the value of the first quantity changes, a corresponding change will occur in the related quantity.

When the value of one quantity uniquely determines the value of the second quantity, we say the second quantity is a function of the first. One way to express these relationships is using ordered pairs (x, y). The x variable is called the **independent variable** and the y variable is called the **dependent variable**, because its value is dependent on the value of x. For example, if the sales tax rate in an area is 6% on purchases made, a $5 purchase will be taxed $0.30. This can be written as the ordered pair ($5, $0.30). The sales tax owed (y) is uniquely determined by the amount of the purchase (x). Sales tax is a function of the amount of the purchase. The tax table shown in Table 3-1 uses ordered pairs to illustrate this concept.

Generally, a function can be represented in four ways:

- Description or rule
- Table of values
- Graph
- Equation or formula

In the case of sales tax, state and local governments set the rule for calculating sales tax. In this example, they have determined that the sales tax will be calculated at 6% of the purchase amount. A table can be created listing all possible purchase amounts and the associated taxes to be charged. Many small businesses or individual entrepreneurs use tax tables provided by the state to determine the amount of sales tax to charge for a specific purchase amount. A graph of this function can be drawn and its properties will show that this is a linear function because its graph is a straight line (Figure 3-1).

Finally, the calculation of sales tax can be expressed as an equation or formula. The formula $y = 0.06(x)$ gives a way of calculating the tax (y in dollars) based on

▨ TABLE 3-1

Purchase Amount	Sales Tax at 6%
$0.50	$0.03 = 6%(0.50)
$1.00	$0.06 = 6%(1.00)
$1.50	$0.09 = 6%(1.50)
$2.00	$0.12 = 6%(2.00)
$2.50	$0.15 = 6%(2.50)
$3.00	$0.18 = 6%(3.00)

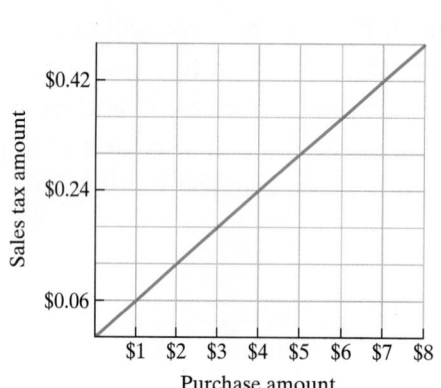

Figure 3-1

the purchase price (*x* in dollars). We will look at these four ways of expressing functions throughout this book.

In mathematics, a **relation** associates members of one set with members of another set. A function is a special kind of relationship between two quantities. Specifically, in a function it must be true that for each value of the independent variable, there is *exactly* one value for the dependent variable. The calculation of sales tax fulfills this requirement because, for each purchase amount possible, there will be only one resulting sales tax.

Definition

Function
A function is a relation in which, for each value of the first component of the ordered pairs, there is exactly one value of the second component.

■ EXAMPLE 1   **The Cricket Function**

The snowy tree cricket is called the thermometer cricket because an accurate estimate of the current temperature can be made using its chirp rate. One can estimate the temperature in degrees Fahrenheit by counting the number of times a snowy tree cricket chirps in 15 seconds and adding 40. Use *R* as the chirp rate per minute and describe this function with words, a table, a graph, and a formula.

Words: Because *R* represents chirps per minute, we will count the value for *R* and divide it by 4 to get the number of chirps in 15 seconds. Then add 40 to that number to estimate the temperature.

Table: See Table 3-2. Notice that each 20 chirps per minute increase corresponds to a 5° increase in temperature.

Graph: The values in the table are plotted on the graph in Figure 3-2. The graph illustrates that if more chirps per minute are counted, the corresponding temperature is warmer.

■ TABLE 3-2

R (chirps/min)	T (temperature, °F)
20	45
40	50
60	55
80	60
100	65

Figure 3-2
Example 1.

Formula: An algebraic rule can be developed using the description as follows:

$$\text{Estimated temperature} = \frac{1}{4}\left(\frac{\text{chirps}}{\text{min}}\right) + 40$$

$$T = \frac{1}{4}R + 40$$

We can use this formula to calculate the estimated temperature for any number of chirps per minute.

All of these descriptions of the cricket function give the same information in different forms. Tables are easy to read, but not all values can be included in a table. The graph gives a picture of the function and may reveal certain patterns, but obtaining exact readings from the graph may be difficult. The formula lets you calculate the exact value of the dependent variable given any value of the independent variable, but patterns in the general function may be difficult to discover if only the formula is used. The best method for presenting a function will vary according to the requirements of the problem.

Graphs are often used to picture numerical data so that relationships can be analyzed and, if possible, trends can be forecast. For example, a scientist may use the graph in Figure 3-3 to indicate the temperature, T, of a certain solution at various times, t, during an experiment. The graph shows that the temperature increased gradually from time $t = 0$ to time $t = 5$. The temperature remained steady from time $t = 5$ to $t = 8$ and then decreased rapidly from time $t = 8$ to $t = 10$. Graphs of this type help us determine the trend of the temperature more clearly than a long table of numerical values.

Functions can often be found in magazines, newspapers, books, or other printed material in the form of tables or graphs. Graphs are usually an easier way to analyze and present lists of data. Closing prices on the stock market, daily high temperatures, and monthly unemployment rates are just a few of the data sets that you may find represented by graphs in newspapers.

Figure 3-3
Graph of temperature versus time.

■ EXAMPLE 2   **Interpreting Graphs**

The graph in Figure 3-4 shows the sunrise time for Asheville, North Carolina, for the year.

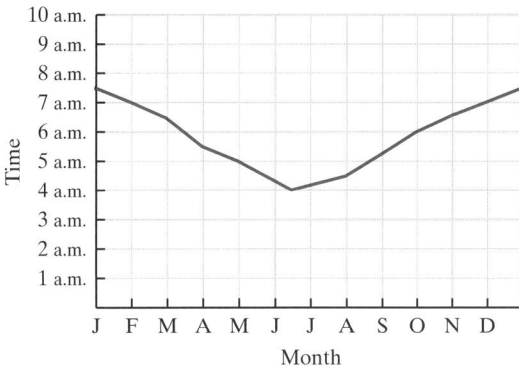

Figure 3-4
Example 2.

Use this graph to answer the following questions.

(a) What is the approximate time of sunrise on February 1?
(b) What are the approximate dates when the Sun rises at 5 a.m.?
(c) During which month does the Sun rise the earliest?

(a) To approximate the time of sunrise on February 1, find the mark on the horizontal axis that corresponds to February 1. From this mark, move vertically upward until the graph is reached. From the point on the graph, move horizontally to the left until the vertical axis is reached. The vertical axis reads 7 a.m.

(b) To approximate the dates when the Sun rises at 5 a.m., find 5 a.m. on the time axis and move horizontally to the right. Notice that you will intersect the graph twice, corresponding to two dates for which the Sun rises at 5 a.m. Follow both points on the graph vertically downward until the horizontal axis is reached. The Sun rises at 5 a.m. at approximately the beginning of the month of May and the middle of the month of August.

(c) June contains the lowest point on the graph, indicating the earliest sunrise.

The key concept in a functional relationship is that *there is only one value of the dependent variable* (y) *for each value of the independent variable* (x). Think of the independent variable as the *input* of the function. This is the variable that you control — the one that you choose or determine. Once you have chosen the value of the independent variable, there will be only one dependent variable or *output* that corresponds to it. (See Figure 3-5.) When trying to determine which variable

Figure 3-5

is a function of which, ask yourself which variable "depends" on the other. This will help you determine the nature of the functional relationship.

■ EXAMPLE 3   **Determining Functional Relationships**

Determine the independent and dependent variables in the following functions. Give a statement that illustrates the functional relationship described.

(a) The altitude and temperature when climbing a mountain

The altitude is the independent variable (input) and the temperature at that altitude is the dependent variable (output). As the altitude of the climb increases, the surrounding temperature will decrease. This is illustrated in Figure 3-6.

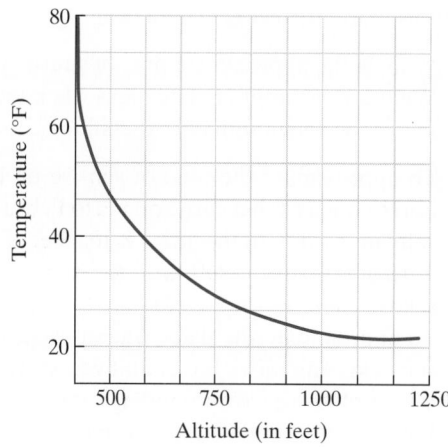

Figure 3-6

■ **TABLE 3-3**

Speed of Car (mph)	Stopping Distance (ft)
45	146
50	175
55	206
60	240
65	276

■ **TABLE 3-4**

Time (sec)	Velocity (ft/sec)
0	0
1	16
2	19.2
3	19.84
4	19.97

(b) The speed of a car and its stopping distance

The stopping distance of a car is dependent on the speed of the car when the brakes are applied. (This is the reason that policemen measure the length of the skid marks at the scene of an accident.) Therefore, the speed of the car is the independent variable (the one that you choose) and the braking distance is the dependent variable (a result of the speed that the car was traveling). The faster the car goes, the longer the stopping distance will be. Table 3-3 gives some stopping distances for cars traveling at different speeds on dry pavement.

(c) The speed of an average-sized man after he jumps from an airplane with a properly opening parachute as shown in Table 3-4

If an average-sized man jumps from an airplane with a properly opening parachute, the speed of the falling man is uniquely determined by the amount of time that he has been falling. Therefore, his velocity is a function of the time that has passed since he jumped from the plane. As the length of time since he jumped increases, his velocity continues to increase.

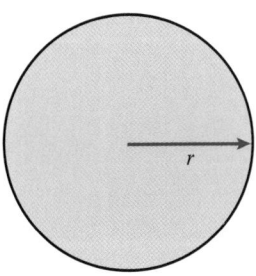

Figure 3-7

(d) The formula for calculating the area of a circle: $A = \pi r^2$

The area of a circle (A) is dependent on the radius of the circle (r) (see Figure 3-7). As the radius of the circle changes, a corresponding change in the area will occur. So the radius is the independent variable (input) and the area is the dependent variable (output) in this function.

Often a function is defined only for certain values of the independent and dependent variables. For instance, in Example 3, several of the independent variables such as the speed of a car, time, and length of the radius of a circle can never be negative numbers. Similarly, the stopping distance of a car, velocity of a falling object, and the area of a circle can only have positive values. This idea leads to the following definition.

Definition

Domain and Range
In a function, the set of all values of the independent variable (x) is the domain, and the set of all values of the dependent variable (y) is the range.

Consider the set $S = \{(1, 5), (2, 6), (3, 7)\}$. The independent variables or x values in this set form the domain of S, which is $\{1, 2, 3\}$. The y values of the ordered pairs, $\{5, 6, 7\}$, make up the range of the function. If a function is expressed as an equation, the **domain** of the function is the set of all possible input values, whereas the **range** is the set of all possible output values. If the domain of a function is not specified, we usually assume it to be all possible real numbers that make sense for a specific function. If we are using a function to model a real-world situation, there are usually some limitations on the values of the domain and range that will occur.

■ EXAMPLE 4   **Identifying the Domain and Range of a Function**

Consider each of the following functions and identify the values of the domain and range of the function.

(a) The sales tax function

The independent variable in this function is the amount of the purchase. Therefore, the domain of the function is all real numbers greater than or equal to 0 (rounded to the nearest hundredth or penny). The dependent variable is the amount of sales tax, and therefore the range is also all real numbers greater than or equal to 0 (rounded to the nearest penny).

(b) $y = 2x + 3$

There are no apparent restrictions on the values of x and y because this is a general linear equation. Therefore, both the domain and the range are all real numbers.

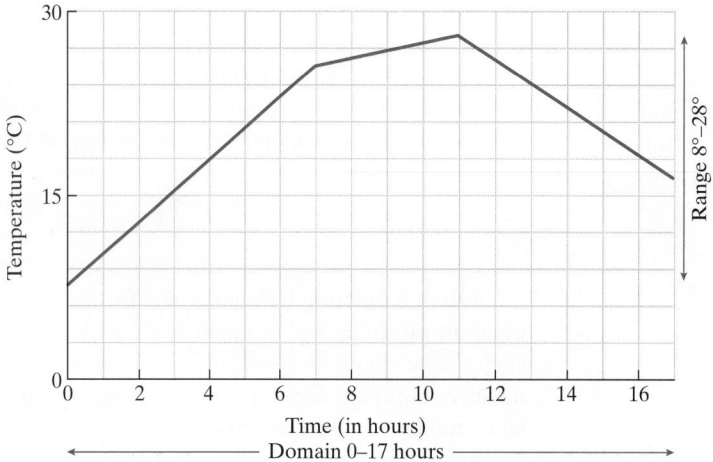

Figure 3-8

(c) Figure 3-8

The independent variable in this function is time in hours and the dependent variable is the temperature in degrees Celsius. The values of the domain (time in hours, h) as shown in the graph are $0 \leq h \leq 17$ and the values for the range (temperature, t) are $8° \leq t \leq 28°$.

In mathematical applications, functions, in any form, are often representations of real events. Thus, we say they are **models**. Using a function to act as a model for a problem is one of the keys to understanding the world around us. We use models in many areas of our lives, including physical science, business, and social science. Models are used to illustrate gains or losses in investments, stopping times for cars traveling at certain speeds, and data gathered in a national census. In this chapter, we will examine the concept of a function, and in later chapters, we will concentrate on applications of functions or models.

Practice Set 3-1

1. What is a *function*? How do we decide which variable is the *independent variable* and which is the *dependent variable* in a function?

2. In your own words, define the domain and range of a function.

3. The following table shows the daily high temperature in degrees Fahrenheit for a week in April.

Date in April	20	21	22	23	24	25	26
High Temperature	73°	77°	74°	68°	70°	68°	72°

(a) What was the high temperature on April 23?
(b) Is the daily high temperature a function of the date or is the date a function of the daily high temperature?

4. The following table lists the fine a driver must pay when she is caught for speeding on a street where the speed limit is 45 mph.

v (mph)	55	60	65	70	75
Fine	$75	$90	$105	$125	$150

(a) What is the fine for someone speeding in a 45-mph zone if she is going 60 mph?

(b) Is the fine a function of the speed or is the speed a function of the fine?

5. The following line graph illustrates the growth in the world's population for the last 30 years.

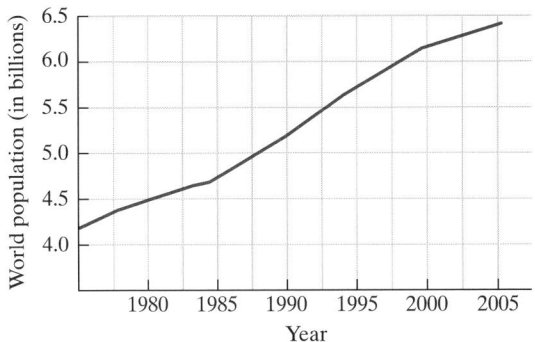

(a) Identify the independent and dependent variables of the function illustrated in the graph.

(b) Give the approximate domain and range of the function.

6. The following graph illustrates the growth in value of a $1000 deposit in a bank account paying 6% interest.

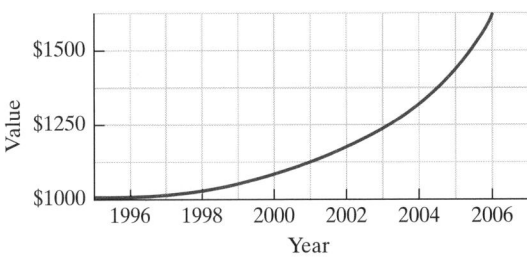

(a) Identify the independent and dependent variables of the function illustrated in the graph.

(b) Give the domain and range of the function.

7. At the end of the semester, students' grades are posted in a table that lists each student's ID number in the left column and the student's grade in the right column. Which quantity must necessarily be a function of the other?

8. Advertisements in newspapers for term life insurance list the applicant's age in the left column of a table and the corresponding monthly insurance premium in the right column. Which quantity is a function of the other?

For problems 9 to 14, write a short statement that expresses a possible function between the quantities. Example: (age, shoe size); solution: As a person's age increases, shoe size also increases up to a point. After that point, shoe size remains relatively constant.

9. (weight of a bag of potatoes, price of the bag)

10. (demand for a product, price of a product)

11. (slope of a hill, speed of a scooter going uphill)

12. (distance from Earth, strength of gravity)

13. (age, target heart rate when exercising)

14. (time, distance an object falls from the top of a building)

The following graph shows the sunset times for Seward, Alaska. Use the graph to solve problems 15 to 20.

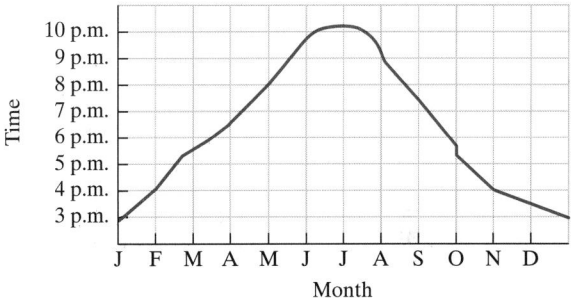

15. Approximate the time of sunset on June 1.

16. Approximate the time of sunset on November 1.

17. Approximate the date(s) when the sunset is 3 p.m.

18. Approximate the date(s) when the sunset is 9 p.m.

19. Approximate the times when the latest and earliest sunsets occur.

20. What are the values of the range of this function?

For each function in problems 21 to 24, use your intuition or additional research, if necessary, to make a rough sketch of the function. Label the axes. Remember that in an ordered pair (x, y) the x variable is the

independent variable and should be plotted on the horizontal axis.

21. (amount of food purchases, 2% sales tax)

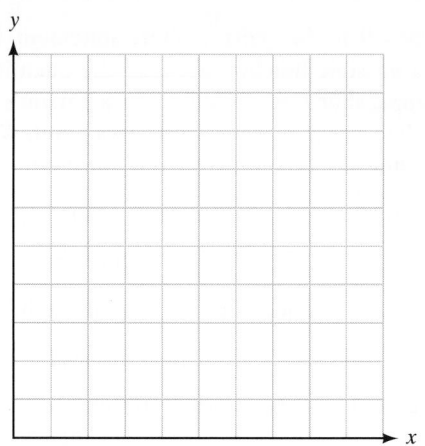

22. (interest rate, number of cars sold per year at a dealership)

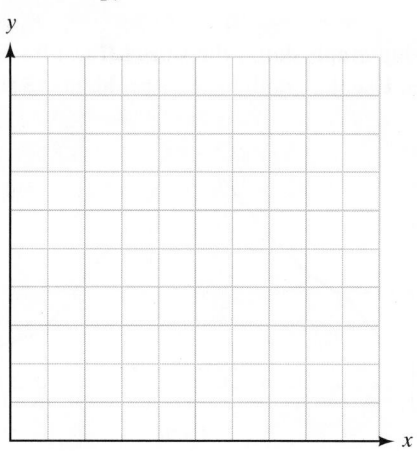

23. (years from 1985 to 2005, percent of homes with a personal computer)

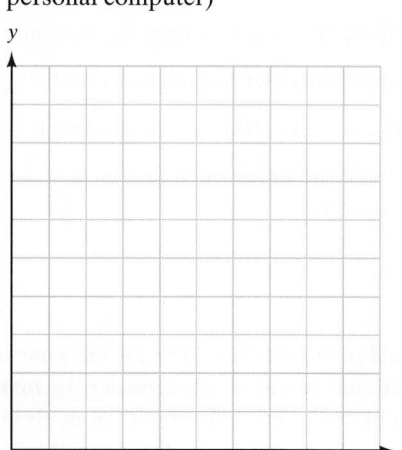

24. (minutes talking on the phone, monthly telephone bill)

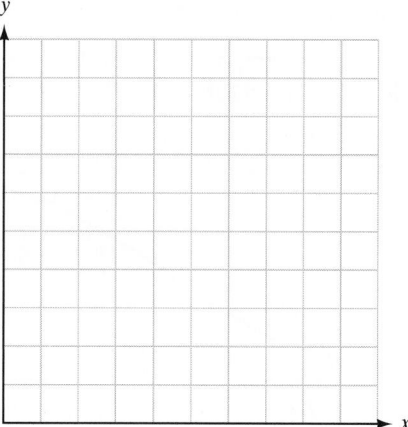

25. Human beings grow rapidly during childhood and then their growth rate slows during the late teens until it eventually levels off. Sketch the graph of a function that represents height as a function of time.

26. A light is turned off for several hours. It is then turned on. After a few hours, it is turned off again. Sketch a possible graph of the lightbulb's temperature as a function of time.

27. Table 3-3 lists some braking distances based on the speed of the car when the brakes are applied. The formula for calculating the braking distance needed when traveling at a certain speed is $d = \frac{x^2}{20} + x$, where x is the speed of the car and d is the stopping distance. Calculate the stopping distance required when a car is traveling 70 mph. Use this result and the results in Table 3-3 to graph this function. Discuss the shape of the graph and its meaning.

28. The ideal weight of a man is a function of his height. One formula that gives this relationship is $w = 110 + 5(h - 60)$, where h is the man's height in inches and w is the weight in pounds. Calculate the ideal weights for men who are 68 in., 69 in., 70 in., 71 in., 72 in., and 73 in. List these results in a table and then use them to graph this function. Discuss the shape of the graph and its meaning.

29. The amount of your monthly house payment is a function of several things: the interest rate, the number of years of financing required, and the

amount of your loan. Assume that you are planning to borrow $125,000 at a fixed interest rate for 30 years. Find a mortgage calculator on the Internet such as the one located at http://www.bankrate.com. Use the online calculator to determine your monthly payment based on interest rates of 5.5%, 5.75%, 6%, 6.25%, 6.5%, 6.75%, and 7%. Create a table of these values and then graph this function. Discuss the shape of the graph and its meaning.

30. Use a newspaper to find an example of a functional relationship. Remember that functions may be given in the form of tables or graphs. Submit your example and answer the following questions.
   (a) What is the independent variable in this function?
   (b) What is the domain of the function?
   (c) What is the dependent variable in this function?
   (d) What is the range of the function?

Section 3-2   USING FUNCTION NOTATION

To indicate that P is a function of x, we use the notation

$$P = f(x)$$

We read this as "P equals f of x." The $f(x)$ symbol is another symbol for the variable P. We use the value of x as the input value for the function, and the value of P is the output value.

As defined in the previous section, the x value is the independent variable because its value can vary. The dependent variable is P because its value depends on what value of x we choose. The f is used to represent the dependence of P on x.

EXAMPLE 5   Sales Tax Function

Let $T = f(p)$ be the amount of sales tax owed on purchases p. Explain in words what the following statement tells you about sales tax:

$$f(\$25) = \$1.25$$

Given $T = f(p)$, the input of the function is p, the amount of the purchase, and T is the output of the function or the amount of sales tax owed. Therefore, $f(\$25) = \$1.25$ says that a purchase amount of $25 would require sales tax of $1.25.

EXAMPLE 6   Velocity and Distance Functions

If an object is dropped from the top of a building and the acceleration of gravity is 32 ft/sec^2, then its downward velocity v after t seconds would be described by the function $v(t) = 32t$. The distance d that the object has fallen would be described by the function $d(t) = 16t^2$.

In both of these functions, time (t) is the independent variable. The velocity (v) of the object and the distance (d) it has fallen both depend on the time that has elapsed since the object was dropped. The domain and range for these functions would be all real numbers greater than or equal to 0.

Many algebraic equations involve the use of two variables, x and y, in the equation. Many of these equations are functions and can be written using **function notation**. This is done by solving the equation for the y variable and replacing it with the notation $f(x)$. Look at the following example.

EXAMPLE 7   Function Notation

Write the equation $2x - 3y = 9$ in function notation.

$$2x - 3y = 9$$
$$-3y = -2x + 9 \quad \text{(subtract } 2x \text{ from both sides)}$$
$$y = \frac{2}{3}x - 3 \quad \text{(divide both sides by } -3\text{)}$$
$$f(x) = \frac{2}{3}x - 3 \quad \text{[replace } y \text{ with } f(x)\text{]}$$

By writing an equation in function notation, we have, in essence, created a formula that allows us to input a value for the independent variable and calculate the value of the dependent variable. For example, in the function $f(x) = \frac{2}{3}x - 3$, the name of the function is "f," the independent variable is "x," and the value of the dependent variable will be "$f(x)$." So, if I want to calculate the value of the function at -3, I write

$$f(x) = \frac{2}{3}x - 3$$
$$f(-3) = \frac{2}{3}(-3) - 3$$
$$f(-3) = -5$$

This is called *evaluating the function*, and we say that the function f has a value of -5 when $x = -3$. If we want to calculate the value of the function at 5, then we write $f(5)$, read as "f of 5," and substitute 5 into the formula and calculate the answer.

Remember:

Name of the function   Independent variable

$$y = f(x) = \frac{2}{3}x - 3$$

Value of the function   Function formula

Although $f(x)$ is the standard notation for a function, other variables are also used to denote functions. For example, $v(x)$ could be used to denote a volume function or $t(x)$ could denote a function used to calculate tax.

■ **EXAMPLE 8**   **Evaluating Functions**

Let $g(x) = 3x^2 - 8$.

(a) Find the value of the function if $x = -2$. We write

$$g(-2) = 3(-2)^2 - 8$$
$$g(-2) = 3(4) - 8 = 12 - 8 = 4$$

Therefore, the value of the function when $x = -2$ is 4, or $g(-2) = 4$.

(b) Evaluate $g(-\frac{1}{2})$.

$$g\left(-\frac{1}{2}\right) = 3\left(-\frac{1}{2}\right)^2 - 8$$
$$g\left(-\frac{1}{2}\right) = 3\left(\frac{1}{4}\right) - 8 = \frac{3}{4} - 8 = -7\frac{1}{4}$$

Therefore, $g(-\frac{1}{2}) = -7\frac{1}{4}$.

Many formulas can be written in function notation and easily evaluated. The equation $y = f(x) = 0.06x$ represents the function that calculates the sales tax owed for the amount of the purchases made by the buyer using a 6% tax rate. Using this equation, the sales tax can be computed for purchases in any amount. Sales tax tables used in stores are generated using this equation. Of course, the exact amounts are rounded to the nearest cent to be practical.

■ **EXAMPLE 9**   **Calculating Sales Tax**

Calculate the sales tax owed for the purchases shown in Table 3-5 if the sales tax rate is 6%.

Function equation:

$$f(x) = 0.06x$$

where x is the purchase amount and $f(x)$ is the amount of tax.

(a) $f(\$12.50) = 0.06(\$12.50) = \$0.75$
(b) $f(\$29.95) = 0.06(\$29.95) = \$1.797 = \$1.80$
(c) $f(\$135.47) = 0.06(\$135.47) = \$8.1282 = \$8.13$

See Table 3-5.

■ **TABLE 3-5**

Purchases (x)	Exact Tax (y)	Rounded Tax
$12.50	$0.75	$0.75
$29.95	$1.797	$1.80
$135.47	$8.1282	$8.13

Note that the set {$12.50, $29.95, $135.47} contains elements of the domain of this function. The set {$0.75, $1.80, $8.13} contains elements of the range of the function.

EXAMPLE 10   Using a Function in a Word Problem

Forensic anthropologists (specialists who work for the police and use scientific techniques to solve crimes) can determine a woman's height in life by using the skeletal remains of her humerus bone. (This is the long bone that forms the upper arm.) The formula is $3.08x + 64.47$, where x represents the bone length in centimeters. Write this formula in function notation and find the estimated height in centimeters of a woman whose humerus measures 31.0 cm. Then convert this measurement to inches.

Because the formula is designed to measure a woman's height, we will use the variable h to represent the name of the function and x, the length of the humerus, will be the independent variable.

(a) Function notation:

$$h(x) = 3.08x + 64.47$$

(b) Evaluate the function if the length of the humerus is 31.0 cm.

$$h(31.0) = 3.08(31.0) + 64.47 = 159.95 \text{ cm}$$

Therefore, the predicted height of this woman, based on the length of her humerus, is 159.95 cm.

(c) There are approximately 2.54 cm in 1 in., so we can convert this answer to inches by dividing.

$$159.95 \text{ cm} \div 2.54 \text{ cm/in.} \approx 62.97 \text{ in. or 63 in. (5 ft 3 in.)}$$

Because graphs and tables are also used to represent functions, we can also evaluate them using function notation. Look at the following examples.

EXAMPLE 11   Evaluating Functions Using a Table

The cost of first-class delivery of a letter by the U.S. Postal Service is a function of the weight of the letter. Table 3-6 gives a list of the prices of first-class letters effective January 8, 2006. Use the table to evaluate the function for the following weights: 3 oz and 4.2 oz. Use the single-piece rates.

TABLE 3-6   First-Class Mail

Letters, Flats, and Parcels Weight Not Over (ounces)	Single-Piece
1	0.39
2	0.63
3	0.87
4	1.11
5	1.35
6	1.59
7	1.83
8	2.07
9	2.31
10	2.55
11	2.79
12	3.03
13	3.27

(a) Evaluate $f(3\text{ oz})$. Using the postal rate table, we locate the 3-oz row and look at the next column to determine a cost of $0.87. Therefore, $f(3\text{ oz}) = \$0.87$.

(b) Evaluate $f(4.2\text{ oz})$. The heading on the first column indicates that a first-class letter with a weight of 4.2 oz would require the customer to pay the rate that applies to the row labeled 5 oz because the letter weighs more than 4 oz. Therefore, $f(4.2\text{ oz}) = \$1.35$.

EXAMPLE 12   Evaluating Functions Using Graphs

Use the graph in Figure 3-9 to evaluate the following values of the domain.

(a) Find $g(1)$ on the graph.
(b) Find $g(2)$ on the graph.

(a) Locate 1 on the horizontal axis. At $x = 1$, the value of y on the graph is 3. Therefore, $g(1) = 3$.
(b) Locate 2 on the horizontal axis. At $x = 2$, the value of y on the graph is 2. Therefore, $g(2) = 2$.

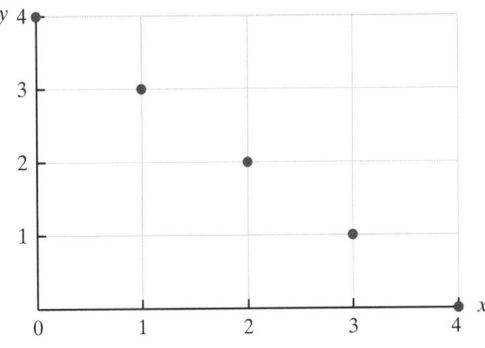

Figure 3-9
Example 12.

Practice Set 3-2

Let the function $g(x) = 3x - 5$. Evaluate $g(x)$ by finding the following values:

1. $g(0)$ **2.** $g(-4)$ **3.** $g(10)$ **4.** $g(-\frac{1}{2})$

Write the following equations in function notation. Then find $f(-2)$ for each function.

5. $y = 2x + 1$ **6.** $2y = 4x - 8$

7. $3x^2 - y = 1$ **8.** $1 = 2x^2 - y$

9. $5x - 2y = 8$ **10.** $2x - 3y = 9$

11. A ball is thrown downward from the top of a 90-story building. The distance, d, in feet, the ball is above the ground after t seconds is given by the function equation $d = f(t) = -16t^2 - 80t + 800$. Determine $f(2)$ and explain what it means.

12. If a ball is dropped from a building and hits the ground in 3 s, how many meters tall is the building? Neglecting air resistance, the ball will reach a constant acceleration of 9.8 m/s. Therefore, the function for this problem will be $d(t) = \frac{1}{2}(9.8)t^2$ or $d(t) = 4.9t^2$. Determine $d(3)$.

13. The femur is the long bone in your leg that connects your hip to your knee. A man's height in centimeters can be predicted from the length of his femur using the function $h(x) = 2.32x + 65.53$, where x is the length of the femur in centimeters. Calculate the approximate height of a man whose femur is 46.5 cm.

14. A woman's height in centimeters can be predicted from the length of her femur using the function $h(x) = 2.47x + 54.10$, where x is the length of the femur in centimeters. Calculate the approximate height of a woman whose femur is 45.5 cm.

15. Alec's height is approximately 1.83 m. Calculate the approximate length of his femur. (Refer to problem 13.)

16. Jennifer's height is approximately 1.55 m. Calculate the approximate length of her femur. (Refer to problem 14.)

17. A checkerboard contains 64 squares. If two pennies are placed on the first square, four pennies on the second square, eight pennies on the third square, 16 pennies on the fourth square, and so on, the number of pennies on the nth square can be found by the function $A(n) = 2^n$.
   (a) Find the number of pennies placed on the 30th square.
   (b) What is this amount in dollars?

18. A house initially costs $85,000. The value, V, of the house after n years if it appreciates at a constant rate of 4% per year can be determined by the function $V = f(n) = \$85,000(1.04)^n$. Determine $f(8)$ and explain its meaning.

19. A movie theater seats 200 people. For any particular show, the amount of money the theater makes is a function of the number of people, n, who buy tickets for a show. Each ticket costs $7.50.
   (a) If 128 tickets are sold for the late show, how much money does the theater make?
   (b) If a ticket costs $7.50, find a formula that expresses the amount of money the theater makes, $M(n)$, as a function of the number of tickets sold, n.
   (c) What is the domain of this function? What is the range of the function?

20. A cab company advertises $1.95 per mile (or part of a mile) with no fixed charge. Therefore, the amount of money a cabbie will make in a day is a result of the number of miles that he drives his customers.
   (a) If a cabbie drives his customers a total of 115 miles on Friday, how much money did he earn?
   (b) Write a function that will represent a method of calculating his total earnings based on miles driven.
   (c) What is the independent variable in this function? The dependent variable?

21. While exercising, a person's recommended target heart rate is a function of age. The recommended number of beats per minute, y, is given by the function $y = f(x) = -0.85x + 187$, where x represents a person's age in years. Determine the number of recommended heartbeats per minute for a 20-year-old. Then calculate $f(60)$ and explain any relationship that your two answers suggest concerning age and target heart rates for people who are exercising.

22. Suppose that the future population of a town *t* years after January 1, 1995, is described in thousands by the function $P(t) = 120 + 4t + 0.05t^2$. Calculate the value of $P(10)$ and explain its meaning.

23. The Texas Education Agency lists its minimum salary schedule for public school teachers on its Web site. The following table represents annual salaries for teachers with 0–5 years of teaching experience. Find $f(3)$ and explain what it means. What are the independent and dependent variables in this function?

**Teacher Salary Schedule
(10-month contract)
2005–2006**

Years of Experience	Annual Salary
0	$24,820
1	$25,410
2	$25,990
3	$26,580
4	$27,820
5	$29,060

24. The monthly salaries for 10-month teachers holding master's degrees in the North Carolina Public School System are listed in the following table. Find $f(6)$ and explain its meaning. What are the independent and dependent variables in this function?

**Master's Degree Certified
Teacher Salary Schedule
2005–2006**

Years of Experience	Monthly Salary
5	$3374
6	$3516
7	$3630
8	$3683
9	$3737
10	$3792

25. The Astronomical Applications Department of the U.S. Naval Observatory in Washington, DC,

has a Web site that lists the sunrise and sunset times for locations throughout the United States. The following table gives these times for Denver, Colorado, for the first part of January 2006. (Time is given in military time.) Consider sunrise times to be the function $f(x)$ and sunset times to be the function $g(x)$. Find $f(4)$ in this table and explain its meaning. Then find $g(10)$ and explain its meaning. What are the independent and dependent variables in these functions?

	January	
	Rise	Set
Day	h m	h m
01	0721	1646
02	0721	1647
03	0721	1648
04	0721	1649
05	0721	1650
06	0721	1651
07	0721	1652
08	0721	1653
09	0721	1654
10	0721	1655

26. The National Climatic Data Center compiles weather data for locations throughout the United States. The average total monthly snowfall in inches (including sleet and ice pellets) for the city of Asheville, North Carolina, is given in the following table. The "T" in the table indicates a month during which there was a trace amount of snowfall. Find $f(02)$ and explain its meaning. What are the independent and dependent variables of this function?

Month	01	02	03	04	05	06
Inches	4.8	4.1	2.9	0.6	T	T

Month	07	08	09	10	11	12
Inches	T	T	0	T	0.7	2.1

27. A cyclist can average 15 mph on a long trip. The following graph shows the distance he can cover as a function of time.

(a) Find the distance he can cover in 5 hr, $f(5)$.
(b) Find $f(8.5)$.

28. An absolute value function is shown in the following graph. Use the graph to evaluate the following.
(a) $f(0)$
(b) $f(-2)$
(c) $f(4)$
(d) $f(-4)$

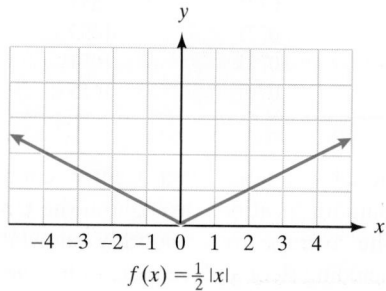

$f(x) = \frac{1}{2}|x|$

29. The cost of a rental car is $25 per day plus $0.05 per mile. The following graph illustrates this cost function. Use the graph to determine $f(100)$ and explain its meaning. What is the domain of this function? The range?

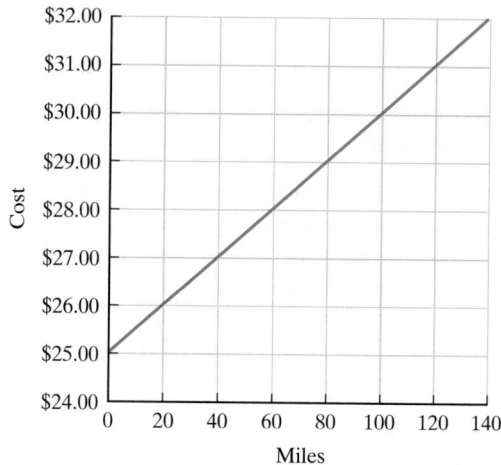

30. A car's value is a function of many things, including the total mileage on the car. The following graph illustrates the depreciation of a car as more miles are driven. Find the value of $f(50,000)$ and explain its meaning. What is the range of this function?

Section 3-3   LINEAR FUNCTIONS

Many functions can be grouped together based on similar characteristics. Functions whose formulas are similar, whose graphs have the same shape, and whose tables display similar patterns form families of functions. In this section, we will study linear functions or functions whose graphs are lines.

A function whose *rate of change* or *slope* is constant is called a **linear function**. Earlier in this chapter, we looked at the sales tax function $T(p) = 0.06p$. This is an example of a linear function. The tax, T, is a function of the amount purchased, p. For every additional dollar a customer spends, her tax will be increased by a constant rate of $0.06. This amount is referred to as the rate of change or slope of the function.

Problems that have constant rates of change can be modeled with linear functions. The cost of renting a car based on mileage is one example of a linear model. The following example illustrates this idea.

■ EXAMPLE 13   Renting a Van

Tran wishes to rent a van for one day to take his baseball team to a tournament in Abilene. The rental cost of the van is $15 per day plus $0.05 for every mile that is driven.

(a) Make a table that gives the rental cost of the van using mileage figures from 0 mi to 200 mi.
(b) Graph the values in the table.
(c) Find a formula for cost (C) in terms of miles (m).

(a) Let us calculate the costs for every 50 mi of the trip and display these in the table.

At the beginning of the trip with $m = 0$, the cost of the van is $15.

If Tran drives 50 mi, the cost will be $15 plus an additional $(50)(\$0.05) = \$2.50$, or a total of $17.50.

If he drives 100 mi, the cost will be $15 plus an additional $(100)(\$0.05) = \$5.00$, or a total of $20.00.

If he drives 150 mi, the cost will be $15 plus an additional $(150)(\$0.05) = \$7.50$, or a total of $22.50.

If he drives 200 mi, the cost will be $15 plus an additional $(200)(\$0.05) = \$10.00$, or a total of $25.00. (See Table 3-7.)

(b) Using the values in the table, our function will form a straight line. (See Figure 3-10.)
(c) From part (a), we see that the cost is calculated using the formula

$$\text{Cost} = \text{rental fee} + \text{mileage charge}$$

$$\text{Cost} = \$15.00 + (\$0.05 \text{ per mile}) \times \text{miles}$$

Therefore, in function format using m for miles, the equation is

$$C(m) = \$15 + \$0.05m$$

■ TABLE 3-7

Cost of Rental Van

Miles	Cost
0	$15.00
50	$17.50
100	$20.00
150	$22.50
200	$25.00

Figure 3-10
Example 13(b).

As you can see from Example 13, the graph of the function models a straight line. This is a fundamental relationship between a linear function and a straight line. In Example 13, the value of the function at $m = 0$ was $15. This is the y-intercept of the graph and is often referred to as the *initial value of the function*. The slope, m, of the line is the *rate of change of the function*, $0.05 per mile. In general, a linear function can be modeled using the slope-intercept form of the equation ($y = mx + b$), where m *is the rate of change* of the function and b *is the initial value* of the function.

Definition

Linear Functions
If $y = f(x)$ is a linear function, then the formula for the function is

$$y = mx + b \qquad \text{or} \qquad y = b + mx$$

Written in function notation, we have

$$f(x) = \text{initial value} + (\text{rate of change})(x)$$

EXAMPLE 14   Long-Distance Rates as a Linear Function

A special discount telephone company offers customers the opportunity to make long-distance calls by paying a $0.39 connection fee and $0.03 per minute used.

(a) Use the definition of a linear function to write a function model for this telephone company's long-distance charges.
(b) Calculate the cost of a 25-minute phone call.
(c) Draw a graph of this function.

(a) The linear function model is $f(x) = $ initial value $+$ (rate of change)(x). In this problem, the connection fee of $0.39 is the initial value because you will pay that charge just for dialing the long-distance call. The rate of change is the $0.03 per minute. This is a constant rate for all minutes regardless of the length of the phone call. Therefore, using this model, the function is

$$f(x) = \$0.39 + \$0.03x$$

where $x = $ number of minutes.
(b) To calculate the cost of a 25-minute phone call, we will evaluate the function at $x = 25$.

$$f(25) = \$0.39 + \$0.03(25) = \$1.14$$

(c) The graph of the function can be drawn using the model by remembering how to graph linear equations of the form $y = mx + b$. In this case, the y-intercept, b, is the initial value $0.39 and the slope, m, is the rate of change of the function, $0.03 per minute. (See Figure 3-11.)

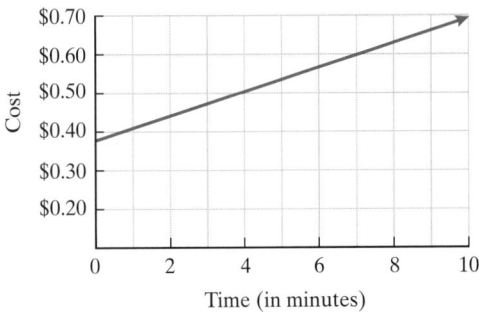

Figure 3-11
Example 14.

In Example 14, the linear function has a constant rate of change, which is $0.03 per minute. The longer the phone call is, the higher the charges will be. This is a direct relationship and is called an increasing function. Note that the graph shows the increase as we look from left to right. Not all linear functions are increasing functions, however. If the rate of change represents a constant loss, it will be negative, and therefore the slope of the line will be negative. When graphed, the line will fall as it moves from left to right, indicating a decreasing function. This concept is illustrated in Example 15.

EXAMPLE 15

Depreciation as a Linear Function

Suppose you buy a new computer for your business. The cost of the computer is $2500. The value of the computer drops or depreciates by $400 each year following your purchase.

(a) Write a formula to estimate the value of the computer based on its age.
(b) Use functional notation to show the value of the computer after 3.5 years.
(c) Make a graph of the function.
(d) What is the meaning of the y-intercept? The x-intercept?

(a) The rate of change for this problem is $-$400, a loss in value of $400 per year. The initial value of the function is $2500, the purchase price of the computer. Therefore, the current value $V = V(t) = \$2500 - \$400t$, where t is time in years.
(b) $V(3.5) = \$2500 - \$400(3.5) = \$1100$. This is the value of the computer after 3.5 years.
(c) See Figure 3-12.
(d) The y-intercept is $2500, which is the initial value of the computer at purchase. The x-intercept is 6.25. This tells us that in 6.25 years the computer will have a value of $0.

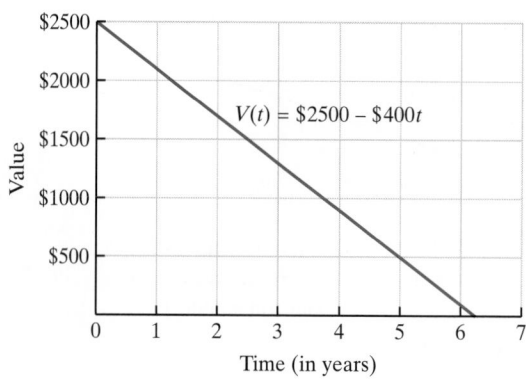

Figure 3-12
Example 15(c).

Linear functions may not always be presented as graphs or equations. Tables of data can also represent linear functions. In a table, the function will be linear if the changes in the y value are proportional to the changes in the value of x. Therefore, if the value of x goes up by equal amounts in the table of a linear function, then the value of y should also go up (or down) by equal amounts.

For example, in Table 3-8, the x values increase by 2 and the y values increase by 4. The slope of any line is the rate of change defined by the ratio

■ TABLE 3-8

x	y
−1	−3
1	1
3	5
5	9

$$\text{Rate of change} = \frac{\text{change in } y}{\text{change in } x}$$

This ratio corresponds to the slope formula presented in Chapter 2: $m = \frac{y_2 - y_1}{x_2 - x_1}$. For the values in Table 3-8, the slope $= \frac{4}{2} = 2$.

To write the equation of a linear function from a table of values, we use the slope-intercept form of the equation, $y = mx + b$. Use the calculated slope and one pair of points from the table to calculate the value of b.

$$\text{Slope} = 2 \qquad \text{Point} = (1, 1)$$

$$y = mx + b$$

$$1 = (2)(1) + b$$

$$1 = 2 + b$$

$$-1 = b$$

Therefore, the function $f(x) = mx + b$ is $f(x) = 2x - 1$.

■ EXAMPLE 16   **Deriving a Linear Function from a Table**

Many fitness centers display tables that list your desirable target heart rate while exercising based on your age. It is recommended that your heart rate not exceed 190 beats per minute at any age. For a 70-year-old, the recommended upper limit

■ **TABLE 3-9**

Age	Target Heart Rate
20	170
30	160
40	150
50	140
60	130
70	120

is 120 beats per minute. Use the information in Table 3-9 to derive a function or formula for calculating your desirable target heart rate based on age.

To write the function, we need to find the rate of change first. We can use any two sets of ordered pairs in our table for the calculations.

$$\text{Rate of change} = m = \frac{y_2 - y_1}{x_2 - x_1} = \frac{170 - 160}{20 - 30} = \frac{10}{-10} = -1$$

Our next step is to calculate the value of b using the rate of change, m, and one set of ordered pairs from the table.

$$\text{Slope} = -1 \qquad \text{Ordered pair} = (20, 170)$$

$$y = mx + b$$

$$170 = -1(20) + b$$

$$170 = -20 + b$$

$$190 = b$$

Using this information, we can write the following function formula:

$$f(x) = -1x + 190 \qquad \text{or} \qquad f(x) = 190 - x$$

where x represents a person's age.

Practice Set 3-3

1. (a) Suppose a taxi driver charges $1.75 per mile. Fill in the following chart with the correct values for $f(x)$, the cost of a trip of x miles.

x	$f(x)$
1	
3	
5	
7	
9	

$f(x)$, the monthly long-distance bill, where x represents total minutes of long-distance time during the month.

x	$f(x)$
0	
15	
30	
45	
60	

(b) What is the initial value of this function? What is the rate of change of this function?

(c) Write a linear function that gives a rule for the amount charged. $f(x) = $ _____.

(d) Evaluate $f(8)$ and explain what it means.

(b) What is the initial value of this function? What is the rate of change of this function?

(c) Write a linear function that gives a rule for the amount charged. $f(x) = $ _____.

(d) Evaluate $f(110)$ and explain what it means.

2. (a) A long-distance company charges a monthly fee of $4.95 and $0.02 per minute. Fill in the following chart with the correct values for

3. Suppose $P(t)$, the population (in millions) of a country in year t, is defined by the formula $P(t) = 5.5 + 0.02t$.

(a) What is the country's initial population?

(b) What is the population growth rate of the country?

(c) Predict the population of the country 5 years from now. (Let $t = 5$.)

4. A plumber's fee schedule can be modeled with a linear function using his service charge to come to your house and his hourly rate for fixing the problem. The fee schedule for J&B Plumbers is $C(h) = \$50 + \$20h$, where h represents the number of hours that the plumber works at your house.

(a) What is the service charge (initial value) at J&B Plumbers?

(b) What is the hourly rate that J&B charges?

(c) Calculate the value of $C(0)$ and explain its meaning.

5. Josh's daughter is getting married in June and he is trying to calculate the cost of the wedding reception. The cost will be a function of the number of guests who attend the reception. The rent for the banquet hall is $525 for the evening. The caterer is charging $17.50 per person for the food.

(a) Write a linear function to model this problem.

(b) How much will the reception cost if 200 people attend?

(c) If Josh has only budgeted $3150 for the reception, approximately how many guests can be invited?

6. Business A and Business B are printing companies. The cost equations for printing wedding invitations at each business are given by

$$\text{Cost}_A = \$200 + \$1.75x$$

$$\text{Cost}_B = \$150 + \$2.00x$$

where x = number of invitations.

(a) Describe in words what these equations tell us about the costs of printing invitations at each business.

(b) If we need 500 wedding invitations, which business will be less expensive?

7. Brandi bought a computer in 2006 for $1800. She estimated the useful life of the computer to be 5 years with a remaining value of $100 at the end of this period. She used the straight-line method of depreciation to estimate her yearly loss in value during this time period.

(a) What is the rate of change for this function?

(b) Write a function that can be used to estimate the value of the computer, V, at any time during the 5-year period.

(c) Calculate $V(4)$ and explain its meaning.

8. Green Giant Daycare Center purchased new furniture for its toddler room. The estimated useful life of the furniture is 10 years. The total cost was $3650 and the value at the end of 10 years is expected to be $250.

(a) What is the rate of change for this function?

(b) Write a function that can be used to estimate the value of the furniture, V, at any time during the 10-year period.

(c) Calculate $V(8)$ and explain its meaning.

Use the data in the tables to write a linear function equation.

9. See Table 3-10.

■ **TABLE 3-10**

x	5	10	15	20	25
y	-1	-2	-3	-4	-5

10. See Table 3-11.

■ **TABLE 3-11**

x	-2	0	4	6
y	$-\frac{5}{2}$	-1	2	$\frac{7}{2}$

11. See Table 3-12.

■ **TABLE 3-12**

x	2	-1	-4	-7	-10
y	5	5	5	5	5

12. See Table 3-13.

■ **TABLE 3-13**

x	0	10	20	30
y	-5	-10	-15	-20

13. The population of a small town grew from 450 in 1996 to 650 in 2006.

(a) Assume that the growth is linear and calculate the rate of change.

(b) Let $x = 0$ correspond to the year 1996. Write a linear function that can be used to predict future population after 1996.

(c) Calculate $f(15)$ and explain its meaning.

14. The deposits at Money Masters Bank grew from $150 million in 1999 to $205 million in 2004.
   (a) Assume that deposits grew at a rate that is linear. Calculate the rate of change.
   (b) Let $x = 0$ correspond to the year 1999. Write a linear function that can be used to predict future deposits of the years after 1999.
   (c) Calculate $f(10)$ and explain its meaning.

15. A businessman decides to purchase a second facility after his annual sales reach $1,500,000. In 1998, annual sales were $600,000 and in 2003, they were $1,000,000.
   (a) Assume that the growth is linear and calculate the rate of change.
   (b) Let $x = 0$ correspond to the year 1998. Write a linear function that can be used to predict future annual sales after 1998.
   (c) Use this function equation to determine the year that his annual sales will reach $1,500,000.

16. The cost of manufacturing goods is a linear function that includes fixed costs, such as utilities and rent, and per unit costs of manufacturing each individual item. In a month, Marvin Stephens Manufacturing Company produces 100 units for $8400 and 250 units for $9000.
   (a) Assume that the cost of production is a linear function and find the rate of change.
   (b) If the fixed costs of production are $8000 per month, write a linear function to model the monthly production of x units.
   (c) How many units can be produced for a cost of $10,000?

17. The average yearly in-state tuition and fees charged by U.S. public universities for the years 2001–2003 are shown in Table 3-14.

   TABLE 3-14

Year	2001	2002	2003
Average Tuition	$3536	$4115	$4694

   (a) What is the rate of change or slope of this function?
   (b) Write the linear function model for these data. Let $3536 be the initial value of the function with 2001 as year 0.

   (c) Plot the data points and use them to draw the line representing the linear function.
   (d) Use the linear function and your graph to predict the average tuition cost in 2005.

18. Table 3-15 records the growth in population of Maryville during the early 2000s.

   TABLE 3-15

Year	2000	2001	2002	2003	2004
Population (in thousands)	124	127	130	133	136

   (a) What is the rate of change or slope of this function?
   (b) Write a linear function for these data. Let 124 be the initial value of the function and let $t = 0$ correspond to the year 2000.
   (c) Plot the data points and use them to draw the line representing the linear function.
   (d) Use the linear function to predict the population in 2008.

19. There is a functional relationship between the height and weight of a person. For women who are 5 ft or taller, a function equation can be written to give the ideal weight of a woman based on her height. The rule used for many years by insurance companies stated that a woman 60 in. tall should weigh 100 lb and for those taller, an additional 5 lb should be added for every inch over 60 in.
   (a) Write a linear function to predict the ideal weight of a woman 60 in. or taller based on this insurance rule.
   (b) According to this rule, what is the ideal weight for a woman who is 5 ft 7 in.?

20. The 2005 Tax Rate Schedule X for single taxpayers states that a taxpayer who is single with taxable income greater than $29,700 but less than $71,950 should pay $4090 plus 25% of the amount over $29,700.
   (a) Use this information to write a function equation for this tax rule.
   (b) If a single taxpayer's taxable income was $35,450, how much tax did he owe the federal government in 2005?

Section 3-4   **DIRECT AND INVERSE VARIATION**

Many functions involve the concepts of direct or inverse proportionality. For example, if a car is traveling at a constant rate of 50 miles per hour, then the distance d traveled in t hours is given by the equation $d = 50t$. The change in distance is directly affected by the change in the time. You can see that as the time increases, the distance traveled also increases. This is an example of a **direct variation**. This equation could also be written $d(t) = 50t$, because distance is a function of time.

In the equation $d = rt$, the relationship between the variables d and t is such that if t gets *larger* then d also gets *larger*, and if t gets *smaller* then d also gets *smaller*. Because of this relationship, we say that d is **directly proportional** to t. Another way to read this equation is that d **varies directly** as t. The number 50 in the equation $d = 50t$ is called the **constant of variation**, or **constant of proportionality**.

Important Equations

Direct Variation

y varies directly as x means that

$$y = kx$$

where k is a nonzero positive constant.

EXAMPLE 17   **Direct Variation**

Suppose y varies directly as the square of x. Find the constant of variation if y is 16 when $x = 2$ and use it to write an equation of variation.

Because this is a direct variation, the general equation will be

$$y = kx^2$$

Replacing y with 16 and x with 2 gives

$$16 = k(2)^2$$

Solve this equation for k.

$$16 = 4k$$

$$4 = k$$

Therefore, the constant of variation is 4. Substituting 4 for k, we get the variation formula for y:

$$y = 4x^2$$

Boyle's law for the expansion of gas is $V = \frac{K}{P}$, where V is the volume of the gas, P is the pressure, and K is a constant. This formula relates a pressure and a volume.

As the pressure, P, increases, the volume of gas, V, decreases, and as the pressure, P, decreases, the volume of the gas, V, increases.

This is an example of **inverse variation**. We say that "V *varies inversely* as P" or "V is **inversely proportional** to P."

Definition

Inverse Variation
y varies inversely as x means that

$$y = \frac{k}{x}$$

where k is a nonzero positive constant.

■ EXAMPLE 18   Inverse Variation

Suppose y varies inversely as the square root of x. Find the constant of proportionality if y is 15 when x is 9 and write the equation of variation.

Because this is an inverse variation, the general equation will be

$$y = \frac{k}{\sqrt{x}}$$

Replacing y with 15 and x with 9 gives

$$15 = \frac{k}{\sqrt{9}}$$

Solve this equation for k.

$$15 = \frac{k}{3}$$

$$15(3) = k$$

$$45 = k$$

Therefore, the constant of proportionality is 45. The variation equation is

$$y = \frac{45}{\sqrt{x}}$$

When working with variation problems, it is important that you pay attention to the words of the problem to determine if the relationship is a direct variation ($y = kx$) or an inverse variation ($y = \frac{k}{x}$). Remember, in direct variation, an increase in one variable causes a corresponding increase in the other. In inverse variation, an increase in one variable causes a corresponding decrease in the other variable.

Look at Example 19 for some practice in determining whether a situation involves direct or inverse variation.

EXAMPLE 19   **Direct or Inverse Variation?**

Use your intuition and the appropriate definitions to determine whether the variation between these variables is direct or inverse.

(a) The time traveled at a constant speed and the distance traveled
(b) The weight of a car and its gas mileage
(c) The interest rate and the amount of interest earned on a savings account

(a) The time traveled at a constant speed and the distance traveled is an example of a direct variation. The longer you travel at a constant speed, the more distance you will cover.
(b) The weight of a car and its gas mileage is an example of inverse variation. Although many things affect a car's gas mileage, in general, the heavier the car, the lower the miles per gallon for that car.
(c) The interest rate and the amount of interest earned on a savings account is an example of a direct variation. The higher the interest rate, the more interest you will earn on your account.

Two additional types of variation equations are **joint variation** and **combined variation**.

Definition

Joint Variation
y varies jointly as x and z means that

$$y = kxz$$

where k is a nonzero positive constant.

Definition

Combined Variation
y varies jointly as u and v and inversely as w and x means that

$$y = \frac{kuv}{wx}$$

where k is a nonzero positive constant.

■ EXAMPLE 20   **Variation Equations**

Write the following statements as a variation equation.

(a) w varies jointly as y and the cube of x.
(b) x is directly proportional to y and inversely proportional to z.

(a) Using the definition for joint variation,

$$w = kyx^3$$

(b) Using the definition for combined variation,

$$x = \frac{ky}{z}$$

■ EXAMPLE 21   **Variation Problem**

Suppose y is directly proportional to x and inversely proportional to the square root of z. Find the constant of variation if y is 4 when x is 8 and z is 36 and write an equation of variation. Determine y when x is 5 and z is 16.

General variation equation:

$$y = \frac{kx}{\sqrt{z}}$$

Substitute 4 for y, 8 for x, and 36 for z and solve for k.

$$4 = \frac{k \cdot 8}{\sqrt{36}}$$

Solve for k.

$$4 = \frac{k \cdot 8}{6}$$

$$4(6) = 8k$$

$$24 = 8k$$

$$3 = k$$

Variation equation:

$$y = \frac{3x}{\sqrt{z}}$$

Substituting 5 for x and 16 for z (from the second set of data), we can find the value of y.

$$y = \frac{3 \cdot 5}{\sqrt{16}} = \frac{15}{4} = 3.75$$

We can use variation equations to solve applied problems. The following guidelines will help you in solving application problems involving variation.

Rule

Steps for Solving Applied Variation Problems

1. Write a general variation equation expressing the stated relationship. Make sure to include a constant of variation, k.
2. Substitute values from the given data into the variation equation and solve for k.
3. Obtain a specific variation formula by replacing k in the variation equation with the value obtained for k in step 2.
4. Solve for the missing value of any variable in the formula you have written using additional data from the problem.

EXAMPLE 22   Applied Variation Problem

The distance a car travels at a constant speed varies directly as the time it travels. Find the variation formula for the distance traveled by a certain car if it is known that the car traveled 220 mi in 4 hr at a constant speed. How many miles will the car travel in 7 hr at that speed?

Let d = distance traveled and t = time.

General variation equation:

$$d = kt$$

Substitute 220 for d and 4 for t.

$$220 = 4k$$

Solve for k.

$$55 = k$$

In this problem, k represents the speed of the car. Therefore, we now know that the car is traveling at a constant speed of 55 mph.

Write the variation equation:

$$d = 55t$$

Now substitute 7 for t and solve for the distance, d.

$$d = 55(7)$$

$$d = 385 \text{ mi}$$

■ EXAMPLE 23   **Ohm's Law**

Ohm's law says that the current, I, in a wire varies directly as the electromotive force, E, and inversely as the resistance, R. If I is 11 A when E is 110 V and R is 10 Ω, find I if E is 220 V and R is 11 Ω.

General variation equation:

$$I = \frac{kE}{R}$$

Substitute 11 for I, 110 for E, and 10 for R.

$$11 = \frac{k \cdot 110}{10}$$

Solve for k.

$$11(10) = 110\,k$$
$$110 = 110\,k$$
$$1 = k$$

Variation equation:

$$I = \frac{1 \cdot E}{R}$$

Now substitute 220 for E and 11 for R and solve for I.

$$I = \frac{1 \cdot 220}{11} = \frac{220}{11} = 20 \text{ A}$$

Practice Set 3-4

Use your intuition and the appropriate definitions to determine whether the variation between these variables is direct or inverse.

1. The diameter of a bicycle wheel and its circumference

2. The number of people in line at the grocery store and the time required to check out

3. The time required to fill a swimming pool and the amount of water coming in from the hose

4. The number of people mowing a lawn and the time it takes to finish the job

5. The amount of water used during a month and the monthly water bill

6. The outside temperature and the time it takes for the snow to melt

Write a variation equation for the following statements.

7. y varies directly as z.

8. p varies inversely as q.

9. a varies jointly with b and c.

10. m varies directly as the square of n.

11. d varies jointly with e and the cube of f.

12. f varies jointly with g and h and inversely with the square of j.

13. m varies directly as the square root of n and inversely as the cube of p.

14. v varies inversely as the square root of g.

Express the following statements as variation equations and find the values of the constants of proportionality and the indicated unknowns.

15. y varies directly as x; $y = 8$ when $x = 24$. Find y when $x = 36$.

16. p varies directly as q; $p = 6$ when $q = 120$. Find p when q is 100.

17. y varies inversely as x; $y = 9$ when $x = 6$. Find y when $x = 36$.

18. r varies inversely as t; $r = 6$ when $t = 2$. Find r when $t = 8$.

19. y varies directly as the square root of x; $y = 24$ and $x = 16$. Find y when $x = 36$.

20. y varies inversely as the square root of x; $y = 6$ when $x = 100$. Find y when $x = 144$.

21. y varies jointly as x and the square of z; $y = 150$ when $x = 3$ and $z = 5$. Find y when $x = 12$ and $z = 8$.

22. y varies jointly as x and the square root of z; $y = 48$ when $x = 2$ and $z = 36$. Find y when $x = 3$ and $z = 25$.

23. p varies directly as q and inversely as the square of r; $p = 40$ when $q = 20$ and $r = 4$. Find p when $q = 24$ and $r = 8$.

24. y varies directly as r and inversely as the product of x and t; $y = 4$ when $r = 6$, $x = 3$, and $t = 1$. Find y when $r = 14$, $x = 1$, and $t = 6$.

Solve the following applied variation problems.

25. The area of a circle varies directly as the square of its radius. If the area of a circle is 78.5 cm^2 when its radius is 5 cm, find the area of the circle when the radius is 7 cm.

26. Hooke's law says that the force required to stretch a spring is directly proportional to the distance

stretched. If a force of 10 lb is required to stretch a spring 5 in., how much force will be required to stretch the spring 10 in.?

27. The distance traveled by a ball rolling down an inclined plane varies directly as the square of the time. If the inclination of the plane is such that the ball traveled 27 ft at the end of 3 sec, what is the distance traveled at the end of 2 sec?

28. The distance that a car travels after the brakes have been applied varies directly as the square of its speed. If the stopping distance for a car going 30 mph is 54 ft, what is the stopping distance for a car going 70 mph?

29. The period of a pendulum varies directly as the square root of its length. If a pendulum of length 16 in. has a period of 0.5 sec, find the length of a pendulum with a period of 0.75 sec.

30. The interest on an investment varies directly as the rate of interest. If the interest is $48 when the interest rate is 5%, find the interest when the rate is 4.75%.

31. The time required to fill a tank varies inversely as the square of the diameter of the pipe used. If it takes 20 hr to fill a given tank with a 2-in. pipe, find the diameter of the pipe needed to fill the same tank in 5 hr.

32. Boyle's law states that the volume of a fixed mass of gas under constant temperature is inversely proportional to the pressure. If the volume is 10 ft^3 when the pressure is 15 lb/in.^{2}, find the volume when the pressure is 60 lb/in.^{2}.

33. The weight of a body above the surface of the Earth varies inversely as the square of the distance of the body from the center of gravity of the Earth. If an astronaut weighs 180 lb on the surface of the Earth, how much would she weigh 500 mi above the surface of the Earth? Assume the radius of the Earth to be 4000 mi.

34. The time it takes to drive a certain distance varies inversely as the speed traveled. If it takes 3 hr at 60 mph to drive a certain distance, how long would it take to drive the same distance at 65 mph?

35. The electric power, P, used in a circuit varies directly with the square of the voltage drop, V, and inversely with the resistance, R. If 180 W of power in a circuit are used by a 90-V drop with a resistance of 45 Ω, find the power used when the voltage drop is 120 V and the resistance is 30 Ω.

36. The weight of a cylindrical container filled with a given substance varies jointly as the height of the container and the square of its radius. If a container with a radius of 10 cm and a height of 30 cm weighs 60 kg, what is the weight of a container filled with the same substance when its radius is 12 cm and its height is 60 cm?

37. The expansion of metal varies jointly as the temperature and the length of the metal. A brass rod expands 2.7 in. when its length is 100 ft and the temperature is 225°F. Find the expansion when the length of the brass rod is 40 ft and the temperature is 150°F.

38. The maximum load that a cylindrical column with a circular cross section can hold varies directly as the fourth power of the diameter of the cross section and inversely as the square of the height. If a 10-m column that is 1.5 m in diameter can support 32.805 t, how many metric tons can be supported by a column 9 m high and 1 m in diameter?

39. The volume, V, of a sphere is given as a function of its radius, r, by

$$V(r) = \frac{4\pi r^3}{3}$$

(a) Is this a direct or inverse variation?
(b) What is the constant of proportionality?
(c) Evaluate $V(9 \text{ in.})$.

40. The area of a circle, A, is given as a function of its radius: $A(r) = \pi r^2$.
(a) Is this a direct or inverse variation?
(b) What is the constant of proportionality, k?
(c) Evaluate $A(3 \text{ in.})$.

Section 3-5   NONLINEAR FUNCTIONS

We examined functions that are linear in the previous section. Now let us look at several types of nonlinear functions: quadratic functions, power functions, and exponential functions.

Quadratic Functions

The first family of nonlinear functions we will discuss is the **quadratic function**.

Definition

Quadratic Function
A quadratic function is a function f defined for all real numbers x by an equation of the form:

$$f(x) = ax^2 + bx + c$$

in which a, b, c are constants and $a \neq 0$.

The graph of a quadratic function is a parabola. One of the simplest quadratic functions is defined by $f(x) = x^2$. To graph this equation, choose several values for x and solve for $f(x)$. (See Table 3-16.)

Now plot these points on a coordinate plane. (See Figure 3-13.) This is the graph of the quadratic function $f(x) = x^2$.

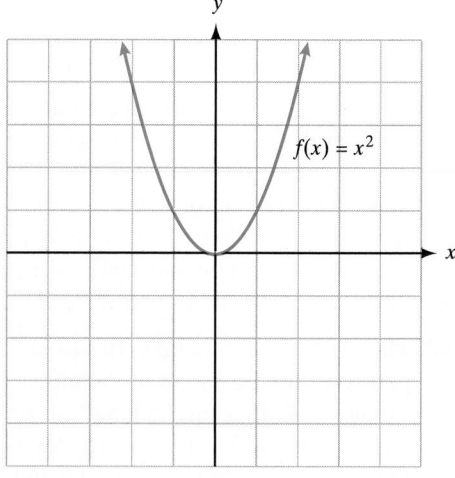

Figure 3-13
Graph of quadratic function $f(x) = x^2$.

■ **TABLE 3-16**

x	$f(x) = x^2$	$f(x)$	Solution
-2	$f(x) = (-2)^2$	4	$(-2, 4)$
-1	$f(x) = (-1)^2$	1	$(-1, 1)$
0	$f(x) = (0)^2$	0	$(0, 0)$
1	$f(x) = (1)^2$	1	$(1, 1)$
2	$f(x) = (2)^2$	4	$(2, 4)$

You will notice that the graph in Figure 3-13 is symmetric to the y-axis. This means that the graph is the same on both sides of the y-axis. The y-axis acts as a mirror.

EXAMPLE 24   **Quadratic Functions**

Sketch the graph of $f(x) = -x^2$.

First, choose several values for x and solve for $f(x)$. (See Table 3-17.) Second, plot these points on a coordinate plane. (See Figure 3-14.) This figure shows the graph of $f(x) = -x^2$.

■ **TABLE 3-17**

x	$f(x) = -x^2$	$f(x)$	Solution
-2	$f(x) = -(-2)^2$	-4	$(-2, -4)$
-1	$f(x) = -(-1)^2$	-1	$(-1, -1)$
0	$f(x) = -(0)^2$	0	$(0, 0)$
1	$f(x) = -(1)^2$	-1	$(1, -1)$
2	$f(x) = -(2)^2$	-4	$(2, -4)$

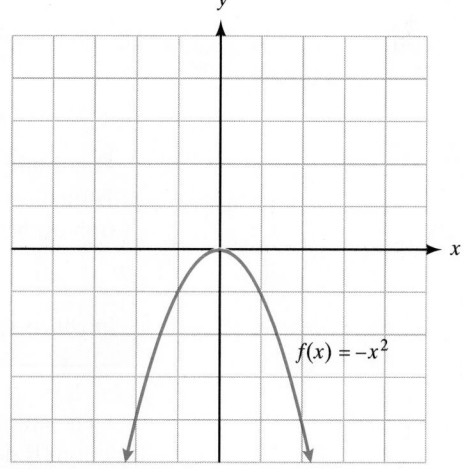

Figure 3-14
Graph of quadratic function $f(x) = -x^2$.

You will notice that the graph of $f(x) = -x^2$ opens down. If the leading coefficient is positive, then the parabola will open upward. If the leading coefficient is negative, the parabola will open downward.

Important Equations

Quadratic Function

$$f(x) = ax^2 + bx + c \qquad \text{(if } a > 0\text{, then the graph opens up)}$$

$$\text{(if } a < 0\text{, then the graph opens down)}$$

Each parabola has a minimum point or a maximum point. The vertex of a parabola is the high or low point of the graph — the maximum (max) or minimum (min) of the function. If the parabola opens downward, the function has a maximum value that is the y-coordinate of the vertex. If the parabola opens upward, the function has a minimum point that is also the y-coordinate of the vertex. The maximum and minimum points are important in many application problems. Another important aspect of a quadratic function are the **roots** or 0s of the function. The roots

Calculator Mini-Lesson

Using a Graphing Calculator to Find Max/Min and Roots

A TI-83 Plus graphing calculator can be used to easily find the maximum or minimum value of a parabolic function and the roots of the function. Follow these steps.

Zeros— these are the x-intercepts or roots of the equation.

1.   Select **2:zero** from the CALCULATE menu (located above the TRACE button). The graph will be displayed with the words **Left Bound?** at the bottom of the screen.
2.   Move the cursor to the left of the location of one of the x-intercepts using the arrow keys. Press ENTER. A small arrow will appear at the top of the screen marking the left boundary. At the bottom of the screen, you should see **Right Bound?** Move the cursor right, past the x-intercept, and press ENTER again. Another arrow should appear at the top of the screen marking the right boundary.
3.   The word **Guess?** is now displayed at the bottom of the screen. Press ENTER one more time and the coordinates of the x-intercept or root should be displayed at the bottom of the screen.

Max/Min— depending on the equation, the graph will have either a maximum point *or* a minimum point.

1.   Select **3:minimum** or **4:maximum** from the CALCULATE menu. The graph of the function will be displayed.
2.   Set the left and right boundaries for the maximum or minimum point following the same steps that were used to find the zeros.

of a quadratic function are the same as the x-intercepts. Remember, the x-intercept of any equation is where the graph crosses the x-axis. To find the x-intercepts, we substitute a 0 for y and solve the equation for x. The x-intercepts or roots of a quadratic function can also be determined using a graphing calculator.

EXAMPLE 25   Finding Roots of Quadratic Functions

Graph the quadratic function $f(x) = -2x^2 + 3x + 2$ using a graphing calculator. Find the value of the maximum or minimum and determine the roots of the function.

Enter the equation using the $\boxed{Y=}$ function as

$$Y_1 = -2x^2 + 3x + 2$$

Use the $\boxed{GRAPH}$ button to display the parabola. Use the $\boxed{TRACE}$ function to move the cursor to the highest point on the graph. This is the maximum point of the function. Record the coordinates shown at the bottom of the screen. Now use the $\boxed{TRACE}$ function to move the cursor to each of the x-intercepts. These are the roots of the equation. Record the coordinates displayed on your screen. Use the $\boxed{CALCULATE}$ feature to verify these points. (See Figure 3-15.)

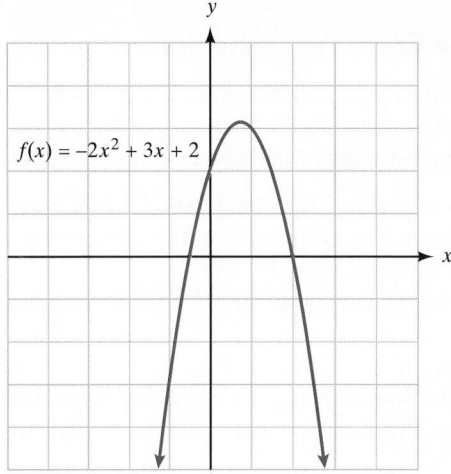

$f(x) = -2x^2 + 3x + 2$

Figure 3-15
Example 25.

Note that the roots are $(-0.5, 0)$ and $(2, 0)$ and the maximum value is 3.13.

Quadratic functions are used to describe many scientific applications, such as throwing objects or shooting projectiles. The force of gravity and the initial velocity of a moving object are used to write a quadratic function that describes a particular situation. Look at the following situation and the function used to describe it.

EXAMPLE 26   Finding the Maximum Height of a Quadratic Function

A rock is thrown upward from the ground. Its height in feet above ground after t seconds is given by the equation

$$f(t) = -16t^2 + 15t$$

Find the maximum height of the rock and the number of seconds it took for the rock to reach its maximum height.

Enter the equation into a graphing calculator. Use the $\boxed{Y=}$ function:

$$Y_1 = -16t^2 + 15t$$

Use the $\boxed{\text{GRAPH}}$ button to display the parabola. Move the cursor to the highest point on the graph using the $\boxed{\text{TRACE}}$ function. The coordinates of the cursor will be displayed at the bottom of your screen. In this application, the t variable is plotted on the x-axis, so the x-coordinate of the maximum represents the time. The y value represents the height. Use the $\boxed{\text{CALCULATE}}$ feature to verify these points. (See Figure 3-16.)

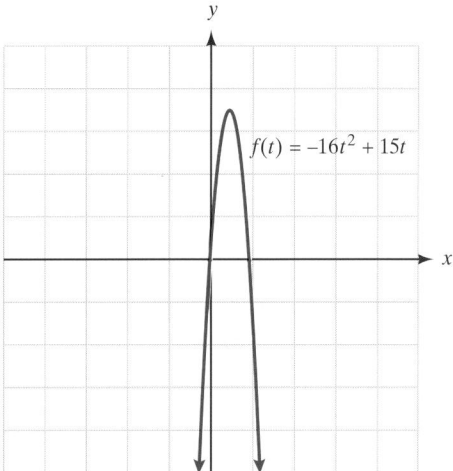

Figure 3-16
Example 26.

Note that the maximum is $(0.469, 3.52)$. This means that the rock's maximum height is 3.5 ft, which was reached in approximately 0.5 sec.

EXAMPLE 27   Profit Function

A company's profit (in thousands of dollars) is given by the equation $P(s) = 230 + 20s - 0.5s^2$, where s is the amount (in hundreds of dollars) spent on advertising.

TABLE 3-18

s = Amount Spent on Advertising (in $100)	Profit (in $1000)
0	$P(0) = 230 + 20(0) - 0.5(0)^2 = 230$
8	$P(8) = 230 + 20(8) - 0.5(8)^2 = 358$
15	$P(15) = 230 + 20(15) - 0.5(15)^2 = 417.5$
25	$P(25) = 230 + 20(25) - 0.5(25)^2 = 417.5$
40	$P(40) = 230 + 20(40) - 0.5(40)^2 = 230$
50	$P(50) = 230 + 20(50) - 0.5(50)^2 = -20$

Figure 3-17
Example 27.

Complete the table with the designated values for s and use the graphing calculator to help you draw a sketch of the function. (You will need to adjust the window settings to view the entire graph.) Use the TABLE or TRACE function to verify the values that have been calculated in Table 3-18. The graph of this function is shown in Figure 3-17.

What does it mean when we obtain a negative number for profit?

Power Functions

A **power function** is an equation that takes the form $f(x) = cx^k$. The number k is called the *power* and is the most significant part of a power function. For most applications, we are interested only in positive values of the variable x and of c, but we allow k to be any number.

In a power function, larger values of the exponent, k, cause the function to increase faster when k is positive. (See Figure 3-18.) If k is negative, the functions decrease toward 0. These functions are easily graphed using a graphing calculator, and the differences in their behaviors can be examined by graphing several functions with increasing powers of the exponent. Using only the first quadrant for graphing, this property is illustrated in Figure 3-19.

Figure 3-18
Power functions.

$f(x) = x$
$f(x) = x^2$
$f(x) = x^3$
$f(x) = x^4$

Figure 3-19
Comparing graphs of power functions.

■ EXAMPLE 28   **Power Function**

When a rock is dropped from a tall structure, it will fall $D = 16t^2$ ft in t sec. Make a graph that shows the distance the rock falls versus time if the building is 70 ft tall. How long does it take the rock to strike the ground?

(a) Using your graphing calculator, enter the equation $D = 16t^2$, letting $D = y_1$, the distance on the vertical axis; x will equal time, which is represented on the horizontal axis. Be sure that the window of the graph has a maximum y (y max) greater than 70, because the building is 70 ft tall. (See Figure 3-20.)

$D = 16t^2$

Figure 3-20
Graph of distance fallen versus time.

(b) We want to know how long it takes the rock to strike the ground. Therefore, we want to solve the equation letting $D = 70$, because it will strike the ground after traveling 70 ft.

$$16t^2 = 70$$

$$t^2 = \frac{70}{16}$$

$$t^2 = 4.375$$

$$t = 2.09 \text{ sec}$$

We can verify this result using the $\boxed{\text{TRACE}}$ function on the calculator.

Exponential Functions

The third type of nonlinear function we will discuss is called an **exponential function**. Many biological systems grow at a rate that is exponential. Compound-interest formulas are also examples of exponential growth. This growth shows a pattern. Exponential functions increase at such a fast rate that it is usually most efficient to graph these using a graphing calculator.

Definition

Exponential Function

$$f(x) = b^x \qquad \text{(if } b \neq 0 \text{ or } 1, \text{ and } x \text{ is a real number)}$$

EXAMPLE 29   Graphing an Exponential Function

Graph the exponential function $f(x) = 2^x$ using a graphing calculator.
Enter the equation using the $\boxed{Y=}$ function as

$$Y_1 = 2\boxed{\wedge}x$$

Use the $\boxed{\text{GRAPH}}$ button to display the exponential function. (See Figure 3-21.)

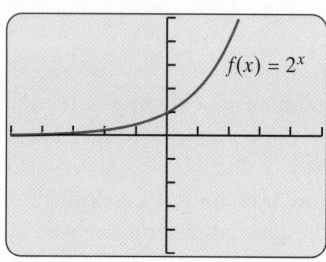

Figure 3-21
Example 28.

The world has many problems that can be modeled using exponential functions. The following example deals with radioactive decay, which is described with an exponential function.

EXAMPLE 30   Radioactive Decay

As a result of the Chernobyl nuclear accident, radioactive debris was carried through the atmosphere. One immediate concern was the impact the debris had on the water supply. The percent y of radioactive material in water after t days is estimated by $y = 100(2.7)^{-0.1t}$. Estimate the expected percent of radioactive material in the water after 30 days.
Enter the equation using the $\boxed{Y=}$ function as

$$Y_1 = 100(2.7)\boxed{\wedge}-0.1x$$

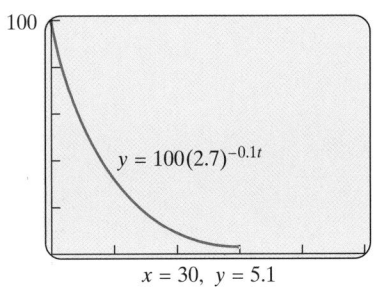

$$y = 100(2.7)^{-0.1t}$$

$x = 30, \; y = 5.1$

Figure 3-22
Example 30.

Use the GRAPH button to display the function. You will need to adjust the WINDOW setting to view the graph. (See settings that follow.) Use the TRACE function to move the cursor to where the x value is 30 on the graph. (In this application, the t variable is plotted on the x-axis.) The coordinates of the cursor will be displayed at the bottom of your screen. Approximate the value of y to the nearest tenth. Use the CALCULATE feature or TABLE feature to verify these points.

WINDOW

$$X_{\min} = 0 \qquad Y_{\min} = 0$$

$$X_{\max} = 50 \qquad Y_{\max} = 100$$

$$X_{\text{scl}} = 10 \qquad Y_{\text{scl}} = 10$$

(See Figure 3-22.)

The values at the bottom of the screen are $x = 30$ and $y = 5.1$, so approximately 5% of the radioactive material still contaminated the water supply after 30 days.

You can also verify this result by substituting $t = 30$ into the equation and calculating the result.

Practice Set 3-5

Sketch the graphs of the following quadratic functions using a graphing calculator. State if the function has a maximum or a minimum. Determine the maximum or minimum value to the nearest tenth. Determine the roots of the quadratic function to the nearest tenth.

1. $f(x) = x^2 + 6x + 5$

2. $f(x) = x^2 - 6x + 5$

3. $f(x) = x^2 + 5x + 4$

4. $f(x) = -x^2 - 4$

5. $f(x) = -3x^2 + 2x + 5$

6. $f(x) = -2x^2 + 5x - 6$

Use your graphing calculator to sketch a graph of the following power functions. Calculate the value of $f(-3)$ for each function in problems 7 to 10.

7. $f(x) = 3x^2$

8. $f(x) = -4x^2$

9. $f(x) = \dfrac{1}{3}x^3$

10. $f(x) = 2x^4$

Draw a sketch of the following exponential functions using a graphing calculator. Find the value of $f(2)$ for each function in problems 11 to 16.

11. $f(x) = 2^x$

12. $f(x) = 3^x - 2$

13. $f(x) = -3^x$

14. $f(x) = -\left(\dfrac{1}{4}\right)^x$

15. $f(x) = \left(\dfrac{1}{2}\right)^x$

16. $f(x) = 2^x - 1$

17. The height h of a ball after it is thrown vertically upward is given in feet by the function $h(t) = 4 + 6t - 16t^2$, where t is the time in seconds. Determine the time when the ball is at its peak. Determine the maximum height of the ball.

18. The distance s (in feet) fallen by an object thrown downward with an initial velocity of v_0 ft/sec is given by $s = 16t^2 + v_0 t$, where t is the number of seconds of fall. If $v_0 = 10$ ft/sec, how far will the object fall after 3 sec?

19. Marcus shoots an arrow straight upward. The velocity of the arrow is 160 ft/sec. The function that models this problem is $f(x) = 5 + 160x - 16x^2$, where x is the number of seconds that have passed since the arrow was shot. Use your graphing calculator to answer the following questions.
    (a) How high is the arrow after 4 sec?
    (b) What is the maximum height that the arrow reaches before it falls back to Earth?
    (c) After how many seconds did the arrow reach the ground?

20. A ball is projected off of a 400-ft-tall building at a velocity of 45 ft/sec. The function $f(x) = -16x^2 + 45x + 400$ (where x is the number of seconds elapsed) models this toss.
    (a) How high is the ball 2 sec after it is thrown?
    (b) What is the maximum height that the ball reaches?
    (c) After how many seconds did the ball reach the ground?

21. The function that relates the price of a certain-quality diamond to its weight is $p(w) = 920w^2$, where w is the weight of the diamond in carats. Sketch this function and use it to find the price of a 1.5-carat diamond.

22. The distance required for a certain automobile to come to a stop after the brakes have been applied can be modeled with the function $d(s) = 0.0273s^2$, where s is the speed the car was traveling when the brakes were applied. Sketch this function and use it to find the estimated stopping distance for a car traveling 45 mph.

23. Suppose that the future population of Pikeville t years after the year 2000 is modeled by $f(t) = 15,000(1.005)^t$, where $t = 0$ corresponds to the year 2000. Sketch a graph of this model and use it to predict the population of Pikeville in the year 2010.

24. At 6% interest compounded monthly, the future value of a $5000 investment can be calculated using the formula $A = 5000(1.005)^x$, where x represents the number of months that the money is invested. Sketch the graph of this equation and find the value of the investment after 5 years (60 months).

Chapter Summary

Key Terms, Properties, and Formulas

combined variation	exponential function	linear function
constant of proportionality	function	models
constant of variation	function notation	power function
dependent variable	independent variable	quadratic function
direct proportion	inverse proportionality	range
direct variation	inverse variation	relation
domain	joint variation	roots

Points to Remember

A function is a relation in which, for each value of the independent variable (domain) of the ordered pairs, there is exactly one value of the dependent variable (range).

The domain of a function is the set of all possible values of the independent variables.

The range of a function is the set of all possible values of the dependent variables.

A linear function is written in the form $f(x) = mx + b$, and its graph is a straight line.

A quadratic function $f(x) = ax^2 + bx + c$ will have a maximum value if the graph opens down and a minimum value if the graph opens up.

Direct variation $y = kx$ Joint variation $y = kxz$

Inverse variation $y = \frac{k}{x}$ Combined variation $y = \frac{kuv}{wx}$

Power function: $f(x) = cx^k$ where c and k are constants and x is a real number

Exponential function: $f(x) = b^x$ if $b \neq 0$ or 1, and x is a real number

Chapter Review Problems

1. Let $T(p) = 0.06p$ be a function that calculates sales tax. Explain the meaning of $T(\$12) = \$0.72$.

2. Explain in your own words the meaning of the domain and range of a function.

3. Are there any restrictions on the domain and range of the tax function in problem 1?

For each problem, write a short statement that expresses a possible functional relationship between the quantities. Example: Age; shoe size. Solution: As a person's age increases, shoe size also increases up to a point. After that point, shoe size remains relatively constant.

4. (age of a person, height of a person)

5. (time, number of bacteria in a culture)

6. (speed of a car, time it takes to drive from home to school)

Use the following graph to solve problems 7 and 8.

Long Distance Bill

7. Identify the independent and dependent variables of the function illustrated in the graph.

8. Give the domain and range of the function.

9. The formula for calculating the braking distance needed when traveling at a certain speed is $d = \frac{x^2}{20} + x$, where x is the speed of the car and d is the stopping distance. Calculate the stopping distance required when a car is traveling 20 mph, 40 mph, 60 mph, and 80 mph. Graph these values and discuss the shape of the graph and its meaning.

10. Let the function $f(x) = 2x - 6$. Find the following values of $f(x)$.
    (a) $f(-2)$ (b) $f(0)$ (c) $f(4)$ (d) $f(\frac{1}{2})$

Write the following equations in function notation.

11. $y = -3x + 2$

12. $-3y = 2x + 6$

13. $x - y = 8$

14. $3x + 2y = 6$

15. $4x = -y + 1$

16. Let $f(x) = 2x^2 - 1$. Complete Table 3-19 for this function.

▨ **TABLE 3-19**

x	-2	-1	0	1	2
$f(x)$					

17. The graph that follows defines $g(x)$. Find the following values.
    (a) $g(0)$
    (b) $g(3)$
    (c) $g(-2)$

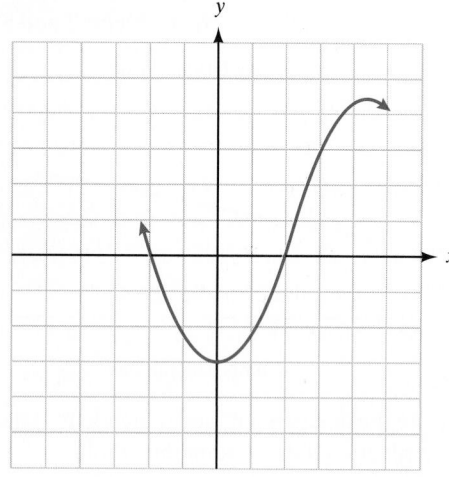

18. The cost of renting a car at Rental City is given by the function $C(m) = \$29 + \$0.06m$, where $m =$ the number of miles driven by the customer. Find $C(120)$ and explain what your answer means.

19. The local community college charges students a $75 activity fee plus $30 for every credit hour a student takes during the semester.
    (a) Write a formula in function notation that can be used to calculate a student's charges.
    (b) Find the cost for a student who enrolls in 12 credit hours for a semester.

20. MidTexas Printing Company prints paperback novels for aspiring young authors. The company charges a $1000 setup fee and $5.50 per book printed. The minimum number of books it will print is 250.
    (a) Write a linear function that models these charges.
    (b) What is the domain for this function?
    (c) Calculate $f(375)$ and explain what it means.

21. Married taxpayers who filed their 2003 taxes jointly used Schedule Y of the taxpayer guide. Those whose taxable incomes were greater than $14,000 but less than $56,800 were required to pay $1400 plus 15% of the amount over $14,000.
    (a) Write a function equation for this tax rule.
    (b) Find $f(\$32,355)$ and explain what your answer means.

22. Kim sells vacuum cleaners. Her salary plan provides her with $1000 per month plus 25% of all sales that she makes during the month.
    (a) Write a linear function to model this problem.
    (b) How much will she make this month if she sells $2500 worth of vacuum cleaners?

23. Use the data in Table 3-20 to write a linear function equation.

▨ **TABLE 3-20**

x	-1	0	1	2	3
y	-5	-3	-1	1	3

24. Use the data in Table 3-21 to write a linear function equation.

▨ **TABLE 3-21**

x	-4	0	2	6	8
y	2	4	5	7	8

25. Your fingernails grow 5 mm per week. Name the independent and dependent variables in this function. Is this a direct or inverse variation problem?

26. The depth of water in a swimming pool decreases at a rate of 0.35 in./hr on a sunny day due to evaporation. Name the independent and dependent variables in this function. Is this a direct or inverse variation problem?

Write a variation equation for each of the following statements.

27. s varies directly as t.

28. z varies inversely as p.

29. m varies jointly as r and s.

30. x varies directly as the cube root of z and inversely as y squared.

Express the following statements as variation equations and find the values of the constants of proportionality and the indicated unknowns.

31. Suppose u varies directly as the cube of v; $u = 8$ when $v = 1$. Find u when $v = 2$.

32. Suppose x varies inversely as the square of y; $x = 2$ when $y = 3$. Find x when $y = 5$.

33. Suppose s varies jointly as t and g; $s = 10$ when $t = 3$ and $g = 2.5$. Find s when $t = 7$ and $g = 6$.

34. N varies directly as the square of L and inversely as the cube of M; $N = 9$ when $L = 2$ and $M = 1$. Find N when $L = 4$ and $M = 2$.

35. The distance a stone falls when dropped off a cliff is directly proportional to the square of the time it falls. If the stone falls 64.4 ft in 2 sec, how far will the stone have fallen in 3 sec?

36. The gravitational force between two objects varies inversely as the square of the distance between the objects. If a force of 50 units results from two objects that are 12 units apart, how much force results from two objects that are 20 units apart?

37. Sketch the graphs of the following quadratic functions, giving the maximum or minimum of the function and the roots of each function.
    (a) $f(x) = 2x^2 - 4x - 6$
    (b) $g(x) = -x^2 - 2x + 8$

38. Sketch the following power functions and evaluate each function at -3.
    (a) $f(x) = \frac{1}{2}x^4$
    (b) $g(x) = -2x^3$

39. Sketch the following exponential functions and evaluate each function at -2.
    (a) $f(x) = 3^x$
    (b) $g(x) = \left(\frac{1}{2}\right)^x$

40. In 2000, the population of Mexico was 100.35 million, and it was growing at a constant 1.53% annual rate. The function that expresses this growth is $P(t) = 100.35(1.0153)^t$ in year t, where $t = 0$ is the year 2000. Calculate the predicted population of Mexico in 2010 ($t = 10$) using this function.

Chapter Test

1. In your own words, give a description of a linear function.

2. The value of an automobile after t years is given by the function $V(t) = \$25,000 - \$1500t$. What is the significance of the $25,000 and of the $1500?

3. Write a short statement that expresses a possible functional relationship between these quantities: the square footage of a house and the cost of the house. Identify the independent and dependent variables.

4. The following graph illustrates the number of widgets produced during the first shift on Monday at Daniel's Widget Shop.

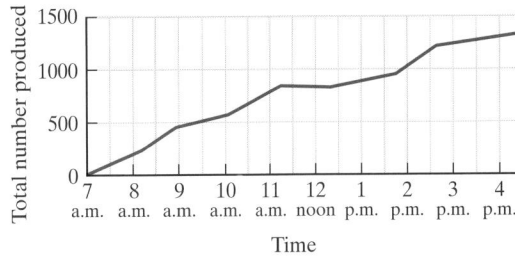

(a) Identify the independent and dependent variables in this graph.

(b) What is the initial value of the function? Is this a linear function?

Write the following equations in function notation. Find $f(-4)$ for each problem.

5. $2x - y = 4$

6. $y = 5$

7. $3x^2 + y = -2$

Use the linear function model to answer problems 8 to 11.

8. A new Ford costs $22,500. The car's value depreciates $2200 per year. Write a formula that expresses its value, V, in terms of its age, t, in years.

9. The cost of a cab ride is modeled by the function $C(d) = 1.50 + 0.75d$, where d is the number of miles traveled and C is the cost in dollars. Evaluate $C(12)$ and explain what the answer tells us.

10. For students at Alvin Community College taking 12–15 credit hours, the charges include a $21 registration fee and $28 per credit hour.
   (a) Write a linear function that models this fee scale.
   (b) What are the domain and range for this function?
   (c) Calculate $f(14)$ and explain what it means.

11. Write a linear function using the data in Table 3-22.

   TABLE 3-22

x	-1	0	1	2
$f(x)$	5	2	-1	-4

Use the definitions of direct and inverse variation to complete problems 12 and 13.

12. The height of a candle is reduced by 0.75 in./hr when it is burning. Name the independent and dependent variables in this function. Is this a direct or inverse variation problem?

13. The diameter of a tree is growing by 0.2 in./yr. Name the independent and dependent variables in this function. Is this a direct or inverse variation problem?

Express the following statements as variation equations and find the values of the constants of proportionality and the indicated unknowns.

14. Suppose t varies directly as B and inversely as the square of P; $t = 7.5$ when $B = 6$ and $P = 2$. Find t when $B = 63$ and $P = 3$.

15. Suppose y varies jointly as the square of x and the cube of z; $y = 135$ when $x = 2$ and $z = 3$. Find y when $x = 0.5$ and $z = 2$.

Solve the following applied variation problems.

16. Charlotte's earnings as an ICU nurse are directly proportional to the number of hours worked. If she earns $260.50 for 8 hr of work, how much money does she earn for 35 hr of work?

17. The mass of a circular coin varies jointly as its thickness and the square of the radius of the coin. A silver coin 2 cm in radius and 0.2 cm thick has a mass of 26.4 g. What is the mass of a silver coin 4 cm in radius and 0.3 cm thick?

18. Sketch the graph of the quadratic function $f(x) = -x^2 + 9$. Find its maximum or minimum and roots.

19. Sketch the graph of the function $f(x) = -2^x$. Calculate $f(4)$.

20. Suppose that the annual inflation rate is 4.5%. College tuition at State University is currently $5200 per year. Using this inflation rate, we can write a function to predict future tuition costs: $C(t) = 5200(1.045)^t$, where t = number of years from now. Predict the tuition cost at State University for a newborn (18 years from now).

Suggested Laboratory Exercises

Tax Bite 2005

The following information was gathered online from the Tax Foundation at www .taxfoundation.org. You may gather more current information of the same kind by visiting this site.

The major portion of a person's work year is spent earning money to pay taxes (federal, state, and local) and to pay for living expenses (food, clothing, and shelter). The Tax Foundation gives the following breakdown for an average calendar year. (See Table 3-23.)

TABLE 3-23

Expense Category	Days
Federal taxes (include Social Security and Medicare)	70
State and local taxes	37
Housing	65
Health care	52
Food	31
Transportation	31
Recreation*	22
Clothing	13
Savings*	2
Miscellaneous*	42
Total time =	365

*These items are not considered to be "essential" and may be called "disposable" income because you are not required to pay for any of these.

(a) If you start work on January 1, 2005, and must work steady 8-hour work days (no weekends off) until you have worked enough days to pay all of your taxes (rows 1 and 2 of the table), on what calendar date would you have finished paying all of the taxes and started working for yourself?

(b) How much of your work year earns you your housing and food money?

(c) What percent of your work year is spent earning money that would be considered "disposable" income?

(d) If you earned $52,000 per year, approximately how much disposable income would you have?

(e) Wages have continued to increase (on the average) over the past few years, and yet disposable income has been decreasing. What might be some of the reasons for this sad state of affairs?

The Growth of McDonald's

The following is information taken from the home page of McDonald's at www. mcdonalds.com/corp.html. It lists the number of systemwide restaurants that were open during the years indicated. (See Table 3-24.)

TABLE 3-24

Year	1999	2000	2001	2002	2003	2004
Restaurants	26,309	28,707	30,093	31,106	31,129	31,561

In the area of mathematics known as statistics, there is a process called linear regression analysis. Using the data from the table as (x, y) pairs (year, number of outlets), it is possible to develop a linear equation that models the growth in the number of McDonald's restaurants. The equation obtained is $y = 987x - 1945320$.

(a) Evaluate the previous equation for each data pair in the chart and record the value obtained (rounded to the nearest whole number) in a table similar to Table 3-25.

TABLE 3-25

	1999	2000	2001	2002	2003	2004
Estimated						

(b) Is the model equation correctly predicting the numbers of restaurants for each year? For which year is it closest? For which year is it the worst predictor?

(c) What is the estimated number of restaurants for 2006 as predicted by the model? Go to the McDonald's home page and see how close you are.

LAB EXERCISE 3

Using a Graphing Calculator for Linear Functions

Use a graphing calculator to analyze the following linear function. We will look at the equation, graph, and table in this exercise.

1. Jennifer makes a base pay of $250 per week. She also receives 5% of all sales that she makes during the week. Write a function equation to calculate her weekly paycheck.

2. Enter this function into your calculator using the $\boxed{Y=}$ button. After the equation is in the calculator, set the window as follows:

$$X_{min} = 0 \qquad Y_{min} = 0$$

$$X_{max} = 2500 \qquad Y_{max} = 400$$

$$X_{scl} = 500 \qquad Y_{scl} = 50$$

Press the $\boxed{GRAPH}$ key and use the display to draw a sketch of this function equation. Be sure to label the axes.

3. Then access the $\boxed{TABLE}$ function above the $\boxed{GRAPH}$ key and use this information to fill in the given table. You may need to access the $\boxed{TBLSET}$ func-

tion above the WINDOW button in order to set up the table to match this chart. Set **TblStart = 0** and **ΔTbl = 500** because the change in sales (x) in the chart is in \$500 increments.

Sales	Pay
\$ 500	
\$1000	
\$1500	
\$2000	
\$2500	

4. Find $f(\$875)$ and explain its meaning for this problem. You can calculate this using the function equation or you can use the CALCULATE feature over the TRACE button to find the answer. Under CALCULATE, select **1:value** and press ENTER. Then you will see the graph and at the bottom of the screen, **x=**. Fill in 875 and press ENTER. The answer will be displayed and the location on the graph will be noted with a blinking cursor.

LAB EXERCISE 4   Rebound Height and Variation

Get a golf, tennis, or hand ball. Drop (do not throw) the ball from some height. Does it rebound to the same height from which it is dropped? Does the height to which the ball rebounds change if the height from which it is dropped changes? Make some measurements and record the drop height and rebound height (approximately). Is rebound height directly or inversely related to drop height? Is this relationship linear or not? Which variable is the dependent variable and which is independent? Is this relationship a function or not? Support your answers with data, graphs, and so forth.

LAB EXERCISE 5   Name That Function!

The tables that follow each contain a list of words or numbers in the first column and a number in the second column. There is some functional relationship between the two columns in each case. Describe the function clearly in your own words. Complete the charts.

(a)
airplane	2
ship	1
automobile	4
boat	1
airliner	?
train	?

(b)
fossil	2
bones	2
dinosaur	4
paleontologist	4
raptor	?
pterodactyl	?

(c)
1	1
2	4
3	9
4	?
5	?

(d)
1	3
2	5
3	7
4	9
5	?

■ **TABLE 3-26**

Name of Pizza	Diameter (all pizzas are round)	Base Price (cheese pizza)	Price per Extra Topping	Base Price per Square Inch	Price per Square Inch with Three Toppings
Chihuahua	9 in.	$6.00	$0.80		
Poodle	12 in.	$9.75	$1.05		
Lab	15 in.	$15.55	$1.75		
St. Bernard	17.5 in.	$19.25	$2.50		

LAB EXERCISE 6   **Do You Want Pizza for Lunch?**

Pizzas come in a bewildering assortment of sizes and with a plethora of topping choices and combinations. In this activity, you will attempt to clear up some of this confusion.

To begin, suppose that Dan's Pizza Parlor and Veterinary Clinic (Hey, this is a small town, what can I say?) serves the best-tasting pizza in town. Table 3-26 lists the sizes and prices of pizzas that are available from Dan's.

1. To begin your research, complete Table 3-26 by filling in the last two columns (base price per square inch of pizza and price per square inch with three additional toppings). Remember, the formula for the area of a circle is $A = \pi r^2$. The base price is for a cheese pizza; all other toppings are at additional cost. This additional cost is different for each size pizza.
2. Rank (from lowest to highest) the cost per square inch of all the sizes of cheese pizza. Which one is the "best" price? How did you determine this answer?
3. Rank the cost per square inch for pizzas with three extra toppings as you did in part 2. Answer the same questions.
4. Is there anything "odd" about Dan's price structure?
5. Make up some questions (be reasonable) that you would like for the other groups in your class to answer about this activity. Be sure that you can answer them also.
6. Research the prices of pizzas in your local area. Check with as many restaurants as you can. Determine the "best" buy in your neighborhood.

LAB EXERCISE 7   **Transformations of Nonlinear Functions**

The "basic" nonlinear functions such as $f(x) = x^2, f(x) = x^3, f(x) = \sqrt{x}$, and $f(x) = |x|$ are all "based" at the origin. These basic graphs can be shifted around the coordinate plane by changes in the equation. Use a graphing calculator to complete the following laboratory exercise.

1. Put the following functions into your graphing calculator in the y_1, y_2, and y_3 locations in the $y =$ list. Then complete the table. Sketch a graph on a piece of graph paper.

Function	y-intercepts	x-intercepts	Domain	Range
$f(x) = x^2$				
$f(x) = x^2 + 1$				
$f(x) = x^2 - 1$				

Answer the following questions:

(a) What do all three graphs have in common?

(b) Are the graphs all congruent (the same size and shape)?

(c) The graph of the general function $f(x) = x^2 + c$ is the graph of the function

$f(x) = x^2$ moved $|c|$ units _____ if $c > 0$ and $|c|$ units _____ if $c < 0$.

2. Put the following functions into your graphing calculator in the y_1, y_2, and y_3 locations in the $y =$ list. Then complete the table. Sketch a graph on a piece of graph paper.

Function	y-intercepts	x-intercepts	Domain	Range
$f(x) = x^2$				
$f(x) = (x + 1)^2$				
$f(x) = (x - 1)^2$				

Answer the following questions:

(a) What do all three graphs have in common?

(b) Are the graphs all congruent?

(c) The graph of the general function $f(x) = (x + c)^2$ is the graph of the function

$f(x) = x^2$ moved $|c|$ units _____ if $c > 0$ and $|c|$ units _____ if $c < 0$.

3. Put the following functions into your graphing calculator in the y_1, y_2, and y_3 locations in the $y =$ list. Then complete the table. Sketch a graph on a piece of graph paper.

Function	y-intercepts	x-intercepts	Domain	Range
$f(x) = x^2$				
$f(x) = 2x^2$				
$f(x) = \frac{1}{2}x^2$				

Answer the following questions:

(a) What do all three graphs have in common?

(b) Are the graphs all congruent? How are they different?

(c) The graph of the general function $f(x) = ax^2$ is the graph of the function

$f(x) = x^2$, which is either narrower or wider

If $a > 1$, then the graph is _____ and if $0 < a < 1$, the graph is _____.

(d) Now, go to the $y =$ screen and insert negative signs in front of each equation.
What happens to your graphs? _____

4. Without using your calculator, using the results from 1–3, sketch a graph of these functions:
(a) $f(x) = 2x^2 - 1$
(b) $f(x) = 2(x - 1)^2$
(c) $f(x) = \frac{1}{2}x^2 - 1$
(d) $f(x) = \frac{1}{2}(x - 1)^2$
(e) $f(x) = -2x^2 - 1$
(f) $f(x) = -\frac{1}{2}(x - 1)^2$
Now use your graphing calculator to verify your drawings.

5. Repeat these same steps for the functions $f(x) = x^3$, $f(x) = \sqrt{x}$, and $f(x) = |x|$.

LAB EXERCISE 8   Patterns in Exponential Functions

Your neighbor is going out of town for the month of July. It costs him $18 per day to board his two small dogs at the local vet. Since this will cost him $558 for the month, he asks you how much you will charge him to feed and walk the dogs for the entire 31 days in July. You tell him that you will work on July 1 for 2 cents, July 2 for 4 cents, July 3 for 8 cents, July 4 for 16 cents, and so on in the same pattern for every day of the month. He thinks this sounds like a real deal and says okay. At the end of the month, how much does he owe you?

1. Complete the table in margin for the first week of July.
2. Do you see a pattern in the pay amounts? How can you obtain the pay on a given day if you know the pay for the previous day?
3. Calculate the pay for days 8–14, 15–21, and 22–31. Then find the totals due to you for each of the last 3 weeks. What is the total amount in cents that your neighbor owes you at the end of the month? Convert this to dollars and cents.
4. The pay on any day can be written as a power of 2. Write each amount in the table in Problem 1 as a power of 2. For example, $2 = 2^1$, and $4 = 2^2$. Do you notice a pattern in the exponents?
5. Let $n =$ the number of days worked. Using your pattern from Problem 4, write an equation for the daily pay in cents as a function of days worked. Name it $P(n)$.
6. Use your function (allowing $n = 25$) to verify the pay for July 25 that you calculated in Problem 3.
7. Put the function into your graphing calculator. Sketch it on a piece of graph paper. Is this a linear function? Explain your answer in terms of the graph and the values in the table.
8. Did your neighbor make a good deal? How are you going to spend your money?

Day in July	Pay in cents
1	
2	
3	
4	
5	
6	
7	
Total first week	

chapter four

Mathematical Models in Personal Finances

"There is no branch of math, however abstract, which may not some day be applied to phenomena of the real world." — Nikolai Lobatchevsky

As we have seen in previous chapters, a function relates two variables to each other. A rule or relationship exists between two sets of data that connects values in one set with values in the other set. Many times, this rule is in the form of an algebraic equation or formula also known as a mathematical model. In this chapter, we will look at various mathematical models in making decisions about your personal finances. We will examine options for purchasing a home, purchasing an automobile, investments, and insurance.

Section 4-1   MATHEMATICAL MODELS IN THE BUSINESS WORLD

There are numerous situations in the life of a business where mathematical models are necessary. Profit calculations, retail sales tax, depreciation, markup, and cost of production are a few of the areas where formulas must be developed and used. Some simple business situations will be presented in this section.

Sales Tax   A large majority of state legislatures have approved a **retail sales tax** on purchases made by consumers. Some local governments also have a sales tax that helps fund local programs. Retail merchants are responsible for collecting the appropriate amounts of sales tax from their retail sales and forwarding it to their state's Department of Revenue and/or local governments. Sales tax is given in the form of a percent that is applied to the total purchase price of goods.

Important Equations

$$\text{Sales tax: } t = rp$$

where: t = sales tax r = tax rate p = amount of purchase

Since the calculation of sales tax usually involves rounding to the nearest penny, many states develop sales tax charts so cashiers can determine the tax owed without doing any calculating. Cash registers can now be programmed to enter the correct amount of sales tax owed based on items purchased. This is especially helpful when sales tax rates on some items differ from sales tax rates on others. For example, the sales tax on food items might be 2% while the sales tax rate on nonfood items is 7%. The cash register can be programmed to distinguish between types of items based on the bar code on each item.

EXAMPLE 1   Sales Tax Revenues

J. Bandera Company operates its business in a location where the state sales tax rate is 4% and the local sales tax rate is 1.5%. The company had $127,250 in retail sales in January. How much sales tax should be sent to the state? How much sales tax should be sent to the local government?

$$t = rp$$

(a)   State sales tax = $(0.04)(\$127,250) = \$5090$
(b)   Local sales tax = $(0.015)(\$127,250) = \$1908.75$

In a small business, the owner records the amount of money that he receives each day for purchases in his store. If the sales tax rate is 7% and he has only the total receipts for the day, he may need to calculate the amount of merchandise sold and the amount of sales tax he collected as separate figures. Look at Example 2 for a model of this problem.

EXAMPLE 2	**Calculating Original Sales from the Sales Total**

Ari owns a small general merchandise store. At the end of the day on Saturday, he counted total receipts in his store of $6045.50. If the sales tax in his county is 7%, how much merchandise did Ari sell on Saturday? How much sales tax did he collect?

Let x = the amount of merchandise sold and $0.07x$ = sales tax collected.
The model for the problem is:

$$\text{merchandise} + \text{tax} = \text{total receipts}$$

Now substitute the variables into the model and solve.

$$x + 0.07x = \$6045.50$$

$$1.07x = \$6045.50$$

$$x = \frac{\$6045.50}{1.07} = \$5650$$

$$\text{Sales tax} = 0.07(\$5650) = \$395.50$$

Therefore, he sold $5650 worth of merchandise and collected $395.50 in sales tax.

Depreciation   The fixed assets or plant assets of a business are its buildings, machinery, equipment, land, and similar items that will be used for more than one year. **Depreciation** is the allowance made in bookkeeping for the decreases in value of property through wear, deterioration, or obsolescence. The **straight-line method of depreciation** is the simplest method used in bookkeeping. The **residual value** (also called scrap value or trade-in value) of an asset is its expected value at the end of its useful life. The total allowable depreciation (original cost − residual value) is divided evenly among the number of years of useful life of the property. Depreciation is considered to be an operating expense of a business and is deducted each year from the business profits when determining the year's taxable income.

Important Equations

Straight-Line Method of Depreciation

$$\text{Annual depreciation} = \frac{\text{original value} - \text{residual value}}{\text{number of years}}$$

EXAMPLE 3   Straight-Line Depreciation

A machine that engraves jewelry is purchased for $6500. It is expected to last 8 years and to have a residual or scrap value of $700. What amount of annual depreciation will be allowed using the straight-line method of depreciation?

Original cost	$6500
Scrap value	− $ 700
Allowable depreciation	$5800

Annual depreciation = $5800 ÷ 8 = $725

A yearly depreciation expense of $725 would be claimed each year for 8 years.

Using this depreciation number, the value of this machine over its useful life can be modeled with a function. If x is the number of years of depreciation and V the value of the machine at the end of each year, then the function is:

$$V(x) = \$6500 - \$725x$$

This function is linear and would have a graph like that shown in Figure 4-1.

Figure 4-1

Most businesses use the straight-line method of depreciation for reporting to their stockholders and creditors on their financial statements. Some companies keep a separate set of depreciation records for computing income taxes. They will then use a different method for calculating depreciation. This is done because it provides the most depreciation expense as quickly as possible, which decreases the amount of tax payments. The company can then apply the money saved to best fit their business needs. These alternate methods are more complicated and covered in all basic accounting courses.

Cost of Production and Profit   For a manufacturing company to be profitable, the gross income from its sales must exceed the cost of the production of inventory. Fixed costs such as buildings, utilities, and wages must be considered as well as the cost of producing individual items. Models can be developed to show both the cost of manufacturing items and the income from sales. Total cost is a function of both fixed costs and per item costs. Gross income is the selling price of each item times the number of items sold to retailers. Net profit is the difference of these two numbers. In business production, if no items are produced in a month, the business must still pay its rent and other fixed costs. Therefore, if laborers go on strike, the business must find a way to continue production if at all possible. Labor unions have used this fact to help them negotiate for higher wages and better conditions in the workplace.

Important Models

Cost of production = fixed costs + (per item cost)(number of items produced)

Gross income = (selling price)(number of items sold)

Net profit = gross income − cost of production

EXAMPLE 4   **Calculating Net Profit**

The Hutchinson Corporation stamps popular designs on T-shirts and then sells them to retail stores. The fixed costs for this business during a month average $32,850. Shirts can be produced at a cost of $6.78 each. During March, the company produced and sold 12,750 T-shirts. Each shirt was sold for $12. Did the company make a profit in March?

(a) Cost of production = fixed costs + production cost of T-shirts

$$f(x) = \$32{,}850 + \$6.78x$$

$$f(12{,}750) = \$32{,}850 + (\$6.78)(12{,}750)$$

$$f(12{,}750) = \$32{,}850 + \$86{,}445$$

$$f(12{,}750) = \$119{,}295$$

(b) Gross income = (selling price)(number of items sold)

$$g(x) = \$12x$$

$$g(12{,}750) = (\$12)(12{,}750) = \$153{,}000$$

(c) Net profit = gross income − cost of production = $153,000 − $119,295 = $33,705

Markup   A retail store buys its merchandise from a wholesaler or manufacturer and uses a markup rate to determine the selling price of each item. The **markup** on items is calculated by multiplying the markup rate times the price the retailer paid to acquire the item (wholesale price). The markup amount is then added to the cost, and this is the selling price or retail price of the item. Businesses such as furniture stores and jewelry stores may have as much as a 200% markup on their inventory. That is the reason that they can still make a profit even if they have a 50%-off sale!

Important Models

Markup amount = markup rate × wholesale price

■ **EXAMPLE 5**   **Finding the Selling Price of an Item**

(a) A manufacturer charges shoe stores $24 for a certain tennis shoe. Bellis Department Store uses a markup rate of 125% on its shoes. What will the selling price of this particular tennis shoe be?

Markup amount = (markup rate)(wholesale price) = (1.25)($24) = $30

Selling price = wholesale price + markup = $24 + $30 = $54

(b) If the suggested retail price of this type of shoe is $60, what is the suggested markup rate?

Markup amount = retail price − wholesale price = $60 − $24 = $36

Markup rate = markup ÷ wholesale price = $\dfrac{\$36}{\$24}$ = 1.5 = 150%

Practice Set 4-1

Write a mathematical model for each problem and use it to find the correct answer.

1. Sales tax in Reagan County is 7.5% on all purchases. Calculate the sales tax on the following purchase totals (round answers to the nearest cent):
   (a) $25.55   (b) $155.75   (c) $256.18

2. You buy a jet ski that costs $1450 plus 6% sales tax. Find the amount of the sales tax and the total bill.

3. Sales tax in San Patricio County is assessed at 8.25%, where 6.25% is designated for the state and 2% is designated for the county. If Johnson Mercantile has total retail sales of $25,615 during the month, how much sales tax will be owed to the state and how much will be owed to the county?

4. Some tourist areas assess a lodging tax to be paid to the local government to provide extra revenue for local projects such as local roads and utilities. If a family rents a beach cottage for $775 a week in the summer, how much will a 13% lodging tax add to the total cost of the cottage?

5. Myron owns a small sporting goods store. At the end of the week before Christmas, he counted total receipts in his store of $27,129.60. If the sales tax in his county is 8%, how much merchandise did Myron sell that week? How much sales tax did he collect?

6. Bart owns a neighborhood Kwik-E-Mart. At the end of the day on Wednesday, he counted total receipts in his store of $8399.70. If the sales tax on food items is 2%, how much merchandise did Bart sell on Wednesday? How much sales tax did he collect?

7. Selma bought a new television for a total cost of $213.95. If the sales tax at the store is 7%, what was the retail price of the television (price before tax)? (Round to the nearest penny.)

8. The total cost of a meal for a couple at a nice restaurant was $66.95. If the sales tax rate was 3%, what was the actual cost of the food?

9. A computer is purchased for a business at a cost of $2150. The computer is expected to be usable for 5 years and has a scrap value of $500. Using the straight-line method of depreciation, what amount of depreciation will be allowed each year?

10. Tate Realty buys new furniture for its waiting room. If the total cost of the furniture is $5475 and the usable life of the furniture is determined to be 10 years, what is the annual allowable depreciation if the residual value of the furniture is estimated at $850?

11. Dickinson's Law Firm buys new furniture for its waiting room. If the total cost of the furniture is $9450 and the usable life of the furniture is determined to be 7 years, using the straight-line method of depreciation, what is the annual allowable depreciation if the residual value of the furniture is estimated at $1000?

12. Motor Parts of Amarillo paid $20,000 for a motor vehicle. They expect to use it for 4 years before replacing it. They estimate that when they sell it in 4 years' time, they will get $8000 for it. Using the straight-line method, determine the annual amount of depreciation.

13. Many people prefer to buy used cars because a new car depreciates in value so quickly. Tyler buys a new car and pays $13,500 for it. A year later, he decides to sell it, and the retail price listed in car guides for a car similar to his is $11,880. What percent has the car depreciated in one year?

14. Computers depreciate very quickly because the technology is changing so rapidly. If a certain computer sells for $799 today and next year it is only worth $575, what percent has it depreciated in one year?

15. The Kerns Pen Company makes ballpoint pens. The fixed costs of operation for one month average $53,500. The cost of producing one pen is $0.75, and the pens are marketed to retailers for $1.05 each. Give the net profit or loss if the company manufactures zero pens in a month.

16. The Kerns Pen Company makes ballpoint pens. The fixed costs of operation for one month average $53,500. The cost of producing one pen is $0.75, and the pens are marketed to retailers for $1.05 each. Give the net profit or loss if the company manufactures 150,000 pens in a month.

17. The Kerns Pen Company makes ballpoint pens. The fixed costs of operation for one month average $53,500. The cost of producing one pen is $0.75, and the pens are marketed to retailers for $1.05 each. Give the net profit or loss if the company manufactures 200,000 pens in a month.

18. The Kerns Pen Company makes ballpoint pens. The fixed costs of operation for one month average $53,500. The cost of producing one pen is $0.75, and the pens are marketed to retailers for $1.05 each. How many pens must be sold in order for the company to break even?

19. The inventor of a new game believes that the variable cost of producing the game is $1.95 per unit, and the fixed costs for a month are $8000. He sells the game to retailers for $5.00 each. Give the net profit or loss if the inventor makes zero games in a month.

20. The inventor of a new game believes that the variable cost of producing the game is $1.95 per unit, and the fixed costs for a month are $8000. He sells the game to retailers for $5.00 each. Give the net profit or loss if the inventor makes 150,000 games in a month.

21. The inventor of a new game believes that the variable cost of producing the game is $1.95 per unit, and the fixed costs for a month are $8000. He sells the game to retailers for $5.00 each. Give the net profit or loss if the inventor makes 200,000 games in a month.

22. The inventor of a new game believes that the variable cost of producing the game is $1.95 per unit, and the fixed costs for a month are $8000. He sells the game to retailers for $5.00 each. How many games must be sold in order for the inventor to break even?

23. Strayhorn Enterprises manufactures toy dogs. The fixed costs of operation are $3500 per month.

A toy poodle costs $2.55 to manufacture, a toy cocker spaniel costs $3.05 to manufacture, and a toy collie costs $4.15 to manufacture. A poodle sells for $6.50, a cocker spaniel sells for $8.95, and a collie sells for $13.50. Give the net profit or loss if the company manufactures and sells 200 of each type of dog.

24. Strayhorn Enterprises manufactures toy dogs. The fixed costs of operation are $3500 per month. A toy poodle costs $2.55 to manufacture, a toy cocker spaniel costs $3.05 to manufacture, and a toy collie costs $4.15 to manufacture. A poodle sells for $6.50, a cocker spaniel sells for $8.95, and a collie sells for $13.50. Give the net profit or loss if the company manufactures and sells 150 poodles, 200 spaniels, and 300 collies.

25. Lloyd runs a copying service in his home. He paid $3500 for the copier and a lifetime service contract. Each sheet of paper he uses costs $0.01, and he gets paid $0.12 per copy he makes.
    (a) Write a model that can be used to calculate the cost of operations $C(x)$ for the first year. Let x be the number of copies he makes.
    (b) Calculate the total cost if he makes 20,500 copies this year.
    (c) If he is paid for all 20,500 copies, what will be his profit for the year?

26. The Dewhurst Company prints graduation announcements for the local high schools. The setup fee for each high school order is $150, and each announcement printed costs $0.05. The announcements cost the students $0.50 each.
    (a) Write a model that can be used to calculate the cost of printing announcements for East High School. Let x be the number of announcements ordered.
    (b) Calculate the total printing costs if the senior class at EHS orders 4500 announcements.
    (c) When all graduation announcements have been paid for by the students at EHS, what will the profit be for this printing job?

27. A sporting goods store uses a markup rate of 55% on all items. The cost of a golf club to the retailer is $35. What is the selling price of the golf club?

28. Jewelry has a 250% markup. If a diamond ring costs Frank's Jewelers $550, what will the retail price be on this ring?

29. A sweater costs a department store $26.95. The selling price of the sweater is $48.51. What is the markup rate of the sweater?

30. Ace Furniture Emporium charges $1425 for a sofa. If the sofa costs the store $475, what is the markup rate of the sofa?

Section 4-2   MATHEMATICAL MODELS IN PERSONAL INCOME

Mathematics becomes a very powerful tool when it can be applied to our personal finances. Calculating a net salary increase after receiving a 5% raise translates into usable dollars for our own daily lives. The ability to correctly calculate the federal income tax owed may keep us from overpaying taxes. Creating a family budget helps us become good money managers. Although there may be general formulas available for some applications, many times we must modify general formulas and write mathematical models to fit specific circumstances.

Many jobs pay workers a specific salary amount per week or month. Other jobs pay an hourly rate to their employees. However, in some professions, sales jobs pay salaries based on the amount of sales someone generates during the pay period. A real estate salesman may net 4% of the total value of the houses he sells during a month. If he sells no houses, he receives no paycheck. The greater the value of his sales in a month, the larger the paycheck. Car sales and life insurance sales are other examples of professions that base income directly on sales. This method of payment is called **straight commission.** A mathematical model can be written to express this idea.

Important Models

Straight Commission

$$\text{Paycheck} = (\text{commission rate})(\text{sales})$$

For the realtor making a 4% commission, the equation would be $P = 0.04s$, where P = paycheck and s = amount of sales.

Other types of sales jobs may pay the salesman a base salary and then a percentage of sales made during the pay period. This concept can be modeled with this equation.

Important Models

Base + Commission

$$\text{Paycheck} = \text{base salary} + (\text{commission rate})(\text{sales})$$

Waiters and waitresses are paid in a similar manner by earning both tips left by customers and a small base pay for coming to work. These salaries are all functions of the amount of money the customer spends. Many salary agreements have similar patterns, but a mathematical model or equation must be written to calculate the amount of pay earned for a specific job situation.

EXAMPLE 6   Retail Store Sales

Coleen works in a retail store. She is paid a base salary of $120 per week plus a commission of 10% of the total weekly retail sales she makes.

(a) Write a mathematical model that can be used to calculate Coleen's weekly salary. Let P = weekly pay and s = total retail sales. Written in functional notation, the model would be:

$$P(s) = 120 + 0.10s$$

(b) Draw a graph to illustrate Coleen's potential salary. (See Figure 4-2.)

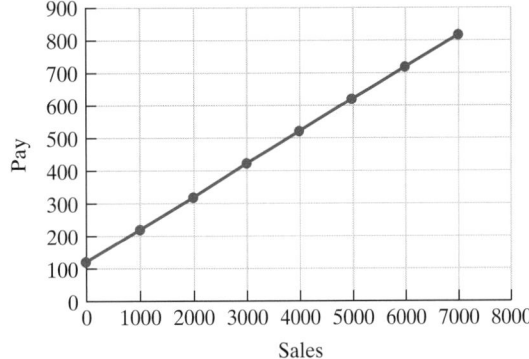

Figure 4-2

(c) Calculate Coleen's paycheck for the week if she makes $6200 in retail sales the week before Christmas.

$$P(s) = 120 + 0.10s$$

$$P(6200) = 120 + 0.10(6200)$$

$$= 120 + 620$$

$$= \$740 \text{ for the week}$$

You should verify this answer using the graph in Part b.

(d) Coleen needs to gross $500 each week in order to meet her expenses. How much in retail sales should she average each day of a 5-day working week in order to gross $500 for the week?

1. Let $P(s) = \$500$ so we can calculate the weekly sales (s) needed.

$$P(s) = 120 + 0.10s$$

$$500 = 120 + 0.10s$$

$$500 - 120 = 0.10s$$

$$380 = 0.10s$$

$$\$3800 = s$$

2. Since $3800 is the total amount of sales needed for the week, we divide by 5 to calculate the average amount of sales needed each day to reach this goal.

$$\$3800 \div 5 = \$760 \text{ of sales needed per day}$$

Tax laws and requirements seem to change on a yearly basis. The deductions allowed, exemptions allowed, and the tax rate may change as Congress passes new laws. However, the general model for calculating income tax can be used to write a specific equation for tax calculations. Deductions are subtracted from gross income to calculate net income or taxable income. Then, tax tables or tax rate schedules are used to find the amount of income tax owed by an individual.

EXAMPLE 7   Calculating State Income Tax

Enrico is single and has a gross salary of $68,500 per year. After taking all legal exemptions and deductions, he calculates his taxable income to be $51,275. Enrico's W-2 form shows that his employer withheld $3150 in state taxes for the year. Use the tax schedule provided in Table 4-1 and calculate the amount of state tax that he owes. Will he file for a refund or will he owe an additional payment to the state?

▦ Table 4-1   2005 State Tax Rate Schedule

If Your Filing Status Is:	And the Amount on Line 11b Is More Than	But Not Over	The Tax Is:
Single	$ 0	$ 12,750	6% of the amount on line 11b
	$ 12,750	$ 60,000	$765 + 7% of the amount over $12,750
	$ 60,000	$120,000	$4072.50 + 7.75% of the amount over $60,000
	$120,000	—	$8722.50 + 8.25% of the amount over $120,000
Head of household	$ 0	$ 17,000	6% of the amount on line 11b
	$ 17,000	$ 80,000	$1020 + 7% of the amount over $17,000
	$ 80,000	$160,000	$5430 + 7.75% of the amount over $80,000
	$160,000	—	$11,630 + 8.25% of the amount over $160,000
Married filing jointly or qualifying widow(er)	$ 0	$ 21,250	6% of the amount on line 11b
	$ 21,250	$100,000	$1275 + 7% of the amount over $21,250
	$100,000	$200,000	$6787.50 + 7.75% of the amount over $100,000
	$200,000	—	$14,537.50 + 8.25% of the amount over $200,000
Married filing separately	$ 0	$ 10,625	6% of the amount on line 11b
	$ 10,625	$ 50,000	$637.50 + 7% of the amount over $10,625
	$ 50,000	$100,000	$3393.75 + 7.75% of the amount over $50,000
	$100,000	—	$7268.75 + 8.25% of the amount over $100,000

According to the State Tax Rate Schedule, a single taxpayer whose taxable income is between $12,750 and $60,000 must pay $765 plus 7% of the amount over $12,750. Written as a mathematical model:

$$\text{Tax} = \$765 + 0.07(I - \$12,750) \qquad \text{where } I = \text{taxable income}$$

Completing the formula:

$$\text{Tax} = \$765 + 0.07(\$51,275 - \$12,750)$$
$$= \$765 + 0.07(\$38,525)$$
$$= \$765 + \$2696.75$$
$$\text{Tax} = \$3461.75$$

Since Enrico owes $3461.75 in state income tax and his employer has only withheld $3150 during the year, he will owe an additional tax payment of:

$$\$3461.75 - \$3150 = \$311.75$$

An important part of personal finances is the use of a family budget. An article on budgeting recently stated that most people spend 10% more than they make. This leads to increased use of credit, meaning a family can incur a great deal of debt. An effective budget puts you in control of your finances and expenditures. Then you can avoid the question, "Where did all our money go?" You will already know the answer because you have a budget.

The first step in developing a budget is to examine your current financial information, including both monthly income and monthly expenditures. You can use a form like the one in Table 4-2 to help organize your figures. You should prepare a summary of your current spending habits and then adjust expenditures based on family goals such as saving for college tuition, a new car, or a down payment on a house.

■ **Table 4-2   Budget Form**

Category	Budget Items	Budgeted Amount	Actual Expense
Housing	Mortgage/Rent		
	Electricity/Gas		
	Water/Sewer		
	Cable		
	Telephone		
Food	Groceries		
	Eating out		
Loans	Car loan		
	Credit cards		
	Other loans		
Miscellaneous	Clothing purchases		
	Medical bills		
	Charitable contributions		
	Entertainment		
	Gasoline/Car maintenance		
	Savings		

The Consumer Credit Counseling Service recommends that you save at least 5% of your take-home earnings each month and that your credit obligations (not including your house payment) should not exceed 15% of your take-home pay. A useful rule in determining the monthly house payment that you can afford is given here:

1. Subtract any monthly bills from your gross monthly income.
2. Multiply this amount by 36%.

Your monthly house payment should not exceed this amount.

EXAMPLE 8   Budgeting Monthly Income

Joanna is single and has just started her first full-time job. Her take-home pay after taxes have been withheld is $2074. She wants to save 7% of her take-home pay each month. Her monthly expenses are: apartment rent—$650, utilities (electricity and water)—$25, cell phone—$40, cable TV—$45, car payment—$225, credit card payments—$100, groceries—$350, entertainment—$250, clothing costs — $50, and gasoline — $120. Fill in a budget table and determine if she will be able to save 7% of her take-home pay.

Category	Budget Items	Budget
Housing	Mortgage/Rent	$650
	Electricity/Gas	$ 25
	Water/Sewer	
	Cable	$ 45
	Telephone	$ 40
Food	Groceries	$350
	Eating Out	
Loans	Car Loan	$225
	Credit Cards	$100
	Other Loans	
Miscellaneous	Clothing Purchases	$ 50
	Medical Bills	
	Charitable Contributions	
	Entertainment	$250
	Gasoline/Car Maintenance	$120
	Savings	?

The total amount that Joanna has budgeted at this point is $1855. If she wants to save 7% of her take-home salary, we must calculate that amount to determine if she will have enough left after expenses to save it.

$$0.07 \times \$2074 = \$145.18 \text{ or approximately } \$145$$

If we add her current expenses to this amount ($1855 + $145), the total is $2000. Therefore, she can save 7% of her take-home pay and still have enough money to meet her monthly expenses (with $74 left over for miscellaneous expenses!).

Practice Set 4-2

For each problem, write a mathematical model and use it to find the correct answer.

1. Cassandra works for CJ Paper Products selling paper products to businesses and restaurants. Her monthly salary is computed based only on her sales per month. If she is paid 9.5% of her total monthly sales, calculate her gross pay this month if she sells $15,670 worth of paper products.

2. After Cassandra has been with the company for 12 months, she receives an increase of 0.75% in her commission percentage. If she sells $15,670 worth of paper products after she receives her raise, what will her gross pay be for the month?

3. Jerry sells cars at Cookie's Used Car Emporium. His monthly salary is calculated each month by adding a commission of 3.5% of his monthly sales to a base pay of $1245. If Jerry sells several cars worth a total of $65,000 during this month, calculate his gross pay.

4. Jerry needs to gross at least $2500 each month in order to pay his bills. Using your mathematical

model from Problem #3, calculate the amount of sales Jerry must make in order to be paid $2500.

5. Casey sells computer equipment. He is paid a base salary of $2200 per month and a commission of 2% of all sales over $7500. If Casey sells $12,350 worth of computer equipment this month, calculate his gross pay for the month.

6. Would Casey make a better salary if he were paid only a straight commission of 15% of total sales? If Casey decides that he wants to be paid with a straight 15% commission, how much computer equipment would he need to sell to make the equivalent of the $2200 base salary he was previously earning?

7. Paolo makes a straight 2.5% commission on his sales of equipment. If he sells $125,000 worth of equipment this month, how much will he be paid this month?

8. Joan makes a base salary of $275 per week and a commission of 4% of sales over $1000. If she sells $1250 of merchandise this week, calculate the amount of her paycheck for the week.

9. A waitress generally expects to receive 15% of the cost of a meal as a tip from her customers. If the total bill for a table is $65.00, how much should be left as a tip for the waitress?

10. The standard tip that a customer should leave in a restaurant is 15%. How much money should a customer leave as a tip for the waitress if the meal costs $22.50?

11. A realtor sells a house for $150,000. The real estate agency that he works for will receive a commission on the sale in the amount of 6% of the selling price. The selling agent (realtor) will then receive 60% of that amount as his commission. How much will the agent earn from this sale?

12. The listing agent for a house receives 20% of the agency fee as commission when a sale occurs even if another realtor sells the house. If a house sells for $250,000 and the agency receives 6% of the selling price, how much will the listing agent be paid?

13. What is the commission rate for a sales employee who earned $425 straight commission on sales of $5000?

14. What is the commission rate for a car salesman who earned $1620 straight commission on a $36,000 car?

15. (a) Use the tax rate schedule from Example 7 to calculate the amount of state tax owed by a married couple filing jointly if the net taxable income is $48,745.
    (b) Calculate the amount of state tax owed by a single person with the same net taxable income.

16. Use the income tax table (Table 4-1) to calculate the tax that is owed by a taxpayer who is a Head of Household with net income of $257,000.

17. Proposals have been made that would implement a single-rate tax with few, if any, deductions allowed. Each person would pay the same fixed percent on his or her gross income. If Gilbert is a single person who grossed $31,000 last year, how much tax would he owe if the tax rate on gross income were 4.5%? If he takes all current allowable deductions, his taxable income would be $22,450. Using Table 4-1, would he owe more or less tax than he would using the 4.5% fixed rate?

18. Use Table 4-1 to determine if a married person with a taxable income of $55,000 will owe more tax if she files her return jointly or separately.

19. Ping is paid a salary based on a commission rate of 4.5% of his total sales in a month. Last year, he averaged sales of $50,000 per month throughout the year. Calculate his gross income for that year. After deductions, his net taxable income was $16,750. If he is filing as a single person, how much tax will he owe? (Use the tax rate schedule in Table 4-1.)

20. Mario is a car salesman, and he sold $1,248,000 worth of cars last year. He receives a 4.75% straight commission on his sales. Calculate his income for last year. After all deductions were taken, his net taxable income was $41,056. If he files as "married filing jointly," how much tax will he owe? (Use the tax rate schedule in Table 4-1.)

21. Suppose that you are a sales representative for the Rooty Tooty Trumpet Co. You earn a commission of 9.5% of your monthly sales made over your base pay of $800 per month.
    (a) Write an equation that models this situation.
    (b) What would the slope of the graph of this model be?

Section 4-3 Mathematical Models in Banking **151**

(c) What are the units of this slope and what do they mean?

(d) Is the relationship between your commission and sales a function?

(e) If you were to graph this equation, which set of numbers (sales or commission) should be plotted on the y-axis and why?

(f) Use your model to determine the amount of sales you would need to make in order to earn $2525 dollars in one month.

22. Ritzy Cars pays their salespersons on a graduated commission scale with no base pay. A salesperson earns 3% on the first $55,000 of a sale, 2% on the next $20,000, and 1% on any amount above $75,000 in sales.

(a) Write a statement, instead of an equation, to model this pay scale. It should be written in such a way as to allow you to calculate the commission earned for any size sale.

(b) Is the relationship between the amount of sales and the amount of commission earned a function in this situation?

(c) What would be the commission paid on a sale of a used car at Ritzy's if the car cost $48,000?

(d) What would the commission be on a luxury car that cost $128,000?

23. Josh is single and has just started his first full-time job. His take-home pay after taxes have been withheld is $1855. He wants to save 7% of his take-home pay each month. His monthly expenses are apartment rent—$590, utilities (electricity and water)—$25, cell phone—$45, cable TV—$45, car payment—$125, groceries—$320, entertainment—$150, and gasoline—$150. Fill in a budget table and determine if he will be able to save 7% of his take-home pay.

24. Marcus has just gotten married and wants to try and save 5% of his take-home pay each month for a down payment on a new house. His take-home pay after taxes have been withheld is $2350. His monthly expenses are apartment rent—$850, utilities (electricity and water)—$35, cell phone for two people—$75, cable TV—$45, car payment (his car)—$225, car payment (her car)—$200, credit card payments—$150, groceries—$550, entertainment—$250, clothing costs—$75, charitable contributions—$50, and gasoline—$250. Fill in a budget table and determine if he will be able to save 5% of his take-home pay.

25. The Consumer Credit Counseling Service recommends that your credit obligations (not including your house payment) should not exceed 15% of your take-home pay. If Ketan's take-home pay is $1978, what is the maximum monthly credit obligation that he should have?

26. The Consumer Credit Counseling Service recommends that your credit obligations (not including your house payment) should not exceed 15% of your take-home pay. If Olivia's take-home pay is $2206, what is the maximum monthly credit obligation that she should have?

27. Research your family's monthly expenses and fill out a chart of approximate costs for each category. In your opinion, are there places in the budget where adjustments in spending could be made?

28. Assume that you are single and earn $2600 per month. Federal and state taxes will be withheld from this total at an approximate rate of 28%. Calculate your take-home pay. Now, using this figure, research costs of apartments, gasoline, groceries, utility bills, cable TV, and other expenses in your local area. Create a reasonable budget, including at least 5% of your take-home pay for savings.

Section 4-3 **MATHEMATICAL MODELS IN BANKING**

The borrowing and lending of money is a practice that dates far back into our history. In the past, many moneylenders charged exorbitant fees for loans. Eventually, regulations concerning lending practices were enacted, and today lending institutions are required to inform consumers of loan rates and methods used to calculate interest owed. Even with these regulations, the "fine print" of many loan agreements is difficult to understand. In this section, we will examine some of the simpler mathematical models that deal with the calculation of interest owed on personal loans and monthly payments.

When you borrow money from a bank or lending institution, you are actually renting the money for your own use. Just as you would expect to pay rent for a house you are living in, you must pay rent, or **interest,** for the money you borrow. The amount of money that you borrow is called the **principal** of a loan. A certain percentage of the loan is charged as interest, and the percent used to calculate this interest is called the **rate.** The rate is usually quoted on a yearly basis. If the interest rate is given as a yearly rate, then the time intervals used in formulas also should be expressed in terms of years.

Simple Interest   One method of charging interest on loans is called **simple interest.** The interest here is calculated on the whole principal for the entire length of the loan. The amount due at the end of the loan, called **maturity value** (M), will be the sum of the original loan amount (P) and the total interest due (I), or $M = P + I$. This is the total amount the borrower will be required to repay the lender by the end of the loan period.

Important Equations

Simple Interest Formulas

Simple interest:

$$I = Prt$$

Maturity value:

$$M = P + I$$

where I = interest, P = principal, t = time (in years), and r = rate

---

EXAMPLE 9   **Maturity Value of a Loan**

A loan of $1200 is made by Citizens State Bank for 3 years at a simple interest rate of 9.5%. Calculate the total amount that must be repaid at the end of the loan period.

(a) Calculate interest owed:

$$I = Prt$$
$$I = (\$1200)(0.095)(3)$$
$$I = \$342$$

(b) Calculate the maturity value:

$$M = P + I$$
$$M = \$1200 + \$342$$
$$M = \$1542$$

At the end of the 3-year period, a total of $342 in interest has been charged and the borrower had to repay a total of $1542 to the lender.

EXAMPLE 10   Borrowing Money Using a Short-Term Note

Latasha borrowed tuition money from the bank using a 6-month short-term note. The principal of the loan was $720 at an annual simple interest rate of 6.5%. What is the maturity value of this note?

(a) Calculate the interest owed. Since the variable t in the simple interest formula represents time in years and this loan is for 6 months, we must use the fraction $\frac{6}{12} = \frac{1}{2}$ in the formula.

$$I = Prt$$

$$I = (\$720)(0.065)\left(\frac{1}{2}\right)$$

$$I = \$23.40$$

(b) Calculate the maturity value of the note.

$$M = P + I$$

$$M = \$720 + \$23.40 = \$743.40$$

Therefore, at the end of 6 months, Latasha will repay the bank the sum of $743.40.

Some loans are made in the form of notes that are repaid in entirety at the end of the loan period. However, most loans require that the borrower repay the loan by making monthly payments. The monthly payment amount is calculated by dividing the number of payments to be made into the maturity value of the loan. Look at the following example.

EXAMPLE 11   Monthly Loan Payments for a Simple Interest Loan

A $2000 loan is made by Bank of the West at a simple interest rate of 12% for 2.5 years. What monthly payment will be required to completely repay the loan in 2.5 years?

(a) Calculate the interest owed:

$$I = Prt$$

$$I = (\$2000)(0.12)(2.5)$$

$$I = \$600$$

(b) Calculate the maturity value:

$$M = P + I$$

$$M = \$2000 + \$600$$

$$M = \$2600$$

(c) Calculate the monthly payments:

$$2.5 \text{ years} = (12)(2.5) = 30 \text{ payments}$$

$$\$2600 \div 30 = \$ 86.67 \text{ per month}$$

Compound Interest   When an investor wishes to earn interest on his savings, he may also consult a bank or credit union. Money can be deposited into a savings account or a money market account. The depositor is paid interest by the bank on the amount of money in the account. Interest may be calculated on a daily, monthly, quarterly, or yearly basis and is credited to these accounts at appropriate intervals. This is called **compound interest,** and most banks and credit unions today pay interest in this manner. This is an advantage to the depositor because interest is paid both on the original deposit and on any interest credited to the account since the original deposit. The effect of paying "interest on interest" causes the account to grow in value more quickly than it would if interest were calculated using the simple interest formula.

To see how this works, let's look at an example. Suppose you deposit $1000 into a savings account that is paying 4.8% interest compounded monthly. This means that the 4.8% rate is divided by 12 ($4.8\% \div 12 = 0.4\%$) and that monthly rate is applied to your account balance each month. During the first month, your account would earn

$$I = Prt = (\$1000)(0.004/\text{month})(1 \text{ month}) = \$4.00$$

This interest is credited to your account to give you a new balance of $1004. At the end of the second month, the monthly interest rate is again applied to your balance.

$$I = Prt = (\$1004)(0.004/\text{month})(1 \text{ month}) = \$4.016 = \$4.02$$

Your new balance at the beginning of the third month is $1008.02. During the second month, you were paid interest on both the original deposit of $1000 and the interest that you earned during the first month. This is the principle of compounding interest.

Most compound interest is calculated with a table or computer program, but we will look at one formula that can be used to calculate compound interest.

Important Equations

Compound Interest

$$M = P\left(1 + \frac{r}{n}\right)^{nt}$$

where M = maturity value, P = original principal, t = number of years, n = total number of compounding periods per year, and r = annual interest rate

By using the compound interest formula, we can calculate the future value of an investment given a certain interest rate and length of time for the account to grow. It is important to know if interest is paid monthly (12 pay periods per year), quarterly (4 pay periods per year), or daily (360 or 365 days a year). Note that some institutions use the **Banker's Rule** for calculating interest based on 30 days in a month, 360 days in a year. Others use **ordinary interest,** which is based on 365 days per year. If interest is compounded monthly and r represents the yearly interest rate, then we use $\frac{r}{12}$ in the formula and let *the exponent be 12t.* If interest is compounded quarterly, we use $\frac{r}{4}$ and *the exponent is 4t.* Using ordinary interest, if interest is compounded daily, we use $\frac{r}{365}$ and *the exponent is 365t.* Do not round any numbers as you work the problem, but leave them in your calculator and only round the final answers. If you round before you have completed the calculations, your final answer will be incorrect.

Important Equations

Quarterly/Monthly Compound Interest

Quarterly:

$$M = P\left(1 + \frac{r}{4}\right)^{4t}$$

Monthly:

$$M = P\left(1 + \frac{r}{12}\right)^{12t}$$

Daily:

$$M = P\left(1 + \frac{r}{365}\right)^{365t}$$

where r = annual rate and t = number of years.

EXAMPLE 12

Using the Compound Interest Formulas

Calculate the maturity value of a $1000 deposit into a savings account paying 5% after 10 years if it is compounded: (a) quarterly, (b) monthly, and (c) daily using ordinary interest.

(a) $M = P\left(1 + \frac{r}{12}\right)^{12t}$

$$= 1000\left(1 + \frac{0.05}{4}\right)^{4\cdot10} = 1000(1 + 0.0125)^{40} = \$1643.62$$

(b) $M = P\left(1 + \frac{r}{12}\right)^{12t}$

$$= 1000\left(1 + \frac{0.05}{12}\right)^{12\cdot10} = 1000(1 + 0.004166\ldots)^{120} = \$1647.01$$

Remember, do not round the number inside of the parentheses when you are calculating the answer. Leave it in your calculator and round the final answer to the nearest penny.

(c)
$$M = P\left(1 + \frac{r}{365}\right)^{365t}$$

$$= 1000\left(1 + \frac{0.05}{365}\right)^{365 \cdot 10} = 1000(1 + 0.00013698\ldots)^{3650} = \$1648.66$$

Notice that the value of the account compounded monthly is more than the account compounded quarterly and that the account compounded daily is larger than either of the other two. The more often the interest is compounded, the better the return will be.

For the sake of clarity, let us look at a comparison of the growth of a savings account. Suppose that you have $1000 to place in a savings account. You want to open an account, deposit your money, and then let the money just sit in the account for 10 years, untouched. The amount of money that would be in the account after 10 years would depend on the interest rate, of course, but also greatly depends on the compounding rate. The value of $1000 at 5% annual interest for various compounding periods is shown in Table 4-3.

Table 4-3   Comparison of the Growth of a Savings Account

Number of Years	Simple Interest	Compounded Yearly	Compounded Quarterly	Compounded Monthly	Compounded Daily	Compounded Continuously
1	$1050.00	$1050.00	$1050.95	$1051.16	$1051.27	$1051.27
5	$1250.00	$1276.28	$1282.04	$1283.36	$1284.00	$1284.03
10	$1500.00	$1628.89	$1643.62	$1647.01	$1648.66	$1648.72

To emphasize the great difference that compounding can make, look at Table 4-4, which compares $1000 at 10% true simple interest (i.e., no compounding at all) for 100 years with 10% interest compounded yearly for 100 years. If you will excuse some poor English here, the difference ain't chicken feed.

Figure 4-3 shows graphically the difference if you were to compare the rate of growth at simple interest to the rate of growth at compound interest.

It is easy to see from the figure that the line showing the growth in the value of your account at simple interest is a linear function (also called arithmetic growth). The curved line shows the function for the growth your account would have at compound interest. This curve shows what is sometimes called geometric or exponential growth.

Table 4-4   Simple Interest versus Compound Interest

Number of Years	Compounded Yearly ($)	Simple Interest Rate ($)
0	1000.00	1000.00
1	1100.00	1100.00
2	1210.00	1200.00
5	1610.51	1500.00
10	2593.74	2000.00
20	6727.50	3000.00
50	117,390.85	6000.00
100	13,780,612.34	11,000.00

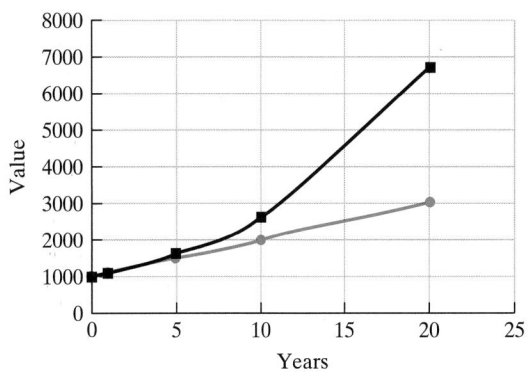

Figure 4-3
Simple interest versus compound interest.

Calculator Mini-Lesson

Exponents

Any *standard scientific calculator* has a key that will allow you to find a base raised to any exponent. Look for a key labeled x^y or y^x. To test this key, find the value of 5^3 by entering 5 followed by y^x, 3 and = button. You should have an answer of 125.

A *graphing calculator* (TI-83 Plus) has a key labeled $\boxed{\wedge}$, which can be used to raise any number or variable to any exponent. Calculate the value of 5^3 using this key. Press ENTER to obtain the correct answer of 125.

EXAMPLE 13   Savings for a Car

Debbie wants to buy a new car in two years. She sold a story to a national magazine and received a check for $5000 that she wants to save as the down payment on her new car. She plans to deposit it into an account at Guaranty Bank, where the interest rate is 6% compounded monthly. How much money will be in the account at the end of 2 years?

$$P = \$5000 \qquad r = 6\% = 0.06 \qquad y = 2$$

$$M = P\left(1 + \frac{r}{12}\right)^{12t}$$

$$M = \$5000\left(1 + \frac{0.06}{12}\right)^{12(2)}$$

$$M = 5000(1 + 0.005)^{24}$$

$$M = 5000(1.005)^{24}$$

$$M = \$5635.80$$

Debbie will have $5635.80 available for her down payment in 2 years.

The effect of compounding interest provides a higher maturity value in a long-term investment. When interest is paid into your account monthly or quarterly, you are then paid interest on that interest at the end of the next compounding period. Compounding can also occur daily and even continuously. As illustrated in Table 4-3, the more often that interest is compounded, the greater the return on your investment. Look at the next example, which compares the effect of compounding quarterly with compounding monthly.

EXAMPLE 14 — Compounding Quarterly versus Monthly

Juan is interested in investing in a savings account that currently pays 4.8%. At First National Bank the interest is compounded quarterly, and at Friendly Bank the compounding is done monthly. If he plans to deposit $2500 for 5 years into the account, how much difference would there be in the maturity value of the investments at the two banks at the end of 5 years?

$$P = \$2500 \quad r = 4.8\% = 0.048 \quad y = 5 \text{ years}$$

(a) First National Bank: compounded quarterly

$$M = P\left(1 + \frac{r}{4}\right)^{4t}$$

$$M = \$2500\left(1 + \frac{0.048}{4}\right)^{4(5)}$$

$$M = \$2500(1 + 0.012)^{20}$$

$$M = \$3173.59$$

(b) Friendly Bank: compounded monthly

$$M = P\left(1 + \frac{r}{12}\right)^{12t}$$

$$M = \$2500\left(1 + \frac{0.048}{12}\right)^{12(5)}$$

$$M = \$2500(1 + 0.004)^{60}$$

$$M = \$3176.60$$

$$\$3176.60 - \$3173.59 = \$3.01 \quad \text{(more interest at Friendly Bank)}$$

By investing his money at Friendly Bank, Juan will earn more interest given the same interest rate and number of years because of the effect of monthly compounding. The difference ($3.01) is small in this example but increases as the size of the investment and the number of years in the account increase.

If a financial institution compounds interest for finite periods such as daily, quarterly, or monthly, the previous formulas apply. However, as the number of compounding periods per year increases (daily to hourly to . . .), we say that interest is **compounded continuously.**

Important Equations

Continuous Compounding

$$A = Pe^{rt}$$

where P = principal dollars invested and A is the amount accumulated after t years at an annual rate, r.

The formula for continuous compounding is one type of an exponential growth function and involves the number e. You will find this number on your calculator above the *ln* button. This symbol represents an irrational number and is approximately equal to 2.71828. Many of the growth and decay formulas of science use applications that are based on powers of this irrational number. Predictions of the future value of an item based on the rate of inflation can also be calculated using this formula.

■ EXAMPLE 15   **Interest Compounded Continuously**

Calculate the maturity value of a $5000 certificate of deposit (CD) paying 6.5% interest compounded continuously if it is held for 5 years. Use $A = Pe^{rt}$ where $P = \$5000, r = 0.065, t = 5$

$$A = 5000e^{(0.065)(5)}$$

$$A = 5000e^{0.325}$$

$$A = \$6920.15$$

The maturity value of this CD will be $6920.15.

Practice Set 4-3

For each problem, write a mathematical model and use it to find the correct answer.

Find the simple interest owed and maturity value of each loan given the following information.

	Principal	Rate	Time
1.	$ 500	9%	1 year
2.	$ 500	9%	6 months
3.	$1200	12%	18 months
4.	$2800	11.5%	5.5 years

5. What was the interest rate on a 2-year loan of $500 if the simple interest paid was $120?

6. What was the interest rate on a 3.5-year, $1000 loan if the simple interest paid was $297.50?

7. What interest will be charged on a $250 loan for 3 months if the rate is 18% simple interest?

8. What interest will be charged on a $1200 loan for 9 months if the rate is 12% simple interest?

Calculate the monthly payments necessary to retire the following loan amounts if simple interest is charged on the note.

	Loan Amount	Rate	Time
9.	$1200	12%	6 months
10.	$1500	8%	9 months
11.	$4500	10%	3 years
12.	$3750	11.5%	1.5 years

13. A refrigerator costs $1600 cash. It may be purchased for $100 down and 24 easy monthly payments of $80 each.
 (a) What are the finance charges (total interest)?
 (b) What is the total cost of this purchase if you finance the refrigerator?
 (c) What simple interest rate is being charged?

14. A man bought his girlfriend a new necklace for $259. Instead of paying cash, he paid $19 down,

financed the balance at 12% simple interest, and agreed to make monthly payments for 12 months.
 (a) What is the amount of these monthly payments?
 (b) What will be the total cost of the necklace if he finances it under these terms?

15. Sara made 10 payments of $108.50 to the credit union. The original loan amount was $1000. After she had made all payments, how much interest did she pay? What simple interest rate was she charged by the credit union?

16. Andrew borrowed $1200 on a 6-month note. The maturity value of the note was $1284. What simple interest rate was he charged for this note?

Calculate the maturity value of the following certificate of deposits if the interest is compounded periodically.

	Principal	Rate	Time	Compounded
17.	$ 2000	7.2%	1 year	monthly
18.	$10,500	5.75%	15 years	monthly
19.	$25,000	6%	5 years	quarterly
20.	$ 3500	3.5%	4 years	daily

21. Find the maturity value and amount of interest earned on an investment of $900 invested for 3 years at 10%
 (a) compounded quarterly.
 (b) compounded monthly.

22. Millie invested $1000 at 9.6% interest, compounded quarterly for a term of 18 months.
 (a) What will be the maturity value of her investment at the end of this term?
 (b) How much interest did her investment earn?

23. Teresa is saving money to pay her daughter's college tuition. She hopes to have $6500 saved 5 years from now. If she buys a $5000 certificate of deposit that pays 6% interest compounded monthly, will she have reached her goal of $6500 five years from now?

24. A plaintiff in a lawsuit was awarded $20,000 by a jury. However, an appeal was filed, so the judge

ordered that the money be held in an escrow account until the appeal was heard. Two years later, the plaintiff finally won the case and the money was paid out of the escrow account. If the escrow account had been paying interest at 8% compounded monthly, how much money did the plaintiff actually receive?

25. Sean plans to invest $10,000 in a savings account that pays 6% compounded quarterly. His friend suggests that he invest in an account paying the same interest rate but that pays interest compounded monthly. How much more interest will he earn at the end of 10 years if he follows his friend's advice?

26. Some certificates of deposit (CDs) pay simple interest that is credited to the deposit when the CD matures. CDs generally pay a higher interest rate because the depositor agrees to leave the money in the bank for a specific length of time. There are penalties for early withdrawal of funds from a CD. Compare the maturity value of a 3-year certificate

of deposit for $5000 that pays 6.5% simple interest with the maturity value of $5000 in a savings account for 3 years that pays 4.8% interest compounded monthly.

27. Calculate the amount of money you will have in the bank after 5 years if you deposit $25,000 into a savings account that pays 4.5% interest compounded continuously.

28. Mary invests $3500 at 8.25% compounded continuously. How much money will be in the account after 6 years?

29. Inflationary estimates use the formula for continuous compounding when predicting future values of items. Use this formula to predict the future value (M) in 10 years of a house that is valued at $140,000 if the inflation rate is 2%.

30. Use the continuous compounding formula to predict the future value in 5 years of a gallon of gasoline if the current price is $2.45 per gallon and the inflation rate is 1.5%.

Section 4-4   MATHEMATICAL MODELS IN CONSUMER CREDIT

When consumers borrow money to finance purchases such as cars or furniture, the money must be repaid in monthly payments. This method of purchasing items is called **installment buying.** There are generally two types of consumer credit available: **closed-end credit,** which involves the financing of a specific purchase amount for a set number of months; and **open-end credit,** where there are no fixed payments and the consumer continues to make payments until the balance is paid in full. Cars, furniture, and appliances are usually financed with closed-end credit (also known as fixed installment loans) while department store credit cards and bank charge cards such as Visa® or MasterCard® are examples of open-end credit.

Do you have a credit card or are you planning to get one soon? Credit limits are usually established when the credit card is issued. The required monthly payment is generally a percent of the balance due with a minimum payment required for low balances. You can save money if you know the interest rate, the annual fee, and the grace period (the interest-free period between purchases and billing given to consumers who pay off their balances entirely) on your cards. The interest rate may be fixed or variable (dependent upon the amount you owe or some standard such as a prime rate, the rate banks charge their best customers). How can you save money? First, you can get a card with no annual fee, saving $5 to $50. Next, you can eliminate interest payments by paying off your entire balance each month.

If you cannot pay off the balance each month, credit card companies will charge interest on the balance due. Some companies still use the **unpaid balance**

method to calculate the interest that you owe. The interest is calculated on the unpaid balance from the previous month, and any new purchases do not affect the interest charge calculation. The next example will show you how to find the new balance using this method.

EXAMPLE 16   Calculating Interest Using the Unpaid Balance Method

Lynn received a statement from a department store where she has a charge card. Her previous balance was $380. This month, she made a $20 payment and charged an additional $31.15 to her account. The charge card has an interest rate of 18% per year. Find the finance charge and the new balance.

(a) First, calculate the interest owed using the simple interest formula.

$$I = Prt$$

If the annual interest rate is 18%, then the rate applied each month will be $18\% \div 12 = 1.5\%$.

$$\text{Interest owed} = (\text{unpaid balance})(\text{monthly rate})(\text{time})$$

$$I = (\$380)(0.015)(1 \text{ month}) = \$5.70$$

(b) Second, calculate the new balance.

$380.00	(unpaid balance)
− $ 20.00	(payment made)
+ $ 5.70	(interest charged)
+ $ 31.15	(new purchase)
$396.85	(new balance)

Most credit card companies today use the **average daily balance method** to calculate interest charges. The companies apply the interest rate to the average balance that you carry on your card that month. Therefore, all payments and new purchases during the month are included in the interest calculation. The next example uses the same problem in Example 16 to illustrate this method.

EXAMPLE 17   Calculating Interest Using the Average Daily Balance Method

Lynn received a statement from a department store where she has a charge card. Her previous balance was $380. She made a $20 payment and charged an additional $31.15 to her account. The charge card has an interest rate of 18% per year. Find the finance charge and the new balance.

June 3   Billing date
June 12   Payment $20.00
June 20   Clothes $31.15
July 3   Next billing date

(a) First make a table that shows all transactions that have taken place during the month. Then compute a running balance for the month.

Date	Transaction	Balance
June 3	Opening balance	$380.00
June 12	Payment	$380.00 − $20.00 = $360.00
June 20	Purchase	$360.00 + $31.15 = $391.15

Next, calculate the balance due figures along with the number of days until the balance changed. Multiply each balance by the correct number of days and find the sum of these balances so that an "average daily balance" can be calculated.

Date	Balance Due	Number of Days Until Balance Changed	(Balance Due) × (Number of Days)
June 3	$380.00	9	$380.00 × 9 = $3420.00
June 12	$360.00	8	$360.00 × 8 = $2880.00
June 20	$391.15	13	$391.15 × 13 = $5084.95
	Total:	30 days	$11,384.95

$$\text{Average Daily Balance} = \frac{\text{sum of daily balances}}{\text{days in billing cycle}} = \frac{\$11,384.95}{30} = \$379.50$$

Lynn's finance charges will be calculated on this balance using the simple interest formula.

(b) The annual interest rate is 18%, so calculate the monthly rate by dividing 18% by 12 = 1.5%. Then calculate the finance charge for June as follows:

$$I = Prt = (\$379.50)(0.015)(1 \text{ month}) = \$5.69$$

The balance due on July 3 will be $391.15 + $5.69 = $396.84.

During the 1960s, Congress enacted several measures designed to protect the well-being of American consumers. One of these was the Consumer Protection Act or **Truth-in-Lending Act** that was enacted in 1969. An important feature of this law was the requirement that the total payment, the amount financed, and the finance charges be included in all credit contracts. This requirement was designed to assist consumers in comparing the different types of credit accounts available to them when making a purchase. All loan agreements must state the true annual interest rate known as the **annual percentage rate** or **APR.** Because the calculation of the APR is somewhat complicated, tables have been prepared so consumers can

■ **Table 4-5** **APR Table (Finance Charge per $100 of Amount Financed)**

Number of Payments	Annual Percentage Rate										
	8.0 %	**8.5%**	**9.0%**	**9.5%**	**10.0%**	**10.5%**	**11.0%**	**11.5%**	**12.0%**	**12.5%**	**13.0%**
6	2.35	2.49	2.64	2.79	2.93	3.08	3.23	3.38	3.53	3.68	3.83
12	4.39	4.66	4.94	5.22	5.50	5.78	6.06	6.34	6.62	6.90	7.18
18	6.45	6.86	7.28	7.69	8.10	8.52	8.93	9.35	9.77	10.19	10.61
24	8.54	9.09	9.64	10.19	10.75	11.30	11.86	12.42	12.98	13.54	14.10
30	10.66	11.35	12.04	12.74	13.43	14.13	14.83	15.54	16.24	16.95	17.66
36	12.81	13.64	14.48	15.32	16.16	17.01	17.86	18.71	19.57	20.43	21.30
48	17.18	18.31	19.45	20.59	21.74	22.90	24.06	25.23	26.40	27.58	28.77
60	21.66	23.10	24.55	26.01	27.48	28.96	30.45	31.96	33.47	34.99	36.52

translate the finance charge per $100 to the APR. See Table 4-5. Look at the next example that illustrates how to find the true APR you are being charged using your loan amount and total interest paid.

EXAMPLE 18 **Finding the APR on a Consumer Loan**

Latoya financed her new $1400 living room set that she bought at Dave's Discount Furniture World. She paid $200 down and financed the balance due for 30 months. Her payments were $46.75 per month. What was the APR for her purchase?

(a) Since the table gives us the finance charges per $100 of amount financed, we must first compute this amount.

$$\begin{aligned} \text{Payments } \$46.75 \times 30 \text{ months} &= \quad \$1402.50 \text{ paid to the store} \\ \text{Amount financed after down payment} &= - \ \underline{\$1200.00} \\ \text{Finance charge} &= \quad \$ \ 202.50 \end{aligned}$$

$$\text{Finance charge per } \$100 = \frac{\text{finance charge}}{\text{amount financed}} \times \$100$$

$$\text{Finance charge per } \$100 = \frac{\$202.50}{\$1200} \times 100 = \$16.88$$

(b) Look in the APR table and read across the row for 30 monthly payments until you find the number closest to $16.88. This number is $16.95 and is in the column under the heading 12.5%. Therefore, the APR on this loan is approximately 12.5%.

The APR table can also be used to calculate the monthly payments that you will be required to make if you finance purchases at a given APR. Comparing interest rates for large purchases such as cars can save consumers a significant amount of money in interest charges.

EXAMPLE 19   Calculating Monthly Payments Using the APR Table

Jeffrey plans to purchase a refrigerator for $1075. The store will finance his purchase at 8.0% APR for 24 months. Calculate the amount of Jeffrey's monthly payment if he makes a down payment on the refrigerator of $75.

(a) First, calculate the balance due that Jeffrey will finance.

$$\text{Cost} - \text{Down Payment} = \$1075 - \$75 = \$1000 \text{ to be financed}$$

(b) Use the APR table to calculate the total amount of interest that Jeffrey will pay on this loan. Go to the row for 24 monthly payments and find the amount in the column labeled 8.0%. This amount, $8.54, is the interest that he will be charged per $100 financed.

$$\text{Total interest due} = \left(\frac{\text{amount financed}}{100}\right) \times \text{amount in chart}$$

$$\text{Total interest due} = \left(\frac{\$1000}{100}\right) \times 8.54 = \$85.40$$

(c) Now, use the total interest due and balance due to calculate his monthly payments.

Balance due	$1000.00
Total interest due	+ $ 85.40
Total needed to pay off loan	$1085.40

$$\$1085.40 \div 24 \text{ payments} = \$45.23 \text{ per month}$$

The actual calculated amount is $45.225, but in order to insure that the entire loan is paid, the company will round up when determining monthly payments and adjust the last payment to make the payoff exact.

Practice Set 4-4

Find the finance charge on each of the following open-end charge accounts using the unpaid balance method of calculating interest.

1. Unpaid balance: $350.75
   annual interest rate: 18%

2. Unpaid balance: $1230.40
   annual interest rate: 21.6%

3. Unpaid balance: $ 655.90
   annual interest rate: 19.8%

4. Unpaid balance: $ 540.35
   annual interest rate: 21%

Complete each of the following tables in Problems 5–10 showing the unpaid balance at the end of each month. Use the unpaid balance method to calculate interest. Assume an 18% annual interest rate.

5.

Month	Unpaid Balance at Beginning of Month	Finance Charge	Purchases
June	$350.10		$ 25.00
July			$150.40
August			$208.75

Month	Purchases	Payments	Unpaid Balance at End of Month
June	$36.75	$ 75.00	
July	$ 0	$200.00	
August	$55.40	$150.00	

6.

Month	Unpaid Balance at Beginning of Month	Finance Charge	Purchases
January	$3071.10		$ 25.00
February			$125.00
March			$ 45.98

Month	Purchases	Payments	Unpaid Balance at End of Month
January	$ 0	$500.00	
February	$13.85	$350.00	
March	$16.79	$375.00	

7.

Month	Unpaid Balance at Beginning of Month	Finance Charge	Purchases
October	$59.75		$325.88
November			$ 59.06
December			$155.67

Month	Purchases	Payments	Unpaid Balance at End of Month
October	$ 34.98	$ 50.00	
November	$295.60	$150.00	
December	$230.75	$ 50.00	

8.

Month	Unpaid Balance at Beginning of Month	Finance Charge	Purchases
April	$312.88		$34.15
May			$45.67
June			$34.99

Month	Purchases	Payments	Unpaid Balance at End of Month
April	$ 0	$125.00	
May	$165.98	$125.00	
June	$ 90.45	$125.00	

9.

Month	Unpaid Balance at Beginning of Month	Finance Charge	Purchases
June	$1295.00		$ 65.00
July			$1325.00
August			$ 415.98

Month	Purchases	Payments	Unpaid Balance at End of Month
June	$ 0	$120.00	
July	$153.85	$350.00	
August	$ 65.09	$575.00	

10.

Month	Unpaid Balance at Beginning of Month	Finance Charge	Purchases
March	$0.00		$ 695.00
April			$ 925.00
May			$4816.92

Month	Purchases	Payments	Unpaid Balance at End of Month
March	$ 0	$ 0.00	
April	$ 58.85	$20.00	
May	$165.90	$75.00	

Find the average daily balance for each of the following credit card accounts (Problems 11–16). Assume one month between billing dates and find the finance charge using an 18% annual rate and the average daily balance method.

11. Billing date: June 3 with a balance of $145.90
    June 17: Payment $ 25.00
    June 22: Groceries $121.95

12. Billing date: May 1 with a balance of $315.98
    May 5: Payment $125.00
    May 20: Birthday present $ 45.75

13. Billing date: March 1 with a balance of $ 35.95
    March 5: Payment $ 35.95
    March 12: Clothing $ 545.75

14. Billing date: July 1 with a balance of $485.52
    July 3: Fireworks $125.00
    July 10: Payment $100.00

15. Billing date: October 5 with a balance of $550.77
    October 5: Plane ticket $405.98
    October 12: Payment $350.00
    October 30: Halloween costume rental $ 45.00

16. Billing date: July 10 with a balance of $126.75
    July 15: Beach cottage rental $950.45
    July 25: Payment $500.00
    August 2: School clothes $245.68

Find the APR (true annual interest rate) to the nearest half percent for each of the following problems (17–22).

	Amount Financed	Finance Charge	Number of Monthly Payments
17.	$9500	$968.05	18
18.	$2000	$366.20	48
19.	$1000	$32	6
20.	$1500	$180	30
21.	$7500	$1841	60
22.	$5000	$850	36

23. Carlos financed a $1250 computer with 24 monthly payments of $56.82. Find the finance charge he paid and the APR he was charged.

24. Joaquin bought a wide-screen, flat-panel plasma TV for $4500. He paid $500 down and financed the balance for 36 months. His monthly payments were $127.20. Find the finance charge he paid and the APR he was charged.

25. Lenese is buying new furniture at Discount Furniture Mart because they are offering to finance her purchase at 8.5% APR for 24 months with no down payment. If her total bill is $3560, calculate the amount of interest she will pay by financing her purchase.

26. Fitness, Inc. is advertising a new exercise machine for $1999.99. They will finance the purchase at 9.5% interest for 24 months. How much interest will be paid if someone pays no money down and finances this equipment purchase?

27. Vanida is planning to buy a boat that costs $10,876 including taxes and tags. She will pay 10% down and finance the balance at 12% APR for 48 months. Calculate her monthly payments for this boat.

28. Appliance Central is having a special sale that offers customers the opportunity to buy a refrigerator with no down payment and with financing at 9% for 18 months. If the cost of a new refrigerator is $1895 including tax, how much will the monthly payments be if John-Paul buys this refrigerator?

29. Kimani's new jet ski cost him $4578 including tax and fees. His down payment was $500, and he financed the balance at 10.5% APR for 36 months. How much is his monthly payment?

30. Marisa is purchasing a new dining room set for $4295. She pays $250 down and finances the balance at 12% APR for 36 months. Calculate her monthly payments.

Section 4-5   **MATHEMATICAL MODELS IN PURCHASING AN AUTOMOBILE**

In the previous section on consumer credit, we discussed installment loans. The most common method for calculating interest on installment loans is by a method known as add-on interest. Add-on interest is an application of the simple interest formula. It is called add-on interest because the interest is added to the amount borrowed so that both the interest and the amount borrowed are paid for over the length of the loan. One of the most common applications of installment loans is in purchasing a car because the interest charged when purchasing a car is add-on interest.

Important Equations

Installment Loan Formulas

$$\text{Simple interest formula: } I = Prt$$

$$\text{Amount to be repaid: } A = P + I$$

$$\text{Number of payments: } N = 12t$$

$$\text{Amount of each payment: } m = \frac{A}{N}$$

where P = amount to be financed, r = add-on interest rate, t = time (years) to repay the loan, I = amount of interest, A = amount to be repaid, m = amount of the monthly payment, and N = number payments

Suppose that you have decided to purchase a new car. You will need to take several things into consideration. You will need to look at the sticker price of the car, the dealer's preparation charges, the tax rate, and the add-on interest rate. You will then need to make an offer for the car. If you are serious about getting the best price, find out the dealer's cost. The dealer's cost is the price the dealer paid for the car. You will need to do some research to find this out. You can consult a reporting service, an automobile association, a credit union, or a periodical like *Consumer Reports*. Most car dealers will accept an offer that is between 3% and 10% over what they actually paid for the car.

EXAMPLE 20   **Making an Offer for a Car**

Allison wants to buy a new Honda Civic. The dealer's cost for the car is $12,750. She decides to offer the dealer 5% over the dealer's cost for this car. How much is Allison offering to pay for the car?

(a) Since she is offering 5% over the dealer's cost, we multiply 5% times $12,750.

$$\$12,750.00 \times .05 = \$637.50$$

To calculate the amount she will offer, add this to the dealer's cost.

$$\text{Amount of offer} = \$637.50 + \$12,750.00 = \$13,387.50$$

(b) An alternative calculation will help you arrive at the same answer. If we offer 5% over the dealer's cost, then we can multiply the dealer's cost by 105% (100% of dealer cost + 5% over) to calculate the amount that we should offer.

$$\text{Amount of offer} = 105\%(\$12,750) = 1.05(\$12,750) = \$13,387.50$$

Suppose that you have now decided to purchase a new car and you want to determine the monthly payment. Most car purchases require a down payment to be paid on the day of purchase. Then, the balance due on the car is financed for a period of 2 to 6 years, generally. Some dealerships provide on-site financing, but auto loans are available at banks, credit unions, and online lenders. Fees such as the cost of taxes and tags for the car must be included in the cost when you purchase a car. Example 21 demonstrates the process of calculating the down payment, balance due to be financed, and the calculation of the monthly payment amount.

EXAMPLE 21   **Purchasing a Car (Add-On Interest)**

Sarah wants to buy a new car. The sticker price of the car is $16,000, the cost of tags is $50, and the tax rate is 7%. The dealership agrees to finance the car for 4 years at an interest rate of 8%. If Sarah pays the sticker price for the car and makes a $2500 down payment, how much will she need to finance? Calculate her monthly payment.

(a) We will first need to determine the amount that Sarah needs to finance.

$$\text{Sales tax} = 7\%(\$16,000) = \$1120$$

$16,000	Sticker price
$ 1120	Sales tax
+ $ 50	Tags
$17,170	Total cost

Amount to finance:	$17,170	Total cost
	− $ 2500	Down payment
	$14,670	

(b) To calculate her monthly payment, we begin by using the installment loan formula to calculate the interest she must pay.

$$I = Prt$$

$$I = \$14,670(0.08)(4) = \$4694.40$$

Next, calculate the total amount to be repaid.

$$A = P + I$$

$$A = \$14,670 + \$4694.40 = \$19,364.40$$

Finally, calculate the monthly payment.

$$M = \frac{A}{N} = \frac{\$19,364.40}{(4)(12)} = \frac{\$19,364.40}{48} = \$403.425 = \$403.43$$

Therefore, Sarah's monthly payment will be $403.43.

Because a car purchase is a closed-end installment loan, another way to calculate monthly payments including finance charges is by using an APR table. This method of calculating monthly payments was introduced in the last section. Example 18 demonstrates the calculation of a monthly payment using the APR table (see Table 4-5).

EXAMPLE 22   Purchasing a Car (APR Table)

Jeffrey plans to purchase a used car for $10,750. The dealership will finance his purchase at 8.0% APR for 36 months. Calculate the amount of Jeffrey's monthly payment if he makes a down payment on the car of $2000.

(a) First calculate the balance due that Jeffrey will finance.

Cost of car − down payment = $10,750 − $2000 = $8750 to be financed

(b) Use the APR table to calculate the total amount of interest that Jeffrey will pay on this loan. Go to the row for 36 payments and find the amount in the column labeled 8.0%. This amount, $12.81, is the interest that will be charged per $100 financed.

$$\text{Total interest due} = \left(\frac{amount\, financed}{100} \right) \times amount\, in\, chart$$

$$\text{Total interest due} = \left(\frac{\$8750}{100} \right) \times \$12.81 = \$1120.88$$

(c) Now use the total interest due and balance due on the car to calculate his monthly payments.

$$
\begin{array}{ll}
\$8750.00 & \text{Balance due} \\
+ \,\underline{\$1120.88} & \text{Total interest due} \\
\$9870.88 & \text{Total needed to pay off loan}
\end{array}
$$

$9870.88 ÷ 36 payments = $247.20 per month

The actual calculated amount is $247.19111, but in order to ensure that the entire loan is paid, the company will round up when determining monthly payments and adjust the last payment to make the payoff exact.

Many people prefer to **lease** a car rather than buy a car. There are big differences between buying and leasing. Typically, if you were to purchase a new car, you would make a down payment and finance the remaining cost. At the end of the term, the car would be yours. Leasing is essentially renting, with your payment going toward the car's depreciation. If the lease includes a purchase option, you may buy it at the end of a specific time period.

There are short-term cost advantages to leasing. Most leases are for 3 years, so the repairs on the car are covered by factory warranty. The sales tax is also less because you only pay tax on the financed portion of the lease. The monthly payments and the down payment on a leased car are usually less than buying a car. You are only paying for the car's depreciation during the lease, plus the lease company's profit. For example, if the car is initially worth $28,000 but after 24 months is only worth $19,000, you pay only $9000 over 24 months. However, at the end of the lease term you have nothing. This is a major disadvantage in leasing a car. If you buy the car at the end of the lease, it will cost you a lot more than if you had just bought the car in the beginning.

Be sure to read the "fine print" on the lease agreement. For example, some banks charge an acquisition fee to initiate the lease. This adds to the initial cost of the car. Leases are also restrictive. If you exceed the yearly mileage limit, you will be charged an additional amount. The mileage surcharge may be 15¢ or more per mile. This can add up to a major expense very quickly. The car must also be returned in good shape. Any wear and tear on the car will be charged to you at the end of the lease.

Comparing lease offers can be very confusing, making it hard to know if you got a good deal. However, the Federal Reserve Board now requires a standardized federal disclosure form. The dealer is required to give details about specific items in the lease agreement. You must also remember that you will find it difficult to get out of your lease early if you want to—a problem if your driving needs or financial circumstances change.

At the end of the lease you have three options.

- Return the car to the dealer, where it will be checked for mileage and wear and tear. A disposition fee may be charged at the end of the lease to offset costs related to pick-up, reconditioning, and sale of the vehicle.
- Return the car and use it to trade on another lease or purchase. This is only possible if the wholesale value is more than the residual value of the car as stated in your contract.
- Purchase the car from the lease company. Most lease companies will allow you to purchase the car at the residual value (plus maybe a few hundred dollars more for profit for the leasing agent).

EXAMPLE 23   Leasing a Car

Martinez plans to lease a red 2005 Ford Mustang 2-door convertible. The sales price of the car is $25,000. The lease agreement states the following:

Due at signing: $478.74	Mileage allowance: 15,000/year
Monthly payment: $478.74	Excess mileage fee: $0.17/mile
36 months	Acquisition fee: $795

(a) If Martinez pays the acquisition fee, the amount due at signing, and the 36 monthly payments, how much has he paid to lease this car?
First calculate the total amount paid after he has made 36 lease payments. Then add this to his initial cost and acquisition fee.

$$\text{Monthly payments} = 36(\$478.74) = \$17,234.64$$

$$
\begin{array}{ll}
\$\quad 478.74 & \text{Initial payment} \\
\$\quad 795.00 & \text{Acquisition fee} \\
+\ \underline{\$17,234.64} & \text{Total of 36 payments} \\
\$18,508.38 &
\end{array}
$$

(b) If he drives 47,550 miles before he turns in the car, how much extra cost will he incur?

Martinez exceeded his mileage allowance for 3 years by 2550 miles (47,550 − 45,000). Therefore, we calculate the additional cost for this mileage by multiplying his excess mileage by \$0.17/mile.

$$2550 \text{ miles}(\$0.17/\text{mile}) = \$433.50$$

Therefore, he will owe the company an additional \$433.50 when he turns in the car.

One advantage of buying a car is that it is yours! You can customize it and drive it as hard and far as you want, penalty-free. Rather than having infinite payments, buying means you will eventually pay the car off. And if you want to sell it, you can do so at any time, as you are not locked into a contract. However, down payments on cars that you purchase can be substantial. Monthly payments are usually higher than payments for a leased car, and once your warranty expires, you will be responsible for the maintenance costs. When you want to sell the car (or trade it in), you will have to go through the hassle of doing so. And, as an investment, new cars depreciate rather than appreciate. Be sure to shop around and do your research before buying or leasing a car.

So which is better? That depends on your individual situation and needs. Some money advisers say that in general, if you buy a new car every 3–4 years, leasing can save you money. However, if you tend to hang on to your car for longer periods and pay it off, buying is a better deal. You will have to decide for yourself by analyzing the advantages and disadvantages of each.

EXAMPLE 24   Comparing the Purchase of a Car with Leasing a Car

Emily is interested in a 2005 Jeep Wrangler 4WD vehicle and negotiates the purchase price to \$22,000. She has \$1200 to pay toward the purchase of this car. She wants to compare the cost of purchasing the vehicle with the cost of a lease agreement. The current rate for car loans is 8% APR, and she plans to finance the car for 5 years if she purchases it. The cost of a 36-month lease agreement is stated as follows:

Payment amount: \$433.45	Excess mileage fee: \$0.17/mile
Purchase price: \$22,000	Lease term: 36 months
Total money due at signing: \$433.45	Disposition Fee: \$395
Residual value: \$10,808	Acquisition Fee: \$795
Current retail value: \$22,700	Purchase Option: \$11,307
Mileage allowance: 15,000/year	

(a) Purchasing the car by financing it at 8% APR for 5 years:

Emily can pay $1200 down for the car, and she will finance the balance. Therefore, she will finance $22,000 – $1200 = $20,800. Use the APR table to determine the total amount of interest she will pay for this purchase.

$$\text{Total interest due} = \left(\frac{amount\,financed}{100} \right) \times amount\,in\,chart$$

$$\text{Total interest due} = \left(\frac{\$20,800}{100} \right) \times \$21.66 = \$4505.28$$

The total amount due for the car: $20,800 + $4505.28 = $25,305.28
If we divide this by 60 (payments for 5 years), her monthly payment will be $421.76.

$$\text{Total paid for the car: } \$25,305.28 + \$1200 = \$26,505.28$$

(b) Lease agreement:

When Emily takes the car home, she will be required to pay the $795 acquisition fee and $433.45 down payment, for a total of $1228.45. She will then make 36 payments of $433.45 for a total of $15,604.20. If she decides at that time to purchase the car, she will owe an additional $11,307.

If she does not finance this amount, the total she has paid for the car by leasing is $1228.45 + $15,604.20 + $11,307 = $28,139.65

Practice Set 4-5

1. What is add-on interest, and how is it calculated?

2. How do you find the monthly payment for add-on interest?

3. Name two advantages of leasing a car.

4. Name two disadvantages of leasing a car.

5. Name two advantages of buying a car.

6. Name two disadvantages of buying a car.

Determine the amount offered for the following cars.

7. Peter offers 5% over dealer cost on a Porsche that has a sticker price of $51,000 and a dealer cost of $46,090.

8. Molly offers 7% over dealer cost on a Volkswagen that has a sticker price of $26,475 and a dealer cost of $16,413.

9. Joseph offers 6% over dealer cost on a Chevrolet that has a sticker price of $32,515 and a dealer cost of $29,460.

10. Megan offers 5% over dealer cost on a Honda that has a sticker price of $24,480 and a dealer cost of $22,998.

11. Charles offers 7% over dealer cost on a BMW that has a sticker price of $63,000 and a dealer cost of $56,904.

12. Laura offers 5% over dealer cost on a Volvo that has a sticker price of $35,750 and a dealer cost of $34,682.

Determine the amount of interest and the monthly payment for each of the car loans in Problems 13–18.

13. Peter purchases a car for $37,884 at 2.9% add-on rate for 5 years.

14. Molly purchases a car for $16,079 at 3.6% add-on rate for 4 years.

15. Joseph purchases a car for $15,747 at 5% add-on rate for 3 years.

16. Megan purchases a car for $34,631 at 4% add-on rate for 5 years.

17. Charles purchases a car for $50,187 at 1.9% add-on rate for 6 years.

18. Laura purchases a car for $29,108 at 8.5% add-on rate for 4 years.

19. A newspaper advertisement offers a $9000 car for nothing down and 36 easy monthly payments of $317.50. What is the total amount paid for the car, and what is the total finance charge?

20. A newspaper advertisement offers a $4000 used car for nothing down and 36 easy monthly payments of $141.62. What is the total amount paid for the car, and what is the total finance charge?

21. A car dealer will sell you a $16,450 car for $3290 down and payments of $339.97 per month for 48 months. What is the total amount paid for the car, and what is the total finance charge?

22. A car dealer will sell you a used car for $6798 with $798 down and payments of $168.51 per month for 48 months. What is the total amount paid for the car and what is the total finance charge?

23. A newspaper advertisement offers a $9000 car for nothing down and 36 easy monthly payments of $317.50. What is the simple interest rate?

24. A newspaper advertisement offers a $4000 used car for nothing down and 36 easy monthly payments of $141.62. What is the simple interest rate?

25. A car dealer will sell you a $16,450 car for $3290 down and payments of $339.97 per month for 48 months. What is the simple interest rate?

26. A car dealer will sell you a used car for $6798 with $798 down and payments of $168.51 per month for 48 months. What is the simple interest rate?

27. Phil bought a used car for $4500. He paid $500 down and financed the balance for 36 months. His monthly payments were $127.20. Find the finance charge that he paid and the APR that he was charged.

28. Vera is planning to buy a car that costs $10,876 including taxes and tags. She will pay 10% down and finance the balance at 12% APR for 48 months. Calculate her monthly payments.

29. Brandon's new motorcycle cost $8578 including taxes and tags. His down payment was $500, and he financed the balance at 10.5% APR for 36 months. How much was his monthly payment?

30. Molly is planning to buy a car that costs $24,095 including taxes and tags. She will pay $5000 down and finance the balance at 9.5% APR for 48 months. Calculate her monthly payments.

Use the following information to answer Questions 31–33.

Matt plans to lease a 2005 Dodge Dakota pick-up truck 4WD. The sales price of the truck is $25,000. The least agreement states the following:

Due at signing: $426.71	Mileage allowance: 15,000/year
Monthly payment: $426.71	Excess mileage fee: $0.18/mile
48 months	Acquisition fee: $895

31. If Matt pays the acquisition fee, the amount due at signing, and the 48 monthly payments, how much has he paid to lease this car?

32. If he drives 67,000 miles before he turns in the truck, how much extra cost will he incur?

33. If Matt buys the truck for $25,000 and pays 10% down, how much will he finance? If he finances this balance for 4 years at 2.9% add-on interest, how much will his monthly payments be? What is the total cost of the truck if he finances it?

Use this information for Problems 34–36.

Mary Alice plans to lease a 2005 Mercedes C230 sport coupe. The sales price of the car is $35,000. The lease agreement states the following:

Due at signing: $615.95	Mileage allowance: 15,000/year
Monthly payment: $615.95	Excess mileage fee: $0.18/mile
48 months	Acquisition fee: $895

34. If Mary Alice pays the acquisition fee, the amount due at signing, and the 48 monthly payments, how much has she paid to lease this car?

35. If she drives 65,200 miles before she turns in the car, how much extra cost will she incur?

36. If Mary Alice buys the car for $35,000 and pays 20% down, how much will she finance? If she finances this balance for 6 years at the special rate of 0.9% add-on interest, how much will her monthly payments be? What is the total cost of the car if she finances it?

Section 4-6   MATHEMATICAL MODELS IN PURCHASING A HOME

For most people, the single largest purchase of their life will be buying a house. This purchase will require many decisions in what may be unfamiliar areas. There are typically three steps in buying and financing a home. First, you will need to find a home you would like to buy and then reach an agreement with the seller on the price of the house. Second, you will need to find a lender to finance the loan. A loan specifically for buying a house is called a **mortgage.** You will need to shop around to find the lender that offers the best interest rates and terms. Finally, you will need to pay certain closing costs in a process called settlement or **closing,** where the deal is finalized. The term *closing costs* refers to money that must be paid above and beyond the down payment on the house. Attorney's fees, taxes, lender's administration fees, and appraisals are some of the items that may be included in closing costs.

The first step in buying a home is to find a house you can afford and come to an agreement with the seller. A realtor can help you find the type of house you want for the amount you can afford to pay for the house. The type of house you can afford depends greatly on your monthly income and the amount of down payment you can make. A down payment will generally be between 5% and 20% of the selling price of the house. The larger the down payment you make, the lower the interest rate may be, in many cases. If you make a down payment of less than 20% of the selling price, you will probably be required to pay mortgage insurance, which will add to your monthly payment amount. When determining the amount of the loan you need for a house, multiply your % down payment times the selling price of the home and subtract that amount from the price. For example, a 15% down payment on a $150,000 house would be (0.15)($150,000) = $22,500, leaving a balance to be financed of $150,000 – $22,500 = $127,500.

A useful rule in determining the monthly payment you can afford is given here:

1. Subtract any monthly bills from your gross monthly income.
2. Multiply this amount by 36%.

Your monthly house payment should not exceed this amount.

Another way of deciding if you can afford a house is to multiply your annual salary by 4. The purchase price of the house should not exceed this amount. The method of multiplying 36% of your gross income is the more commonly used way of determining the maximum amount you can afford to pay monthly for a house. The following example illustrates this method.

■ **EXAMPLE 25**   **Maximum House Payment**

Betty Menendez is looking for a new home in the Abilene area. Her gross monthly income is $4200, and her current monthly payments on bills total $515. What is the maximum amount she should plan to spend for house payments each month?

(a) The first step is to subtract her monthly bills from her gross monthly income.

$$\$4200 - \$515 = \$3685$$

(b) Multiply $3685 by 36%.

$$\$3685.00 \times 0.36 = \$1326.60$$

Her maximum house payment should be $1326.60 per month.

Once you have determined the maximum amount of monthly payment you can afford, you need to know the maximum amount you can borrow. This will help you decide what price range to look at in buying a house. An **amortization table** like the one in Table 4-6 can help determine the amount of money that you can afford to borrow. These tables are typically used by bankers and real estate agents to determine the monthly mortgage payments required at various rates on home loans.

Table 4-6   Amortization Table: Monthly Cost to Finance $1000

Rate of Interest	10 Years	15 Years	20 Years	25 Years	30 Years
5.0%	10.61	7.91	6.60	5.85	5.37
5.5%	10.85	8.17	6.88	6.14	5.68
6.0%	11.10	8.44	7.16	6.44	6.00
6.5%	11.35	8.71	7.46	6.75	6.32
7.0%	11.61	8.99	7.75	7.07	6.65
7.5%	11.87	9.27	8.06	7.39	6.99
8.0%	12.13	9.56	8.36	7.72	7.34
8.5%	12.40	9.85	8.68	8.05	7.69
9.0%	12.67	10.14	9.00	8.39	8.05
9.5%	12.94	10.44	9.32	8.74	8.41
10.0%	13.22	10.75	9.65	9.09	8.78
10.5%	13.49	11.05	9.98	9.44	9.15
11.0%	13.77	11.37	10.32	9.80	9.52

You can use the following formula to determine the amount of money you can afford to borrow using the amortization table.

Important Equation

Maximum Amount of a Loan Formula

$$\text{Maximum Loan} = \frac{monthly\ payment\ you\ can\ afford}{Table\ 4\text{-}6\ entry} \times 1000$$

EXAMPLE 26   Finding the Maximum Amount of a Loan

Charles can afford to make a maximum house payment of $900 per month. What is the maximum loan he should seek if he will finance his house over 30 years at 7.5% interest?

The maximum monthly payment is $900. Since the loan is being financed for 30 years at 7.5% interest, the table entry is 6.99. Substitute these values into the formula.

$$\text{Maximum Loan} = \frac{\$900}{6.99} \times 1000 = \$128{,}755.36$$

Charles can afford to borrow $128,755.36.

Help is available from many sources to help you make financial decisions and to help you manage your money. One of these is www.aliaterra.com. This site has a mortgage calculator and links to 11 types of calculators that give you information about mortgages. Suppose you wish to find out about what price of house you might be able to afford using this website. Look at the hypothetical situation in Example 27.

EXAMPLE 27   How Much Can I Borrow?

First, go to www.aliaterra.com, scroll down to the bottom of the screen and find the link *How Much Can I Afford?* A nice spreadsheet page comes up with slots for inserting financial information. Suppose you enter the following information:

Gross monthly income = $2085

Monthly payments: auto loan = $300

Monthly payments: other = $50

Other debts: monthly credit card payment = $75

Interest rate available = 5.0%

Term (years) = 30

Down payment = 10%

Front ratio (%) = 30

Back ratio (%) = 40

Now click on the results tab on the web page.

The front ratio indicates that your mortgage payment should be no more than 30% of your gross income. The back ratio indicates that your other debt should be no more than 40% of your gross income. The results of the search indicate that you can afford a loan of $59,490. With a down payment of 10%, or $6610, the total value of a house would be $66,100. Your mortgage payment, including taxes and insurance, is estimated to be $435.09. Houses in this price range are rare. If you were this person, you would need to get the car paid off and do some other things in order to get financing on a higher priced home.

Problems 40–41 give you some other hypothetical situations to use with this financial calculator.

When you have determined the amount of money that you need to borrow to purchase the house you have chosen, you can use the amortization table to calculate your actual monthly payment, or you can use a formula to calculate the monthly payment. The table and the formula are typically used for a **fixed-rate mortgage.** A fixed-rate mortgage is a loan in which the interest rate is guaranteed over the life of the loan. Fixed-rate loans usually range from 15 to 30 years.

First, we will use Table 4-6 to calculate the amount of the monthly payment for a fixed-rate loan. You will need to know the amount to be financed, the interest rate, and the length of time the loan is to be financed. The simple formula using the table is given in the following box.

Important Equations

Fixed-Rate Mortgage Monthly Payment Formula (Using Amortization Table)

$$P = \frac{A}{1000} \times Table\,4\text{-}6\,entry$$

where P = monthly payment and A = amount borrowed

EXAMPLE 28   Payments on a Fixed-Rate Mortgage Using the Amortization Table

The McIntyres are buying a $175,000 home. They plan to make a down payment of $67,000. If they get a fixed-rate mortgage for 30 years at 6.0%, what is their monthly payment? Use the amortization table to calculate their monthly payment.

(a) The amount borrowed (A) is the price of the house minus the down payment.

$$A = \$175,000 - \$67,000 = \$108,000$$

(b) Now use the formula $P = \frac{A}{1000} \times Table\ 4\text{-}6\ entry$, substituting the value $A =$ $108,000 and looking up the entry in Table 4-6. Since the rate is 6.0% and the loan is being financed for 30 years, the number from the table is 6.00.

$$P = \frac{\$108,000}{\$1000} \times 6.00$$

$$P = \$108 \times 6.00 = \$648.00$$

Therefore, the McIntyre family's monthly payment will be $648.00.

The formula to calculate the monthly payment directly is very complicated. However, it can be programmed into a computer, and by entering the required data, the monthly payment is easily calculated. Look at the formula and its use in calculating the monthly payments in Example 29.

Important Equations

Fixed-Rate Mortgage Monthly Payment Formula

$$P = A\left[\frac{\frac{r}{12}\left(1 + \frac{r}{12}\right)^{12t}}{\left(1 + \frac{r}{12}\right)^{12t} - 1}\right]$$

where P = monthly payment, A = amount borrowed, r = annual rate, and t = number of years.

EXAMPLE 29   **Payments on a Fixed-Rate Mortgage Using the Formula**

The Hamiltons are buying a $156,000 home. They plan to make a down payment of $55,000. If they get a fixed-rate mortgage for 30 years at 7.2%, what is their monthly payment? Use the fixed-rate monthly payment formula to calculate their monthly payment.

(a) The amount borrowed (A) is the price of the house minus the down payment.

$$A = \$156,000 - \$55,000 = \$101,000$$

(b) Now use the formula, substituting the values $r = 0.072$, $t = 30$ and $A = \$101,000$. Remember not to round any numbers in the problem until you have the final answer.

$$P = 101,000\left(\frac{\frac{0.072}{12}\left(1 + \frac{0.072}{12}\right)^{12 \cdot 30}}{\left(1 + \frac{0.072}{12}\right)^{12 \cdot 30} - 1}\right)$$

$$P = 101,000\left(\frac{0.006(1.006)^{360}}{(1.006)^{360} - 1}\right)$$

$$P = \$685.58$$

Therefore, the Hamilton family's monthly payment will be $685.58.

In addition to conventional fixed-rate loans, there are **adjustable-rate mortgages (ARM)** available to consumers that generally start out with a lower interest rate than similar fixed-rate mortgages. However, even though the monthly mortgage payments remain the same for a 1-, 2-, or 5-year period, the interest rates change periodically, reflecting prevailing rates in the economy. After the introductory period of fixed mortgage payments, the payments are then adjusted to reflect the new interest rates. There are also additional monthly costs to consider when financing a house, including required homeowners insurance and property taxes. Closing costs when financing a home will also impact the final loan agreement. Some of these charges include a loan origination fee, lender document and underwriting fees, fees to the title company, title insurance fees, appraisal costs, and document recording fees.

Purchasing a house can be a complicated transaction. After you find your "dream house," be sure to shop for the lender offering the best interest rates and services. Rates offered by banks, savings and loans, credit unions, and online lenders should be compared as you make a decision about financing. Realtors and mortgage officers can help you make wise decisions about your home purchase. There are also many loan calculation tools available online to help you determine the amount of money you can reasonably afford to invest in a house given your monthly income and expenses.

Practice Set 4-6

Answer the following in your own words.

1. What factors are important when looking for a home loan?

2. What factors influence the amount of monthly payment for a home loan?

3. What is the general rule for determining the monthly payment that you can afford?

4. How do you determine the monthly payment for a home loan?

5. How do you determine the maximum amount of money that you can afford to borrow?

Determine the down payment and the amount to be financed for each home described in Problems 6–11.

6. Cost of house: $148,700
   Down payment: 5% of cost of house

7. Cost of house: $153,250
   Down payment: 10% of cost of house

8. Cost of house: $195,000
   Down payment: 20% of cost of house

9. Cost of house: $179,900
   Down payment: 25% of cost of house

10. Cost of house: $273,450
    Down payment: 15% of cost of house

11. Cost of house: $315,500
    Down payment: 30% of cost of house

In Problems 12–17 determine the maximum monthly payment you could afford for a house. Use the formula discussed in Example 25.

12. Gross monthly income: $1240
    Current monthly payments: $275

13. Gross monthly income: $985.65
    Current monthly payments: $135.50

14. Gross monthly income: $2750
    Current monthly payments: $560

15. Gross monthly income: $2200
    Current monthly payments: $550

16. Gross monthly income: $1680
    Current monthly payments: $520

17. Gross monthly income: $3700
    Current monthly payments: $650

Determine the monthly payment for each loan described in Problems 18–23. Use the fixed-rate mortgage monthly payment formula.

18. Cost of house: $148,500
    Interest rate: 6%
    Term: 30 years

19. Cost of house: $185,000
Interest rate: 7.25%
Term: 25 years

20. Cost of house: $375,000
Interest rate: 7.5%
Term: 15 years

21. Cost of house: $110,500
Interest rate: 6.25%
Term: 30 years

22. Cost of house: $175,000
Interest rate: 5%
Term: 30 years

23. Cost of house: $113,650
Interest rate: 5.85%
Term: 20 years

Determine the monthly payment for each loan described in Problems 24–29. Use Table 4-6 (amortization table formula).

24. Cost of house: $248,500
Interest rate: 8%
Term: 20 years

25. Cost of house: $85,000
Interest rate: 6.5%
Term: 25 years

26. Cost of house: $169,900
Interest rate: 5.5%
Term: 20 years

27. Cost of house: $112,000
Interest rate: 7%
Term: 15 years

28. Cost of house: $175,000
Interest rate: 6%
Term: 30 years

29. Cost of house: $265,000
Interest rate: 6.5%
Term: 30 years

In Problems 30–35, determine the maximum amount of a loan that you could obtain.

30. Maximum monthly house payment: $1215.75
Interest rate: 7.5%
Term: 30 years

31. Maximum monthly house payment: $750
Interest rate: 6.5%
Term: 30 years

32. Maximum monthly house payment: $942
Interest rate: 8%
Term: 20 years

33. Maximum monthly house payment: $1850
Interest rate: 7%
Term: 25 years

34. Maximum monthly house payment: $1235
Interest rate: 5.5%
Term: 15 years

35. Maximum monthly house payment: $635
Interest rate: 8.5%
Term: 30 years

36. Charlotte wishes to buy a house that sells for $90,000. Her credit union requires her to make a 20% down payment. The mortgage rate is 5% on a 20-year loan. Determine the amount of the required down payment and find the monthly mortgage. (Use the amortization table.)

37. The Petersons are buying a $250,000 house and planning to make a 25% down payment. The bank is financing the balance at 5.75% for 30 years. Calculate the amount of their monthly payments. (Use the fixed-rate mortgage formula.)

38. Johnny and Eunice Harris are buying a house that sells for $104,000. The bank is requiring a minimum down payment of 20%. The current mortgage rate is 7.5% for 25 years. (Use the amortization table.)
  (a) Determine the amount required for the down payment and the amount of their monthly payment.
  (b) Using the monthly payment amount that you have calculated, determine the total amount that they will have paid for their house in 25 years.

39. The Bergmanns are buying a new condo that is priced at $118,500. They will make a 15% down payment and finance the balance at 6.25% for 30 years. (Use the fixed-rate mortgage formula.)
  (a) Determine the amount required for the down payment and the amount of their monthly payment.

(b) Using the monthly payment amount you have calculated, determine the total amount they will have paid for their condo in 30 years.

40. Go to www.aliaterra.com and enter the following amounts: wages = $6500, student loan = $123, other payments = $40, interest rate = 5.0% for 30 years with 20% down payment, property tax estimate = $1550, and homeowners insurance = $500.

What is the conservative estimate for the price of house you might be able to purchase? What is the aggressive estimate?

41. Repeat Problem 40, but this time use a 15-year loan instead of a 30-year loan. Note the major changes. Go back now and enter your own data and see how much money you might be able to borrow.

Section 4-7   MATHEMATICAL MODELS IN INSURANCE OPTIONS AND RATES

In the previous sections, we have discussed mathematical models in buying a car and buying a home. In this section we will look at mathematical models involved in purchasing insurance. Insurance is an economical way of helping an individual deal with a severe financial loss by pooling the risk over a large number of people. Many people purchase insurance protection, and their payments are pooled in order to provide funds with which to pay those who experience losses. This helps to lower the rates when many different people purchase the same protection and divide the risk. Rates would have to be much higher if only a few people chose to pay in enough money to provide reimbursement for a major loss.

The risk that an insurance company assumes by insuring a person influences how high the rates will be. The insurance company does not know who will suffer loss, but it knows from experience how many losses are expected and the cost of the claim. This is why car insurance is more expensive for inexperienced drivers. Teenagers will pay a much higher premium than an experienced adult driver will. This is determined by looking at the claims filed by young inexperienced drivers. Likewise, life insurance premiums are determined by the age of the client, health concerns, and the lifestyle of the client.

The payment made to purchase insurance coverage is called a **premium.** An **insurance policy** defines in detail the provisions and limitations of the coverage. The amount of insurance specified by the policy is called the **face value** of the policy. Insurance premiums are paid in advance, and the term of the policy is the time period for which the policy will remain in effect. The insurance company is referred to as the **insurer** or **underwriter.** The person that purchases the insurance is called the **insured** or **policyholder.** When an insured loss occurs, the payment that the insurance company makes to reimburse the policyholder is often called an **indemnity.**

Individual states have insurance commissions that regulate premium structure and insurance requirements (such as required automobile insurance) passed by their legislatures. This causes insurance practices and premiums to vary from state to state.

We will now look specifically at automobile insurance. Automobile insurance is usually written for a maximum term of one year. The main reason for a one-year policy is the high nationwide accident rate. These accidents increase rates for automobile insurance. Since insurance rates always reflect the risk taken by the insurance company, the driving record and the age of the driver is another major factor in determining the cost of automobile insurance. This is another reason for having a one-year policy, since a driver's record may change over a period of years.

Automobile insurance is divided into two basic categories: liability coverage and comprehensive/collision coverage. **Liability insurance** pays for bodily injury, property damage, and some additional expenses of other drivers, their passengers, and your passengers when you or a driver covered by your policy causes an accident. Most states require the owners of all vehicles registered in the state to purchase minimum amounts of liability insurance. Each state determines the minimum liability coverage for its drivers. Texas law requires proof of financial responsibility for anyone who drives an automobile in the state. The minimum liability insurance required by law is $20,000 bodily injury per person, $40,000 bodily injury per accident, and $15,000 for property damage per accident. This is commonly called "20/40/15" coverage. Liability insurance does not pay for damage to your own vehicle.

The following two tables show the base annual premiums for automobile liability insurance. Most insurance companies will reduce the total premium cost by a certain percent when two or more vehicles are covered under one insurance policy.

Table 4-7   Automobile Liability Insurance Base Annual Premium

Bodily Injury Coverage	Territory 1	Territory 2	Territory 3
20/40	$ 81	$ 91	$221
25/40	$ 83	$ 94	$115
25/50	$ 86	$ 97	$120
50/50	$ 88	$101	$125
50/100	$ 90	$103	$129
100/100	$ 91	$104	$131
100/200	$ 94	$108	$136
100/300	$ 95	$110	$139
200/300	$ 98	$112	$141
300/300	$100	$115	$144

Table 4-8   Automobile Liability Base Annual Premiums

Property Damage Coverage	Territory 1	Territory 2	Territory 3
$ 15,000	$83	$ 95	$100
$ 20,000	$85	$ 97	$103
$ 25,000	$86	$ 99	$104
$ 50,000	$87	$101	$107
$ 100,000	$90	$103	$108

Table 4-9 contains excerpts of the driver classifications used to determine the annual cost of liability insurance.

◼   **Table 4-9   Automobile Insurance Multiples of Base Annual Premium**

		Pleasure; Less Than 3 Miles to Work Each Way	Drives to Work 3 to 9 Miles Each Way	Drives to Work 10 Miles or More Each Way	Used in Business
Mature drivers	All others	1.00	1.10	1.40	1.50
Young females	Age 16	1.40	1.50	1.80	1.90
	Age 20	1.05	1.15	1.45	1.55
Young males	Age 16	1.60	1.70	2.00	2.10
(married)	Age 20	1.45	1.55	1.85	1.95
	Age 21	1.40	1.50	1.80	1.90
	Age 24	1.10	1.20	1.50	1.60
Young males	Age 16	2.05	2.15	2.45	2.55
(unmarried	Age 20	1.60	1.70	2.00	2.10
not principal	Age 21	1.55	1.65	1.95	2.05
operator/owner)	Age 24	1.10	1.20	1.50	1.60
Young males	Age 16	2.70	2.80	3.10	3.20
(unmarried	Age 20	2.55	2.65	2.95	3.05
and owner)	Age 21	2.50	2.60	2.90	3.00
	Age 24	1.90	2.00	2.30	2.40
	Age 26	1.50	1.60	1.90	2.00
	Age 29	1.10	1.20	1.50	1.60

As you can see from the table, drivers under 21 are classified according to sex and age. Males under 25 are classified according to marital status and whether they are the owners or principal operators of the cars. Unmarried males may continue to be so classified until they reach age 30. Most mature drivers would be classified "all others." Since younger drivers are more inexperienced and tend to have more accidents, their liability insurance will be much higher.

▌ **EXAMPLE 30**   **Automobile Liability Insurance Premiums**

Joshua Windsor is 16 years old and drives his car to work at the local grocery store each day, a one-way distance of 6 miles. He is not the principal operator of the car. The area in which he lives is classified Territory 1. Determine the cost of 20/40/15, or the minimum liability coverage required in the state of Texas. (Remember that 20/40/15 means $20,000 bodily injury per person, $40,000 bodily injury per accident, and $15,000 for property damage per accident.) Use Tables 4-7, 4-8, and 4-9 to determine his total annual premium.

First, look at Table 4-7 and determine the premium amount for $20,000 single and $40,000 total bodily injury, or 20/40. This amount is $81.00. Then look at Table 4-8 to determine the premium amount for $15,000 property damage. This amount is $85.00. Then add these two amounts together, $81.00 + $85.00 = $166.00 for the total base premium. Next, look at Table 4-9 to determine what you need to multiple the base amount times in order to get the annual premium amount. Since he is 16 years old, is not the principal operator, and drives 6 miles to work, multiply $166.00 × 2.15 = $356.90. Therefore, Joshua's total annual premium is $356.90.

EXAMPLE 31   Automobile Liability Insurance

Gerald Sluder of Sluder's Construction Company was driving a company truck when it hit an automobile, injuring a mother and her son. Sluder Construction was sued for $130,000 in personal injuries and $5500 property damage. The court awarded the victims a $70,000 personal injury judgment and the entire property damage suit. Sluder Construction carries 25/50/15 liability coverage. How much will the insurance company pay? How much of the award will Sluder Construction have to pay?

The insurance company will pay the $50,000 maximum total bodily injury coverage ($25,000 maximum per person) and the total award for property damage ($5500). Therefore, the insurance company will pay a total of $55,500.

Since the court awarded the claimants more than Sluder Construction's bodily injury coverage, the firm will be responsible for the excess:

$70,000	Bodily injury awarded
− $50,000	Liability coverage for bodily injury
$20,000	Amount to be paid by Sluder Construction

The second category of automobile insurance is comprehensive and collision insurance. Comprehensive and collision insurance protect against damage to the policyholder's own automobile. Comprehensive insurance covers damage to the car resulting from fire, theft, vandalism, acts of nature, falling objects, and so on. Collision insurance covers damage resulting from one-car accidents. Collision insurance pays for repairs to the vehicle of the insured when the policyholder is responsible for an accident, when the insured's car was damaged by a hit-and-run driver, or when another driver was responsible for the collision but did not have liability insurance and was unable to pay for the property damage caused by the accident. Collision insurance does not pay for loss or damage to other vehicles or property. Collision policies are available with various deductible amounts. Both collision and comprehensive coverage become considerably less expensive as the policyholder pays a higher percentage of each repair cost. Comprehensive/collision rates also depend on the make, model, and age of the vehicle. For example, newer automobiles are more expensive to repair, so the insurance premiums will cost more than those for an older car.

Uninsured motorist insurance is also available. This offers financial protection for the policyholder's own bodily injuries or those of a family member when hit by a driver who did not carry bodily injury liability insurance. It does not cover the uninsured motorist.

Table 4-10 lists excerpts of base annual comprehensive and collision insurance rates for vehicles of various ages. Automobiles of the current model year are

■ **Table 4-10   Comprehensive and Collision Insurance Base Annual Premiums**

Model Class	Age Group	Comprehensive	$250 Deductible Collision	$500 Deductible Collision
A–G	1	$55	$ 82	$ 76
	2, 3	$52	$ 77	$ 73
	4	$49	$ 71	$ 67
J–K	1	$63	$111	$101
	2, 3	$59	$103	$ 95
	4	$54	$ 93	$ 86
L–M	1	$68	$123	$112
	2, 3	$64	$125	$104
	4	$57	$102	$ 94
N–O	1	$77	$140	$126
	2, 3	$70	$130	$117
	4	$62	$115	$105

classified as "Age Group 1"; cars in Group 2 (the first preceding model year) and Group 3 (the second preceding model year) both pay the same rate; and models 3 or more years old are classified in Group 4. Each automobile model is assigned an identification letter from A to Z. (Typically, less expensive models are identified by letters near the beginning of the alphabet, and successive letters identify increasingly expensive models.) As in the case of liability insurance, the base annual comprehensive/collision premiums must be multiplied by a multiple reflecting the driver's classification.

EXAMPLE 32   **Comprehensive/Collision Insurance Premiums**

Kevin Widderich, who is 26 years old and single, uses his car for business. His car is a Nissan Altima, which is considered a Model K, less than 1 year old. Find his annual premium for the following insurance: 50/50/20 liability insurance in Territory 3, with full comprehensive and $500-deductible collision.

Tables 4-7 and 4-8 are used to determine the base annual liability (bodily injury and property damage), as in the previous example. The comprehensive and collision base premiums are shown in Table 4-10. The total of all these base annual premiums must then be multiplied by the driver classification multiple from Table 4-9 to obtain the total annual premium.

```
    $ 125    50/50 Bodily injury
      103    $20,000 Property damage
       63    Comprehensive (Model K, Age Group 1)
 +    101    $500-deductible collision (Model K, Age Group 1)
    $ 392    Base annual premium
 ×   2.00    Driver classification—unmarried male, age 26, business use
    $ 784    Total annual premium
```

■ EXAMPLE 33   **Comprehensive/Collision Insurance**

Suzie Sharpe carries 10/20/5 liability insurance and $250-deductible collision insurance. Suzie was at fault in an accident that caused $900 damage to her own car and $1200 damage to the other vehicle. How much of this property damage will Suzie's insurance company pay? Suppose that a court suit results in a $12,000 award for personal injuries to the other driver. How much would the insurance company pay and how much is Suzie's responsibility?

The property damage to the other car is $1200, which will be paid by the insurance company since Suzie has a $5000 property damage policy. The property damage to Suzie's car is $900 − $250 (deductible) = $650. So the total property damage settlement is $1200 + $650 = $1850. Under Suzie's $10,000 single and $20,000 total bodily injury policy, the maximum amount the insurance company will pay to any one victim is $10,000. Suzie is personally liable for the remaining $2000 of the $12,000 settlement. Therefore, her total obligation is $2000 + $250 (deductible) = $2250.

As you can see, insurance is a complex topic. We have talked exclusively about purchasing automobile insurance in this section, but there are many other types of insurance that you will need to consider in your lifetime. Examples of other kinds of insurance include medical, home, renters, flood, and life insurance. Annuities are a type of retirement insurance. There are many factors to consider when purchasing insurance. You will want to shop around for the best rates and look at the reputation of the insurance company that you are considering.

Practice Set 4-7

1. What is insurance?

2. What is a premium?

3. What is face value?

4. Who is the insurer?

5. What is indemnity?

6. What is liability insurance?

7. What is the minimum amount of liability insurance in the state of Texas?

8. What is comprehensive insurance?

9. What is collision insurance?

Determine the amount of liability insurance premiums for the following automobile insurance problems using the tables in this section.

10. Driver classification: Male, 47, drives 8 miles to work
    Liability coverage: 25/50/15
    Territory: 1

11. Driver classification: Female, 32, business use
    Liability coverage: 50/50/25
    Territory: 2

12. Driver classification: Unmarried male, 16, drives 3 miles to work, not principal operator
    Liability coverage: 50/100/25
    Territory: 3

13. Driver classification: Female, 25, drives 6 miles to work
    Liability coverage: 20/40/15
    Territory: 2

14. Driver classification: Female, 30, drives 12 miles to work
    Liability coverage: 50/50/25
    Territory: 1

15. Driver classification: Unmarried male, 21, drives 5 miles to work, principal operator
    Liability coverage: 100/200/50
    Territory: 3

Determine the total comprehensive/collision premiums for the following. Use the tables in this section.

16. Model: G
    Age group: 2
    Deductible on collision: $250
    Driver classification: Female, 54, drives 1 mile to work

17. Model: L
    Age group: 4
    Deductible on collision: $500
    Driver classification: Male, 35, drives 11 miles to work

18. Model: N
    Age group: 1
    Deductible on collision: $500
    Driver classification: Unmarried male, 24, drives 6 miles to work, principal operator

19. Model: A
    Age group: 3
    Deductible on collision: $500
    Driver classification: Female, 47, drives 30 miles to work

20. Model: J
    Age group: 1
    Deductible on collision: $250

Driver classification: Married male, 20, drives 12 miles to work, principal operator

21. Model: L
    Age group: 2
    Deductible on collision: $250
    Driver classification: Female, 65, drives 15 miles to work

22. Everett McCook, age 42, lives in Territory 3. Each day he drives 5 miles each way to the college where he teaches. His liability insurance includes $50,000 for single bodily injury, $100,000 for total bodily injury, and $15,000 for property damage. Determine his annual payment.

23. Kenny Sluder, age 26, is unmarried and owns a Volkswagen Jetta, considered a Model D car in Age Group 1. Each day he commutes 15 miles each way to work from his home in Territory 1. His auto insurance includes 25/50/15 liability coverage. He also has comprehensive and a $250 deductible on collision coverage. How much is his annual premium?

24. Erika Chavez was liable for an accident in which two people were injured. Her insurance included 50/100/25 liability protection. The court awarded one person $30,000 and the other $65,000 for personal bodily injuries. An award of $25,000 for damages to the other car was also part of the court settlement.

   (a) How much of the court settlement will the insurance company pay?
   (b) How much of the expense must Ericka pay personally?

25. During a hurricane, Leslie Hull-Ryde's car was struck by a falling tree, which caused $8000 in damages. Leslie carries comprehensive and $250-deductible collision insurance.

   (a) How much of the damages will her insurance cover?
   (b) How much of the repair bill will Leslie have to pay?

Section 4-8

MATHEMATICAL MODELS IN STOCKS, MUTUAL FUNDS, AND BONDS

Good financial planning includes the use of various types of investments as you examine your goals for the future. Planning for retirement at an early age may seem unimportant to you, but as you learned in an earlier section, the effect of compounding can lead to a significant amount of savings after 30 or more years. For example, if at age 16, you were to invest $2000 in a retirement account each year for 6 years ($12,000 invested by age 22), you would have more than $1 million by the time you are 65 if your account returns an average of 10% per year (the historical average for the stock market). In this section, we will examine different investment options that are available as you learn to manage your finances and plan for the future.

One type of very safe investment is a savings account. Though the interest rates may be relatively low, bank accounts up to $100,000 are insured by the federal government, so there is no risk of losing the principal you have invested. The interest rate of the account guarantees a certain increase in the value of your account. You have already examined these interest rates and the effects of compounding in Section 4-3.

Other types of investments are riskier but may offer better returns over a long period of time. These investments include stocks, bonds, and mutual funds.

Stocks   A **stock** represents ownership in a particular company. When stocks are openly traded, they "go public," and each ownership unit is called a **share.** For example, if you buy 100 shares of stock in WalMart, you are now a proud owner of that company (so you own some of the bricks in the local store!). Any investor who owns stock in a company is called a **shareholder.**

Most stocks are traded on the New York Stock Exchange (NYSE) or National Association of Securities Dealer Automated Quotations (NASDAQ). Individual investors most often use licensed stockbrokers or online brokerages to purchase shares of stock. Investors pay a brokerage fee for the purchase and sale of stocks. These costs vary based on the brokerage being used and sometimes on the number of shares being traded. Online brokerages may charge a flat fee, such as $9.99 per purchase for all stock purchases regardless of the size of the investment. However, they offer no investment advice or assistance with decisions about investment opportunities. Brokers who work directly with clients and their stock investments may charge a commission fee that is based on the number of shares bought or sold.

EXAMPLE 34   Purchasing Shares of Stock

An investor wishes to purchase 5000 shares of Disney® stock (NYSE symbol DIS). The current price of Disney stock is $27.32 per share. His stockbroker charges 2% of the cost of the stock as her commission. Find the total cost of this purchase.

(a) First, find the cost of the stock.

$$5000 \text{ shares} \times \$27.32 \text{ per share} = \$136,000$$

(b) Now calculate the stockbroker's commission based on this purchase price.

$$\$136,000 \times 2\% = \$136,000 \times 0.02 = \$2732$$

(c) The total cost of this purchase is the cost of the stock plus the broker's fee.

$$\$136,000 + \$2732 = \$138,732$$

The value of a stock will fluctuate daily depending on the economy and the particular company. If a large number of people are trying to buy a particular stock when only a limited number of shares are available, the price of the stock will increase. Conversely, if many shareholders are trying to sell a stock and few people are purchasing, the prices will fall. Most large company stocks are considered to be a lower risk than the newer, small company stocks. There is some risk associated with all stocks.

EXAMPLE 35   **Calculating Profit from Stock Transactions**

Suppose that you bought 750 shares of Dell stock (NASDAQ symbol DELL) at $35.15. The current price is $42.50, and you decide that you should sell this stock. You use an online brokerage firm that charges $9.99 per transaction. Calculate the amount of profit you will have after you sell your stock.

(a) First, calculate the cost of the original stock purchase and the amount you will receive from the sale.

$$\text{Sale} = 750 \text{ shares} \times \$42.40 = \$31,800.00$$

$$\text{Cost} = 750 \text{ shares} \times \$35.15 = \$26,362.50$$

$$\text{Difference} = \$5437.50$$

(b) The brokerage costs include a $9.99 fee for the original purchase and an additional $9.99 fee for the sale. Therefore, the total brokerage cost is $19.98.

$$\text{Net profit} = \text{profit} - \text{costs}$$

$$\text{Net profit} = \$5437.50 - \$19.98 = \$5417.52$$

If a company is profitable, it may pay owners all or part of its profits in the form of **dividends.** These dividends will be sent to you quarterly or can be used to automatically reinvest in the company by purchasing additional shares of stock for your portfolio. Newer companies often pay no dividends and choose to use the profits of the company to invest in the growth and expansion of the company. Currently, WalMart pays an annual dividend of $0.56. Therefore, as a shareholder with 100 shares, you would receive a dividend of $\frac{0.56}{4} \times 100 = 14.00$ four times a year.

Over the last 75 years, the return on stocks has averaged more than 10% per year. However, it is important to view investments in stocks as long-term investments (more than 5 years). Monthly and yearly returns can be much more volatile than this average, and you can lose a great deal of money as a short-term investor.

Mutual Funds   Most people do not have the time or expertise to choose good stock investments from the thousands of stocks that are available. For this reason, many small investors purchase **mutual funds** instead of individual stocks. A mutual fund is a group of stocks managed by a professional who invests your money in a portfolio of various investments. This portfolio may be a blend of various stocks or bonds or a combination of both. Shares of mutual funds are purchased in a manner similar to stock purchases. You will generally pay a fee to the manager, sometimes called the "load" fee. The money you invest is combined with the money of other investors, and the fund manager buys and sells stocks to try and obtain the best return possible. Some funds specialize in an area such as technology or health care, while others are more broad-based and include stocks from many types and sizes of businesses.

Bonds   Another investment option available to the public is **bonds.** Bonds are traded like stocks, and their price is a function of the law of supply and demand. Companies and municipalities may issue bonds when they need to borrow money for a project. For example, if a county needs funds to build a new school, it may issue school bonds. People who buy these bonds are lending money to the county for its project. The county then agrees to pay the purchaser the **face value** (price paid at purchase) plus interest at a fixed rate. These are long-term investments with a typical term of 10 years or more. If a company goes bankrupt, the bondholders are the first to claim the assets of the company, even before the stockholders of the company. Bonds earn simple interest, which is typically paid periodically to the purchaser. Generally, investments in bonds are considered safer than investments in stocks, but the returns are usually lower. Bonds may also be included in mutual fund portfolios.

Reading a Stock Table   Most daily newspapers and online finance websites include stock tables of the most widely traded stocks on the New York Stock Exchange, NASDAQ, and American Stock Exchange. They will also include a list of widely held mutual funds and their current values. There are many facts that can be included in a stock table, so we will examine a few of the most common by looking at Table 4-11.

■ **Table 4-11   Reading a Stock Market Table**

NAME	DIV	VOL	LAST	NET CHG.
HarleyD	0.35	14047	48.40	+.05

Table 4-11 refers to a recent listing for Harley Davidson stock. The heading DIV refers to the dividends that the company pays per share to its stockholders annually. According to this table, Harley Davidson paid a $0.35 dividend per share to its shareholders during the last year. Therefore, if you own 2000 shares of this stock, you would have received $0.35 \times 2000 = \$700$ during the last 12 months from the company in four quarterly payments. The heading VOL refers to the unofficial daily total of shares traded, expressed in hundreds. A listing of 14047 indicates that 14047 × 100 = 1,404,700 shares of Harley Davidson stock were traded yesterday. The heading LAST stands for the price at which shares traded when the market closed yesterday at 4:00 p.m. The closing price for Harley was $48.40 per share at the close of trade yesterday. The NET CHG column represents the net change in value from the price at the close of the market two days ago. Since the value in this column is +.05, Harley Davidson's closing stock price of $48.40 was 5 cents higher than its closing price the day before.

EXAMPLE 36   Reading a Stock Table

Use the stock table for Pepsi stock to answer the following questions.

(a) If you owned 2500 shares of Pepsi stock last year, what annual dividend did you receive?

NAME	DIV	VOL	LAST	NET CHG.
PepsiCo	0.92	42504	56.01	−.89

The table lists an annual dividend of $0.92 for Pepsi. Therefore, someone with 2500 shares will receive 2500 × 0.92 = $2300.

(b) How many shares of Pepsi stock were traded yesterday?
The volume traded yesterday was 42504 × 100 = 4,250,400 shares.

(c) What was the price at which Pepsi stock closed yesterday?
The closing price of the stock yesterday was $56.01.

(d) What was the price at which Pepsi stock closed the day before yesterday?
Because the net change is −.89, that indicates that the closing price on the previous day was $56.01 + 0.89 = $56.90.

(e) What was the percent decrease in the value of the stock from two days ago until yesterday?
The percent decrease is calculated as follows:

$$\frac{\text{new value} - \text{original value}}{\text{original value}} \times 100 = \frac{\text{net change}}{\text{price before the change}} \times 100$$

$$= \frac{-0.89}{56.90} \times 100 = -1.56\%$$

The use of computer spreadsheets is becoming more popular in today's society. People who own shares of stock, for example, can design a spreadsheet program to calculate the value of their portfolios. The mathematical models involved are fairly simple. Once a formula is programmed into the computer, the values of the variables can be changed easily, and the recalculation of the portfolio value is quickly completed.

▪ Table 4-12   Stock Portfolio

A	B	C	D	E	F
Stock Name	**# of Shares**		**Price Per Share**		**Current Value**
LU	150		2.84		$ 426.00
WEN	250		44.88		$11,220.00
JNJ	120		66.44		$ 7972.80
				Total	$19,618.80

In Table 4-12, mathematical models are used to calculate the values in cells F2, F3, F4, and F5. Formats will differ according to the specific spreadsheet program, but the models will use the following relationships:

$$F2 = B2 * D2 \qquad F3 = B3 * D3$$

$$F4 = B4 * D4 \qquad F5 = SUM(F2..F4)$$

As the daily price of each stock fluctuates, the price can be updated and the values in column F will automatically be recalculated using the same formulas or mathematical models that were previously programmed into the spreadsheet.

Practice Set 4-8

1. An investor purchases 1500 shares of Exxon-Mobile stock at $57.15 per share.
   (a) Find the cost of the stock.
   (b) If the broker charges 2% of the cost of the stock, find his commission on this purchase.

2. An investor purchases 500 shares of McDonald's stock at $30.51 per share.
   (a) Find the cost of the stock.
   (b) If the broker charges 2.5% of the cost of the stock, find his commission on this purchase.

3. An investor purchases 50 shares of Intel stock at $27.33 per share.
   (a) Find the cost of the stock.
   (b) If the broker charges 1.5% of the cost of the stock plus 10¢ per share, find his commission on this purchase.

4. An investor purchases 75 shares of Reebok stock at $41.64 per share.
   (a) Find the cost of the stock.
   (b) If the broker charges 1.75% of the cost of the stock plus 12.5¢ per share, find his commission on this purchase.

5. An investor purchases 1100 shares of eBay stock at $37.80 per share.
   (a) Find the cost of the stock.
   (b) If the broker charges 2.1% of the cost of the stock, find his commission on this purchase.

6. An investor purchases 700 shares of Microsoft stock at $25.43 per share.
   (a) Find the cost of the stock.
   (b) If the broker charges 2.5% of the cost of the stock, find his commission on this purchase.

7. An investor purchases 40 shares of Honda stock at $24.74 per share.
   (a) Find the cost of the stock.
   (b) If the broker charges 2.5% of the cost of the stock plus 12.5¢ per share, find his commission on this purchase.

8. An investor purchases 85 shares of Nike stock at $83.75 per share.
   (a) Find the cost of the stock.
   (b) If the broker charges 2.75% of the cost of the stock plus 7.5¢ per share, find his commission on this purchase.

9.

NAME	DIV	VOL	LAST	NET CHG.
FordM	0.40	178606	29.90	−0.37

(a) If you owned 500 shares of Ford stock last year, what annual dividend did you receive?

(b) How many shares of Ford stock were traded yesterday?

(c) What was the price at which Ford stock closed yesterday?

(d) What was the price at which Ford stock closed the day before yesterday?

(e) What was the percent decrease in the value of the stock from two days ago until yesterday?

10.

NAME	DIV	VOL	LAST	NET CHG.
GeneralElectric	0.84	120468	36.70	−0.20

(a) If you owned 2000 shares of General Electric stock last year, what annual dividend did you receive?

(b) How many shares of General Electric stock were traded yesterday?

(c) What was the price at which General Electric stock closed yesterday?

(d) What was the price at which General Electric stock closed the day before yesterday?

(e) What was the percent decrease in the value of the stock from two days ago until yesterday?

11.

NAME	DIV	VOL	LAST	NET CHG.
HewlettPackard	0.32	68540	22.72	+0.04

(a) If you owned 50 shares of Hewlett Packard stock last year, what annual dividend did you receive?

(b) How many shares of Hewlett Packard stock were traded yesterday?

(c) What was the price at which Hewlett Packard stock closed yesterday?

(d) What was the price at which Hewlett Packard stock closed the day before yesterday?

(e) What was the percent increase in the value of the stock from two days ago until yesterday?

12.

NAME	DIV	VOL	LAST	NET CHG.
Sprint	0.50	110227	24.20	+0.12

(a) If you owned 750 shares of Sprint stock last year, what annual dividend did you receive?

(b) How many shares of Sprint stock were traded yesterday?

(c) What was the price at which Sprint stock closed yesterday?

(d) What was the price at which Sprint stock closed the day before yesterday?

(e) What was the percent increase in the value of the stock from two days ago until yesterday?

13. Maria plans to invest $2155 in a mutual fund. James Large Cap Fund is currently selling for $8.62 per share. How many shares can she buy at this price?

14. Juan inherited $9280 from his grandmother and is planning to invest in a mutual fund called John Hancock Classic Value Fund. The current price per share of this fund is $23.20. How many shares of this fund can he purchase?

15. Georgio is saving for his son's college education by investing in mutual funds. He sells some land for $10,150 and plans to invest it in Texas Value Capital Funds. The current price of this fund is $29.00 per share. How many shares can he purchase?

16. Joseph is planning to buy shares in a mutual fund that invests in companies in China. He has $10,260 to invest, and his broker recommends Templeton China World A Fund, which is currently selling for $20.52 per share. How many shares of this fund can he buy?

17. What is a bond? Describe the difference between a bond and a stock.

18. What is a mutual fund? What advantage is there to investing in a mutual fund?

19. If you are a financial advisor, you assist your clients in making decisions about the amount of money they invest in each kind of investment — savings, stocks, bonds, and mutual funds. If you were advising a 25-year-old client who is interested in saving for retirement in 30 years, what advice would you give if he plans to invest at least some money in each type of account?

20. As a financial advisor, what investments would you recommend to a 50-year-old client who plans to retire at age 65? Why?

Chapter Summary

Key Terms, Properties, and Formulas

adjustable-rate mortgage (ARM)
amortization table
annual percentage rate (APR)
average daily balance method
Banker's Rule
bonds
closed-end credit
closing costs

commission
compound interest
depreciation
dividends
fixed-rate mortgage
installment buying
lease
markup
maturity value

mortgage
mutual funds
open-end credit
ordinary interest
shareholders
simple interest
stocks
unpaid balance method
variable-rate mortgage

Formulas to Remember

Simple Interest:

$$I = Prt$$

Maturity Value:

$$M = P + I$$

Compound Interest Formulas

Quarterly:
$$M = P\left(1 + \frac{r}{4}\right)^{4t}$$

Monthly:
$$M = P\left(1 + \frac{r}{12}\right)^{12t}$$

Daily:
$$M = P\left(1 + \frac{r}{365}\right)^{365t}$$

where r = annual rate and t = number of years.

Fixed-Rate Mortgage Monthly Payment Formula

$$P = A\left[\frac{\frac{r}{12}\left(1 + \frac{r}{12}\right)^{12t}}{\left(1 + \frac{r}{12}\right)^{12t} - 1}\right]$$

where P = monthly payment, A = amount borrowed, r = annual rate, and t = number of years

Chapter Review Problems

1. The tax rate in Wake County is 7%. The county rate is 2.5% and the state rate is 4.5%. If Qwik-E-Mart sells $12,548 worth of merchandise this weekend, how much sales tax will the owner owe to the county and how much will be owe to the state?

2. TJ Sports had gross receipts of $4285.75 on Tuesday. This total included an 8.5% sales tax. What were the receipts from the merchandise (without tax) sold on Tuesday?

3. The local sales tax on food is 5% and the sales tax on other items is 6%. If Marie purchases $12.80 worth of food items and $26.50 worth of nonfood items at X Mart, what amount of sales tax will she be charged?

4. John gave a barber $15 for a service that costs $12.50. What is the tip rate?

5. You are depreciating a $25,000 van over 10 years. At the end of 10 years, the salvage value of the van is expected to be $1500. How much does the van depreciate each year?

6. The Jon-Jon Company makes small fishing boats. Each boat costs $125 to produce. The fixed costs of production are $1250 per month. These boats sell for $275 each. If the company produces 75 boats this month, how much net profit will be earned?

7. The Ace Furniture Store uses a 200% markup on all furniture. If a sofa costs them $475, how much will the retail price be?

8. Julian has the choice of two salary plans as a salesman for TurboVac Company. He can earn his salary by taking a straight 25% commission on his monthly sales, or he can earn a fixed amount of $1000 per month and 5% of total monthly sales. If he sells $5000 in merchandise in July, which plan would yield the higher paycheck?

9. What is the commission rate for an employee who earned $812.50 straight commission on sales of $12,500?

10. The weekly salary of an employee is $400 plus a 6.5% commission on the employee's sales over $1200. Find the employee's gross pay for a week when the sales amounted to $6000.

11. Use the income tax table in Section 4-2 to write a model that can be used to calculate the amount of tax owed by a person who is married filing jointly if his income is between $21,250 and $100,000.

12. The Meltons had a net taxable income of $22,500 this year. How much income tax do they owe if they file jointly?

13. The Consumer Credit Counseling Service recommends that your credit obligations (not including your house payment) should not exceed 15% of your take-home pay. If Caitlyn's take-home pay is $2386, what is the maximum monthly credit obligation that she should have?

14. An amount of $5000 was deposited in a savings account paying simple interest. After 6 months, the account had earned $162.50 in interest. What is the annual interest rate on this account?

15. You borrow $15,000 on a 2-year note. The interest rate is 13% simple interest. What is the maturity value of the note? If monthly payments are made, how much will each payment be?

16. Find the interest on a $1000 bond paying 6% simple interest for 6 years.

17. James buys an $8000 certificate of deposit. It pays 5.8% compounded quarterly. If it matures after 2 years, what will the value of the investment be?

18. How much interest will be earned at the end of 5 years on a deposit of $2500 in an account paying 5% interest compounded monthly?

19. A person invests $10,000 at 8% for 20 years compounded continuously. How much will be in the account at the end of 20 years?

20. Find the finance charge for this month on an open-end charge account using the unpaid balance method of calculating interest if the unpaid

balance is $3150.75 and the annual interest rate is 21.6%.

21. Find the average daily balance for the following credit card account. Assume one month between billing dates and find the finance charge using an 18% annual rate and the average daily balance method.

June 1: Billing date with a balance of $1415.90
June 15: Payment $ 125.00
June 23: Birthday present $ 21.95

22. Marisa bought a new surround-sound stereo system for $2350. She paid $500 down and financed the balance for 36 months at 8%. Calculate the amount of her monthly payment. (Use the APR table found in Section 4-4.)

23. Michael plans to offer 5% over dealer cost on a Honda that has a sticker price of $32,480 and a dealer cost of $26,998. Calculate the amount of his offer.

24. Determine the amount of interest owed and the monthly payment if Pietro purchases a car for $27,885 at 0.9% add-on rate for 5 years.

25. A newspaper advertisement offers a $6500 used car for nothing down and 36 easy monthly payments of $196.80. What is the total amount paid for the car, and what is the total finance charge? Calculate the simple interest rate charged.

26. Anna plans to lease a 2005 Mini Cooper 2-door coupe. The sales price of the car is $25,000. The lease agreement states the following:

Due at signing: $395.59   Mileage allowance: 15,000/year
Monthly payment: $395.59   Excess mileage fee: $0.15/mile
48 months   Acquisition fee: $849

If Anna pays the acquisition fee, the amount due at signing, and the 48 monthly payments, how much has she paid to lease this car?

27. If Anna drives 62,148 miles before she turns in the car, how much extra cost will she incur?

28. If Anna purchases the Mini Cooper for $25,000 at a 3.6% add-on rate for 5 years, how much will her monthly payments be?

29. Determine the maximum monthly payment you could afford for a house if your gross monthly income is $4988 and your current monthly payments are $500.30. Use the formula discussed in Section 4-6.

30. The Dalton family is purchasing a $145,000 house. They plan to make a 20% down payment. The credit union will finance the balance for 30 years at a 6.25% fixed rate. Calculate the amount of their monthly payments.

31. Determine the monthly payment for this loan by using Table 4-6 (amortization table).

Cost of house: $148,500   Interest rate: 5.5%
Term: 30 years

32. Kristen Robinson is 16 years old and drives a Honda Accord, which is a Model L. The car is in Age Group 2. She drives the car for pleasure. Her parents own the car. Determine her annual premium for comprehensive and $500-deductible collision coverage.

33. Determine the annual premium for 50/100/100 liability insurance for a 45-year-old male who drives 25 miles to work and lives in Territory 3.

34. Janet's car was stolen while parked outside her home. The car had a market value of $20,000. Janet carries comprehensive and $500-deductible collision insurance. How much indemnity will the insurance company pay?

35. John bought 150 shares of Apple Computer stock and paid $36.54 per share. He also had to pay a $10.99 online broker fee to make the purchase. What was the total cost to him for this transaction?

36. An investor purchases 450 shares of Texas Instruments stock at $27.28 per share.
   (a) Find the cost of the stock.
   (b) If the broker charges 2.5% of the cost of the stock, find her commission on this purchase.

37. Travis plans to invest $87,250 in a mutual fund. Century Shares Trust is currently selling for $34.90 per share. How many shares can he buy at this price?

Chapter Test

1. Jerry purchases a new car for $24,500. If the sales tax on this purchase is 3.5%, how much sales tax will the dealer add to his cost?

2. A retailer pays $12.40 for a coffee maker. He uses a 125% markup on small appliances. Find the retail price of this coffee maker.

3. A business buys an $18,000 car for its courier to use for delivering correspondence between branch offices. If the business office plans to depreciate the car using the straight-line method over a 10-year period, find the yearly depreciation allowance if the residual value of the car is $2500.

4. BMA Corporation manufactures beanies at a cost of $0.82 each. Their fixed costs per month are $3575. Each beanie sells for $2.20. If BMA produces 14,500 beanies this month, calculate their net profit.

5. Mary makes a 12% commission on her weekly sales at Stereo Extravaganza. She also receives a base pay of $200 per week. If she sells $1275 worth of stereo equipment this week, what will her gross pay be?

6. One proposal in Congress has been to change the tax laws and have a "flat tax rate." This would require all citizens to pay the same percent of their gross pay to the federal government. If Jose's gross income this year is $55,250 and the flat tax rate is 18%, how much income tax would Jose owe the government?

7. Find the amount of money that you will have in the bank at the end of 15 years if you deposit $2500 into an account that pays 4.5% interest compounded quarterly.

8. Jeff earned $250 on his $5000 certificate of deposit last year. What simple interest rate did the bank pay him?

9. Jeremy deposits $7500 in a savings account that pays 5.5% compounded continuously. How much will be in this account in 6 years?

10. Find the finance charge for this month on an open-end charge account using the unpaid balance method of calculating interest if the unpaid balance is $5250.05 and the annual interest rate is 15%.

11. Find the average daily balance for the following credit card account. Assume one month between billing dates, and find the finance charge using an 18% annual rate and the average daily balance method.

July 1: Billing date with a balance of	$115.90
July 15: Payment	$ 25.00
July 20: Clothes purchase	$225.55

12. Robin bought a new washing machine for $1385. She paid $100 down and financed the balance for 24 months at 9%. Calculate the amount of her monthly payment. (Use the APR table.)

13. Determine the amount of interest owed and the monthly payment if Martin purchases a Lexus for $57,885 with no down payment at 0.9% add-on rate for 6 years.

14. Darrius plans to lease a 2005 Jeep Grand Cherokee 4WD. The sales price of the car is $36,200. The lease agreement states the following:

Due at signing: $571	Mileage allowance: 15,000/year
Monthly payment: $571	Excess mileage fee: $0.17/mile
54 months	Acquisition fee: $795

    If Darrius pays the acquisition fee, the amount due at signing, and the 54 monthly payments, how much has he paid to lease this car?

15. If Darrius purchases the Jeep for $36,200, pays $600 down, and finances it at a 1.9% add-on rate for 6 years, how much will his monthly payment be?

16. The Rasmussen family is purchasing a $375,000 house. They plan to make a 25% down payment. The credit union will finance the balance for 30 years at a 5.5% fixed rate. Calculate the amount of their monthly payments using the amortization table.

17. Determine the annual liability insurance premium for 50/100/50 for a 16-year-old female who drives 4 miles one way to work in Territory 2.

18. Janet's car was stolen while parked outside her home. The car had a market value of $20,000. Janet carries comprehensive and $500-deductible

collision insurance. How much out-of-pocket expense will Janet incur to replace the car, assuming that she can buy one for $20,000?

19. Larry purchased 175 shares of stock A at a price of $49.50 and 250 shares of stock B at $29.88. He also paid $9.99 in online broker's fees for each of the two purchases. What was the total cost of his purchases?

20. An investor purchases 50 shares of Wendy's stock at $44.50 per share.
    (a) Find the cost of the stock.
    (b) If the broker charges 1.5% of the cost of the stock plus $0.15 per share, find his commission on this purchase.

Suggested Laboratory Exercises

LAB EXERCISE 1

Saving for College Expenses

On Polly's 6th birthday her parents bought a $10,000 CD that pays at the rate, r, of 4% *compounded annually*. Use the simple interest formula to fill in the following table or set up a spreadsheet to calculate the values for you.

■ **Table 4-13   Lab Exercise 1**

Polly's Age	Principal (P)	Interest Earned (I)	Total of Account ($P + I$)
7	$10,000.00	$400.00	$10,400.00
8	$10,400.00		
9			
10			
⋮ 18			

Now, use a calculator and the following formula to calculate the total value of Polly's CD on her 11th birthday. In this formula, A = the total value, P = the original principal at age 6, r = the interest rate, and t = the number of years that have elapsed since Polly's 6th birthday.

$$A = P(1 + r)^t$$

Now fill in the last line of the chart with Polly's 18th birthday and calculate the total value of her CD at that time.

LAB EXERCISE 2

Depreciation

Equipment purchased for use by business will decrease in value due to use and age as time goes by. The IRS recognizes this fact by allowing businesses to decrease the value of assets on their books for tax purposes. This is cleverly called *depreciation*.

Suppose that you own a company and you purchase a new widget maker for $50,000. This machine will depreciate in value so that after 5 years it will have a book value of $10,000. This depreciation is linear, that is, straight-line.

1. Write an equation for the book value, V, as a function of the number of years of use, x.
2. What is the slope of this line and what does it mean here?
3. What would the book value be after 4 years?
4. Set up a spreadsheet to do all of the calculations for you for all 5 years.

LAB EXERCISE 3   ## Phone 'Em Up

One of the many long-distance phone companies (call this company X) charges a base fee of $2.75 per month plus 10 cents per minute of use. A new company (call this company Y) decides to charge 12 cents per minute of use and no base fee.

1. Write an equation to model the charges of company X.
2. Write an equation to model the charges of company Y.
3. Write an inequality for numbers of minutes of use where the charges of company X will be less than the charges of company Y.
4. What is the minimum number of minutes per month that you would have to talk long-distance so that company X's charges would be less than those of company Y?

LAB EXERCISE 4   ## Purchasing Furniture

1. Using the given diagram of the sample apartment, you must "purchase" furniture for the living/dining room and for the master bedroom. Use the Internet site, www.furniturefind.com to shop for the furnishings you wish to purchase. List the items you are buying and their costs below. You must purchase enough furniture to comfortably live, including a dining table and chairs, living room furniture, and a bedroom set. Don't forget to buy a mattress.

   Draw the furniture in the room where you plan to place it.

Item Description	Cost
Total cost of furnishings	

2. For the current promotion, you can purchase the furniture interest-free under the following condition:

   Monthly payments are based on
   20% down payment and 24 monthly payments.

   Based on this plan, calculate the amount of your down payment: _____
   Calculate the amount of each monthly payment: _____

3. The fine print!

Until January 2009, interest will accrue at 23.4%.
If the balance is paid in full by end of deferral period,
all finance charges will be credited, resulting in no interest to you.

If you do not pay off this loan by the end of December 2008, then you will pay interest on the entire balance due at the time of purchase. Using the simple interest formula and the 24 months of financing available, how much interest would you pay if you weren't able to pay off the total balance due by the end of 2008? _____

4. Use the Annual Percentage Rate (APR) Table (Table 4-5) to answer these questions.
  (a) You plan to pay 10% down on your purchase. How much do you pay at the time of purchase? _____ How much is left to finance? _____
  (b) If you finance the balance due at 7.5% for 36 months, how much interest will you owe? _____
  (c) What will your monthly payment be? _____
5. Using the installment loan table, calculate the monthly payments for your purchase if you decide to finance the purchase for 4 years at 8.5% APR.

  Total interest due _____
  Monthly payment _____

LAB EXERCISE 5   ## Creating a Stock Portfolio

In Section 4-8 of this chapter, there was a brief discussion of the use of spreadsheets for tracking the value of a stock portfolio. Divide the class into groups of 4 and have each group choose 8 stocks for a portfolio. Each group should research the companies chosen and write a brief paragraph for each describing the type of company chosen, the products it markets or produces, the location of the headquarters, and other interesting facts about the company. Each group should then "invest" $1000 in each company by "purchasing" the maximum number of whole shares possible with $1000. Students should use the Internet or newspaper to get the current per share cost of the chosen stocks. Using a spreadsheet, each group should first record the data for the stock market purchases that are made. Then each group should follow the closing prices of their stocks each day for two weeks. The ups and downs of these closing prices should be tracked and recorded on graph paper. At the end of two weeks, each group should calculate its portfolio's percent gain or loss. Which group made the most money?

Systems of Equations

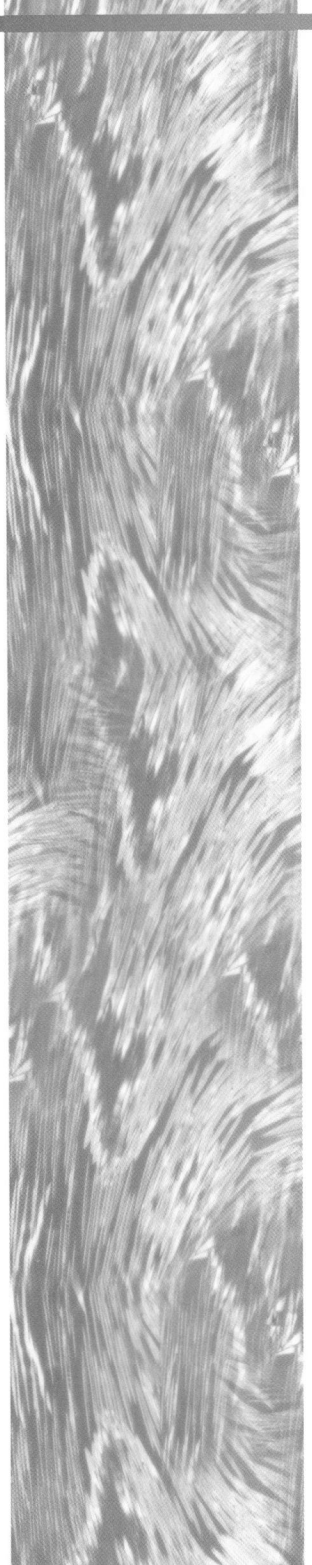

IN THIS CHAPTER

"Mathematicians do not deal in objects, but in relations between objects; thus, they are free to replace some objects by others so long as the relations remain unchanged." – Poincaré

Some problems or situations involve the interaction of two or more variables. Business profit, for example, is based on the cost of production and the income from selling a product. A break-even point can be determined using a system of equations so the business will be sure to make a profit. Several methods for solving systems of equations such as these will be explored in this chapter.

Section 5-1   SOLVING SYSTEMS BY GRAPHING

Many problems involve more than one unknown quantity and involve using a **system of equations**. In these problems, there are usually two conditions that must be met. For example, you might be asked to make a specific volume of a solution having a certain concentration. The two requirements that must be satisfied are the volume of the solution and the strength of the solution. It is often easier to solve a problem like this with two equations that relate the unknown quantities. Then we look for the one solution that satisfies both sets of requirements — the one solution that satisfies both equations algebraically. This may be done by graphing, using algebraic techniques, or using a process with determinants called Cramer's rule. In this section, we will look at the graphing method used to solve systems.

A system of linear equations consists of two equations containing two related variables. For example, the following system involves the related variables x and y.

$$y = 2x - 8$$
$$3x + 4y = 12$$

Many ordered pairs (x, y) can be found that will satisfy the first equation. There are many ordered pairs that will satisfy the second equation as well. The **solution** of the system, however, is the single ordered pair that will satisfy *both* of the equations. The single ordered pair that will satisfy the system shown in the previous equations is $(4, 0)$. In this section, we will learn to find this solution graphically.

In Chapter 2, you learned to graph a linear equation using both a table of ordered-pair solutions and the slope-intercept form ($y = mx + b$) of the equation. We can use either of these techniques to graph each of the equations in the system. Both lines are graphed on the same set of axes. The point of intersection of the two lines is the solution of the system.

EXAMPLE 1   Solving a System by Graphing

Find the solution of the following system of equations graphically.

$$x + 3y = 7$$
$$y = 3x - 1$$

Use a table for each equation to find at least three points for each line. Although you may choose any values for x or y, we will let $x = 0$, $y = 0$, and $x = 1$. (See Table 5-1.)

Line 1: $x + 3y = 7$.

$$(0) + 3y = 7 \qquad x + 3(0) = 7$$
$$3y = 7 \qquad\qquad x = 7$$
$$y = 2\frac{1}{3}$$
$$1 + 3y = 7$$
$$3y = 7 - 1$$
$$3y = 6$$
$$y = 2$$

See Table 5-2.

■ **TABLE 5-1**

Example 1

x	y
0	
	0
1	

■ **TABLE 5-2**

Example 1, Line 1

x	y
0	$2\frac{1}{3}$
7	0
1	2

Now graph these three points on the grid to show the line representing the equation $x + 3y = 7$.

Line 2: $y = 3x - 1$.

$$y = 3(0) - 1 \qquad 0 = 3x - 1$$
$$y = -1 \qquad\qquad 1 = 3x$$
$$\frac{1}{3} = x$$
$$y = 3(1) - 1$$
$$y = 3 - 1 = 2$$

See Table 5-3.

Graph these three points representing the line $y = 3x - 1$ on the same grid and locate the point of intersection of the two lines. (See Figure 5-1.)

The two lines intersect at the point $(1, 2)$, so this is the solution of this system of equations.

TABLE 5-3

Example 1, Line 2

x	y
0	-1
$\dfrac{1}{3}$	0
1	2

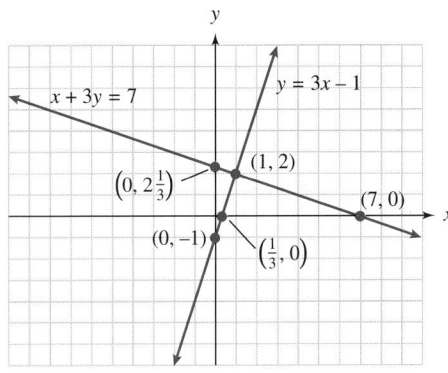

Figure 5-1
Example 1.

When the solution to a linear system has been found, it should be checked in the original equations. It should satisfy both equations.

EXAMPLE 2   Checking a Solution

Show that the ordered pair $(1, 2)$ is the correct solution of the system in Example 1:

$$x + 3y = 7$$
$$y = 3x - 1$$

(a) Substitute $(1, 2)$ into the first equation.

$$x + 3y = 7$$
$$1 + 3(2) = 7$$
$$1 + 6 = 7$$
$$7 = 7 \quad \text{(true)}$$

(b) Substitute $(1, 2)$ into the second equation.

$$y = 3x - 1$$
$$2 = 3(1) - 1$$
$$2 = 3 - 1$$
$$2 = 2 \quad \text{(true)}$$

Because the ordered pair $(1, 2)$ checks in both equations, it is the solution of this system of equations.

When a system of two linear equations is graphed, three different outcomes are possible. The two lines may intersect in one point. This system is said to be **consistent**. The two lines may be parallel. In this case, there is no solution because the two lines do not intersect. These lines are said to be **inconsistent**. The third possible outcome results in two lines that coincide. In this case, all ordered pairs that satisfy the first equation also satisfy the second equation. Thus, infinitely many solutions are possible. These lines are said to be **dependent**. See Figure 5-2.

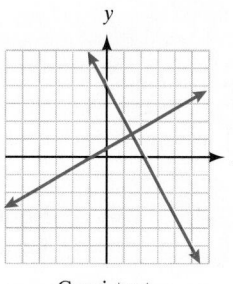
Consistent,
one solution (x, y)

Inconsistent,
no solution

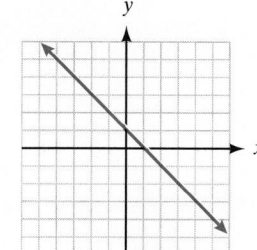
Dependent,
infinite number of solutions

Figure 5-2
Solutions of systems of equations.

Notice that when a system consists of parallel lines or lines that coincide, the directions of the two lines, and therefore the slopes of the two equations, are identical. On the other hand, if the lines intersect in one point, their directions must be different, so their slopes will also be different. If you graph the system using the slope-intercept form of the equation ($y = mx + b$), it is easy to determine the slope of each line. The slope numbers can give you important information about the solution of a system. Look at the following example.

EXAMPLE 3   **Graphing a System with No Solution**

Solve the following system graphically.

$$2x + 4y = 8$$
$$x + 2y = -2$$

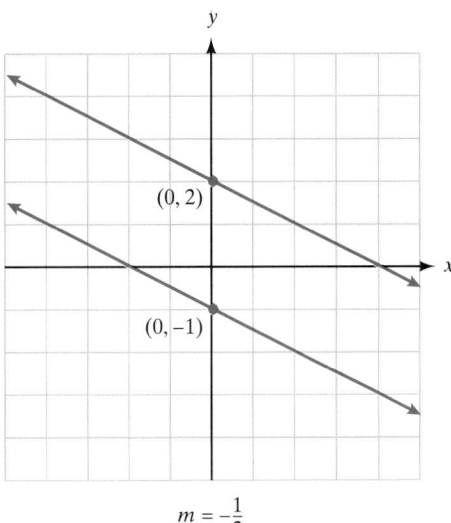

$m = -\dfrac{1}{2}$

Figure 5-3
Example 3.

(a) Put both equations into $y = mx + b$ form.

$$2x + 4y = 8$$

$$4y = -2x + 8 \qquad \text{(add } -2x \text{ to both sides)}$$

$$y = -\frac{1}{2}x + 2 \qquad \text{(divide by 4)}$$

In this case, the slope $= -\frac{1}{2}$ and the y-intercept $= 2$.

$$x + 2y = -2$$

$$2y = -x - 2 \qquad \text{(add } -x \text{ to both sides)}$$

$$y = -\frac{1}{2}x - 1 \qquad \text{(divide by 2)}$$

In this case, the slope $= -\frac{1}{2}$ and the y-intercept $= -1$.

(b) Because both slopes are equal to $-\frac{1}{2}$, we know that the directions of the lines will be the same. Because the y-intercepts are different, the lines are not identical but must be parallel. (See Figure 5-3.)

Because the lines are parallel, this system is inconsistent, and the answer is "no solution."

EXAMPLE 4   **Solving a System That Is Dependent**

Solve the following system graphically.

$$3x - 2y = 8$$

$$6x - 4y = 16$$

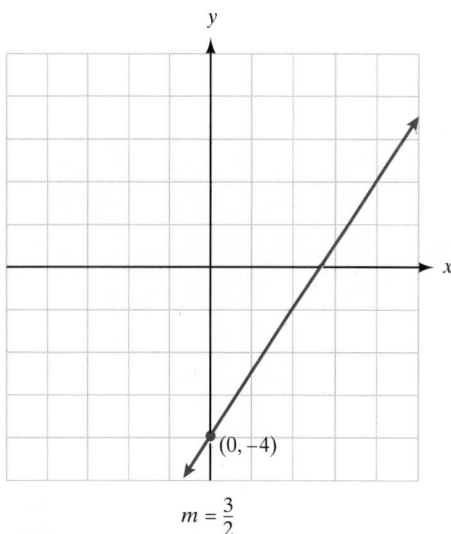

$(0, -4)$

$m = \dfrac{3}{2}$

Figure 5-4
Example 4.

(a) Put both equations into $y = mx + b$ form.

$$3x - 2y = 8$$

$$-2y = -3x + 8 \qquad \text{(add } -3x \text{ to both sides)}$$

$$y = \frac{3}{2}x - 4 \qquad \text{(divide by } -2)$$

In this case, the slope $= \frac{3}{2}$ and the y-intercept $= -4$.

$$6x - 4y = 16$$

$$-4y = -6x + 16 \qquad \text{(add } -6x \text{ to both sides)}$$

$$y = \frac{3}{2}x - 4 \qquad \text{(divide by } -4)$$

In this case, the slope $= \frac{3}{2}$ and the y-intercept $= -4$.

(b) Because the slopes and the y-intercepts are the same, the lines are identical. Therefore, any solution of the first equation also satisfies the second equation, and there are infinitely many solutions that will satisfy this system. (See Figure 5-4.)

A TI-83 Plus graphing calculator may be used to find the solution of a system of equations graphically. Solve each equation for y and enter the equations using the $\boxed{Y=}$ key. When you press $\boxed{\text{GRAPH}}$, both lines will be displayed. Use the $\boxed{\text{TRACE}}$ feature to move the cursor as close as possible to the point of intersection. The coordinates will be displayed at the bottom of the screen. They may not be exactly correct because the pixels on the screen cause slightly differing answers. There is a $\boxed{\text{CALCULATE}}$ function located above the $\boxed{\text{TRACE}}$ button; you can use it to calculate the exact point of intersection.

◼ EXAMPLE 5   **Solving a System Using a Graphing Calculator**

Solve the following system using a graphing calculator.

$$4x + 3y = 24$$

$$2x - y = 2$$

(a) Solve each equation for y.

$$4x + 3y = 24 \qquad\qquad 2x - y = 2$$

$$3y = -4x + 24 \qquad\quad -y = -2x + 2$$

$$y = -\frac{4}{3}x + 8 \qquad\qquad y = 2x - 2$$

(b) Enter the equation using the $\boxed{\text{Y=}}$ function as

$$Y_1 = \left(-\frac{4}{3}\right)x + 8$$

$$Y_2 = 2x - 2$$

(c) Use the $\boxed{\text{GRAPH}}$ button to display the lines. Use the $\boxed{\text{TRACE}}$ function to move the cursor to the point of intersection. Use the $\boxed{\text{CALCULATE}}$ feature to verify this point. (See Figure 5-5.)

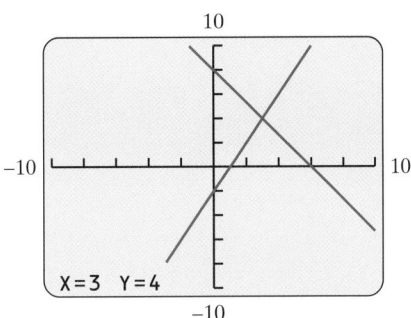

Figure 5-5
Example 5.

Practice Set 5-1

Which ordered pair is a solution of the system of equations?

1. $3x + 4y = 1$ 　　$(7, 2)$ 　　$(3, -2)$

　　$x - y = 5$

2. $3x - 7y = -22$ 　　$(2, 4)$ 　　$(1, 3)$

　　$x - y = -2$

3. $x - 4y = 1$ 　　$(3, 1)$ 　　$(-3, -1)$

　　$5x - 3y = -12$

4. $2x - 3y = 6$ $(0, 3)$ $(3, 0)$

  $4x + 3y = 12$

5. $2x + y = 2$ $\left(1, \dfrac{1}{2}\right)$ $\left(\dfrac{1}{2}, 1\right)$

  $6x - 4y = -1$

6. $4x + 9y = 12$ $\left(-\dfrac{3}{2}, \dfrac{2}{3}\right)$ $\left(\dfrac{3}{2}, \dfrac{2}{3}\right)$

  $2x - 3y = 1$

Solve the following systems graphically. Check your solution.

7. $x + y = 3$

  $x - y = -1$

8. $x + 3y = 2$

  $2y = x + 3$

9. $2x - y = 4$

  $x + 2y = 2$

10. $3x - 7 = y$

  $y = 3x + 5$

11. $x = 4$

  $x + y = 5$

12. $4y - 3x = 8$

  $y = 5$

13. $2x - y = -1$

  $2x + y = 1$

14. $3x + 2y = 20$

  $x + y = 8$

15. $\dfrac{1}{3}x + 2y = 9$

  $x + 6y = 27$

16. $x + y = 9$

  $6x - 5y = 10$

17. $x - 10 = 5y$

  $x + 10 = 5y$

18. $x = 2$

  $y = 3$

19. $x + 2y = -10$

  $\dfrac{1}{2}x - 3 = y$

20. $3x = 2y + 5$

  $6x - 4y = 10$

21. $x - 4y = 1$

  $5x - 3y = -12$

22. $x + y = 13$

  $x - y = 3$

23. $x + y = 4$

  $3x + 3y = 12$

24. $3x - 2y = 6$

  $15x - 10y = -2$

25. $4x - 9y = 6$

  $\dfrac{1}{3}x - \dfrac{3}{4}y = 1$

Solve each system using a graphing calculator.

26. $y = \dfrac{3}{4}x + 2$

  $y = x + 1$

27. $2x + y = 4$

  $x - y = 2$

28. $2x - 5y = 10$

  $6x - 15y = 75$

29. $3x + 2y = 4$

  $-x + 3y = -5$

30. $x + 2y = -1$

  $2x - 3y = 12$

31. $2x - 3y = 1$

  $-6x + 9y = -3$

32. $x + y = -2$

  $-3x - 3y = 6$

Section 5-2   **SOLVING SYSTEMS ALGEBRAICALLY**

Solving a system of equations graphically is useful, but it is less accurate than solving a system algebraically. When the solution of a system is fractional, for example, it is difficult to give a precise solution from a graph.

  The goal of solving systems algebraically is to reduce the system that has two equations in two variables to a single equation that has only one variable. This can be done using either of two methods: **substitution** or **linear combination**. In the substitution method, we substitute an expression for one variable to eliminate that variable, resulting in an equation containing only one unknown. In the linear combination method, the two equations are added together (based on the addition property of equality) in such a way that one of the two variables is eliminated from the new equation. Look at the following examples.

■ EXAMPLE 6   **Substitution Method**

Solve:

$$4x - 3y = 16$$

$$y = 7x + 6$$

(a) In the second equation, y is defined to be $7x + 6$. Using substitution, we will replace the y in the first equation with the expression $7x + 6$ and then solve for x.

$$4x - 3y = 16$$

$$4x - 3(\mathbf{7x + 6}) = 16 \qquad \text{(substitute)}$$

$$4x - 21x - 18 = 16 \qquad \text{(distributive property)}$$

$$-17x - 18 = 16 \qquad \text{(combine like terms)}$$

$$-17x = 34 \qquad \text{(add 18 to both sides)}$$

$$x = -2 \qquad \text{(divide by } -17)$$

(b) Now that we have solved for the value of x, we can easily calculate the value of y using the second equation.

$$y = 7x + 6$$

$$y = 7(-2) + 6 \qquad \text{(substitute } -2 \text{ for } x)$$

$$y = -8 \qquad \text{(simplify)}$$

Therefore, the solution of this system is the ordered pair $(-2, -8)$.

Check this solution by substituting these values into both of the original equations.

Rule

The Substitution Method

1. Solve one of the equations for one variable in terms of the other. Choose the variable with a coefficient of 1 to solve for, if possible.
2. Substitute the expression obtained in step 1 into the other equation and solve the resulting one-variable equation.
3. Solve for the remaining variable by substituting the value you obtained in step 2 into either of the original equations.
4. Check your answer to be sure that it satisfies both equations.

In the previous example, we did not have to do step 1 of this method because one of the equations was already in the correct form for substitution. Let us look at a problem where the first step must be done before substituting.

EXAMPLE 7   **Substitution Method**

Solve the system:

$$2x + 6y = 16$$

$$6x + 5y = 9$$

We must first solve one of the equations for one variable in terms of the other. It appears to be easiest to solve for x in the first equation because all terms are divisible by 2.

$$2x + 6y = 16$$

$$2x = -6y + 16 \quad \text{(subtract } 6y \text{ from both sides)}$$

$$x = -3y + 8 \quad \text{(divide by 2)}$$

Now we take the expression $-3y + 8$ and substitute it in place of the x variable in the second equation.

$$6x + 5y = 9$$

$$6(-3y + 8) + 5y = 9 \quad \text{(substitute for } x)$$

$$-18y + 48 + 5y = 9 \quad \text{(distributive property)}$$

$$-13y + 48 = 9 \quad \text{(simplify)}$$

$$-13y = -39 \quad \text{(add } -48 \text{ to each side)}$$

$$y = 3 \quad \text{(solve for } y)$$

Now complete the solution by substituting 3 for y in one of the equations and solving for x.

$$x = -3y + 8$$

$$x = -3(3) + 8 \quad \text{(substitute 3 for } y)$$

$$x = -1 \quad \text{(simplify)}$$

The solution of this system is $(-1, 3)$. Check to verify the solution.

The second algebraic method for solving systems is the linear combination method. The key step is to obtain, for one of the variables, coefficients that differ only in sign so that the two equations can be combined or added together to eliminate that variable. This method is illustrated in the following example.

EXAMPLE 8   **Linear Combination Method**

Solve the system:

$$2x + y = 4$$
$$x - y = 2$$

Notice that the y variables have coefficients of -1 and 1. Because these are opposites, if the two equations are added together, the y terms will be eliminated from the new equation.

$$2x + y = 4$$
$$\underline{x - y = 2}$$
$$3x = 6 \quad \text{(add the equations)}$$
$$x = 2 \quad \text{(divide both sides by 3)}$$

Now substitute 2 for x in either equation to solve for the value of y.

$$2x + y = 4$$
$$2(2) + y = 4 \quad \text{(substitute 2 for } x)$$
$$4 + y = 4 \quad \text{(simplify)}$$
$$y = 0 \quad \text{(add } -4 \text{ to both sides)}$$

Therefore, the solution of the system is $(2, 0)$. Check this solution in both equations to verify the results.

Sometimes one or both equations will need to be modified so that the coefficients of one of the variables are opposites. This can be achieved by multiplying either or both of the equations by a constant as shown in the next example.

EXAMPLE 9   **Linear Combination Method**

Solve the system:

$$5x + 2y = 7$$
$$3x - 6y = -3$$

You can obtain coefficients of y that are opposites by multiplying the first equation by 3.

$$5x + 2y = 7 \rightarrow \qquad 15x + 6y = 21 \qquad \text{(multiply by 3)}$$
$$3x - 6y = -3 \rightarrow \qquad \underline{3x - 6y = -3} \qquad \text{(same equation)}$$
$$18x \qquad = 18 \qquad \text{(add equations)}$$
$$x \qquad = 1 \qquad \text{(solve for } x)$$

Now substitute $x = 1$ into either of the two original equations to find the value of y.

$$5x + 2y = 7$$
$$5(1) + 2y = 7 \qquad \text{(substitute 1 for } x)$$
$$5 + 2y = 7 \qquad \text{(simplify)}$$
$$2y = 2 \qquad \text{(add } -5 \text{ to both sides)}$$
$$y = 1 \qquad \text{(divide both sides by 2)}$$

Therefore, the solution of the system is $(1, 1)$. Be sure to check your answer.

Rule

The Linear Combination Method

1. Obtain coefficients of either x or y that are opposites of each other. You may multiply one or both equations by a constant to achieve this goal.
2. Add the two equations together, producing a new equation containing only a single variable. Solve this equation for the value of that variable.
3. Solve for the remaining variable by substituting the value you obtained in step 2 into either of the original equations.
4. Check your answer to be sure that it satisfies both of the original equations.

Remember that a linear system of equations may intersect in one point and therefore have one solution (consistent), may be parallel and have no solution (inconsistent), or may be the same line and have an infinite set of solutions (dependent). It is easy to see these results graphically, but we need to examine how linear systems having no solution and those systems that are dependent behave algebraically.

EXAMPLE 10   Linear Systems with No Solution

Solve the system:

$$2x - 6y = 3$$
$$x - 3y = \frac{4}{3}$$

First, it will be simpler to work with the equations if there are no fractions in the problem. Therefore, we will multiply the second equation by 3 to clear the fractions.

$$3\left(x - 3y = \frac{4}{3} \right)$$

$$3(x) - 3(3y) = 3\left(\frac{4}{3} \right)$$

$$3x - 9y = 4$$

To obtain coefficients of x that are opposites, multiply the first equation by 3 and the second by -2.

$$2x - 6y = 3 \rightarrow \quad 6x - 18y = 9 \qquad \text{(multiply by 3)}$$

$$3x - 9y = 4 \rightarrow \quad \underline{-6x + 18y = -8} \qquad \text{(multiply by } -2\text{)}$$

$$0 = 1 \qquad \text{(add the equations)}$$

Both the x and y variables have been eliminated at the same time. Because $0 = 1$ is a false statement, there is no ordered pair (x, y) that satisfies this system. Therefore, there is no solution for this system of equations. If the system were graphed, the lines would be parallel.

EXAMPLE 11   Linear Systems with an Infinite Number of Solutions

Solve the system:

$$2x = 4y - 8$$

$$x - 2y = -4$$

First, each equation needs to be written in standard form. Then the second equation can be multiplied by -2 to eliminate the x variable.

$$2x = 4y - 8 \rightarrow 2x - 4y = -8 \rightarrow \quad 2x - 4y = -8 \quad \text{(write in correct order)}$$

$$x - 2y = -4 \quad \rightarrow \ x - 2y = -4 \rightarrow \underline{-2x + 4y = 8} \qquad \text{(multiply by } -2\text{)}$$

$$0 = 0 \qquad \text{(add equations)}$$

Both sides of the new equation are eliminated, leaving the identity $0 = 0$. This means that the two equations are identical. Such equations are called **dependent equations** and all solutions of the first equation are also solutions of the second equation. There are **infinitely many solutions** that satisfy both equations in this case. If the two equations were graphed, the same line would result from both equations.

Practice Set 5-2

Solve the following systems using the substitution method.

1. $x = 2y$

$x + y = 18$

2. $x - 2y = 0$

$3x = y$

3. $5x + 3y = 11$

$x = 5y + 5$

4. $3x + 2y = 0$

$x + 2y = 4$

5. $3x - y = 4$

$9x - 5y = -10$

6. $x - 2y = 5$

$6y - 3x = -15$

Solve the following systems using the linear combination method.

7. $2x - 3y = 7$

$4x + 3y = 5$

8. $x + 3y = 2$

$x - 2y = -3$

9. $x + 7y = 12$

$3x - 5y = 10$

10. $5x + 2y = 7$

$3x - 6y = -3$

11. $x = y + 3$

$3y = x + 2$

12. $6x - 5y = 3$

$10y = 5 + 12x$

13. $3x - 2y = 6$

$-6x + 4y = -12$

14. $3x + 3y = 7$

$2x + 5y = 3$

Solve the following systems using either method.

15. $2x - y = 2$

$4x + 3y = 24$

16. $x = y + 1$

$2x - 2y = -5$

17. $y = 2x - 1$

$y = x + 1$

18. $6x + 21y = 132$

$6x - 4y = 32$

19. $5x - 2y = 14$

$6x - 5y = 9$

20. $x - 2y = 7$

$3x + y = \dfrac{7}{2}$

21. $x - y = 8$

$3y = x + 2$

22. $2x - 8y = 4$

$\dfrac{5}{2}x + y = 5$

23. $14x - 6 = -2y$

$7x + y = 3$

24. $8y + 8x = 8$

$y = 2x + 4$

25. $7x + 3y = -8$

$5x - 4y = -61$

26. $3x - 4y = 6$

$5x - 3y = -12$

27. Is $(2, 3)$ a solution of the following system?

$$3x + 5 = y$$
$$2y + x = 8$$

28. Is $\left(-1, \dfrac{2}{5}\right)$ a solution of the following system?

$$x + 5y = 1$$
$$x + y = -\dfrac{2}{5}$$

29. The sum of two numbers is 20 and their difference is 2. Write a system of equations that will model this problem. Then solve the system using any method you choose.

30. The sum of two numbers is 63. Their difference is 19. Write a linear system to model this problem and use it to find the two numbers.

31. The sum of two numbers is 30. If twice one of them is 3 times the other, what are the numbers?

32. The difference between two numbers is 18. Find the two numbers if their sum is 0.

33. One-half the sum of two numbers equals their difference. What are the numbers if their sum is 64?

34. The difference between two numbers is 2. If 3 times the larger plus 5 times the smaller is 94, what are the numbers?

35. Three times one number is 4 times another. If the sum of the two numbers is 46, what are the numbers?

36. Find two numbers whose sum is 15 if one of the numbers subtracted from twice the other is also 15.

Section 5-3   **SOLVING SYSTEMS WITH CRAMER'S RULE**

Another method used to solve linear systems is **Cramer's rule**, named after a Swiss mathematician who lived more than 200 years ago. Cramer's rule involves the use of an array of numbers called a determinant to calculate the values for the solution (x, y) of the system.

A **determinant** is a *square array of numbers* such as

$$\begin{vmatrix} a & b \\ c & d \end{vmatrix}$$

where the array has the same number of rows as columns and is enclosed between two vertical lines. The numbers $a, b, c,$ and d are called **elements**. The value of a determinant is calculated as follows:

Important Equations

Value of a Second-Order Determinant

$$\begin{vmatrix} a & b \\ c & d \end{vmatrix} = ad - bc$$

Look at the following example of this process.

EXAMPLE 12   **Determining the Value of a Determinant**

(a) Evaluate

$$\begin{vmatrix} 2 & 5 \\ 6 & 3 \end{vmatrix}$$

$$\begin{vmatrix} 2 & 5 \\ 6 & 3 \end{vmatrix} = (2)(3) - (5)(6) = 6 - 30 = -24$$

(b) Evaluate

$$\begin{vmatrix} -1 & -3 \\ 5 & 2 \end{vmatrix}$$

$$\begin{vmatrix} -1 & -3 \\ 5 & 2 \end{vmatrix} = (-1)(2) - (-3)(5) = -2 - (-15) = 13$$

We can use determinants to help us solve a system of equations by using the coefficients of the variables and the constants in each equation to form arrays. Cramer's rule can be written as follows:

Rule

Cramer's Rule
Given the system:

$$ax + by = c$$
$$dx + ey = f$$

$$x = \frac{\begin{vmatrix} c & b \\ f & e \end{vmatrix}}{\begin{vmatrix} a & b \\ d & e \end{vmatrix}} \qquad y = \frac{\begin{vmatrix} a & c \\ d & f \end{vmatrix}}{\begin{vmatrix} a & b \\ d & e \end{vmatrix}}$$

To use this rule, the equations must be written in standard form. If the determinant of the numerator is not 0 and the determinant of the denominator is 0, the system is inconsistent (the lines would be parallel). If the determinants of both the numerator and the denominator are 0, the system is dependent (same line). If the determinant of the denominator is a nonzero number, then the lines are consistent and there is a solution (x, y) for the system. The following examples use Cramer's rule to solve the given systems of equations.

EXAMPLE 13   Solving a System Using Determinants

Solve the system:

$$3x + 5y = -1$$
$$2x - 3y = 12$$

(a) Let $a = 3, b = 5, c = -1, d = 2, e = -3$, and $f = 12$.
(b) Substitute values into Cramer's rule:

$$x = \frac{\begin{vmatrix} c & b \\ f & e \end{vmatrix}}{\begin{vmatrix} a & b \\ d & e \end{vmatrix}} = \frac{\begin{vmatrix} -1 & 5 \\ 12 & -3 \end{vmatrix}}{\begin{vmatrix} 3 & 5 \\ 2 & -3 \end{vmatrix}} = \frac{(-1)(-3) - (5)(12)}{(3)(-3) - (5)(2)} = \frac{-57}{-19} = 3$$

$$y = \frac{\begin{vmatrix} a & c \\ d & f \end{vmatrix}}{\begin{vmatrix} a & b \\ d & e \end{vmatrix}} = \frac{\begin{vmatrix} 3 & -1 \\ 2 & 12 \end{vmatrix}}{\begin{vmatrix} 3 & 5 \\ 2 & -3 \end{vmatrix}} = \frac{(3)(12) - (-1)(2)}{(3)(-3) - (5)(2)} = \frac{38}{-19} = -2$$

(c) Therefore, this system is consistent and has a solution $(3, -2)$. Check this solution by substituting it into the original equations as previously discussed.

$3x + 5y = -1$	$2x - 3y = 12$
$3(3) + 5(-2) = -1$	$2(3) - 3(-2) = 12$
$9 + (-10) = -1$	$6 - (-6) = 12$
$-1 = -1$ (Yes)	$12 = 12$ (Yes)

■ EXAMPLE 14   **Solving a System Using Determinants**

Solve the system:

$$2x = 8 - y$$

$$4x + 2y = 3$$

(a) To use Cramer's rule, we must first put our equations in standard $Ax + By = C$ order.

$$2x = 8 - y \rightarrow 2x + y = 8$$

$$4x + 2y = 3$$

Now let $a = 2$, $b = 1$, $c = 8$, $d = 4$, $e = 2$, and $f = 3$.

(b) Substitute values into Cramer's rule:

$$x = \frac{\begin{vmatrix} c & b \\ f & e \end{vmatrix}}{\begin{vmatrix} a & b \\ d & e \end{vmatrix}} = \frac{\begin{vmatrix} 8 & 1 \\ 3 & 2 \end{vmatrix}}{\begin{vmatrix} 2 & 1 \\ 4 & 2 \end{vmatrix}} = \frac{(8)(2) - (1)(3)}{(2)(2) - (1)(4)} = \frac{13}{0} = \text{undefined}$$

(c) Because the denominator has a value of 0 and the numerator is a nonzero number, this system is inconsistent and has no solution. The lines, if graphed, would be parallel.

■

In Example 14, the denominator of the fraction is 0 and the numerator is a nonzero number. That result indicates that there is no solution because the lines are parallel. If both the numerator and the denominator have a value of 0, this indicates that the lines are dependent and that there are an infinite number of solutions.

Practice Set 5-3

Evaluate the following determinants.

1. $\begin{vmatrix} 1 & 2 \\ 2 & 5 \end{vmatrix}$ **2.** $\begin{vmatrix} 2 & 3 \\ 4 & 5 \end{vmatrix}$ **3.** $\begin{vmatrix} 3 & 2 \\ 6 & 4 \end{vmatrix}$

4. $\begin{vmatrix} -2 & 2 \\ 3 & 5 \end{vmatrix}$ **5.** $\begin{vmatrix} 3 & 5 \\ -2 & 4 \end{vmatrix}$ **6.** $\begin{vmatrix} 7 & 5 \\ -3 & -2 \end{vmatrix}$

Solve each system using Cramer's rule.

7. $x - 4y = 1$

  $2x + 3y = 13$

8. $3x - 8y = -43$

  $-9x - 6y = -21$

9. $6x - 2y = 36$

  $5x + 4y = 47$

10. $15x - 6y = -15$

  $9x + 12y = 4$

11. $6x - 7y = 28$

  $-4x + 5y = -20$

12. $3x - 4y = 6$

  $15x - 20y = 36$

13. $2x - y = -10$

  $x + y = 4$

14. $2x + 3y = 7$

  $x - 6y = 11$

15. $3x - 2y = 13$

  $-6x + 4y = -26$

16. $2x = 3 - 7y$

  $10x + 3y = -1$

17. $y = 3x$

  $2x - 15y = 86$

18. $2x - 3y = 6$

  $-4x + 6y = 8$

25. $0.2x - 0.4y = 2.2$

  $0.5x - y = 1.6$

26. $0.5x - 0.75y = -0.5$

  $0.125x - 0.75y = 2.375$

19. $2x - 3y = 10$

  $2x + 5y = 2$

20. $x + y = -25$

  $2x = 3y + 70$

27. $2x + 3y = 1$

  $3x + 2y = 2$

28. $2x + y = 1$

  $x - 7y = -2$

21. $x = -4y$

  $3x = 5y + 17$

22. $x + 2y = 4$

  $3x - y = 1$

29. $\dfrac{2}{3}x - \dfrac{2}{5}y = 1$

  $\dfrac{5}{2}x - \dfrac{3}{2}y = 2$

30. $\dfrac{1}{2}x + \dfrac{3}{4}y = \dfrac{7}{4}$

  $\dfrac{1}{3}x - \dfrac{1}{6}y = \dfrac{1}{2}$

23. $3y + 2x = -36$

  $3x = 5y + 22$

24. $0.3x + y = 0.1$

  $0.1x + 0.2y = -0.1$

Section 5-4   APPLICATIONS OF LINEAR SYSTEMS

There are many applied problems in science, business, and health services for which the correct mathematical model is a system of linear equations. These models involve situations requiring two or more variables and two or more conditions on those variables. An appropriate system should be constructed and then solved using any of the methods previously discussed. Look at some of the following examples of applications involving linear systems.

■ EXAMPLE 15   **Problems of Quantity and Cost**

The newly renovated Morris Theater will seat 1500 people. Reserved seats will cost $8 each and all other seats will cost $5 each. How many of each type of ticket must be sold for the opening performance if the new owners want to generate a total of $10,500 in sales?

  Let

$$x = \text{reserved seats @ \$8}$$

$$y = \text{general seats @ \$5}$$

(a) There are two conditions present in this problem. One involves the total number of tickets available (1500). The other condition involves the amount of money from sales that needs to be generated ($10,500). Write two equations that reflect these two conditions.

  Total ticket sales: $x + y = 1500$

  Total revenues: $\$8x + \$5y = \$10,500$

(b) Solve the system using any of the methods we have studied. Here we will use linear combination.

$$x + y = 1500 \quad \rightarrow \quad -5x - 5y = -7500 \qquad \text{(multiply by } -5)$$

$$8x + 5y = 10{,}500 \rightarrow \quad \underline{8x + 5y = 10{,}500}$$

$$3x \qquad = 3000 \qquad \text{(add the equations)}$$

$$x \qquad = 1000 \qquad \text{(solve for } x)$$

(c) Now substitute $x = 1000$ into either of the original equations to find y.

$$x + y = 1500$$

$$1000 + y = 1500 \qquad \text{(substitute } x = 1000)$$

$$y = 500 \qquad \text{(add } -1000 \text{ to both sides)}$$

Therefore, 1000 seats at $8 and 500 seats at $5 should be sold.

(d) Check to see if this satisfies the original requirements of the problem.

$$\text{Total seats should be } 1500 = 1000 @ \$8 + 500 @ \$5 \qquad \text{(true)}$$

$$\text{Total revenue is } \$10{,}500 = (1000)(\$8) + (500)(\$5)$$

$$= \$8000 + \$2500$$

$$= \$10{,}500 \qquad \text{(true)}$$

The next example involves mixture problems. These types of problems occur in chemistry labs, where chemists mix solutions of differing concentrations, in metallurgy and the production of metal alloys, and even in the production of food products such as mixed nuts. Concentrations of items being mixed may be given in the form of a percent. Remember to convert the percent to its equivalent decimal form before using it in an equation.

EXAMPLE 16

Mixture Problems

How many milliliters of a 25% solution should be mixed with a 55% solution to produce 50 mL of a 46% solution?

There are two conditions that must be satisfied in this problem. The total volume of the mixture must be 50 mL and the concentration of the new mixture must be 46%.

(a) Write two equations to reflect these conditions. Let $x =$ amount of 25% solution and $y =$ amount of 55% solution.

In general, the concentration of a mixture of solutions can be modeled as follows:

$$\text{(conc. of } x)(\text{vol. of } x) + (\text{conc. of } y)(\text{vol. of } y) = (\text{new conc.})(\text{total vol.})$$

Concentration $\rightarrow$ $(0.25)x + (0.55)y = (0.46)(50 \text{ mL})$

$$(0.25)x + (0.55)y = 23$$

Total volume $\rightarrow$ $x + y = 50$

(b) In this problem, we will use Cramer's rule to find the solution.

$$x + y = 50$$

$$0.25x + 0.55y = 23$$

$$x = \frac{\begin{vmatrix} c & b \\ f & e \end{vmatrix}}{\begin{vmatrix} a & b \\ d & e \end{vmatrix}} = \frac{\begin{vmatrix} 50 & 1 \\ 23 & 0.55 \end{vmatrix}}{\begin{vmatrix} 1 & 1 \\ 0.25 & 0.55 \end{vmatrix}} = \frac{(50)(0.55) - (1)(23)}{(1)(0.55) - (1)(0.25)} = 15$$

$$y = \frac{\begin{vmatrix} a & c \\ d & f \end{vmatrix}}{\begin{vmatrix} a & b \\ d & e \end{vmatrix}} = \frac{\begin{vmatrix} 1 & 50 \\ 0.25 & 23 \end{vmatrix}}{\begin{vmatrix} 1 & 1 \\ 0.25 & 0.55 \end{vmatrix}} = \frac{(1)(23) - (50)(0.25)}{(1)(0.55) - (1)(0.25)} = 35$$

This means that 15 mL of 25% solution and 35 mL of 55% solution will produce 50 mL of a 46% solution.

Check these solutions to see if they meet the original conditions of the problem.

Supply and demand are two important concepts in economics. **Supply** is the number of items manufacturers are willing to produce. **Demand** is the number of items consumers are willing to purchase. The equations or functions used to define supply and demand for a particular item are usually based on the selling price of the item. Each is a function of the selling price. If demand is greater than supply, then stores will continually have empty shelves and unhappy customers asking for a particular product. If supply is greater than demand, then the manufacturer will have warehouses filled with a product that consumers will not buy. Businesses strive for the **equilibrium point**, where supply equals demand. This point would be the intersection point of the supply and demand equations for a business.

EXAMPLE 17   Supply and Demand Equations

The supply S and demand D (in thousands) for a certain product are given by the equations $S = f(p) = 3p - 15$ and $D = h(p) = 30 - 2p$, where p represents the price of the product in dollars. Find the value of p at the equilibrium point.

At the equilibrium point, supply equals demand, so we set the two equations equal to each other. (See Figure 5-6.)

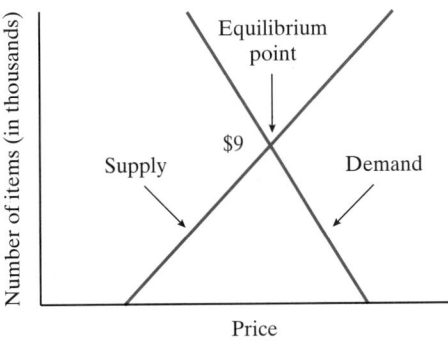

Figure 5-6
Example 17. Supply and demand equations.

$$3p - 15 = 30 - 2p$$
$$3p + 2p - 15 = 30 - 2p + 2p$$
$$5p - 15 = 30$$
$$5p - 15 + 15 = 30 + 15$$
$$5p = 45$$
$$p = 9$$

Therefore, the equilibrium point where supply equals demand is $9. Notice that the demand exceeds the supply to the left of the equilibrium point (when the price is below $9) and supply exceeds demand to the right of the equilibrium point (when the price is above $9).

If we wish to also calculate the number of items that should be produced at this price, we substitute $9 into either equation to calculate the answer.

$$S = f(p) = 3p - 15$$
$$f(9) = 3(9) - 15 = 27 - 15 = 12 \text{ (or 12,000) items}$$

Some manufacturers use a technique called **break-even analysis** to help them determine the number of items they must produce and sell to cover expenses. All income after the break-even point is profit for the company. To determine the break-even point, we let the equation that defines total cost of production equal the equation that defines total revenue from sales. Cost of production and total revenue are both functions of the number of items produced and sold. The graph shown in Figure 5-7 illustrates this idea.

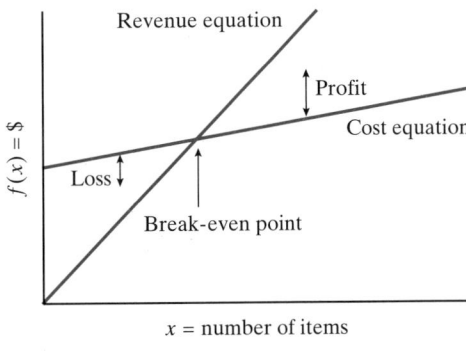

Figure 5-7
Break-even analysis.

■ EXAMPLE 18   Break-Even Point

DSC Printing Company prints textbooks at a charge of $15 per book plus a setup fee of $1200. The company sells each book for $25. How many books must be printed and sold before the company begins to make a profit?

First, we will write mathematical models to represent the cost equation and the revenue equation. Then we will calculate the break-even point by setting the cost equation equal to the revenue equation.

(a) Let b be the number of books printed.

$$\text{Cost} = C(b) = \$1200 + 15b$$

$$\text{Revenue} = R(b) = \$25b$$

(b) Set the equations equal to each other.

$$C(b) = R(b)$$

$$25b = 1200 + 15b$$

$$25b - 15b = 1200$$

$$10b = 1200$$

$$b = 120$$

Therefore, the company breaks even when 120 books have been printed and sold. If less than 120 books are printed and sold, the company will lose money, and if more than 120 books are printed and sold, the company will make a profit.

Practice Set 5-4

Write a system of equations for each problem and then solve using any method we have studied.

1. A chemist wants to mix a solution containing 10% acid with another solution containing 25% acid. She needs to produce a total of 30 mL, and the concentration of acid in the final solution should be 18%. How much of each acid should she use?

2. Everett wishes to clean his boat with a 15% soap solution. How much of a 10% soap solution and a 20% soap solution should he add to a quart of pure water to make 30 qt of a 15% solution?

3. The McCook apartment building contains 20 rental units. One-bedroom apartments rent for $650 per month and two-bedroom apartments rent for $825 per month. The total monthly in-come from all apartments is $14,400. How many one-bedroom and two-bedroom apartments are in the apartment building?

4. Tickets to a band concert were $5.00 for balcony and $10.00 for orchestra seats. If attendance at one show was 800, and if total receipts for that show were $7000, how many people bought orchestra seats?

5. Timjon Company produces children's cartoon watches. It has determined that the following equations describe the supply and demand curves for the watches. Demand: $D(p) = 30 - 3p$. Supply: $S(p) = 4p - 5$, where p = the price of a watch. Determine the equilibrium price for these supply and demand functions. Graph these functions to show the equilibrium price.

6. Windsor Company produces video games. It has determined that the following equations describe the supply and demand curves for the games. Demand: $D(p) = 60 - 2p$. Supply: $S(p) = 4p - 6$, where p = the price of a video game. Determine the equilibrium price for these supply and demand functions. Graph these functions to show the equilibrium price.

7. Sonya needs to purchase a new refrigerator. Model A costs $950 to purchase and $32 in electricity per year to operate. Model B costs $1275 to purchase but costs only $22 in electricity per year to operate. After how many years will the total cost of both units be equal? If she expects to keep the refrigerator for about 15 years, which model is the best buy?

8. Maribeth bought three leotards and four pairs of tights at the Dancer's Studio for $185.00, while Beth bought two leotards and three pairs of tights for $127.50. What is the price of a leotard and the price of a pair of tights?

9. A silversmith uses two silver alloys. The first alloy is 60% silver and the second is 40% silver. How many grams of each should be mixed together to produce 20 g of an alloy that is 52% silver?

10. Annette wishes to mix a tomato sauce that is 17% sugar with a sauce that is 30% sugar to obtain 26 L of a tomato sauce that is 24% sugar. How much of each should she mix?

11. John's Rent-a-Car Agency charges $26 a day plus 15¢ per mile for a compact car. The same type of car can be rented from Cookie's Rental Agency for $18 a day plus 20¢ per mile. How many miles would you need to drive in one day for the cost of the cars to be the same? If you plan to drive 200 miles, which rental agency should you use?

12. Joan bought 3 heads of lettuce and 2 lb of tomatoes at Ingles for $4.05. Betty bought 2 heads of lettuce and 3 lb of tomatoes for $4.35 at the same store. What is the price of a head of lettuce and a pound of tomatoes at Ingles?

13. Daniel is paid $200 plus a 5% commission on sales per week. He is considering a new salary plan that would pay him a straight 15% commission on sales. What amount of sales would he need to make for the two salaries to be equal? If he normally aver-

ages $1500 per week in sales, which plan should he choose?

14. Use the following supply and demand equations to determine the equilibrium price. Supply: $S(p) = 1200 - 2.8p$. Demand: $D(p) = 800 + 3.2p$. Explain what your answer means.

15. The Math Club and the Physics Brain Bunch both meet at the local pizza parlor once a month. The math club purchases three large pepperoni pizzas and four pitchers of soda for a total cost of $61. The physics club has two large pepperoni pizzas and three pitchers of soda for a total cost of $42. Find the cost of a large pepperoni pizza and a pitcher of soda.

16. The length of a rectangle is 3 ft greater than its width. If its perimeter is 14 ft, find the length and width of the rectangle.

17. The perimeter of a rectangular window is 200 cm. The length of one side is 20 cm less than 11 times the other. What are the dimensions of the window?

18. A grocer plans to mix candy that sells for $3.40 per pound with candy that sells for $4.60 per pound. He wants to make 10 lb of a mixture that will sell for $4 per pound. How much of each type of candy should he use?

19. Cathy purchased 16 shares of Coca-Cola® stock and 10 shares of Pepsi® stock for $1097.40. Nancy bought 48 shares of Coca-Cola and 12 shares of Pepsi for $2509.20. What is the price of a share of Coca-Cola and a share of Pepsi?

20. A company produces backpacks and charges $32 per pack. The monthly cost of manufacturing the backpacks includes a fixed cost of $25,500 and $15 per backpack. Find the number of backpacks that need to be sold in a month for the company to break even. Draw a sketch of these functions.

21. Daniel Widget Company produces widgets at a cost of $18 each and has a fixed production cost of $5500 per month. Each widget is sold to stores for $38. Draw a sketch of the graph of these two equations and label the break-even point. How many widgets must be sold before the company begins to make a profit?

22. The fence surrounding a backyard playground has a length 3 times its width. The perimeter of this

rectangular playground is 296 ft. Find the dimensions of the playground.

23. The perimeter of a rectangular painting is 60 in. and its area is 216 in.^{2} What are the dimensions of a frame for this painting?

24. A hotel charges $90 per day for a double room and $80 per day for a single. If there are 80 rooms that are occupied for a total revenue of $6930, how many rooms of each kind are there?

25. At an office supply store, Mary buys seven packages of notebook paper and four pens for $6.40. At the same store, Sue buys two packages of notebook paper and 19 pens for $5.40. What was the cost of each of these items?

26. Jerry has available a 10% acetic acid solution and a 60% acetic acid solution. Find how many milliliters of each solution he should mix to make 50 mL of a 40% acetic acid solution.

27. How many ounces of pure water and how many ounces of a 16% butterfat solution should Charlotte mix to obtain 32 oz of a 10% butterfat solution?

28. The perimeter of Kevin's lawn is 54 m. It is in the shape of a rectangle with the length of one side 3 m less than twice the width. What are the dimensions of the lawn?

29. When not at the lake, Cassie spends her time in a rectangular dog pen that her master constructed with 28 yd of fencing. If the length of the pen is 2 yd longer than twice the width, what are its dimensions?

30. The perimeter of an isosceles triangle is 48 in. If the length of the shortest side is 3 in. less than either of the other two sides, what are the lengths of the sides of the triangle?

Section 5-5 SYSTEMS OF NONLINEAR FUNCTIONS

Not all problems or relationships can be described using linear equations. We have previously discussed graphing nonlinear equations using a graphing calculator. In this section, we will look at the solutions of **nonlinear systems of equations**. In a nonlinear system of equations, at least one of the two equations contains a variable with an exponent greater than 1, and its graph will be a curve.

EXAMPLE 19

Solving a Nonlinear System of Equations with a Graphing Calculator

Solve the following system of equations.

$$x^2 - y = 0$$
$$2x - y = 0$$

The first equation is a nonlinear equation because the x variable has an exponent of 2. We will use the graphing calculator to show us the intersection points of these two equations. Unlike linear systems, nonlinear systems may have more than one intersection point.

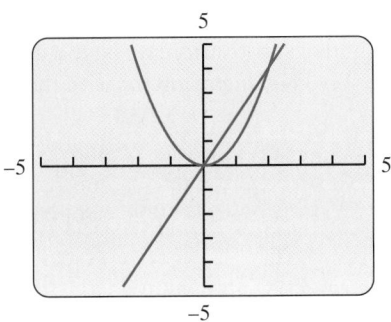

Figure 5-8
Example 19.

(a) Solve each equation for y and use the $\boxed{Y=}$ function to enter the equations into the calculator. Then use the $\boxed{\text{GRAPH}}$ button to display the graphs. Use the following values in the $\boxed{\text{WINDOW}}$ setting:

$$X_{min} = -5 \qquad Y_{min} = -5$$

$$X_{max} = 5 \qquad Y_{max} = 5$$

$$X_{scl} = 1 \qquad Y_{scl} = 1$$

See Figure 5-8.

(b) Notice that the line ($y = 2x$) intersects the parabola ($y = x^2$) at two points. Use the $\boxed{\text{TRACE}}$ function on the calculator to get the approximate values of these solutions. Use the $\boxed{\text{CALCULATE}}$ function to get the exact values. The solution set is $\{(0, 0), (2, 4)\}$.

You can see from this example that the graphing calculator will help us visualize the problems and the number of intersection points in the solution set. However, using the $\boxed{\text{TRACE}}$ function does not always give us an exact answer. We can use an algebraic method to solve some systems and calculate an exact answer.

■ EXAMPLE 20   Solving a Nonlinear System of Equations Algebraically

Solve the system:

$$x^2 - y = 0$$

$$2x - y = 0$$

(a) First solve each equation for y.

$$y = x^2$$

$$y = 2x$$

(b) Because both x^2 and $2x$ equal y, they must be equal to each other. Now, using the method of substitution, we have a quadratic equation in one variable that can be solved by factoring (or with the quadratic formula).

$$\left. \begin{array}{l} y = x^2 \\ y = 2x \end{array} \right\} \rightarrow \quad x^2 = 2x$$

$$x^2 = 2x = 0 \qquad \text{(set equation equal to 0)}$$

$$x(x - 2) = 0 \qquad \text{(factor)}$$

$$x = 0 \qquad x - 2 = 0 \qquad \text{(set each factor equal to 0)}$$

$$x = 2 \qquad \text{(solve for } x)$$

(c) Calculate the y values for each of the x values by substituting $x = 0$ and $x = 2$ into either equation.

$$\begin{array}{ll} \text{If } x = 0 & \text{If } x = 2 \\ y = x^2 & y = x^2 \\ y = 0^2 & y = 2^2 \\ y = 0 & y = 4 \end{array}$$

Solution: $(0, 0)$ and $(2, 4)$.

In the last section, we discussed the law of supply and demand. Remember that supply and demand functions express the quantities of items supplied or demanded as functions of their selling prices. When the supply produced is equal to the demand for the product, we have achieved market equilibrium. Often these supply and demand equations will be nonlinear functions.

EXAMPLE 21 **Supply and Demand Functions**

The demand function for a specific toy is given by the function $p(x) = -2x^2 + 90$. The corresponding supply function is given by the function $p(x) = 9x + 34$. In both equations, p is the price in dollars and x is in thousands of units. Find the equilibrium price and number of units produced at this price.

(a) At market equilibrium, the price given by the demand function will equal the price given by the supply function.

Because $p(x) = -2x^2 + 90$ and $p(x) = 9x + 34$, we let

$$9x + 34 = -2x^2 + 90 \qquad \text{(and solve it by factoring)}$$

$$2x^2 + 9x - 56 = 0 \qquad \text{(set equation equal to 0)}$$

$$(2x - 7)(x + 8) = 0 \qquad \text{(factor)}$$

$$2x - 7 = 0 \qquad x + 8 = 0$$

$$2x = 7 \qquad x = -8 \qquad \text{(solve each factor for } x)$$

$$x = 3.5 \qquad \varnothing$$

Xmin = 0
Xmax = 8
Xscl = 1
Ymin = 0
Ymax = 100
Yscl = 10

market equilibrium

X=3.5 Y=65.5

Figure 5-9
Example 21.

Because x represents the number of toys in thousands, the answer cannot be negative. Therefore, $x = -8$ is an extraneous root and is not a possible answer.

The correct number of toys is 3.5 thousand or 3500.

(b) Now we need to calculate the equilibrium price. Use $x = 3.5$ and substitute into either equation to find p.

$$p(x) = 9x + 34$$

$$p(x) = 9(3.5) + 34$$

$$p(x) = 31.5 + 34 = 65.5 = \$65.50$$

Therefore, the equilibrium price for these toys is $65.50.

(c) Use your graphing calculator to sketch these functions and verify the answer you have calculated. Use the window setting shown in Figure 5-9.

Practice Set 5-5

Use a graphing calculator to sketch each system of equations. Find the solution of the system algebraically and verify with the calculator.

1. $y = x^2$
$3x + y = 10$

2. $y = x$
$y = 2x^2 + 1$

3. $y = x$
$y = -2x^2 + 1$

4. $y = x^2 + 2$
$y = -x^2 + 4$

5. $y = x^2 - 5x + 6$
$y = 2x$

6. $y = x^2 - 2$
$y = -2x^2 + 6x + 7$

7. $y = x^2 - 4$
$y = 2x - 1$

8. $y = x^2 + 1$
$x + y = 3$

9. $2x + 3y^2 = 2$
$x - y = 1$

10. $x + xy = -1$
$xy = -6$

11. $x^2 + y^2 = 13$
$x^2 - y^2 = 5$

12. $x^2 + y^2 = 5$
$x + 2y = 3$

13. The sum of two numbers is 7 and the sum of their squares is 25. What are the numbers?

14. Find two numbers whose sum is 19 if the sum of their squares is 185.

15. The sum of the squares of two numbers is 58 and their difference is 10. Find one pair of such numbers.

16. The sum of two numbers is 12. Their difference is 2. Find the numbers.

17. The area of a room is 143 ft^2, and its perimeter is 48 ft. Let x be the width and let y be the length of the room. Write a system of equations that models this situation. Determine the length and the width of the room.

18. The area of the desktop is 1000 in.^{2}, and its perimeter is 130 in. Let x be the width and let y be the length of the desktop. Write a system of equations that models this situation. Find the length and the width of the desktop.

19. The product of two positive numbers is 60 and their difference is 7. Let x be the smaller number and let y be the larger number. Write a system of equations that models this situation. Find the two numbers.

20. The product of two numbers is 4 and the sum of their squares is 8. Find the numbers.

21. The demand function for a certain type of sunglasses is given by the equation $p = -0.1x^2 - 2x + 90$, and the corresponding supply function is given by the function $p = 0.1 x^2 - x + 30$, where p is in dollars and x is in thousands of pairs of sunglasses. Find the equilibrium price and the number of sunglasses produced at that price.

22. From 1980 through 1994, the northeastern part of the United States grew at a slower rate than the western part. Two models that represent the populations of the two regions are

Northeast: $p = 49{,}152.2 + 164.9t$

West: $p = 43{,}131.7 + 921t + 5.3t^2$

where p is the population in thousands and t is the calendar year, with $t = 0$ corresponding to 1980. Use a graphing calculator to determine when the population of the West overtook the population of the Northeast.

Chapter Summary

Key Terms, Properties, and Formulas

break-even analysis	determinant	nonlinear system of equations
consistent	elements	solution
Cramer's rule	equilibrium point	substitution
demand	inconsistent	supply
dependent	infinitely many solutions	system of equations
dependent equation	linear combination	

Points to Remember

Solving a system of equations graphically: Graph both lines on the same set of axes and locate their point of intersection. If they are parallel, the lines are inconsistent and there is no solution. If the two equations are for the same line, the equations are dependent and there are infinitely many solutions.

     Solving a system algebraically: Use substitution or linear combination. The substitution method involves replacing one of the variables in one equation with its equivalent from the other equation, resulting in a single equation with one variable. In linear combination, the two equations are added together in such a way as to produce a new equation with only one variable.

Cramer's rule: Use determinants to find the solution of a system of linear equations. Given the system:

$$ax + by = c$$
$$dx + ey = f$$

$$x = \dfrac{\begin{vmatrix} c & b \\ f & e \end{vmatrix}}{\begin{vmatrix} a & b \\ d & e \end{vmatrix}} \qquad y = \dfrac{\begin{vmatrix} a & c \\ d & f \end{vmatrix}}{\begin{vmatrix} a & b \\ d & e \end{vmatrix}}$$

A nonlinear system of equations includes at least one equation that is not linear. These systems may have two, one, or no solutions. A graphing calculator can help you visualize the system and its solutions.

Many application problems involve the use of systems of equations. Some of the more common types of problems include problems of quantity and cost, mixture problems, supply and demand problems, and break-even analysis problems.

Chapter Review Problems

Decide if the given ordered pair is a solution of the given system.

1. $x - 2y = 4 \qquad (0, -2)$
   $2x + y = -2$

2. $3x - y = -13 \qquad (-5, -2)$
   $x - 2y = -1$

3. $x + y = 4 \qquad (1, 3)$
   $2x - y = 5$

4. $3x + y = 7 \qquad (2, 1)$
   $x = 2y$

Solve each system of equations by graphing.

5. $2x - y = 13$
   $x + y = 8$

6. $2x + y = 3$
   $4x + 2y = 1$

7. $5x - 3y = 9$
   $x + 2y = 7$

8. $x + y = 4$
   $2x - y = -1$

9. $2x - 3y = -6$
   $y = -3x + 2$

Solve each system of equations algebraically.

10. $3x - y = 7$
    $2x + y = 3$

11. $8x - 5y = 32$
    $4x + 5y = 4$

12. $8x + 2y = 2$
    $3x - y = 6$

13. $3x + 5y = 69$
    $y = 4x$

14. $6x + 3y = 0$
    $18x + 9y = 0$

15. $6x - 8y = 6$
    $-3x + 2y = -2$

16. $2x + 10y = 3$
    $x = 1 - 5y$

17. $4x + 5y = 44$
    $x + 2 = 2y$

18. $2x + 3y = -5$
    $3x + 4y = -8$

Use Cramer's rule to solve the following systems of equations.

19. $2x - y = 4$
    $3x + y = 21$

20. $4x + 2y = 2$
    $5x + 4y = 7$

21. $4x + 5y = 2$
    $-8x - 10y = 1$

22. $2x + y = -4$
    $x = y + 7$

23. $0.8x - 0.1y = 0.3$

$0.5x - 0.2y = -0.5$

24. Solve the following system of equations using all methods — graphing, algebraic process, and Cramer's rule.

$$2x + y = 8$$
$$5x - 2y = -16$$

Solve the following nonlinear systems of equations. Use a graphing calculator to verify your solutions.

25. $x^2 + y = 0$ **26.** $y = 3x + 6$

    $y = 2x - 3$ $y = 2x^2 + 1$

Write a system of equations for each problem and then solve the system.

27. For the school fundraiser, Tyler sold doughnuts at $4 per box and stadium cushions for $6.50 each. He sold 62 items and collected a total of $318. How many of each item did he sell?

28. A 40% acid solution is to be mixed with a 70% acid solution. The chemist needs to produce 120 mL of a 50% acid solution. How much of each acid will be needed to produce the correct mixture?

29. A company manufactures and sells digital clocks. The fixed costs of production are $20,000 and the variable costs per unit produced are $25. The sell-ing price per clock is $125. How many clocks must the company sell to break even?

30. The demand function for a particular lamp is $D(p) = 20 - p$, and the supply function for the same lamp is $S(p) = 2p - 115$. Find the equilibrium price, where supply equals demand.

31. Cheryl has a total of 60 coins in her piggy bank. If the coins consist of only dimes and nickels and the total value of the coins in her bank is $5.75, how many of each coin does she have?

32. The cost of 10 lb of potatoes and 4 lb of bananas is $6.16. Four pounds of the same potatoes and 8 lb of bananas cost $6.88. What is the cost per pound of potatoes and of bananas?

33. A printer recently purchased $3000 worth of new equipment to offer personalized stationery. The cost of producing a package of stationery is $3, and it is sold for $5.50 per package. Find the number of packages that must be printed for him to break even.

34. The total of 10 gal of premium gas and 15 gal of regular gas is $35.50. Premium costs $0.20 more per gallon than regular. What is the cost per gallon of premium gas?

35. Write a word problem that is modeled by the following linear system:

$$a + s = 40$$
$$4.50a + 2.00s = 100$$

Chapter Test

1. Is the ordered pair $(-3, 4)$ a solution of the following system?

$$2x + 3y = 6$$
$$2x + y = -2$$

2. Find the determinant of $\begin{vmatrix} 2 & -5 \\ -1 & 6 \end{vmatrix}$.

Solve each of the following systems of equations by graphing.

3. $x - y = 3$ **4.** $x = 2$ **5.** $2x - y = 4$

   $x + y = 5$ $3x + 2y = 4$ $6x = 3y + 15$

Solve each of the following systems of equations algebraically.

6. $y = 4 - 3x$ **7.** $x - 2y = 4$

   $3x + y = 5$ $3x + 4y = 2$

8. $4x + 3y = 15$ **9.** $2x + 4y = 7$

   $2x - 5y = 1$ $5x - 3y = -2$

Solve each of the following systems of equations using Cramer's rule.

10. $3x - 7y = 13$ **11.** $0.5x - 1.2y = 0.3$

    $6x + 5y = 7$ $0.2x + y = 1.6$

12. Solve the following nonlinear system of equations. Use a graphing calculator to verify your solutions.

$$2x^2 - y = 0$$

$$3x - y = -2$$

13. Solve the following nonlinear system of equations. Use a graphing calculator to verify your solutions.

$$x + 2y = 4$$

$$y = x^2 + 3x + 2$$

Write a system of equations for each problem and solve the system.

14. A company manufactures and sells calculators. The fixed costs are $10,000 and each unit costs $5 to manufacture. The selling price of each calculator is $25. Find the number of calculators that must be sold for the company to break even.

15. The rooms at a motel are priced at $80 for a single and $100 for a double. If there are 65 rooms occupied on Friday night, and the total revenue for the night is $6400, how many double rooms have been rented?

16. Two vats contain milk, one sample testing 3% butterfat and the other testing 7% butterfat. How much milk should be taken from each vat to produce a 10-gal mixture that will test 4.5% butterfat?

17. A combined total of $12,000 is invested in two bonds that pay 10.5% and 12% simple interest. The annual interest is $1380. How much is invested in each bond?

18. The perimeter of a rectangle is 76. The length of the rectangle is 5 more than twice the width. Find the length.

19. Find the equilibrium point for the following demand and supply functions: $D(p) = 89 - 7p$ and $S(p) = 29 + 3p$.

20. The Turning Pointe is planning a new line of leotards. For the first year, the fixed costs for setting up the production line are $17,000. The per item cost for each leotard is $6.00, and each leotard will be sold to a retailer for $10.00. Find the break-even point.

Suggested Laboratory Exercises

LAB EXERCISE 1   ## Which Salary Option?

James is applying to be a salesperson for Daniel's Dandy Used Cars. He has a choice to make that may greatly affect his income. He may choose a base salary of $25,000 per year plus a commission of 10% on sales that he makes, or he may choose a base salary of $35,000 per year plus 7.5% commission on all sales he makes.

(a) Letting x = the number of dollars in sales that James may make, and y_1 and y_2 = the first and second annual earnings options, respectively, write two equations (a system) as described by the options given to James.

(b) Solve this system of equations. Graph this system.

(c) What is the meaning of this solution as applied to this situation?

(d) For what level of annual sales will each of the two methods yield the same gross annual income for James?

(e) For what range of sales should James choose option 1? Option 2?

LAB EXERCISE 2   ## Catering Business

A local caterer has kept good records over the years and has a good idea of just how long it takes to prepare food and set up to serve the food for several different types of possible events. Normally, the food is prepared on the day before the event (if

■ **TABLE 5-4   Lab Exercise 2: Catering Business**

	Hours to Prepare the Food	Time to Set Up
Banquet	12	7
Reception	4	5
Maximum work hours available	38	40

possible) and then tables and decorations are set up and the food is laid out on the day of the event. Table 5-4 shows the estimated time required to prepare food and set up to serve for banquets and for receptions. Of course, there is a limit to the total number of hours that the caterer works during any given week.

(a) Write a system of inequalities for this situation.
(b) Graph this system and shade the region of the graph showing the number of banquets and receptions that may be catered in one week.
(c) Can this caterer handle three banquets and two receptions in one week?
(d) How about two banquets and four receptions?
(e) What is the maximum number of receptions that may be catered if no banquets are catered?
(f) What is the maximum number of banquets that may be catered if no receptions are catered?

LAB EXERCISE 3   **Applying to Medical School**

The following equations model the number of medical school applicants across the nation. There are two separate equations, one for male and one for female applicants. The letter y represents the number of applicants in thousands and the letter x represents the number of years since 1995 (i.e., 1995 equates to $x = 0$, 1996 equates to $x = 1$, and so forth).

$$\text{Female applicants:} \quad y = 1.55x + 4.32$$

$$\text{Male applicants:} \quad y = 0.98x + 16.10$$

(a) The equations are written in the slope-intercept form. What do the slopes tell us about the application rate of males versus females?
(b) What is the solution to this system of equations? What does this solution mean in this application?

chapter six

Probability Models

IN THIS CHAPTER

"It is a truth very certain that, when it is not in our power to determine what is true, we ought to follow what is most probable." – René Descartes

The first formal theories of probability were proposed by Blaise Pascal and Pierre Fermat from France. Their theories applied primarily to games of chance. However, in our time, many things in business, the sciences, and other areas are described in terms of probabilities. This chapter will give a brief introduction to the laws of probability and how they are used to assist in decision making.

Section 6-1 **WHAT IS PROBABILITY?**

Probability theory attempts to describe the predictable long-run patterns of random processes. To a mathematician, a process is **random** if individual outcomes are uncertain but long-run patterns are predictable.

For example, if you were to toss a coin into the air, would it land so that the "head" is up or would it land "tails" up? You may not be able to correctly guess what any particular toss will show, but you should be able to guess that, for a large number of tosses, approximately half the time heads will show and half the time tails will show. Thus, tossing a coin is a random process.

To a mathematician, probability is not a guessing game. It is a matter of determining the relationship between various possible outcomes. For tossing a coin, there are limited results possible. For events that occur in our daily lives, the situation is very complicated. We will begin by looking at some familiar objects with limited possible outcomes.

As with any new topic, there are some terms and expressions that are commonly used in probability problems. These terms need to be defined before beginning a discussion of the particulars of probability.

Definition

Experiment
An experiment in probability is a controlled operation that yields a set of results.

If we set out to gather information in a systematic way so that a reasoned decision may be made, then an **experiment** has been done. An experiment in probability will not necessarily be like an experiment in physics or chemistry. An experiment can be as simple as flipping a coin and recording whether the result was "heads" or "tails." These possible results are called **outcomes**. It is usually important to know the number of possible outcomes to a given experiment.

Definition

Outcomes
The possible results of an experiment are called outcomes. It is also important to know the number of possible outcomes. This is denoted by N in formulas related to probability.

An **event** is a subset of the outcomes of an experiment. For example, when a die is rolled the *event* of rolling a number less than 6 can be satisfied by any one of five outcomes: 1, 2, 3, 4, or 5. The event of rolling a 3 can be satisfied by only one outcome: the 3 itself. The event of rolling an odd number can be satisfied by any of three outcomes: 1, 3, or 5.

Definition

Event
A subset of the outcomes of an experiment is called an event. This is denoted by E in formulas related to probability.

There are two classifications of probability: **empirical probability**, which is experimental, and **theoretical probability**, which is mathematical. Empirical probability is the relative frequency of the occurrence of an event and is determined by *actual* observations of an experiment. We will indicate the probability of an event E by $P(E)$. Theoretical probability is determined through a study of the possible outcomes that *can* occur for the given experiment. The following formula is used for computing the empirical probability:

Important Equations

Empirical Probability (Relative Frequency)

$$P(E) = \frac{\text{number of times the event has occurred}}{\text{total number of times the experiment has been performed}}$$

The probability of an event, whether it is empirical or theoretical, will always be a number between 0 and 1, inclusive, and may be expressed as a fraction, decimal, or percent. An empirical probability of 0 means that the event *never* occurred, and an empirical probability of 1 means that the event *always* occurred.

EXAMPLE 1   Calculating an Empirical Probability

A coin is tossed 100 times and lands heads up 56 of those times. Find the empirical probability of the coin landing heads up.

Let E be the event that the coin lands heads up.

$$P(E) = \frac{56}{100} = 0.56 \text{ or } 56\%$$

The coin lands on heads 56% of the time.

EXAMPLE 2   Calculating an Empirical Probability

A pharmaceutical company is testing a new drug that is supposed to reduce high blood pressure. The drug is given to 600 individuals with the following outcomes.

Blood pressure reduced = 402

Blood pressure increased = 48

Blood pressure remained the same = 150

If this drug is given to an individual, find the empirical probability that

(a) the blood pressure is reduced.
(b) the blood pressure is increased.
(c) the blood pressure remains the same.

(a) Let E be the event that the blood pressure is reduced.

$$P(E) = \frac{402}{600} = 0.67 \text{ or } 67\%$$

(b) Let E be the event that the blood pressure is increased.

$$P(E) = \frac{48}{600} = 0.08 \text{ or } 8\%$$

(c) Let E be the event that the blood pressure remains the same.

$$P(E) = \frac{150}{600} = 0.25 \text{ or } 25\%$$

Empirical probability is used when probabilities cannot be theoretically calculated. Insurance companies use empirical probability to determine the chances of a 16-year-old male driver having an automobile accident based on data collected about past automobile accidents. This information is then used to determine the cost of car insurance for all 16-year-old male drivers.

Most of us accept the fact that if a fair coin is tossed many times, it will land heads up approximately half of the time. We can guess that the probability a fair coin will land heads up is $\frac{1}{2}$. Does this mean that if a coin is tossed 2 times, it will land heads up exactly once and tails up exactly once? Obviously, this is not the case. The probability that a coin will land heads up is determined by looking at the relative frequency over the long run. In other words, the more times an experiment is performed, the more accurately we can predict the probability. This is referred to as the **law of large numbers**.

Theorem

The Law of Large Numbers
The law of large numbers states that probability statements apply in practice to large numbers of trials — not to a single trial. It is the relative frequency over the long run that is accurately predictable, not individual events or precise totals.

What does it mean to say that the probability of rolling a 3 on a die is $\frac{1}{6}$? It means that over the long run, on the average, one of every six rolls will result in a 3.

A related topic to empirical probability is conditional probability. Suppose that you are interested in the probability of two events occurring and you already know what will happen in the first event. In other words, you want to know the probability that a particular *second event* will occur *given* that you already know the results of the first event. This is called **conditional probability**. Conditional probabilities are written in a shorthand as $P(A \mid B)$. This is read as "find the probability that A will occur given that B has already occurred."

■ EXAMPLE 3   **Finding a Conditional Probability**

You have a standard deck of 52 playing cards. Find the probability of drawing a card that is a club (♣) given each of the following conditions. Let C = drawing a club. Whenever two cards are drawn in this example, the first card drawn is not replaced in the deck before drawing the second card. (See Figure 6-3.)

(a) $P(C)$
(b) $P(C \mid$ the card is a black card)
(c) $P(C \mid$ a club was not drawn on the first draw)

(a) This is a simple probability of drawing one club from the deck. Because there are 13 clubs in the deck out of 52 cards,

$$P(C) = \frac{13}{52} = \frac{1}{4}$$

(b) We know that a black card has been drawn from the deck, and there are 13 clubs in the 26 black cards in a deck.

$$P(C \mid \text{the card is a black card}) = \frac{13}{26} = \frac{1}{2}$$

(c) On the first draw, a club was not chosen, so we know that all 13 clubs are still in the 51 remaining cards.

$$P(C \mid \text{a club was not drawn on the first draw}) = \frac{13}{51}$$

Practice Set 6-1

1. What is empirical probability and how is it determined?

2. What is an experiment? What are outcomes of an experiment? What is an event?

3. What is the law of large numbers?

4. The probability of rolling a 5 on a die is $\frac{1}{6}$. Does this probability mean that if a die is rolled 6 times, one 5 will appear? If not, what does it mean?

5. To determine life insurance premiums, life insurance companies must compute the probable date of death. On the basis of research done by the company, Mr. Timmons, age 53, is expected to live another 23.25 years. Does this mean that Mr. Timmons will live until he is 76.25 years old? If not, what does it mean?

6. Explain how you would find the empirical probability of rolling a 3 on a die.

7. Explain how you would find the empirical probability of rolling an odd number on a die. What do you believe is the empirical probability of rolling an odd number? Find the empirical probability of rolling an odd number by rolling a die 40 times.

8. In a sample of 60,000 births, 155 were found to have Down's syndrome. Find the empirical probability that Mrs. Cosgrove's first child will be born with this syndrome.

9. A certain community recorded 4000 births last year, of which 2350 were female. What is the empirical probability that the next child born in the community will be a female? What is the

empirical probability that the next child born will be a male?

10. The last 30 birds that fed at the McCooks' bird feeder were 20 robins, 5 cardinals, 3 blue jays, and 2 doves. Find the empirical probability that the next bird to feed from the feeder will be a cardinal. Find the empirical probability that the next bird will be a robin.

11. Some years ago, a survey was done of men aged 35 and women aged 35 who were married to each other. A total of 81,800 couples was surveyed. Thirty years later, only 64,528 men and 71,862 women were still living. Based on these limited data:
    (a) What is the probability that a male aged 35 will live another 30 years?
    (b) What is the probability that a female aged 35 will live another 30 years?

12. Of the last 70 people who went to the cash register at Wal-Mart, 12 had blond hair, 20 had black hair, 33 had brown hair, and 5 had red hair. Determine the empirical probability that the next person to come to the cash register will have red hair.

13. Of the last 70 people who went to the cash register at Wal-Mart, 12 had blond hair, 20 had black hair, 33 had brown hair, and 5 had red hair. Determine the empirical probability that the next person to come to the cash register will have blond hair.

14. Mr. Harclerode's grade distribution over the past 3 years in Algebra I is shown in the following chart.

Grade	Number of Students
A	41
B	183
C	265
D	96
F	85
Incomplete	2

If Sharon Odell plans on taking Algebra I with Mr. Harclerode, determine the empirical probability that she will receive a grade of A.

15. If Lafawn Oliver plans on taking Algebra I with Mr. Harclerode, determine the empirical proba-

bility that she will receive a grade of C. (Use the table in the previous problem.)

16. Six friends chartered a deep-sea fishing boat for a day's fishing trip. They caught a total of 72 fish. The following chart provides information about the type and number of fish caught.

Fish	Number Caught
Shark	8
Flounder	35
Kingfish	10
Grouper	19

Determine the empirical probability that the next fish caught will be a shark.

17. Six friends chartered a deep-sea fishing boat for a day's fishing trip. They caught a total of 72 fish. Determine the empirical probability that the next fish caught will be a flounder. (Use the chart in the previous problem.)

18. A single card is selected from a deck of cards. Find the probability it is a diamond, given that it is red.

19. A single card is selected from a deck of cards. Find the probability it is a spade, given that it is black.

20. Given that a family has two children, and assuming that boys and girls are equally likely, find the probability that the family has two girls if you know at least one of the children is a girl.

21. Given that a family has two children, and assuming that boys and girls are equally likely, find the probability that the family has two girls if you know that the older child is a girl.

22. The following table is based on some recent customer surveys done at various automobile repair shops. Some are shops at automobile dealerships and some are independent repair shops. Customers are asked to rate the services that they received on their cars.

	Good Service	Poor Service	Total
Car dealer shop	20	9	29
Independent shop	35	27	62
Total	55	36	91

Suppose that your car breaks down and you do not know anything about these repair shops, so you just choose one at random.

(a) What is the probability that the repair shop that you choose will be one that provides good service?

(b) What is the probability that you will randomly choose an independent shop?

(c) What is the probability that you will choose an independent shop that also provides good service?

(d) What is the probability that you will get poor service given that you chose an independent shop?

23. The results of a survey of the service at a local restaurant are summarized in the following table.

Meal	Service Good	Service Poor	Total
Lunch	50	15	65
Dinner	45	35	80
Total	95	50	145

Find the probability that the service was rated
(a) good.
(b) good, given that the meal was lunch.
(c) poor, given that the meal was dinner.
(d) poor, given that the meal was lunch.

24. Each person in a sample of 300 residents in Austin County was asked whether he or she favored having a single countywide police department. The county consists of one large city and a number of small townships. The response of those sampled, with their place of residence specified, is given in the following table.

Residence	Favor	Oppose	Total
Live in city	130	50	180
Live outside city	85	35	120
Total	215	85	300

If one person from the sample is selected at random, find the probability that the person

(a) favors a single countywide police force.

(b) favors a single countywide police force if the person lives in the city.

(c) opposes a single countywide police force if the person lives outside the city.

25. A group of individuals were asked which evening news they watch most often. The results are summarized in the following table.

Viewers	ABC	NBC	CBS	Other	Total
Men	35	25	45	30	135
Women	50	10	20	15	95
Total	85	35	65	45	230

If one of these individuals is selected at random, find the probability that the person watches

(a) ABC or NBC.

(b) ABC, given that the individual is a woman.

(c) ABC or NBC, given that the individual is a man.

(d) a station other than CBS, given that the individual is a woman.

Section 6-2   **THEORETICAL PROBABILITY**

What are the chances of winning the lottery? If you go to a carnival, which games provide the greatest chance of winning? These and similar questions can be answered using theoretical probability. Recall from the previous section that theoretical probability is determined through the study of the *possible* outcomes that can occur in a given experiment. The rest of this chapter will be spent studying theoretical probability.

In Section 6-1, we learned that the results of an experiment are called the outcomes of the experiment. If each outcome has the same chance of occurring as any other outcome, they are said to be **equally likely outcomes**. For example, when you roll a die, the possible outcomes are 1, 2, 3, 4, 5, and 6. These are said to be equally likely outcomes because one has an equal chance of getting each number on any roll of the die.

The process of predicting how a series of events might occur must always begin by studying the situation. A good starting point is to make a list of all possible outcomes of a given event. This list is called the **sample space**.

Definition

Sample Space
The set of all possible outcomes of a random phenomenon is called the sample space. A sample space is listed using set notation:

$$s = \{\text{list of outcomes}\}$$

Remember that when a probability experiment is performed and the results are observed, each individual result is called an event.

EXAMPLE 4   Rolling One Die One Time

Pictured in Figure 6-1 are the sides of a die "unfolded" to show the number of pips on each face. We will do a simple experiment — rolling the die one time. What is the number of possible outcomes? List these outcomes as a sample space.

Any one of the six sides may be face up when the die is rolled. The sample space is $s = \{1, 2, 3, 4, 5, 6\}$ and the number of possible outcomes is $N = 6$.

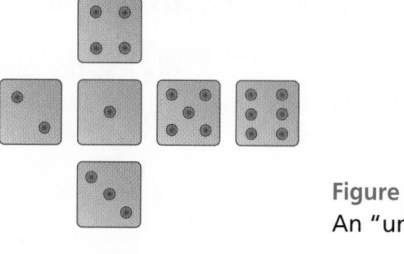

Figure 6-1
An "unfolded" die.

We are now ready to state a formal definition of theoretical probability.

Theorem

Theoretical Probability

$$P(E) = \frac{\text{number of successful outcomes possible}}{\text{total number of possible outcomes}} = \frac{s}{N}$$

EXAMPLE 5 Calculating a Theoretical Probability

A "fair" die is to be rolled one time. Calculate each of the following probabilities:

(a) $P(2)$
(b) $P(\text{even number})$
(c) $P(7)$
(d) $P(\text{number less than 7})$

(a) There is only one favorable outcome out of six. We have one chance to roll a 2 and there are six possible outcomes $\{1, 2, 3, 4, 5, 6\}$. This means that $s = 1$ and $N = 6$, so

$$P(2) = \frac{s}{N} = \frac{1}{6}$$

or one chance in six.

The value of P may be given as a fraction, decimal (rounded appropriately), or percent. In this case, $\frac{1}{6}$ is a nonending, repeating decimal, so to express the value of $P(2)$ as a decimal it must be rounded. The value of $P(2)$ may thus be given as follows if decimal numbers or percentages are preferred.

$$P(2) = \frac{1}{6} = 0.167 = 16.7\%$$

(b) There are three even numbers on the die (2, 4, and 6), so $s = 3$. Any one of these three would fulfill the desired conditions for $P(\text{even number})$.

$$P(\text{even number}) = \frac{s}{N} = \frac{3}{6} = \frac{1}{2}$$

or one chance in two. Also,

$$P(\text{even number}) = 0.5 \text{ or } 50\%$$

(c) There are no 7s on a standard die. This means that $s = 0$.

$$P(7) = \frac{s}{N} = \frac{0}{6} = 0$$

Also,

$$P(7) = 0\%$$

This means that it is not possible to roll a 7 at all on a single die.

(d) All numbers on the die are less than 7. This means that for $P(\# \text{ less than 7})$, $s = 6$.

$$P(\# \text{ less than 7}) = \frac{s}{N} = \frac{6}{6} = 1$$

Also,

$$P(\# \text{ less than 7}) = 1.00 = 100\%$$

This means that no matter what number turns up, the desired result will occur. You cannot miss if you bet on this one.

The following **laws of probability** can be easily understood if you refer to the example just completed.

Rule

Probability Laws

LAW 1
Every probability is a number between 0 and 1 (inclusive).

LAW 2
The sum of the probabilities for all outcomes for a particular sample space is exactly 1.

LAW 3
The probability of an event occurring that cannot possibly happen is 0.

LAW 4
The probability of an event that must occur is 1.

■ EXAMPLE 6   **Marbles in a Jar**

Figure 6-2
Marbles in a jar.

Suppose that a jar contains 10 marbles. (See Figure 6-2.) Two are red, three are green, four are blue, and one is yellow. Each marble is the same size and weight as all of the others, so each has an equal chance of being chosen. What is the probability that you will reach into the jar without looking and draw out

(a) a red marble?
(b) a green marble?
(c) a blue marble?
(d) a yellow marble?
(e) a purple marble?
(f) a red, green, blue, or yellow marble?
(g) Referring to the laws of probability, is law 1 true here?
(h) Is law 2 true here also?

(a) There are two red marbles out of ten marbles in the jar. The probability of drawing a red marble may be abbreviated as $P(\text{red})$.

$$P(\text{red}) = \frac{2}{10} = \frac{1}{5}$$

(b) $$P(\text{green}) = \frac{3}{10}$$

(c) $$P(\text{blue}) = \frac{4}{10} = \frac{2}{5}$$

(d) $$P(\text{yellow}) = \frac{1}{10}$$

(e)
$$P(\text{purple}) = \frac{0}{10} = 0$$

A probability of 0 means that the event is an *impossible event*. In this case, it means that it is not possible to draw a purple marble from the jar because there are none of that color in the jar.

(f)
$$P(\text{red, green, blue, or yellow}) = \frac{10}{10} = 1$$

A probability of 1 means that the event is *certain to occur*. In this example, if a marble is drawn at all it will be one of the four colors, so we are certain to draw a red, green, blue, or yellow marble.

(g) All of the individual probabilities are between 0 and 1 (inclusive), so law 1 is true here.

(h)
$$P(\text{red}) + P(\text{green}) + P(\text{blue}) + P(\text{yellow}) = \frac{2}{10} + \frac{3}{10} + \frac{4}{10} + \frac{1}{10}$$

$$= \frac{10}{10} = 1$$

Law 2 is also true here.

Here are a couple of simple mathematical relationships to formalize some of the results of the experiment just shown in Example 6.

Important Equations

Mathematical Relationships

$$P(A) + P(\text{not } A) = 1$$

$$P(\text{not } A) = 1 - P(A)$$

If the probability that an event will occur is $\frac{3}{8}$, then the probability that it will not occur is $1 - \frac{3}{8}$ or $\frac{5}{8}$. If the probability that some event, A, will occur is 0.25, then the probability that it will not occur is $1 - 0.25$ or 0.75.

EXAMPLE 7   **Using the Mathematical Relationships**

Referring to Example 6, what is the probability of reaching into the jar of colored marbles and *not* drawing out a red one?

In Example 6(a), $P(\text{red}) = \frac{1}{5}$. Thus, $P(\text{not red}) = 1 - P(\text{red}) = 1 - \frac{1}{5} = \frac{4}{5}$.

EXAMPLE 8   Probability of Drawing a Particular Card

Figure 6-3 shows a standard deck of playing cards. This deck has four suits: spades, ♠; hearts, ♥; diamonds, ♦; and clubs, ♣. The spades and clubs are numbered in black, the hearts and diamonds in red. There are 13 cards in each suit and 52 cards in the entire deck. Each suit has three face cards, a king, a queen, and a jack. The other cards are numbered 1, the ace, through 10.

You are to draw one card from a well-shuffled deck of playing cards. Find each of the following.

(a) P(red card)
(b) P(king)
(c) P(not a face card)

(a) All of the hearts and diamonds are red cards, so drawing any heart or diamond will satisfy this probability. There are 13 hearts and 13 diamonds in the deck.

$$P(\text{red}) = \frac{13 + 13}{52} = \frac{26}{52} = \frac{1}{2}$$

(b) There is one king in each of the four suits, so

$$P(\text{king}) = \frac{4}{52} = \frac{1}{13}$$

(c) Each suit contains 3 face cards and 10 nonface cards. Thus, the deck contains 12 face cards and 40 nonface cards. The probability of not drawing a face card is the same as the probability of drawing a nonface card, and so

$$P(\text{not a face card}) = \frac{40}{52} = \frac{10}{13}$$

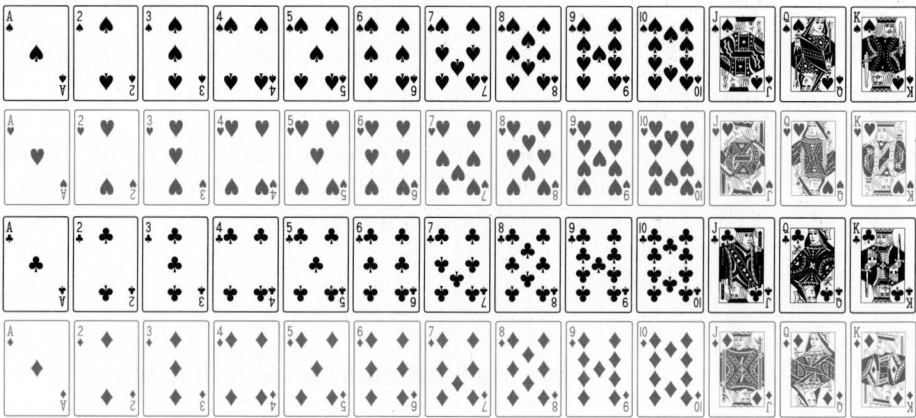

Figure 6-3
Standard deck of 52 playing cards.

■ EXAMPLE 9   **An Application to Human Characteristics**

Assume that in the general population 55% of persons have eyes that would be in the brown-color category, 15% blue, 10% green, and 20% other color variations.

(a) Based on these percentages, if you are in a classroom with 25 persons (including yourself), how many should have brown eyes?

(b) What is the probability that the next person entering the room will have blue eyes?

(a) Because 55% of the general population has brown eyes, we would expect that about 55% of persons in any general group would have brown eyes.

$$55\% \text{ of } 25 = 0.55(25) = 13.75$$

This means that about 14 of the 25 persons would be expected to have brown eyes.

(b) Because 15% of the general population has blue eyes,

$$P(\text{blue eyes}) = 15\% = 0.15$$

or, as a fraction, $P(\text{blue eyes}) = \frac{15}{100} = \frac{3}{20}$.

Practice Set 6-2

1. What are "equally likely outcomes"?

2. How does theoretical probability differ from empirical probability?

3. Can a theoretical probability ever exceed 1? Why or why not?

4. What is a "sample space"?

All of the letters in the word *Mississippi* are written on separate pieces of paper and put in a hat.

5. What is the probability of drawing the letter *s* from the hat?

6. What is the probability of drawing the letter *p*?

7. What is the probability of drawing the letter *a*?

8. What is the probability of drawing the letter *m* or *i*?

Each of the whole numbers 1–20 are written separately on 20 ping-pong balls and placed in a hat.

9. What is the probability that you will reach into the hat and draw out an even number?

10. What is the probability that you will draw a number that is evenly divisible by 5?

11. What is the probability that you will draw the number 3 on the first draw?

12. Suppose 48% of the general population of the world has blood type O, 27% blood type A, and 23% blood type B.
    (a) What is the probability that someone has type AB blood? (Assume that there are only four blood types.)
    (b) If there are 30 people in a room, how many would you expect to have type A blood?

13. A certain baseball player has a batting average (number of hits/number of times at bat) of 0.375. What is the probability that he will not get a hit in his next at bat?

A card is drawn from a standard deck of playing cards.

14. What is the probability that the card is a 3?

15. What is the probability that the card is not a 3?

16. What is the probability that the card is a heart?

17. What is the probability that the card is a red card?

18. What is the probability that the card is a red spade?

19. What is the probability that the card is a black face card?

20. What is the probability that the card is a face card?

21. What is the probability that the card is a card with a value greater than 5 but less than 9?

A bag contains three red, four green, and five blue balls. One ball is drawn from the bag.

22. What is the probability that the ball is red?

23. What is the probability that the ball is not blue?

24. What is the probability that the ball is red or green?

A die is rolled once.

25. What is the probability that the number shown is even?

26. What is the probability that the number shown is less than 3?

27. What is the probability that the number shown is greater than 6?

M&Ms® are packaged so that 24% in a given package are blue, 20% orange, 16% green, 14% yellow, 13% red, and 13% brown.

28. What is the probability that you will reach into a bag of these candies and remove a brown-colored candy?

29. What is the probability of pulling out a green one?

30. What is the probability of drawing out a purple one?

A die is tossed.

31. What is the probability of tossing a 5?

32. What is the probability of tossing an odd number?

33. What is the probability of tossing a 1 or a 4?

34. What is the probability of tossing a number greater than 5?

35. What is the probability of tossing an odd number or a 6?

36. What is the probability of tossing an odd number and a 6?

A card is drawn from an ordinary deck of 52 playing cards.

37. What is the probability of drawing an ace?

38. What is the probability of drawing a red four?

39. What is the probability of drawing a queen or king of hearts?

A TV remote has keys for channels 0–9. You select one key at random.

40. What is the probability that you select channel 6?

41. What is the probability that you select a channel that is an odd number?

42. What is the probability that you select a channel less than 8?

A multiple-choice test has six possible answers for each question.

43. If you guess at an answer, what is the probability that you select the correct answer for one particular question?

44. If you eliminate two of the six possible answers and guess from the remaining possibilities, what is the probability that you select the correct answer to that question?

A traffic light is red for 35 sec, yellow for 10 sec, and green for 45 sec.

45. What is the probability that when you reach the light, the light will be red?

46. What is the probability that when you reach the light, the light will be yellow?

47. What is the probability that when you reach the light, the light will not be red?

48. What is the probability that when you reach the light, the light will not be red or yellow?

A bin contains 100 batteries (all size C). There are 40 Eveready, 24 Duracell, 20 Sony, 10 Panasonic, and 6 Rayovac batteries. One battery is selected at random from the bin.

49. Find the probability that the battery selected is a Duracell.

50. Find the probability that the battery selected is a Duracell or Eveready.

51. Find the probability that the battery selected is a Duracell, Eveready, or Sony.

52. Find the probability that the battery selected is a Kodak.

Section 6-3   ODDS

The **odds** of an event occurring or not occurring are directly related to the probability of the events. There is only a minor difference. Instead of forming ratios relating the success of an experiment to the total number of possible outcomes, ratios of the success of an experiment to the failure of the experiment are formed. These ratios are usually given using a colon (:) to represent the ratio.

Definition

Odds

If s represents the number of successes and f the number of failures, then

$$\text{Odds in favor of an event} = s \text{ to } f = s{:}f$$

$$\text{Odds against an event} = f \text{ to } s = f{:}s$$

EXAMPLE 10   Odds of Drawing an Ace

What are the odds in favor of and the odds against drawing an ace from a standard deck of playing cards?

There are 52 cards in a standard deck of playing cards. Only 4 are aces and the other 48 cards are not aces (see Figure 6-3). This means that $s = 4$ and $f = 48$ for this experiment.

Therefore, the odds in favor of drawing an ace $= s$ to $f = 4{:}48 = 1{:}12$. This means that the odds in favor of drawing an ace are 1 to 12.

The odds against drawing an ace $= f$ to $s = 48{:}4 = 12{:}1$ (or 12 to 1 against).

Note: Do *not* write $12{:}1$ as 12, because odds must be expressed as ratios even when the "fractions" can be reduced to whole numbers.

Odds are given for many games in gambling casinos and at horse races. Usually, these odds are the odds against winning. If the odds on a game are given as

14:1, then the game is estimated to be lost 14 times for each win. Definitely a long shot! The probability of winning can be calculated from the odds by writing the ratio of wins to total outcomes. In this case, the probability of winning would be $\frac{1}{15}$.

EXAMPLE 11   Odds of Being Born with an IQ of 130 or Above

Three percent of the U.S. population is born with an IQ of 130 or above.

(a) What are the odds against a person being born with an IQ of 130 or greater?
(b) What are the odds in favor of a person being born with an IQ of 130 or greater?

(a) If 3% of the population has an IQ of 130 or greater, this means that every 3 births out of 100 will be gifted and every 97 births out of 100 will not be gifted. Therefore, $s = 3$ and $f = 97$. So the odds against = f to s = 97:3.
(b) The odds in favor of being born gifted are 3:97.

EXAMPLE 12   Calculating Probabilities from Odds

If the odds of a new business going bankrupt after its first year in business are 3:7, what is the probability that Mario's Pizza Parlor will go bankrupt at the end of its first year?

Because the odds of bankruptcy are 3:7, this means that three businesses go bankrupt for every seven that do not. The total of all outcomes is thus $7 + 3 = 10$. Therefore,

$$P(\text{bankruptcy}) = \frac{3}{10}$$

EXAMPLE 13   Calculating Odds from Probabilities

Suppose the probability that you will sell your car this week is 0.3. Find the odds against selling your car this week.

Because the probability of selling your car is 0.3, the probability of not selling your car is $1 - 0.3 = 0.7 = \frac{7}{10}$. Therefore, $s = 3$ and $f = 7$. So the odds against selling your car = f to s = 7 to 3 or 7:3.

Practice Set 6-3

1. The odds in favor of winning the door prize are 3 to 17. Find the odds against winning the door prize.

2. The odds against Sparkles Pretty winning the horse race are 5:2. Find the odds in favor of Sparkles Pretty winning.

3. A committee of 3 is to be chosen from your math class members. If there are 20 members in your class, what are the odds that you will be chosen to be on this committee?

4. You roll a fair die one time. Find:
   (a) the probability of rolling a 5.
   (b) the odds of rolling a 5.
   (c) the probability of not rolling a 5.
   (d) the odds against rolling a 5.

5. You roll a fair die one time. Find the odds against rolling an odd number.

6. You roll a fair die one time. Find the odds against rolling a number greater than 4.

7. You roll a fair die one time. Find the odds in favor of rolling a number less than 3.

8. Given a standard deck of 52 playing cards, you draw one card. Find:
   (a) P(club).
   (b) the odds of drawing a club.

9. Given a standard deck of 52 playing cards, you draw one card. Find the odds in favor of selecting a 6.

10. Given a standard deck of 52 playing cards, you draw one card. Find the odds in favor of selecting a heart.

11. Given a standard deck of 52 playing cards, you draw one card. Find the odds against selecting a face card.

12. Given a standard deck of 52 playing cards, you draw one card. Find the odds against drawing an ace.

13. One person is selected at random from a class of 19 males and 13 females. Find the odds against selecting
    (a) a female.
    (b) a male.

14. Suppose the probability that you are asked to work overtime this week is $\frac{5}{8}$. Find the odds in favor of your being asked to work overtime.

15. Suppose that the probability that a mechanic fixes your car right the first time is 0.7. Find the odds against your car being repaired right on the first attempt.

16. One million tickets are sold for a raffle. If you purchase one ticket, find your odds against winning (odds of losing).

17. One million tickets are sold for a raffle. If you purchase 10 tickets, find your odds against winning (odds of losing).

18. You bet on a horse in a race. If the odds on the horse are 5:1, what is the probability that the horse will win the race?

19. If the odds in a certain game are 5:9 in your favor, what is the probability that you will win the game?

20. The odds against Julie Wilson being admitted to the college of her choice are 9:2. Find the probability that Julie will be admitted.

21. The odds against Julie Wilson being admitted to the college of her choice are 9:2. Find the probability that Julie will not be admitted.

22. The odds against Jason getting promoted are 5:9. Find the probability that Jason will get promoted.

23. The odds against Jason getting promoted are 5:9. Find the probability that Jason will not get promoted.

24. The odds in favor of Kristen winning the spelling bee are 7:5. Find the probability that Kristen will win the spelling bee.

25. The odds in favor of Kristen winning the spelling bee are 7:5. Find the probability that Kristen will lose the spelling bee.

26. The odds in favor of Tim winning the tennis match are 1:6. Find the probability that Tim will win the match.

27. The odds in favor of Tim winning the tennis match are 1:6. Find the probability that Tim will not win the match.

28. The odds against Brian winning the 100-yard dash are 5:2. Find the probability that Brian will win.

29. The odds against Brian winning the 100-yard dash are 5:2. Find the probability that Brian will lose.

Section 6-4   COUNTING PRINCIPLE AND TREE DIAGRAMS

Even when situations seem simple, the number of possible results can be quite large. It is often important to know the number of possibilities that a situation may present before beginning to calculate the probability of any individual event.

As stated earlier, the possible results of an experiment are called outcomes. To solve more difficult probability problems, you must first be able to determine all the possible outcomes of the experiment. There are two methods that may be used to help you determine the number of outcomes. These methods are the **counting principle** and tree diagrams.

Rule

Counting Principle
If a first experiment can be performed in X distinct ways and a second experiment can be performed in Y distinct ways, then the two experiments in that specific order can be performed in X times Y distinct ways.

EXAMPLE 14   Using the Counting Principle: A Simple Case

What is the total number of outcomes for tossing two coins?

The first coin has two possible outcomes: heads or tails. The second coin also has two possible outcomes: heads or tails. Thus, the two experiments together have 2(2) or 4 possible outcomes.

EXAMPLE 15   Using the Counting Principle: A Not-So-Simple Case

A license plate is to consist of two letters followed by three digits. Use the counting principle to determine how many different license plates are possible if repetition of letters and digits is permitted.

There are 26 letters and 10 digits (0–9). We have five positions to fill, as follows:

$$\underline{L} \quad \underline{L} \quad \underline{D} \quad \underline{D} \quad \underline{D}$$

Because repetition is permitted, there are 26 possible choices for the first and second positions. There are 10 possible choices for the last three positions.

$$\underline{26} \quad \underline{26} \quad \underline{10} \quad \underline{10} \quad \underline{10}$$

Therefore, the counting principle says that we have 26(26)(10)(10)(10) = 676,000 different possible license plates.

EXAMPLE 16   **License Plates Again**

Repeat the problem in Example 15 but do not allow repetition of letters and digits.

There are 26 possible choices for the first position. Because repetition of letters is not permitted, there are only 25 choices for the second position. There are 10 choices for the third position. Because repetition of digits is not permitted, there are only 9 choices for the fourth position and 8 for the fifth position.

Therefore, the counting principle says that we have $26(25)(10)(9)(8) =$ 468,000 different possible license plates.

A second method used to determine the sample space is to construct a **tree diagram**. As long as the numbers of possible events is small, tree diagrams work very well. They provide a list of all possible events as well as giving the size of the sample space. However, tree diagrams can rapidly become very large and complicated for experiments involving several possible events. Another drawback of tree diagrams is that they are very time consuming to construct.

EXAMPLE 17   **Constructing a Tree Diagram for Tossing Two Coins**

In Example 14, we used the counting principle to help us determine the number of possible outcomes for this experiment. The tree diagram pictured in Figure 6-4 shows us that there are four outcomes and lists the individual outcomes for the experiment.

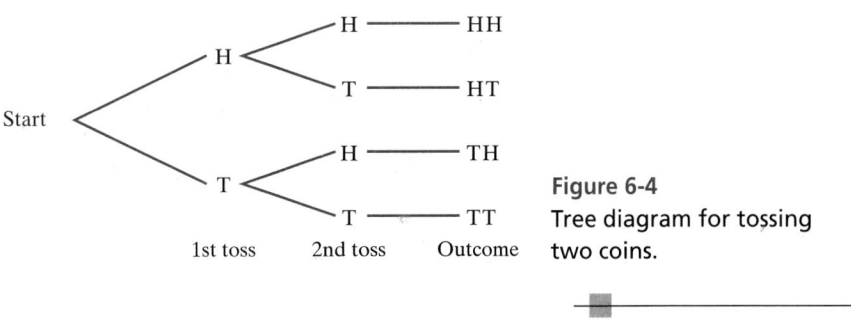

Figure 6-4
Tree diagram for tossing two coins.

Recall from a previous section that the sample space is a list of all possible outcomes. Tree diagrams can be very helpful in determining the sample space.

EXAMPLE 18   **Another Tree Diagram**

Construct a tree diagram and determine the sample space if a coin is tossed and a die is rolled.

    If we want to find the number of possible outcomes when a coin is tossed and a die is rolled, we can use the counting principle. There are two possible outcomes for the coin — head or tails — and there are six possible outcomes for the die — 1, 2, 3, 4, 5, and 6. Therefore, there are 2(6) or 12 possible outcomes for this problem. Figure 6-5 illustrates these 12 outcomes. As you can see from Figure 6-5, the sample space is $S = \{$H1, H2, H3, H4, H5, H6, T1, T2, T3, T4, T5, T6$\}$.

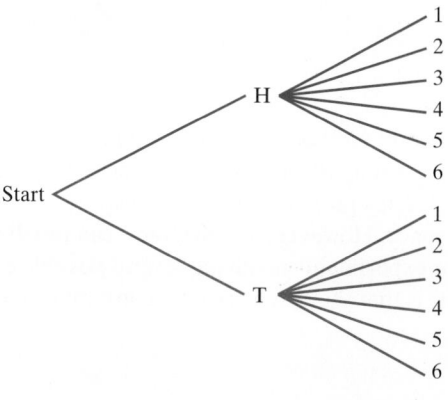

Figure 6-5
Tree diagram for flipping a coin and rolling a die.

EXAMPLE 19   **Choosing without Replacement**

Two marbles are to be selected without replacement from a bag that contains one red, one purple, one green, and one blue marble.

(a) Use the counting principle to determine the number of items in the sample space.
(b) Construct a tree diagram and list the sample space.
(c) Find the probability that one purple marble is selected.
(d) Find the probability that a blue marble followed by a green marble is selected.

(a) The first selection may be any one of the four marbles. Once the first marble is selected, only three marbles remain for the second selection. Therefore, there are 4(3) = 12 items in the sample space.
(b) See Figure 6-6. The sample space is $S = \{$RP, RG, RB, PR, PG, PB, GR, GP, GB, BR, BP, BG$\}$.
(c) Recall that

$$P(E) = \frac{\text{number of successful outcomes}}{\text{number of possible outcomes}} = \frac{s}{N}$$

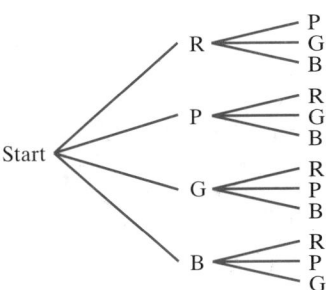

Figure 6-6
Tree diagram for drawing marbles.

The total number of outcomes is 12. Six outcomes have one purple marble:
PR, PG, PB, RP, GP, or BP.

$$P(\text{one purple marble is selected}) = \frac{6}{12} = \frac{1}{2}$$

(d) One possible outcome meets the criteria for this problem: BG

$$P(\text{blue followed by green}) = \frac{1}{12}$$

Practice Set 6-4

Use the counting principle to determine the number of possible outcomes for each of the following.

1. How many different four-digit numbers can be formed from the digits 0–9 if the first digit must be even and cannot be 0? (You may repeat digits.)

2. How many different four-digit numbers can be formed from the digits 0–9 if the first digit must be even and cannot be 0? (You may not repeat digits.)

3. A bag contains five different lightbulbs. The bulbs are the same size, but each has a different wattage. If you select three bulbs at random, how many different outcomes will be in the sample space if the bulbs are selected with replacement?

4. A bag contains five different lightbulbs. The bulbs are the same size, but each has a different wattage. If you select three bulbs at random, how many different outcomes will be in the sample space if the bulbs are selected without replacement?

5. Two balls are to be selected from a bag without replacement. The bag contains one red, one blue, one green, one yellow, and one purple ball. How many possible outcomes will there be for this experiment?

6. Two balls are to be selected from a bag with replacement. The bag contains one red, one blue, one green, one yellow, and one purple ball. How many possible outcomes will there be for this experiment?

Draw a tree diagram for tossing a coin 3 times and then answer the following questions.

7. What is the size of this sample space?

8. What is the sample space for this experiment?

9. What is the probability that tossing a coin 3 times will result in one head and two tails?

10. What is the probability of tossing two or more heads?

A penny is tossed and a die is rolled.

11. Use the counting principle to determine the number of outcomes in the sample space.

12. Construct a tree diagram illustrating all the possible outcomes and list the sample space.

13. What is the probability of tossing a head and rolling a 3?

14. What is the probability of tossing a head and rolling an even number?

15. Complete the following chart to show all of the possible outcomes for rolling two dice. Then answer the following questions.

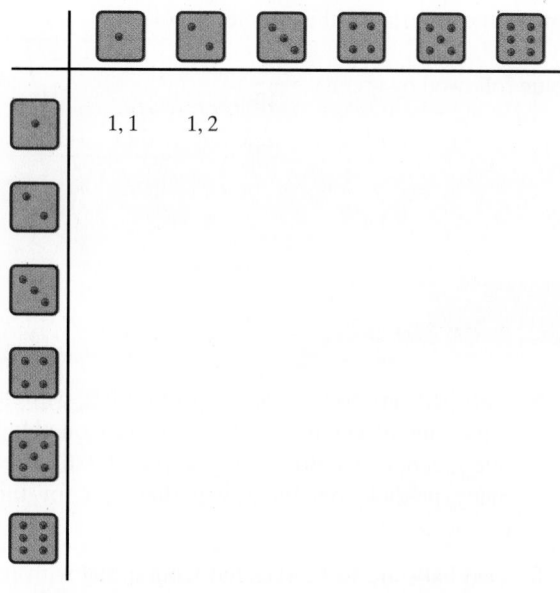

      1, 1   1, 2

  (a) What is the size of this sample space?
  (b) What is the probability of rolling a total of 7 on two dice?
  (c) What is the probability of rolling 13 on two dice?
  (d) What is the probability of rolling a 3 on both dice?

You perform an experiment that involves flipping a coin twice and then rolling a die once.

16. What is the size of the sample space?

17. What is the sample space?

18. Find P(HH3).

19. Find P(HT (in any order) and then roll a 5).

20. Find P(TT and then roll an even number).

A bag contains three cards: an ace, a jack, and a queen. Two cards are to be selected at random with replacement.

21. Construct a tree diagram and determine the sample space.

22. Find the probability that two aces are selected.

23. Find the probability that a jack and then an ace are selected.

24. Find the probability that at least one queen is selected.

A couple plans to have two children.

25. Construct a tree diagram and list the sample space of the possible arrangements of boys and girls.

26. Find the probability that the family has two girls.

27. Find the probability that the family has at least one boy.

28. Find the probability that the family has at least two boys.

Suppose that you are going to make up a password for access to some files on your computer. You are going to choose three lowercase letters from the alphabet and then choose two digits (like *kuy76*).

29. How many different passwords are possible if repetition is allowed?

30. What is the probability that someone could guess your password on the first guess if the person knew to choose three letters and two digits?

A monkey types the letters *o*, *k*, and *a* in random order. Answer the following questions.

31. How many different three-letter "words" could the monkey type using just these three letters? (You cannot repeat the letters.)

32. What is the probability that the monkey would type a meaningful word using these three letters?

Section 6-5   *OR* AND *AND* PROBLEMS

Suppose that a series of events could occur in a given situation. You might wish to calculate the probability for the occurrence of one particular series of events as opposed to other possible outcomes. For example, suppose that you wanted to find the probability of tossing a coin 3 times and having the coin come up heads every time. This is a series of three events.

There are some complications that have not yet been discussed in this chapter. First, can the possible events all occur at once or must they be entirely separate from each other? **Mutually exclusive events** are events that cannot occur together. If you are flipping coins, the events of the coin turning up heads or tails are mutually exclusive. The coin cannot turn up both sides at once.

Definition

Mutually Exclusive Events
Two events *A* and *B* are mutually exclusive if it is impossible for both events to occur at the same time.

Also, the result of each flip of the coin is an **independent outcome**. This means that the result of the first flip of the coin has no effect on the probability of the next flip of the coin.

Definition

Independent Events
Two events *A* and *B* are **independent events** if the occurrence of either event in no way affects the probability of occurrence of the other.

To find the total probability of a series of events, the probability of each individual event must first be calculated. Therefore, for tossing a coin once, the probability of heads showing up on any single toss is $\frac{1}{2}$ (see Section 6-2). Thus, each time you flip the coin the probability of heads showing up will be the same, $\frac{1}{2}$.

Now what do you do with the three probabilities of $\frac{1}{2}$? Look at the original proposed experiment and the outcome desired. Are each of the events (individual coin flips) tied together in the experiment by *and* or *or*? This may seem to be a silly question but it is not. For example, suppose someone asked these questions of you, how would you answer?

Question 1: Do you want coffee *and* cream?

Question 2: Do you want coffee *or* cream?

Answering "yes" to question 1 gets you coffee with cream mixed in it. Answering "yes" to question 2 is meaningless. Question 2 says that you can have either coffee or you can have cream but you cannot have a mixture. There are two different rules to take care of this situation.

If the events are described as "this happens *or* that happens," then the **addition**

rule tells us that we should add up the probabilities of the mutually exclusive events to determine the probability that any one of these events might occur.

Rule

Addition Rule for Mutually Exclusive Events

$$P(A \text{ or } B) = P(A) + P(B)$$

EXAMPLE 20   Mutually Exclusive Events

If A is the event of drawing an ace from a standard deck of 52 playing cards and B is the event of drawing a king, then what is the probability of drawing an ace or a king from the deck on a single draw?

Can you draw *both* an ace and a king on one draw? No! There is no single card in the deck that is both an ace and a king. Thus, these two events, drawing an ace or drawing a king, are mutually exclusive events and the probability can be calculated with the addition rule as follows:

$$P(A) = P(\text{ace}) = \frac{4}{52} = \frac{1}{13}$$

$$P(B) = P(\text{king}) = \frac{4}{52} = \frac{1}{13}$$

$$P(A \text{ or } B) = P(A) + P(B) = \frac{1}{13} + \frac{1}{13}$$

$$P(\text{ace or king}) = \frac{2}{13}$$

Of course, not all events are mutually exclusive. For example, what if you were asked to choose the name of a student in your class from the class roll or choose a male student from the same class. Would it be possible to choose one name and have both events occur? Yes, you could draw the name of a class member who was also a male. Thus, the events are not mutually exclusive. Here is a modification of the addition rule to cover this situation.

Rule

Addition Rule for Events That Are Not Mutually Exclusive

$$P(A \text{ or } B) = P(A) + P(B) - P(A \text{ and } B)$$

EXAMPLE 21   **Drawing Objects from a Container**

A container holds 15 balls and 15 cubes. Seven balls and 7 cubes are painted red, 4 balls and 4 cubes are painted blue, and 4 balls and 4 cubes are painted green. You are to reach into the container and draw out one object at random. Determine whether each of the following pairs of events are mutually exclusive and then calculate $P(A \text{ or } B)$ for each pair.

(a) $P(\text{a cube or a red object})$
(b) $P(\text{a cube or a ball})$
(c) $P(\text{a blue ball or a blue object})$

(a) Because it is possible to draw both a cube and a red object in one draw, these events are *not mutually exclusive*.

$$P(\text{a cube}) = \frac{15}{30} = \frac{1}{2}$$

$$P(\text{a red object}) = \frac{14}{30} = \frac{7}{15}$$

$$P(\text{a cube and a red object}) = \frac{7}{30}$$

$$P(\text{a cube or a red object}) = P(\text{a cube}) + P(\text{a red object})$$
$$- P(\text{a cube and a red object})$$

$$P(\text{a cube or a red object}) = \frac{15}{30} + \frac{14}{30} - \frac{7}{30} = \frac{22}{30} = \frac{11}{15}$$

(b) Because you cannot draw one object and have it be both a cube and a ball, these are *mutually exclusive* events.

$$P(\text{a cube}) = \frac{15}{30} = \frac{1}{2}$$

$$P(\text{a ball}) = \frac{15}{30} = \frac{1}{2}$$

$$P(\text{a cube or a ball}) = P(\text{a cube}) + P(\text{a ball}) = \frac{1}{2} + \frac{1}{2} = 1$$

It is certain that you will draw a cube or a ball if there are no other objects in the container.

(c) Because a blue ball and a blue object can be drawn at the same time, this is *not a mutually exclusive* event.

$$P(\text{a blue ball}) = \frac{4}{30} = \frac{2}{15}$$

$$P(\text{a blue object}) = \frac{8}{30} = \frac{4}{15}$$

$$P(\text{a blue ball and a blue object}) = \frac{4}{30} = \frac{2}{15}$$

$$P(\text{a blue ball or a blue object}) = \frac{2}{15} + \frac{4}{15} - \frac{2}{15} = \frac{4}{15}$$

A second type of problem is the "*and*" probability problem that requires obtaining a favorable outcome in each of several different events. If the events are described as "this happens *and* that happens," then the **multiplication rule** tells us to multiply the probabilities of the outcomes for each event in the series to find the probability that these events will all occur together. *Note:* We must always assume that event A has occurred before calculating the probability of event B.

Rule

Multiplication Rule

$$P(A \text{ and } B) = P(A) \cdot P(B)$$

EXAMPLE 22   Selecting Cards from a Deck with Replacement

Two cards are selected at random from a standard deck of 52 playing cards. Find the probability that two aces will be selected in a row if the first card is replaced into the deck before drawing the second card.

We are asked to calculate the following:

$P(\text{ace and ace, with replacement})$

$P(\text{ace}) = \dfrac{4}{52} = \dfrac{1}{13}$, each time

$P(\text{ace and ace, with replacement}) = \left(\dfrac{1}{13}\right)\left(\dfrac{1}{13}\right) = \dfrac{1}{169}$

EXAMPLE 23   Selecting Cards without Replacement

Two cards are selected at random from a standard deck of 52 playing cards. Find the probability that two aces will be selected in a row if the first card is *not* replaced into the deck before drawing the second card.

We are asked to calculate the following:

$P(\text{ace and ace, without replacement})$

This will change the probability of drawing a second ace. We are to assume that an ace is selected on the first draw before calculating the probability of the second event (see the note that precedes the multiplication rule). Because there are only 3 aces remaining in the deck of 51 cards, the probability of drawing a second ace is changed.

$$P(\text{first ace}) = \frac{4}{52} = \frac{1}{13}$$

$$P(\text{second ace, without replacement}) = \frac{3}{51} = \frac{1}{17}$$

$$P(\text{ace and ace, without replacement}) = \left(\frac{1}{13}\right)\left(\frac{1}{17}\right) = \frac{1}{221}$$

Compare the result for this example with the previous one and note the differences.

EXAMPLE 24   Calculating the Probability of a Series of Events

What is the probability that you would flip a coin twice and then roll a pair of dice and have the results be two tails and a total of 5 on the dice?

Is this an "and" or an "or" type of problem? It can be restated this way: The result desired is tails and another tails and a total of 5. Therefore, use the multiplication rule. First, determine all the individual probabilities and multiply them together.

$$P(\text{T}) = \frac{1}{2} \text{ each time}$$

$$P(\text{total of 5 on 2 dice}) = \frac{4}{36} = \frac{1}{9} \text{ (see Practice Set 6-4, problem 15)}$$

$$P(\text{T and T and 5}) = \left(\frac{1}{2}\right)\left(\frac{1}{2}\right)\left(\frac{1}{9}\right) = \frac{1}{36}$$

Practice Set 6-5

1. One card is selected at random from a deck of cards. Find the probability of selecting a king or a queen. Are these events mutually exclusive? Why or why not?

2. One card is selected at random from a deck of cards. Find the probability of selecting an ace or a club. Are these events mutually exclusive? Why or why not?

3. One card is selected at random from a deck of cards. Find the probability of selecting a black card or a spade. Are these events mutually exclusive? Why or why not?

4. One card is selected at random from a deck of cards. Find the probability of selecting a red card or a black card. Are these events mutually exclusive? Why or why not?

5. One card is selected at random from a deck of cards. Find the probability of selecting a face card or a black card. Are these events mutually exclusive? Why or why not?

6. One card is selected at random from a deck of cards. Find the probability of selecting a 2 or a 5. Are these events mutually exclusive? Why or why not?

7. Each of the numbers 0, 2, 4, 6, 8, 10, 12, and 14 is written on a separate sheet of paper and placed into a box. One piece of paper is selected at random. Find the probability that the piece of paper selected contains the number 2 or a number greater than 2.

8. Each of the numbers 0, 2, 4, 6, 8, 10, 12, and 14 is written on a separate sheet of paper and placed into a box. One piece of paper is selected at random. Find the probability that the piece of paper selected contains the number 8 or a number less than 12.

9. A single die is rolled one time. Find the probability of rolling an odd number or a number greater than 2.

10. A single die is rolled one time. Find the probability of rolling a number greater than 5 or less than 3.

11. What is the probability of drawing two face cards when two cards are selected from a deck of cards without replacement?

12. What is the probability of drawing two face cards when two cards are selected from a deck of cards with replacement?

A package of 24 zinnia seeds contains 7 seeds for red flowers, 12 seeds for white flowers, and 5 seeds for yellow flowers. Three seeds are randomly selected and planted.

13. Find the probability that all three seeds will produce white flowers.

14. Find the probability that the first seed selected will produce a yellow flower, the second seed will produce a red flower, and the third seed will produce a yellow flower.

15. Find the probability that none of the seeds will produce red flowers.

16. Find the probability that the first seed selected will produce a red flower, the second seed will produce a yellow flower, and the third seed will produce a white flower.

Dan is a good, but not great, chess player. Based on past tournament experience, his chances of winning any single game are $\frac{2}{5}$.

17. What is the probability that Dan will win the second and third games of a five-game match and lose all the others?

18. What is the probability that he will win all five games?

19. What is the probability that he will lose all five games?

20. Each letter of the word *Mississippi* is placed on a piece of paper and all 11 pieces of paper are placed in a hat. Three letters are selected at random from the hat and are not replaced.
    (a) Find the probability that three consonants are selected.
    (b) Find the probability that the first letter selected is a vowel, the second letter is a consonant, and the third letter is a vowel.

21. Repeat problem 20 with replacement.

A family has three children. Assuming independence, find the following probabilities.

22. All three are boys.

23. The youngest child is a boy and the older children are girls.

24. The youngest child is a girl, the middle child is a girl, and the oldest child is a boy.

25. All three are girls.

Section 6-6   **PERMUTATIONS AND COMBINATIONS**

An alternative to creating tree diagrams is to mathematically calculate the number of possible outcomes for a single experiment (tossing a coin once) or for each experiment in a series (tossing a coin twice) and then use these calculated values to count the number of items in the sample space. Using the appropriate formula will require that you first understand some new terms.

The counting principle was introduced in Section 6-4. It is repeated here for your convenience.

Rule

Counting Principle
If a first experiment can be performed in X distinct ways and a second experiment can be performed in Y distinct ways, then the two experiments in that specific order can be performed in X times Y distinct ways.

■ EXAMPLE 25   **Arranging Books on a Shelf: The Counting Principle**

In how many ways can nine different books be arranged on a shelf?

Because there are nine different books, by the counting principle the number of possible arrangements will be $9(8)(7)(6)(5)(4)(3)(2)(1) = 362{,}880$.

Another way to calculate $9(8)(7)(6)(5)(4)(3)(2)(1)$ is to use what is called a **factorial**. A factorial is an algebraic shorthand. Nine factorial is written as 9!.

Important Equations

Factorial

If n is a positive integer, then n factorial ($n!$) is given by

$$n! = n(n-1)(n-2)(n-3)\ldots(2)(1)$$

This definition is usually extended to include zero factorial, although it is not usually needed. By definition, $0! = 1$.

Calculator Mini-Lesson

Factorial

Any *standard scientific calculator* has a key that will automatically calculate the value of a factorial. Look for a key or the second function of a key labeled $\boxed{x!}$. To test this key, simply type in a number like 9 and then press the $\boxed{x!}$ key. The calculator should show you the same value as was obtained in Example 26.

A *graphing calculator (TI-83 Plus)* also has a factorial function, but it is harder to find. Type in a number like 9. Press the $\boxed{\text{MATH}}$ key and use the right arrow key to highlight $\boxed{\text{PRB}}$ at the top of the screen. Use the down arrow key to highlight $\boxed{4:!}$. Press $\boxed{\text{ENTER}}$ and then press $\boxed{\text{ENTER}}$ again to see the result.

EXAMPLE 26   Calculating Factorials

Find the value of each of the following.

(a)
$$3! = ?$$
$$3! = 3(2)(1) = 6$$

(b)
$$7! = ?$$
$$7! = 7(6)(5)(4)(3)(2)(1) = 5040$$

EXAMPLE 27   More on Factorials and the Calculator

Using your calculator, find the value of each of the following.

(a) $5! = ?$
(b) $9! = ?$
(c) $12! = ?$
(d) $3.8! = ?$
(e) $0! = ?$

Here are the answers that the calculator should give you:

(a) $5! = 120$
(b) $9! = 362{,}880$
(c) $12! = 479{,}001{,}600$
(d) $3.8! = $ E or Error (remember, integers only)
(e) $0! = 1$

We must also consider the idea of the *order* in which events occur. Consider the experiment of tossing a coin twice, as shown in Example 14. The sample space is $S = \{HH, HT, TH, TT\}$. If you determine the probability of tossing heads once and tails once (and it does not matter which is tossed first), then $P(HT \text{ or } TH) = \frac{2}{4} = \frac{1}{2}$. However, if you wish to determine the probability of tossing heads on the first of two tosses and tails second (i.e., order does matter), then $P(HT) = \frac{1}{4}$. It is clear that whether or not order is important does affect the probability of individual events.

The number of different ways that a set of objects or events can be placed in a specific order is called a **permutation**, and the number of ways that a set of objects or events can be selected without regard to order is called a **combination**. Referring to the example mentioned previously, HT and TH are two different permutations of the same combination. If order matters, then the number of permutations will be calculated, and if order does not matter, then the number of combinations will be calculated.

Important Equations

Permutations

If there are n distinct objects or events possible and you are going to choose r objects or events each time ($r \leq n$), then the number of permutations is given by

$$_nP_r = \frac{n!}{(n-r)!}$$

Note: Order is important here.

Combinations

If there are n distinct objects or events possible and you are going to choose r objects or events each time ($r \leq n$), then the number of combinations is given by

$$_nC_r = \frac{n!}{r!(n-r)!}$$

Note: Order is not important here.

Calculator Mini-Lesson

Combinations and Permutations

There are two keys on a *standard scientific calculator* that are used to determine the number of combinations or permutations. These keys have the same symbols on them as shown in the definitions given previously, $\boxed{_nC_r}$ and $\boxed{_nP_r}$. Using these keys is simple. First, enter the value of n. Next, press the $\boxed{_nC_r}$ or $\boxed{_nP_r}$ and then enter the value of r. The calculator should then display the value.

On a *graphing calculator (TI-83 Plus)*, enter the value of n. Press $\boxed{\text{MATH}}$ and use the right arrow key to highlight $\boxed{\text{PRB}}$. Move down to $\boxed{3:_nC_r}$ or $\boxed{2:_nP_r}$ and press $\boxed{\text{ENTER}}$. Type in the value of r and then press enter to display the answer.

■ EXAMPLE 28   **Choosing a Committee (Combinations)**

Suppose that a committee is to be chosen by drawing names from members of your math class. We will say that there are 20 persons in your class and that a committee will consist of three names drawn at random. If the order in which names are to be drawn has no effect on the final makeup of the committee, then how many different committees are possible?

Because order is unimportant, the number of possible combinations should be calculated.

$$n = 20 \qquad r = 3$$

$$_nC_r = \frac{n!}{r!(n-r)!} = \frac{20!}{3!(20-3)!} = 1140$$

As complicated as this looks, wouldn't a shortcut or some mechanical assistance be nice?

Using the calculator as described in the last Calculator Mini-Lesson,

$$_nC_r = {}_{20}C_3 = 1140$$

This seems large, but it is the number of different possible committees of three persons that can be chosen from a class of 20.

■ EXAMPLE 29   **Choosing Officers for a Committee (Permutations)**

Suppose that officers are to be chosen by drawing names from members of your math class. We will say that there are 20 persons in your class and that the officers will consist of three names drawn at random. If the order in which names are to be drawn has some effect on the final makeup (e.g., the first name drawn will be chair, the second the secretary, and the third person will do all the work), then how many different sets of officers are possible?

Because order does make a difference, we will calculate the number of permutations possible.

$$_nP_r = {}_{20}P_3 = 6840$$

This is a much larger number than in the previous example. Why is that? If order does not matter (see Example 28), then if James, Jane, and Joe are chosen, it will be the same committee no matter whose name is chosen first, second, or third. However, if order matters because of the office and duties assigned, then the list of possibilities for James, Jane, and Joe actually form six *different* sets of officers.

■ EXAMPLE 30   **Winning the Lottery: Fat Chance!**

What are your chances of winning the Texas Lottery? The Texas Lottery Cash Five game requires that you choose five numbers from 1 to 37. You may not choose the same number twice.

(a) How many different combinations of the 37 numbers are possible?
(b) What is the probability that your five numbers would win?

(a) $_nC_r = {}_{37}C_5 = 435{,}897$ different lottery tickets are possible.
(b) If you buy one ticket, your chance of picking the correct five-number combination is 1 in 435,897. In other words, you are wasting your money to enter because you are not going to win.

$$P(\text{win}) = \frac{1}{435{,}897}$$

■ EXAMPLE 31   **Letter Arrangements**

Consider the five letters a, b, c, d, and e. In how many distinct ways can three letters be selected and arranged if repetition is not allowed?
This is a permutation of five things taken three at a time.

$$_5P_3 = 60$$

We could also solve this problem using the counting principle. There are five possible letters for the first choice, four for the second choice, and three for the third choice:

$$5(4)(3) = 60$$

Therefore, there are 60 possible ordered arrangements or permutations.

Practice Set 6-6

Determine each of the following combinations, permutations, and factorials.

1. $_7C_2$ **2.** $_{15}C_5$ **3.** $_7P_2$ **4.** $_{13}P_8$

5. 9!   **6.** 18!   **7.** $(-8)!$ **8.** 5.65!

9. Describe the differences between combinations and permutations.

10. A student must select and answer any four of five essay questions on a test. In how many ways can she do so?

11. There are 10 girls on the golf team at East High. How many different four-girl teams may be chosen by the coach if Jane must be on the team?

12. A standard deck of playing cards has 52 different cards. A poker hand contains five cards. How many different poker hands are possible?

13. You are the coach of a nine-person baseball team. How many different batting orders are possible?

14. You have seven different books. How may different ways may they be arranged on a bookshelf?

15. Angelo's Pizza offers its customers a choice of pizza toppings. You may choose from onions, green peppers, hot peppers, mushrooms, and pepperoni. The base for all of the pizzas is cheese. A pizza may have any number of toppings that the customer desires. How many different pizzas are possible?

16. To win the jackpot of a state lottery, the six numbers chosen by a person, from 1 through 54, must be the same as the six numbers selected at random by the state lottery system. On each lottery ticket purchased, there are two separate selections for the six numbers. (Repetition of numbers is not permitted.) What is the probability of winning the jackpot with one ticket?

17. In how many different ways may four persons be seated in a row of four rocking chairs?

18. In how many different ways may six students be seated in a row with eight seats?

19. Using the letters of the word *algorithm* and calling any arrangement of letters a word:
    (a) How many different nine-letter words may be formed?
    (b) How many different four-letter words may be formed?

20. In how many different ways may three boys and three girls be seated in a row if they must alternate boy, girl?

21. In boating, colored flags, arranged in various orders and combinations, have been used for centuries to convey messages to other boats and ships or the persons on shore. If you have three red, three green, and two blue flags, how many different messages (arrangements) could you put up on the mast of the ship if you used

(a) all eight flags at one time?
(b) only three flags at one time?
(c) only four flags at one time?

22. Alvin Community College's identification number consists of a letter followed by four digits. How many different identification numbers are possible if repetition is not permitted?

23. The daily double at most racetracks consists of selecting the winning horse in both the first and the second races. If the first race has eight entries and the second race has nine entries, how many daily-double tickets must you purchase to guarantee a win?

24. The Stereo Shop's warehouse has 12 different receivers in stock. The owner of the chain calls the warehouse requesting that a different receiver be sent to each of five stores. How many ways can the receivers be distributed?

25. A social security number consists of nine digits. How many different social security numbers are possible if repetition of digits is permitted?

26. An ice cream parlor has 31 different flavors. Maribeth orders a banana split and has to select three different flavors. How many different selections are possible?

27. At a car rental agency, the agent has 10 midsized cars on his lot and six people have reserved midsized cars. In how many different ways can the six cars to be used be selected?

28. If your class has 10 males and 14 females in it, how many different committees consisting of 4 males and 4 females may be chosen?

29. A committee of three judges is considering nine people for a reality show. The committee has decided to select three of the nine for further consideration. In how many ways can it do so?

30. At the beginning of the semester, your teacher informs the class that she marks on a curve and exactly 5 of the 26 students in the class will receive a final grade of A. In how many ways can this result occur?

Section 6-7   APPLIED PROBABILITY PROBLEMS

There are many applications of probability in our daily lives. The weather forecast may give the probability of rain for today. Prescription information may give the probability of a particular side effect occurring if you use that drug. Calculating probabilities can be quite complicated. In this section, we will demonstrate some simple applications of the probability techniques that we have studied.

EXAMPLE 32   Delegations

The National Honor Society at Williams High School has 18 members. A delegation of four members must be chosen to attend an upcoming national meeting. The members decide to draw names at random.

(a) How many different delegations are possible?
(b) How many different delegations that include Jose are possible?
(c) How many that do not include Jose?

(a) Order is not a factor, so the number of possible combinations should be calculated as follows:

$$_nC_r = {}_{18}C_4 = 3060$$

(b) If Jose is sure to be in the delegation, then the other three members must be chosen at random from the 17 remaining members as follows:

$$_nC_r = {}_{17}C_3 = 680$$

(c) If Jose is sure not to be in the delegation, then it is as if Jose's name was not even in the hat to be drawn. The delegation of 4 will be drawn from the other 17 members who are not Jose as follows:

$$_nC_r = {}_{17}C_4 = 2380$$

Note: The total of all delegations with Jose plus the total of all delegations without Jose equals the total number of possible delegations that could be chosen:

$$680 + 2380 = 3060$$

EXAMPLE 33   A Quality Control Problem

A manufacturer of computer chips requires that four chips from each lot of 25 be tested for proper function by the company's quality control department. If one or more of the chips tested are defective, then the entire lot of 25 will be rejected. If a certain lot were to contain 3 defective chips and 22 good chips, what is the probability that this lot would pass inspection?

First, what is the size of the sample space? In other words, how many different combinations of four computer chips can be chosen?

$$_nC_r = {}_{25}C_4 = 12{,}650$$

Second, how many different ways can four chips be chosen involving only the 22 good ones?

$$_nC_r = {}_{22}C_4 = 7315$$

Thus, the probability that the lot will pass inspection is

$$P(\text{lot passes}) = \frac{7315}{12{,}650} = 0.578 \,(= \text{about a } 60\% \text{ chance})$$

EXAMPLE 34   **Choosing a Cereal**

The Kellogg Company is testing 14 new cereals for possible production. It is testing 4 oat cereals, 5 wheat cereals, and 5 rice cereals. If we assume that each of the 14 cereals has the same chance of being selected and 4 new cereals will be produced, find the probability that no wheat cereals will be selected for production.

If no wheat cereals are to be selected, then only oat or rice cereals can be selected. A total of 9 cereals are oat or rice. So the number of ways that 4 oat or rice cereals may be selected from the 9 possible oat or rice cereals is $_9C_4$. The total number of possible selections is $_{14}C_4$.

$$P(\text{no wheat cereals}) = \frac{_9C_4}{_{14}C_4} = \frac{126}{1001} = \frac{18}{143}$$

Practice Set 6-7

1. A bag contains five red balls and four blue balls. You plan to draw three balls at random without replacement. Find the probability of selecting three red balls.

2. Repeat problem 1 with replacement.

3. Each of the numbers 1–6 is written on a piece of paper, and the six pieces of paper are placed in a hat. If two numbers are selected at random without replacement, find the probability that both numbers selected will be even.

4. Repeat problem 3 with replacement.

5. A box contains four good and four defective batteries. If you select three batteries at random without replacement, find the probability that you will select three good batteries.

6. Repeat problem 5 with replacement.

7. Dan's wallet contains eight bills of the following denominations: four $5 bills, two $10 bills, one $20 bill, and one $50 bill. If Dan selects two bills at random without replacement, determine the probability that he will select two $5 bills.

8. Repeat problem 7 with replacement.

9. How many different "words" (the "words" do not have to be meaningful) can be made using
   (a) all the letters in the word *modern*?
   (b) only four letters at a time?

10. You have a penny, a nickel, a dime, and a quarter in your pocket and no other coins. You reach into your pocket and remove two coins at random.
    (a) What is the sample space?
    (b) What is the probability that one of the coins is a nickel?
    (c) What is the probability that the total value of the two coins is greater than 10 cents?

11. An airplane has 10 empty seats left: six aisle seats and four window seats. If four people about to board the plane are given seat numbers at random, what is the probability that they are all given aisle seats?

12. Some slot machines in Las Vegas, Nevada, have three wheels that spin when you pull the "arm" of these one-armed bandits. To win, each wheel must show a picture of an apple when they all stop turning. Each wheel has 20 pictures on it. Wheel 1 has five apples on it, wheel 2 has three apples on it, and wheel 3 has two apples on it. What is the probability that you will win on the first pull?

13. Lowest Bidder Computer Chip Company ships out its memory chips in lots of 100. Three memory chips chosen at random from each lot are inspected by its quality control department. If any chip inspected is found to be defective, then the entire lot is rejected.
    (a) What is the probability that a lot containing two defective chips will pass this inspection?
    (b) What do you think of this quality control procedure?

14. Four friends join the army at the same time. They will be assigned duties at random in either the infantry or the artillery. What is the probability that two of these friends will be assigned to each service area?

15. Suppose that you have invited 10 relatives to a party at your house. You invite your mom, two

uncles, three brothers, and four cousins. What is the probability that the first guest to arrive will be one of your uncles?

16. You are dealt five cards from a deck of 52 cards. Find the probability that you are dealt five red cards.

17. A committee of four is to be randomly selected from a group of seven administrators and eight instructors. Find the probability that the committee will consist of four instructors.

18. A three-person committee will be selected at random from five Democrats and three Republicans. Find the probability that all three selected will be Democrats.

19. Each of the digits 0, 1, 2, 3, 4, 5, 6, 7, 8, and 9 is written on a slip of paper, and the slips are placed in a hat. If three slips of paper are selected at random without replacement, find the probability that the three numbers selected will be greater than 4.

20. Repeat problem 19 with replacement.

Investigate each of the following situations involving telephone numbers. In each case, determine the total number of phone numbers that could be made available for use.

21. At Laredo Community College (LCC), each office extension begins with a 5 and has four digits. How many different telephone extensions can LCC have?

22. Local phone numbers are seven digits long. No local phone number may begin with a 0 or 1. How many different local phone numbers are possible within a given area code?

23. Recently the central area of North Carolina was split into two area codes by BellSouth. The old area code was 910 and the new area code is 336. Some people had to change their area code to 336 and some kept the 910 area code. Speculate about why this was done.

24. If, in the not-too-distant future, a worldwide government wanted each individual to have his or her own personal phone number, would the current 10-digit system (counting the three area code digits) work? Explain your answer.

Chapter Summary

Key Terms, Properties, and Formulas

addition rule	factorial	outcomes
combination	independent events	permutation
conditional probability	independent outcome	probability
counting principle	law of large numbers	random
empirical probability	laws of probability	sample space
equally likely outcomes	multiplication rule	theoretical probability
event	mutually exclusive events	tree diagram
experiment	odds	

Formulas to Remember

Empirical probability:

$$P(E) = \frac{\text{number of times the event has occurred}}{\text{total number of times the experiment has been performed}}$$

Theoretical probability:

$$P(E) = \frac{\text{number of successful outcomes possible}}{\text{total number of possible outcomes}} = \frac{s}{N}$$

Calculating a factorial:

$$n! = n(n - 1)(n - 2) \ldots (2)(1)$$

Zero factorial — definition:

$$0! = 1$$

Permutations:

$$_nP_r = \frac{n!}{(n - r)!}$$

Combinations:

$$_nC_r = \frac{n!}{r!(n - r)!}$$

$$\text{Odds in favor of an event} = s : f$$

$$\text{Odds against an event} = f : s$$

Probability laws

Law 1:
Every probability is a number between 0 and 1 (inclusive).

Law 2:
The sum of the probabilities for all outcomes for a particular sample space is exactly 1.

Law 3:
The probability of an event occurring that cannot possibly happen is 0.

Law 4:
The probability of an event that must occur is 1.
Mathematical relationships:

$$P(A) + P(\text{not } A) = 1$$

$$P(\text{not } A) = 1 - P(A)$$

Chapter Review Problems

1. What is probability?

2. Two of the basic rules used in computing probabilities are the addition rule and the multiplication rule. Explain when each of these rules should be used.

3. What is the difference between the "probability" of an event and the "odds in favor" of that same event?

4. If you toss a pair of dice, what is the probability that the sum of the two numbers shown will be 8?

5. If you toss a pair of dice, what is the probability that the sum of the two numbers shown will be 13?

6. If you toss a pair of dice, what is the probability that the sum of the two numbers shown will be less than 7?

A small box contains 20 marbles. Eight of them are green, seven are red, and five are blue.

7. What is the probability that you will reach into the box and draw out a red marble?

8. What is the probability that you will reach into the box and draw out a green or a blue marble?

9. If you are going to draw out three marbles, one at a time, and you are not going to replace the marbles in the box once they are drawn, what is the probability that all three will be blue?

A group of students chosen at random were asked if they drank beer or not. The following table summarizes the results of this brief survey.

	Drinkers	Nondrinkers	Total
Men	63	50	113
Women	39	48	87
Total	102	98	200

10. If you chose one of these students at random, what is the probability that the person chosen will be a male who drinks beer?

11. What is the probability that you will choose a female who does not drink beer?

12. What is the probability of choosing a student who drinks given that the person chosen is a male?

13. What is the probability of choosing a woman given that the person chosen is a nondrinker?

14. What are the odds in favor of drawing a face card from an ordinary deck of 52 cards?

A social security number has nine digits, such as 000-00-0000.

15. How many different social security numbers are possible?

16. If the population of the United States in 2000 was about 300 million people, and we assume that the population will double each 25 years, will this numbering system need to be changed before 2050?

17. A certain manufacturing operation is known to produce two bad parts out of 75, on the average. If you walk up to the production line and choose one part, what is the probability that it is a good part?

18. Last year it rained on 92 days in Midville, Arkansas. If you pick a calendar date from last year at random, what is the probability that it rained on that day?

The following table gives the results of a poll concerning the evening news watched most often.

	ABC	NBC	CBS	Fox	Total
Men	30	20	40	25	115
Women	50	10	20	20	100
Total	80	30	60	45	215

19. If one of the individuals involved in this poll is selected at random, find the probability that this person watches ABC or NBC.

20. If one of the individuals involved in this poll is selected at random, find the probability that this person watches ABC or the individual is a woman.

21. If one of the individuals involved in this poll is selected at random, find the probability that this person watches Fox, given that the person is a male.

22. A \$100, a \$50, and a \$20 prize are to be awarded to three different people. If seven people are being considered for the prizes, how many different arrangements are possible?

23. How many different committees can be formed from six teachers and 50 students if the committee is to consist of two teachers and three students?

24. An ice cream parlor has 15 different flavors. Cynthia orders a banana split and has to select three different flavors. How many different combinations are possible?

25. Alan bought eight raffle tickets to try to win a TV. What are his odds of winning if 1500 tickets were sold altogether?

Find the numerical value of each of the following.

26. $4!$ 27. $-2!$ 28. $5.2!$

29. $_7C_3$ 30. $_7P_5$ 31. $_{23}C_3$

Chapter Test

You are going to flip a coin once and roll a single die once.

1. What is the sample space for this experiment?

2. What is the probability of flipping the coin and getting heads and rolling a 5 on the die?

3. What is $P\{$tail, and an even number$\}$?

One hundred and fifty residents of Lamb County were surveyed. They were asked first whether or not they lived within the city limits of the city of Littlefield. Second, they were asked if they thought that they had adequate fire protection services available in the event of a fire at their home. The city of Littlefield has a full-time fire department with several fire stations, whereas the county has only volunteer fire protection services available. The following table gives the results of this survey.

Residence	Adequate	Inadequate	Totals
In city	56	34	90
In county	29	31	60
Total	85	65	150

4. Find P(adequate fire protection is available).

5. Find P(adequate fire protection is available | the person lives in the county).

6. Find P(inadequate protection | the person lives in the city).

7. A code is to consist of three digits followed by three letters. Find the number of possible codes if

the first digit cannot be a 0 or 1 and replacement is not permitted.

You are bet by a friend that he can roll a single die one time and have an even number show up.

8. What are the odds that you will win if you take the bet?

9. What is the probability of rolling an even number?

10. Three accountants, Bill, Jane, and Doris, are all up for promotion in the CPA firm where they work. If the probability that Bill will be promoted is 0.25 and the probability that Jane will be promoted is 0.34, then what is the probability that Doris will be promoted?

Bob has three Scrabble tiles with the letters *t*, *o*, and *a* on them.

11. How many three-letter "words" can Bob make using just these letters?

12. How many of these "words" are meaningful in English?

13. If Bob closes his eyes and places these three tiles on the game board, what is the probability that he will create a meaningful word?

14. The state of "Confusion" issues license plates with four digits on them. The digits used are 1–9 (no 0s) and digits may be repeated. You are going to get a new license plate for your new car. What is the probability that the new plate will have all four numbers the same (like 8888)?

A standard deck of playing cards has four suits and two colors as follows: spades (♠) are black, hearts (♥) are red, diamonds (♦) are red, and clubs (♣) are black. Each suit has 13 cards: an ace (A); cards numbered 2–10; and three face cards, a king (K), a queen (Q), and a jack (J).

15. What is the probability of drawing a red card?

16. What is the probability of drawing a queen?

17. What is the probability of drawing the 3 of diamonds, replacing it in the deck, shuffling, and then drawing the 3 of diamonds again?

18. What is the probability of drawing a face card or a diamond?

19. At a horse race, such as the Kentucky Derby, the tote board gives those betting the odds assigned to each horse. These are the odds against winning. Using the following tote board, calculate the probability of winning for a bet placed on each horse.

Horse Name	Odds
Ringo	3 to 1
Bonnie	15 to 1
Clyde	8 to 5
Zero	3 to 2

20. A new family has just moved into the house next door. You have heard that they have four children. What is the probability that they have two boys and two girls?

21. How many different ways can six photos be arranged from left to right on a hallway wall?

22. If the probability of an event is 1, what is the probability that it will not occur?

23. There are 10 true/false questions on a test. If you guess the answers to all 10, what is the probability that you will miss all of the questions, resulting in a grade of 0?

A group of 60 married couples were surveyed and then went to marriage counseling classes. Thirty-six of the 60 couples reported that their marital relations were improved by the counseling. Of these 36 couples, 27 had children.

24. What is the probability of selecting a couple at random that reported no improvement in their relations due to counseling?

25. What is the probability of selecting a couple with children if your choices are limited to those who reported an improvement?

26. What is the probability of selecting, from among all 60 couples, a couple who reported improvement but has no children?

Suggested Laboratory Exercises

LAB EXERCISE 1 ## A Simple Survey

Certain physical traits are not evenly distributed in the general population. For example, there are more right-handed than left-handed people. Conduct a survey of persons chosen at random at your high school. Do *not* ask any members of your class itself. To do this survey in a short time, the questions will be limited to three: (1) Are you right- or left-handed? (2) What color is your hair? (3) What color are your eyes? Complete the following table by filling in all of the data collected. Ask a total of at least 100 students.

Handedness	Number of Persons
Right-handed	
Left-handed	

Eye Color	Number of Persons
Brown	
Blue	
Green	
Other	

Hair Color	Number of Persons
Brown	
Blond	
Black	
Red	

Now compare your class members to the survey results. What proportion of your class should be right-handed? Does this match your class? What is the probability that a student will have brown hair? How many students in your class should have brown hair? How many actually do? Answer the same questions about eye color (you pick the color).

LAB EXERCISE 2 ## Devising a Game

Make up a game using dice like a game of 8s. If you roll a total of 8 on two dice, you win. Find the probability of rolling an 8 and see if this probability seems to be true by rolling the dice a large number of times. Will you win a lot of money at this game?

LAB EXERCISE 3 ## A "Tacky" Lab

Get an ordinary thumbtack. Flip the thumbtack into the air and let it land on a hard surface. When it stops moving, note whether it lands point up. Do this 100 times and record the results each time. What is the probability of the thumbtack landing point up? Is the probability of landing point down the same? Why or why not?

LAB EXERCISE 4   ## Don't Lose Your Marbles

Get a jar and a series of colored marbles, such as five red, two blue, and three yellow. Do an experiment to show that the probability of drawing three red marbles in a row is different if you keep each marble drawn rather than replacing each one before drawing the next.

LAB EXERCISE 5   ## Walk On By

Pick a well-traveled hallway or sidewalk at your school. Choose a short time period (5 or 10 minutes) and count the number of persons walking past during each time interval. It may take several days, counting for an hour or so at the same time each day, to get sufficient data. The data may look something like the following data set.

Number of Students Walking Past	Number of 10-Minute Periods
0–5	6
6–10	15
11–15	17
16–20	15
21–25	5
26 or more	2
Total	60

(a) Determine the probability for each count. For example, 0–5 persons walked by during 6 of the 60 time periods $= \frac{6}{60} = \frac{1}{10}$.

(b) Determine the probability that 16 students will walk by during the next 10-minute counting period.

(c) Determine the probability that more than five persons will walk by during the next 10-minute counting period.

(d) Determine the probability that more than 5 but fewer than 16 persons will walk by during the next 10-minute counting period.

(e) What are the important considerations in setting up an experiment such as this?

chapter seven

Modeling with Statistics

"He uses statistics as a drunken man uses lampposts — for support rather than illumination."
– Andrew Lang

Collecting, classifying, and summarizing quantitative information or facts and then using this information to make *informed* decisions is the basic aim of the area of mathematics called *statistics*. In this chapter, you will be introduced to the fundamentals of this topic. Even if all that you learn from this chapter is how to recognize when statistical procedures have been misused by some group, business, organization, or government agency, then this chapter will have been worth your time.

Section 7-1 INTRODUCTION TO STATISTICS

Statistics is the area of mathematics that is involved with collecting, classifying, summarizing, and presenting data that have been collected. Businesses of all kinds collect data about sales, customer preferences, national trends, and their own costs. Manufacturers collect data about the quality and reliability of their products and compare theirs with those of the competition. Researchers in medicine, environmental areas, computer science, physics, astronomy, and so forth all collect volumes of data. Advertisers and politicians use polls to collect data that are then used to fine-tune their messages. Sports fans collect reams of data on their favorite sports or sports figures.

We are surrounded by data. A fundamental knowledge of statistics will allow us to deal with data in an honest and skillful manner. It will also help us to look objectively and critically at someone else's presentation of data and form our own conclusions. We must become good consumers of data.

This chapter is not intended to be a complete course in statistics. It will just introduce the topic and explore some of the fundamentals of statistics. The basics of data collection and analysis will be studied. A lot of new terminology will be used, but even though the words may be strange, the meanings are usually fairly simple.

There are two broad areas of statistics, **descriptive statistics** and **inferential statistics**. The area of descriptive statistics classifies, sorts, and summarizes data. Generally speaking, **data** are numerical facts or information. Once the data have been presented in a uniform way, they may be used to calculate averages and other numerical values as well as to construct tables or graphs. As long as only the quantitative *facts* are presented, you are working in the area of descriptive statistics. Most of this chapter deals with the area of descriptive statistics.

Although the area of descriptive statistics has been around for centuries, the area of inferential statistics is a 20th-century development. An inference is a conclusion or presumption that is made based on reasoning from the evidence that is available. Inferential statistics involves drawing a conclusion or generalizing based on the data. It involves estimation and "guesstimation." It is from this area of statistics that most of the confusion arises.

There are also two categories into which data fall. **Quantitative data** are numbers that indicate amounts, differences, or counts. This is the easiest type of data to deal with. The second type of data is called **qualitative data**. These types of data are generally words (though some *numerical codes* are used) that indicate observations and are indicative of differences in kind. Before beginning to analyze a set of data, it is important to know which type of data you have. We cannot deal with both types of data in the same way.

EXAMPLE 1 Quantitative versus Qualitative Data

Suppose that you are preparing questions for a survey of students at your school. If you ask questions to gain information about students in the following areas, would you expect to get quantitative or qualitative data as a response?

(a) What is your age? The data provided in this instance should be numbers of years and thus would be quantitative.

(b) What is favorite course? The data in this instance should be the name of an area of study such as history or math. This type of data is qualitative.

(c) What is your IQ score? The word *score* (and similar words like *scale* or *rating scale*) typifies quantitative data.

(d) What is your sex? We would expect the answer to be male or female. This is qualitative data.

Two more commonly used terms in statistics are *sample* and *population*. When you are gathering information for a statistical analysis, you must be aware of which of these two categories your data will fall into.

Suppose that you were doing a survey to find the average age of a person in your math class. It would be easy to pick a day when 100% of the class was in attendance, ask everyone their ages, and then find the average. This set of data would be called a population. If you are sure that you can get the required information from absolutely all possible sources, missing none, then you have a set of data called a **population**.

However, if you wanted to calculate the average age of persons living in your county, it would be virtually impossible to get the age of every individual person living in the county at any given time. You might be able to get a large number of ages but certainly not all of them. This set of data would be called a **sample**.

Definition

Population versus Sample
Population: a complete set of observations
Sample: a subset of observations taken from a population

In most situations, we will be dealing with samples of data and will be calculating sample statistical values. The formulas and rules used are very similar for both sample and population statistics, but there are some differences to allow for the fact that sample values are based on incomplete information. This means that a "fudge factor" is built into many of the formulas for sample statistics.

To come up with a sample that is representative of the population, we will look at several different sampling techniques. Because samples are used to draw conclusions about the whole population, you must be careful to avoid **bias**. Bias is the difference between the results obtained by sampling and the truth about the whole population. Many statisticians use **random sampling** to help eliminate bias. The most common way to satisfy this requirement is to select the sample in such a way that every different member of the population has an equal probability (or chance) of being selected. To produce a random sample, statisticians often use a random number table. Random sampling is one of the most widely used sampling techniques, but there are other techniques that may be used. We will look more closely at the following types of sampling: stratified, systematic, cluster, and convenience.

Groups or classes inside a population that share a common characteristic are called **strata**. In the method of **stratified sampling**, the population is divided into distinct strata. For example, in the population of all undergraduate college students, some strata might be freshmen, sophomores, juniors, or seniors. Other strata might be men or women, in-state students or out-of-state students, and so forth. Then a simple random sample of a certain size is drawn from each strata and the information obtained is carefully adjusted or weighted in all resulting calculations.

Another type of sampling is **systematic sampling**. In this method, it is assumed that the elements of the population are arranged in some natural sequential order. Then a random starting point is selected and we select every "nth" element for our sample. For example, to obtain a systematic sample of 20 students going through the cafeteria line at lunch, we could pick a random number between 0 and 10. Then between 12:00 noon and 12:10 (the actual time determined by our random number), we could begin the sampling process of taking every fifth student in line. The advantage in systematic sampling is that it is easy to get. However, there are dangers in using systematic sampling. When the population is repetitive or cyclical in nature, systematic sampling should not be used. For example, consider a fabric mill that produces dress material. Suppose the loom that produces the material makes a mistake every 17th yard, but we only check every 16th yard with an automated scanner. In this case, a random starting point may or may not result in detection of the fabric flaws before a large amount of fabric is produced.

Cluster sampling is used extensively by government agencies and certain private research organizations. In cluster sampling, we begin by dividing the demographic area into sections. Then we randomly select sections and randomly select individuals in those sections. The resulting calculations are weighted to correct for disproportionate representation of groups. For example, in conducting a survey of schoolchildren in a large city, we could first randomly select 30 schools and then randomly select a certain number of children from each school.

Finally, **convenience sampling** uses results or data that are conveniently and readily obtained. In some cases, this may be all that is available, and in many cases it is better than no information at all. However, convenience sampling does run the risk of being severely biased. For instance, consider a newsperson who wishes to get the "opinions of the people" about a proposed seat tax to be imposed on tickets to all sporting events. The revenues from the seat tax will then be used to support the local symphony. The newsperson stands in front of a classical music store at noon and surveys the first five people coming out of the store who will cooperate. This method of choosing a sample will produce some opinions, and perhaps some human interest stories, but it certainly has bias. It is good advice to be very cautious when the data come from the method of convenience sampling.

EXAMPLE 2 — Which Type of Sampling Method?

Memorial Mission Hospitals (MMH) is a national for-profit chain of hospitals. Management wants to survey patients discharged this past year to obtain patient satisfaction profiles. It wishes to use a sample of such patients. Several sampling techniques are described next. Categorize each technique as simple random sampling, stratified sampling, systematic sampling, cluster sampling, or convenience sampling.

(a) Obtain a list of patients discharged from all MMH facilities. Divide the patients according to length of hospital stay (3 days or less, 4–7 days, 8–14 days, more than 14 days). Draw random samples from each group.

— **Stratified sampling (discharged patients divided into groups depending on number of days in hospital)**

(b) Obtain lists of patients discharged from all MMH facilities. Number these patients and then use a random number table to obtain a sample.

— **Simple random sampling (random number table)**

(c) Randomly select some MMH facilities from each of five geographic regions and then take a random sample from each of these hospital discharge lists.

— **Cluster sampling (geographic regions)**

(d) At the beginning of the year, instruct each MMH facility to survey every 500th patient discharged.

— **Systematic sampling (every 500th patient)**

(e) Instruct each MMH facility to survey 10 discharged patients this week and send in the results.

— **Convenience sampling (any 10 discharged patients in one week)**

As you learn more about statistics, you will begin to see that statistics can be used to mislead as well as inform the public. Mark Twain said, "Get the facts first and then you can distort them as much as you please." Many polls are deliberately misleading. For example, the way a question is asked in a survey can dramatically change the results. Respondents are primed to answer the way a survey's sponsor wishes. The group that is chosen for the poll can also create bias in the survey. This course should help you learn how to interpret results and determine the reliability of these results.

"In earlier times they had no statistics, and so they had to fall back on lies. They did it with lies, we do it with statistics; but it's all the same." – Stephen Leacock

Practice Set 7-1

Decide whether each of the following is in the area of descriptive or inferential statistics.

1. Last month, the federal government announced that approximately 5.2% of the workforce in the United States was unemployed.

2. The age of students at a particular community college ranges from 18 to 78 years.

3. My GPA has been near 3.5 for the past 3 years.

4. The state Highway Safety Council predicts that 15 persons will die in traffic accidents over the Labor Day weekend.

5. Sammy Sosa's batting average is 0.455 this week.

6. In a recent study of a sample of 100 volunteers, eating garlic was shown to lower blood pressure.

7. The average number of students in a class at Alvin Community College is 22.6.

8. The New Mexico Department of Transportation has predicted that the average number of automobiles per household will increase by 0.2% next year.

9. The total attendance for all of the football games held at Southern High School this season was 8653.

10. If you live your entire life in New York City, the chances that you will be robbed at least once are about 15%.

Each of the following words or terms describes some data that are to be collected. Will the data be quantitative or qualitative in each case?

11. Years of education that you have had

12. Your favorite TV show

13. Your daily caloric intake

14. Your place of birth

15. Your blood type

16. Your favorite brand of candy bar

17. Audience ratings of films on a scale of 1 to 5

18. The high temperature at Salt Lake City, Utah, each day

19. The average time you spend standing in the checkout line of a grocery store

20. Your telephone number, including area code

Categorize each of the following as simple random sampling, stratified sampling, systematic sampling, cluster sampling, or convenience sampling.

21. Randomly select five high schools from different geographic regions and survey all students at each of the chosen schools.

22. Survey each 10th student who walks in the front entrance of the school.

23. Obtain a list of students enrolled at Western High School. Number these students and then use a random number table to obtain the sample.

24. Obtain a list of students enrolled at a community college. Draw a random sample from the horticulture students, transfer students, and nursing students.

25. Survey the first five students who walk in the classroom.

26. Once every year, a popular magazine surveys its readers, and, based on the results that are obtained from the responses, the magazine names the best- and worst-dressed celebrities of the year.

27. An instructor at Texas Tech teaches five classes in a semester. Two of the classes are chosen by the dean, and all students in those classes fill out an instructor evaluation form about that instructor.

28. Students at Hampton University obtain the voting records for Norfolk, Virginia. They randomly select 60 Democrats, 50 Republicans, and 10 Independents (the numbers chosen are based on the percentage of registered voters in each category in the county) and survey them concerning their favorite candidate for mayor in the upcoming fall election.

29. At a club meeting, the names of all members are written on identical slips of paper and placed in a bowl. The names of five members are drawn and these will participate in face-to-face interviews with a pollster.

30. You are approached by a lady at the shopping mall who asks you to answer a few questions about the facilities at the mall.

Section 7-2   DESCRIPTIVE STATISTICS

In this section, we will look at some of the common manipulations that can be done with quantitative data once they have been collected. The main topic will be averages for data. As we shall see, there can be several different averages for a given set of data. This means that we cannot just use the word **average** to stand for all of them. All averages are called **measures of central tendency**. There are three commonly used measures of central tendency: the **mode**, the **median**, and the **mean average**.

Definition

The Mode
The mode of a set of data is the most often repeated observation(s) or item(s).

■ EXAMPLE 3   **Finding the Mode of Qualitative Data**

In a recent survey of the senior class at Jones High School, 60 students had brown eyes, 30 had blue eyes, 5 had green eyes, and 10 had hazel eyes. What is the mode of this set of data (i.e., the modal eye color)?

   The most often repeated observation is brown eye color; therefore, the mode = brown.

■ EXAMPLE 4   **Finding the Mode of Quantitative Data**

Find the mode of the following sets of numbers:

(a) 2, 4, 6, 8, 8, 10, 12
(b) 2, 2, 3, 4, 4, 4, 5, 6, 6
(c) 2, 2, 3, 4, 4, 4, 5, 5, 6, 6, 6, 7, 7
(d) 1, 1, 2, 2, 3, 3, 4, 4, 5, 5, 6, 6

(a) In this set of numbers, 8 is the only repeated number, so the mode = 8.
(b) The numbers 2, 4, and 6 are all repeated, but 4 is repeated more than any of the others, so the mode = 4.
(c) There are three 4s and three 6s. These numbers are repeated more than any other numbers in the list and are repeated the same number of times. So there are two modes, 4 and 6. (This is called *bimodal*.)
(d) There are repeated numbers, but none is repeated any more than another. There is no mode.

   This example illustrates that a set of data may have no mode, one mode, or more than one mode.

Definition

The Median
The **median** of a set of observations is the observation in the center or middle of the list of items after they have been placed in some kind of meaningful order. This average has its own symbol, $\tilde{x}$, called "*x*-tilde."

■ EXAMPLE 5   **Finding the Median of Qualitative Data**

In a recent survey of the senior class at Jones High School, 60 students had brown eyes, 30 had blue eyes, 5 had green eyes, and 10 had hazel eyes. What is the median of this set of data?

For a set of data to have a median, it must be data that can be placed in a meaningful order. There is no meaningful order for eye color, so there is no median.

■ EXAMPLE 6   **Finding the Median of Quantitative Data**

Find the median of the following sets of data:

(a) 1, 2, 3, 3, 5, 6, 7, 9, 9
(b) 3, 6, 3, 1, 4, 8, 9, 5, 6
(c) 2, 6, 4, 7, 8, 1, 2, 9

(a) Because these numbers are already in a meaningful order, simply find the middle of the list. There are nine numbers in the list, so the fifth one (counting from either end) would be in the middle of the list. The median = $\tilde{x} = 5$.

(b) First, sort the numbers into numerical order as follows:

$$1, 3, 3, 4, 5, 6, 6, 8, 9$$

Now find the middle number.

$$\tilde{x} = 5$$

(c) Again, sort the numbers into numerical order.

$$1, 2, 2, 4, 6, 7, 8, 9$$

Finding the number in the middle is not as easy this time. There are eight numbers in this list. Counting four from each end places the middle *between 4 and 6*. When this happens, the median must be calculated by adding the two numbers on either side of the middle and then dividing by two.

$$4 + 6 = 10$$

$$10 \div 2 = 5$$

$$\tilde{x} = 5$$

Whenever a set of numerical data has an even number of items, the median will be between two of the items. If there is an odd number of items in the list, then the median will be one of the items, the one in the middle.

Definition

The Mean Average

The **mean average** is found by totaling the observations in a set of data and then dividing the total by the number of items in the original list. This average has its own symbol, $\bar{x}$, called "*x*-bar."

$$\bar{x} = \frac{\Sigma x}{n}$$

■ EXAMPLE 7   **Finding the Mean of Qualitative Data**

In a recent survey of the senior class at Jones High School, 60 students had brown eyes, 30 had blue eyes, 5 had green eyes, and 10 had hazel eyes. What is the mean average of this set of data?

For a set of data to have a mean average, it must be numerical data so that the amounts may be added. Therefore, there is no mean average.

■ EXAMPLE 8   **Finding the Mean of Quantitative Data**

Find the mean average of the following sets of data:

(a) 3, 4, 5, 5, 7, 8, 9, 11, 0, 15
(b) 2.3, 6, 7.3, 4, 6, 7, 6.3

(a) First, add the numbers and then divide by 10, which is the number of items in this list of numbers.

$$3 + 4 + 5 + 5 + 7 + 8 + 9 + 11 + 0 + 15 = 67$$

$$67 \div 10 = 6.7$$

The mean average = 6.7.

(b) Again add and this time divide by 7.

$$2.3 + 6 + 7.3 + 4 + 6 + 7 + 6.3 = 38.9$$

$$38.9 \div 7 = 5.557142857\ldots$$

The mean average is about 5.6.

When you are asked to find some kind of average of a list of numbers or a group of items, you must first determine which of the several averages may apply. This depends on the kind of data with which you are working. As shown in the examples, not all types of data have a median or a mean average.

If a set of data has several valid averages, as most numerical data will, the question then becomes, "Which is the *best average*?" If a set of data has only one valid average (see Examples 3, 5, and 7), then this question is easy to answer. However, if there are several averages available, some thought must be given to this question.

EXAMPLE 9 Which Average Is the Best?

Find the mode, median, and mean of the following sets of data. Then determine the "best" average for each set.

(a) 2, 2, 3, 4, 5, 6, 7, 8, 8
(b) 2, 2, 3, 4, 5, 6, 7, 8, 80

(a) The modes are 2 and 8. Because the numbers are already in order, the middle of the list is easy to find. The median = 5. To find the mean average, add and divide:

$$2 + 2 + 3 + 4 + 5 + 6 + 7 + 8 + 8 = 45$$

$$45 \div 9 = 5$$

The mean average is 5.

The averages are not all the same number, so which is "best"? First, reconsider what averages are supposed to tell us about a set of data. They are *measures of central tendency*. They are supposed to tell us about the value of items near the middle of the set of items once they are arranged properly. Are 2 and 8 near the middle of the list? No. How about 5? Yes, it is near the middle of the list. Therefore, either the mean or the median could be chosen. If you *must* pick one, the average of choice is the *mean*, because all numbers in the list contribute to its calculation.

(b) This list is almost identical to list (a), with one major difference: one extremely large data item. This will have an effect on the averages. The mode = 2. The median = 5. The mean = 117 ÷ 9 = 13.

Now all three of the averages are a different value. Again, which number is closest to the middle of this list? In this case, 5 is, not 13. The value of one of the numbers, 80, is so extreme compared to the rest of the list that it skews the mean average. Because the median is not affected by the size of the numbers, its value is the same as it was in list (a). The *median* is the "best" average.

As a matter of practice in everyday life, we use the word "average" to refer to all three measures of central tendency. However, a builder who builds houses for the "average American family" is interested in the most common family size or the mode. The "average cost of college tuition" is best described using the median cost of college tuition, because tuition at a few very expensive colleges may distort or skew the mean average of college tuition. When computing a "grade point average," the mean average is used in order to reflect *all* grades made by that student during the course. Our correct use of the statistical terms *mean*, *median*, and *mode* will reflect the differences in meaning of these measures of central tendency.

The Weighted Mean

In some situations, data items vary in their degree of importance. For example, a final exam might be 25% of your final average in a particular course, whereas each test counts 20% and homework 15%. Because of these differences in values, computing the final average would not be done by just adding grades and dividing. The following formula is needed to calculate the **weighted mean** by assigning different weights (w) to different values (x).

$$\text{Weighted mean:} \quad \bar{x} = \frac{\sum(w \cdot x)}{\sum w}$$

EXAMPLE 10

The Final Course Average: An Example of a Weighted Mean Average

Suppose your grades in a course are as follows: tests — 80, 85, 75; homework average — 91; final exam — 78. If homework is 15% of your final grade, tests are 20% each, and the final exam is 25%, we can calculate your final average as follows:

$$\bar{x} = \frac{\sum(w \cdot x)}{\sum w}$$

$$\bar{x} = \frac{(15 \times 91) + (20 \times 80) + (20 \times 85) + (20 \times 75) + (25 \times 78)}{15 + 20 + 20 + 20 + 25}$$

$$\bar{x} = \frac{8115}{100} = 81.15$$

College grade point averages are also computed with a weighted mean. Each letter grade is assigned the appropriate number of points (A = 4, B = 3, C = 2, etc.), and each course is assigned a weight equal to the number of credit hours for the course. For a good exercise in calculating a college grade point average, do Lab Exercise 5, titled GPA Mania, at the end of this chapter. The pattern used in Example 10 may be used to calculate the GPA.

Practice Set 7-2

1. Write a brief paragraph discussing possible sources of confusion about the word *average*.

2. Define and distinguish among the mean, the median, and the mode.

Find all possible averages (mean, median, and mode) of the following sets of data. Then choose the "best" average from among them.

3. 2, 3, 4, 6, 2, 3, 8, 2, 7, 9

4. 2.3, 4.5, 6.8, 2.2, 5.8, 9.0, 2.5

5. 3, 5, 6, 72, 4, 8, 9, 9, 3, 9, 2, 5, 7, 77, 4, 3, 8, 2, 9, 6

6. 200, 258, 265, 236, 298, 195, 300, 199, 245, 245, 227

7. 1.23, 2.85, 3.21, 1.54, 2.65, 0.35, 6.88, 4.25, 2.88, 2.69, 3.27, 11.99

8. 23.6, 25.1, 22.5, 20.4, 26.9, 24.7

9. According to the *2004 World Almanac*, the average (median) income for a family of 4 in the United States in 2002 was $42,409, whereas the average (mean) per capita income in the United States in 2002 was $22,851. The per capita average would indicate that a family of 4 should have an income of 4(22,851) = $91,404. This result is about double the median income for a family of 4 that was given. What is going on here?

10. Sonya's Dress Shop sold 23 dresses yesterday as shown on the chart that follows.

Brand	Price	Number Sold
A	$62	3
B	$45	7
C	$38	5
D	$29	2
E	$22	6

(a) What was the mean price per brand?
(b) What was the mean price per dress sold?
(c) What was the median price of the dresses sold?
(d) What was the modal selling price of a dress?

11. Would you use the mean, median, or mode to give a fair representation of the "average" in the following situations?
(a) Builders planning houses are interested in the average size of an American family.
(b) The grade point average for students at a community college.
(c) The average cost of a house in Cook County is $95,000.
(d) The average American's share of the national debt is $8000.

12. For each of the following statements, determine which average, the mean, median, or mode, was likely to have been used to draw the conclusion that was reached.
(a) Half of the workers at PrimoWidgets make more than $6.32 per hour and half make less than $6.32 per hour.
(b) The average number of children in each family renting apartments in Yonkers Heights is 1.82 children per family.
(c) In a recent survey of people purchasing convertibles, it was found that most prefer the color red.
(d) The average age of professors in the University of Texas system is 43.7 years.
(e) The most common fear today is the fear of having to speak at a public gathering.

13. The mean is the "most sensitive" average because it is affected by any change in the data.
(a) Determine the mean, median, and mode for 1, 2, 3, 4, 4, 7, 11.
(b) If you now change the 7 to a 10 in the same list, which average(s) will be affected by this change? What is (are) the new average(s)?

14. Mary is taking three courses this semester. Her biology course is a four-hour course and she received an A in the course. She made Bs in her history course and her English course, both of which are three-hour courses. What is her GPA for this semester? (Use Example 10 as your guide.)

15. Mary drove across town to the mall and went a distance of 9 mi in 14 min. What was her average speed during the trip?

16. Sonya has a mean average of 77.6 on the first five of six tests. To get an overall average of 83.0, what must Sonya score on the sixth test?

17. Following are the ages of students in a math class at a local community college.

18, 18, 19, 19, 19, 20, 20, 22, 22,
22, 23, 23, 25, 27, 42, 43, 57

What is the average age of a student in this class? Briefly justify your answer with a brief discussion or explanation.

18. The following is a list of daily high temperatures as measured in Uranium City, Saskatchewan, Canada, for several consecutive days last January. The temperatures are measured on the Celsius scale.

2, 5, 3, 0, 0, −3, −7, 1

Find the mean, median, and mode for these temperatures.

19. In a recent trade magazine, the average price of a new car in the United States was said to be about $19,000.00. Discuss how you think the person writing the magazine article got this value, and whether you think it represents a mean, median, or mode, and why.

20. The mean of five numbers is 8. If one of the numbers is removed from the list, the mean becomes 7. What is the number that was removed?

21. A doctor's office is advertising for a receptionist. If there are two doctors, four nurses, and a nurse's aid on staff, and the mean average salary of the staff in this office is $60,000.00 per year, can you expect to earn this amount if you apply for the receptionist job? Why is this average skewed?

22. Rubber Baby Buggy Bumper Manufacturing Company has only three employees. Their salaries are $25,000, $30,000, and $35,000 per year. If each employee were to receive a $2000 raise, how would this affect the mean of these salaries?

23. Referring to problem 22, if all the employees received a 4% raise, how would that affect the mean average of the salaries?

24. Find the mean, median, and mode of the ages of cars driven to school by you and your classmates in this class.

25. Find the mean, median, and mode of the manufacturers of the cars driven to school by you and your classmates in this class.

26. Create a set of eight test scores so that the mean score is higher than the median score.

Section 7-3   ORGANIZING AND DISPLAYING DATA

To conduct a reliable experiment, a statistician may need to analyze thousands of pieces of data. Usually, large amounts of data need to be condensed into more manageable forms so that a good evaluation is possible. This may be accomplished in a number of different ways, depending on the desired end use of the data and whether the data are *qualitative* or *quantitative* in nature.

First, we will look at methods of condensing and graphing large amounts of *qualitative data*. The problem with this type of data is that things such as mean averages and meaningful ordering of such data may not be possible. One way to handle such data is to sort the data into some meaningful categories and then use these categories to draw a bar graph. Another option is to determine the percent of data in each category and create a **circle or pie graph**.

EXAMPLE 11   Constructing a Bar Graph of Qualitative Data

Mrs. Johnson's math class had a test last week. After grading all the papers, she sorted the results for her 31 students and found that 3 students made an A, 8 made a B, 10 made a C, 6 made a D, and 4 made an F. Make a bar graph of these data.

First, if Mrs. Johnson had not already done so, the data would need to be sorted into meaningful categories. Here those are the letter grades given by the teacher. The grades have been placed in chart form as follows.

Grade	Frequency
A	3
B	8
C	10
D	6
F	4
Total	31

Now each row of the chart will become a bar on our bar graph, as shown in Figure 7-1.

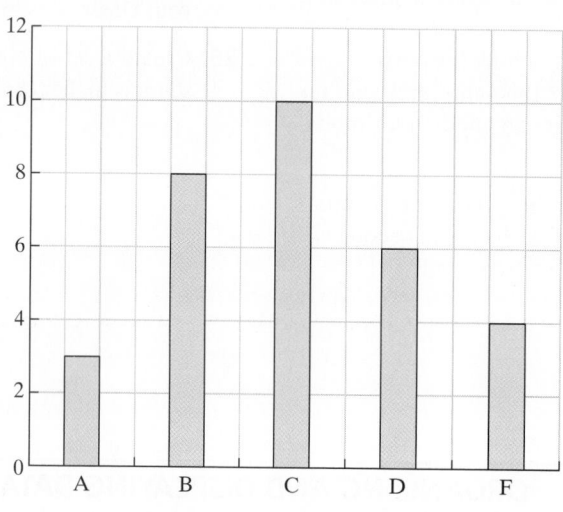

Figure 7-1
Grades on a math test.

EXAMPLE 12   Constructing a Circle Graph

Where do you hide your "mess" when unexpected company shows up at your front door? Believe it or not, statistical data do exist related to this question. In *USA Today* some time ago, the following results were reported based on a survey of about 1000 adults. It was found that about 68% quickly throw stuff in the closet before answering the door, 23% shove things under the bed, 6% throw

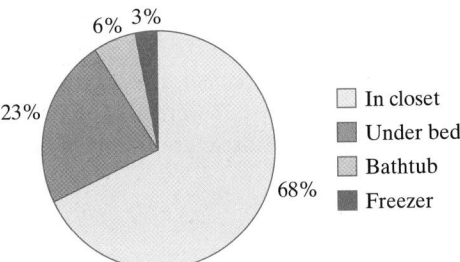

Figure 7-2
Typical circle graph.

items into the bathtub (that is kind of odd!), and 3% put stuff in the freezer or some other strange place. Make a circle graph of these data.

To do this by hand with a calculator, a protractor for measuring angles, and a pencil and paper can be time consuming, but, in brief, this is how to do it.

First, recall that a full circle measures 360°. Find and measure on your circle 68% of 360°.

$$(0.68)(360°) = 245°$$

Then find and measure "pie" slices that correspond to each of the other percentages. The size of the pie slice corresponds to the percentage for each category.

This procedure is much more easily done with a computer program or spreadsheet such as Excel, with the results as shown in Figure 7-2.

These same data would also look good in the form of a horizontal or vertical bar graph, as shown in Figure 7-3. Bars on a bar graph represent categories, so each bar is separate from the others. The bars are of uniform width, but the actual width chosen is arbitrary.

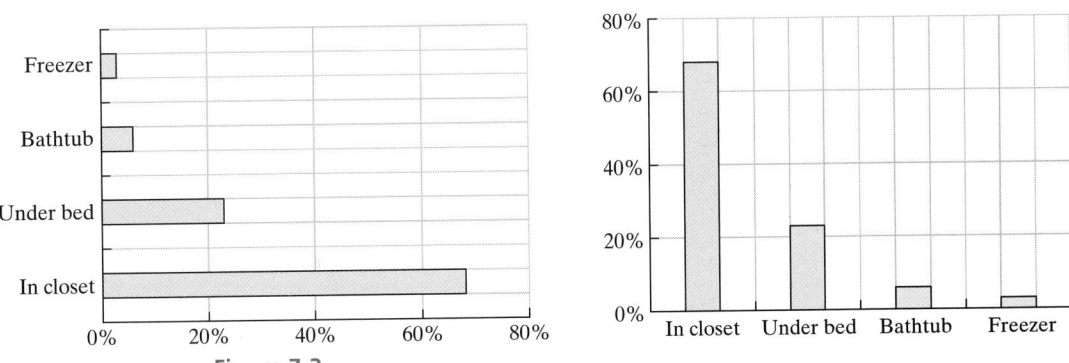

Figure 7-3
Typical horizontal and vertical bar graphs.

EXAMPLE 13   Extracting Information from a Circle Graph

In the 2004 edition of the *Statistical Abstract of the United States*, the number of AIDS cases estimated in 2002 were broken down by race. These data are represented in the form of the circle graph shown here.

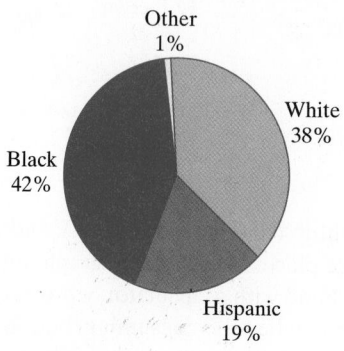

(a) If the total number of cases represented by the circle graph is 384,906, about what number of the cases were reported by persons classified as Hispanic?

(b) What percentage does the whole circle represent?

(c) Why would the percentage of those persons with AIDS who are classified as Black be said to be "disproportionate"?

(a) 19% of 384,906 = 0.19(384,906) = 73,132. Thus, about 73,132 cases of AIDS were reported by persons classified as Hispanic.

(b) The whole circle represents all the data. This means that the whole circle represents 100% of the data.

(c) The percentage of those persons classified as Black is disproportionate because the percentage of African Americans in the United States is much less than 42% of the total population. Thus, in these data, the number of cases reported by persons classified as Black appears to be too high. Why this is the case cannot be determined from these data alone.

Now let us look at organizing and graphing *quantitative data*. A **stem-and-leaf display** is one way of summarizing numerical data. This method organizes the data into groups but still allows us to see the individual data items. It is a combination of a graphing technique and a sorting technique.

Rule

Stem-and-Leaf Display
To make a stem-and-leaf display, break the digits of each data value into two parts. The leading digit becomes the stem and the trailing digit becomes the leaf. You are free to choose the number of digits to be included in the stem.

■ EXAMPLE 14   **Stem-and-Leaf Display**

The grades on the final exam in a history class are given in the following table.
Use a stem-and-leaf display to summarize these grades.

92	63	75	82	73	70	61	52	84	91
83	55	61	75	60	84	88	90	78	71
70	79	68	89	93	68	75	59	73	82

The grades range from a low score of 52 to a high score of 93. Because scores
are all in the 50s, 60s, 70s, 80s, and 90s, we will use the first digits (tens place) as
our stems and the trailing digits (ones place) as our leaves. Draw a vertical line
and place the stems in order, to the left of the line.

$$
\begin{array}{c|}
5 & \\
6 & \\
7 & \\
8 & \\
9 & \\
\end{array}
$$

Stem   Leaf

Now look at each individual grade and place the ones digits for that grade
on the correct row. For example, $9 \mid 2$ represents a grade of 92.
Complete the chart as follows.

Exam Grades in Statistics

$$
\begin{array}{c|l}
5 & 2\ 5\ 9 \\
6 & 3\ 1\ 1\ 0\ 8\ 8 \\
7 & 5\ 3\ 0\ 5\ 8\ 1\ 0\ 9\ 5\ 3 \\
8 & 2\ 4\ 3\ 4\ 8\ 9\ 2 \\
9 & 2\ 1\ 0\ 3 \\
\end{array}
$$

The stem-and-leaf display in Example 14 allows us to see that most grades cen-
tered around the 70s. If grades are assigned on a 10-point scale, it will be easy for
the teacher to see that there were four As (90s) and three Fs (50s). The individual
grades are also displayed for further use, if needed.

A **frequency distribution** is used when the amount of data is very large. Individual data items are grouped in "classes" to help in the analysis of the distribution
of the sample.

Definition

Frequency Distribution
A frequency distribution is a listing in chart form of the observed values in a set
of data and the corresponding frequency of that value.

When constructing a frequency distribution, there are several guidelines that should be followed:

1. Each class should be the same "width" — that is, span the same number of possible data items.
2. Classes should not overlap. Each data item should belong to only one class.
3. Frequency distributions should contain approximately 5 to 12 classes.
4. Use an even or "easy to count" class width whenever possible.

Look at the following example that constructs a frequency distribution for a set of 50 final exam grades in a biology class.

EXAMPLE 15   Constructing a Frequency Distribution

Construct a grouped frequency distribution of the following final exam grades of 50 biology students.

45	85	63	72	60	49	51	68	76	65
48	73	65	66	72	71	78	65	84	80
73	61	94	40	59	75	73	76	85	80
91	72	60	80	58	51	78	72	68	71
85	79	83	64	69	73	50	60	75	82

1. Identify the high and low scores and find the range.

High = 94   Low = 40

Range = 94 − 40 = 54 points

Counting by 5s will be a convenient unit for a class width. If we divide 54 by 5, the result is 10.8 or 11 classes. This falls within the recommended 5 to 12 classes for a frequency distribution.

2. Pick a starting point that is consistent with the data. The lowest class must include the smallest data item (40), and the largest class must include the highest data item (94). The numbers used to define each class should not overlap.

Classes
90–94
85–89
↑
55–59
50–54
45–49
40–44

3. Now set up a table using these classes and sort the data into those classes. Use a tally column to count items and total these in a frequency column.

Final Exam Grades

Classes	Tally	Frequency
90–94	11	2
85–89	111	3
80–84	1111 1	6
75–79	1111 11	7
70–74	1111 1111	10
65–69	1111 11	7
60–64	1111 1	6
55–59	11	2
50–54	111	3
45–49	111	3
40–44	1	1
	Total	50

Once the data have been classified in a frequency distribution, we lose some information. Individual data items are no longer identifiable. However, we can look at the range of numbers in each class to answer specific questions about the data. In the frequency distribution given previously, the class 70–74 is the **modal class** because it is the class with the greatest frequency. We can also see that a majority of the data fell in the classes that include grades ranging from 60 to 84.

A histogram is a bar graph used to picture a frequency distribution. Each bar represents a class of numbers in the frequency distribution. The height of each bar indicates the frequency in that particular class. The bars should always touch because the width of a bar represents a range of numbers (a quantitative value). Because each bar represents a range of values, it is usually labeled with one number called the **midpoint of the class**. This number is calculated by adding the lower and upper class limits of one class and dividing by 2.

EXAMPLE 16   **Drawing a Histogram**

Use the frequency distribution in Example 15 to draw a histogram.

1. Calculate the class midpoints for each class

$$\frac{40 + 44}{2} = \frac{84}{2} = 42 \qquad \frac{45 + 49}{2} = \frac{94}{2} = 47$$

and use these to label each bar.

2. A histogram of final exam grades for biology students is presented in Figure 7-4.

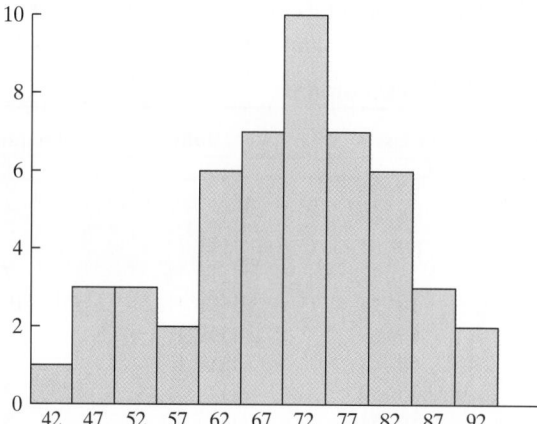

Figure 7-4
Histogram of exam grades.

Notice that a histogram is different from a bar graph. The bars in a histogram represent classes of data on a number line. Therefore, there are no gaps between the bars unless an intervening class has a frequency of 0. The width of the bars on a histogram is determined by the class width and the scale of the base number line for the graph.

Histograms are valuable tools. For example, the histogram of a sample should have a distribution shape that is similar to that of the population from which the sample was taken. Many distributions are normal or bell shaped with a symmetrical distribution. Others are skewed where a few very high or very low values cause one tail of the distribution to be longer than the other. A bimodal distribution has two high-frequency classes separated by classes with lower frequencies. Look at the typical distribution shapes illustrated in Figure 7-5.

Test scores, IQ scores, measurements of height and weight, and thousands of

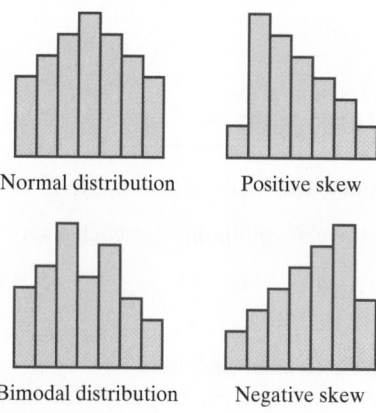

Figure 7-5
Various histogram shapes.

other things are normally distributed in the general population. Therefore, we would expect a random sample of IQ scores to also approximate a normal distribution. In a classroom, students usually hope that the distribution of grades will be negatively skewed — lots of higher grades and only a few low ones!

Some statistical analysis involves the comparison of a sample with the distribution shape of the underlying population. For example, test scores on standardized tests are normally distributed or bell shaped when graphed. If the scores from a sample of students in a particular school are positively skewed (lots of low scores and a few high ones), the administration may ask questions about the difference in actual outcome from the expected bell-shaped outcome. Underlying causes of the difference will be closely examined and remedied if possible.

Practice Set 7-3

1. A class of high school students was asked to tell the number of miles each drove to school (one way). Use these numbers to construct a stem-and-leaf display of commuting distances.

6	5	15	12	25	16	12	4	8	12
21	25	11	10	14	22	9	3	13	10
8	29	31	12	16	4	15	12	11	36

2. The speeds of 50 cars were measured by a radar device on a city street with a posted limit of 25 mph as follows:

27	23	22	38	43	24	35	26	28	25
23	22	52	31	30	41	45	29	27	43
29	28	27	25	29	36	28	37	28	29
28	26	33	25	27	25	34	32	22	32
21	23	24	18	48	23	16	26	21	23

(a) Classify these data into a grouped frequency distribution (lowest class 15–19).

(b) Construct a histogram of these data with the same number of classes as in the frequency distribution.

(c) Does this histogram approximate any of the theoretical curves we have studied? If so, which one (skewed, normal, bimodal)? Is this the shape you would expect from this problem? Why or why not?

3. Trade winds are one of the beautiful features of island life in Hawaii. The following data represent total air movement in miles each day over a weather station in Hawaii, as determined by a continuous anemometer recorder. The period of observation is January 1 to February 14.

26	28	18	14	26	40	13	22	27
28	50	42	15	13	16	33	18	16
26	11	16	17	37	10	35	20	21
18	28	18	28	21	13	19	25	19
19	15	29	14	25	54	32	34	22

(a) Classify these data into a grouped frequency distribution with the first class of 10–14.

(b) Construct a histogram of these data with the same number of classes as in the frequency distribution. Does this approximate any of the curves we have studied?

4. In the past year, 900 cases of accidental in-home poisonings were reported to authorities in a large western city. The location within the home where the poisoning occurred is given, along with the number of cases reported. Use these data to draw a circle graph.

Location in Home	Number of Cases
Kitchen	369
Bathroom	189
Bedroom	108
Other location	234
Total	900

5. The U.S. Immigration and Naturalization Service keeps records of where persons entering the

United States and seeking to stay come from originally. The following graph shows where immigrants came from during the 1990s.

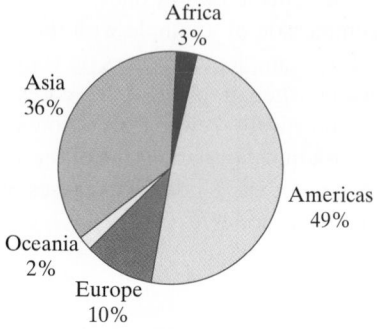

Africa
3%

Asia
36%

Americas
49%

Oceania
2%

Europe
10%

(a) What percentage of immigrants entered the
United States from Africa?

(b) Did more than one-third of immigrants come
from Asia?

(c) If there were approximately 7.5 million immigrants to the United States during the 1990s,
about how many came from the Americas?

(d) Where did the least number of immigrants
come from?

6. The following list of the weights of bears was com-
piled by wildlife officers in eastern North Carolina
over the course of several years.

80	344	416	348	166	220	262	360	204
140	180	105	166	204	26	120	436	125
220	46	154	116	182	150	65	356	316
270	202	202	365	79	148	446	62	236
114	76	48	29	514	140	94	86	150
144	332	34	132	90	40	212	60	64

(a) Make a frequency distribution of this information. Begin with the lowest class (0–49).

(b) Use the frequency distribution to construct a
histogram.

7. A task force carried out a study of one-way commuting distances in miles for workers in the down-
town Dallas area. A random sample of 60 of these
workers was taken. The commuting distances of
the workers in the sample are as follows:

13	47	10	3	16	20	17	40	4	2
8	21	19	15	3	17	14	6	12	45
4	16	11	18	23	12	6	2	14	13
46	12	9	18	34	13	41	28	36	17
29	9	14	26	10	24	37	31	8	16
7	25	1	8	7	15	24	2	12	16

(a) Make a frequency distribution to represent
this information using 10 classes.

(b) Use this distribution to construct a histogram.
Which of the shapes we have studied is most
like the shape of this distribution?

8. Northeast Texas Community College holds
evening classes on United States history. The
director of studies, who wants to know the age
distribution of students in the class, obtained
the following information (ages rounded to nearest years):

41	28	22	45	30	43	46	35	56
20	31	19	22	32	55	54	31	63
19	27	53	51	33	58	29	65	53
27	18	29	51	39	29	56	19	63

(a) Construct a stem-and-leaf display of these
data.

(b) Construct a frequency table of these data using seven classes.

(c) Construct a histogram to display this frequency table.

9. Pleasant temperatures are one of the beautiful
features of island life in Tahiti. The following data
represent the high temperature each day at the
weather station in Tahiti. The period of observation is January 2003.

76	74	78	74	81	70	73	82	77	77
72	75	73	76	83	78	76	72	76	81
77	80	75	80	81	74	78	80	76	77
78									

(a) Classify these data into a grouped frequency
distribution with a first class of 70–74.

(b) Construct a histogram of these data with the
same number of classes as in the frequency
distribution.

10. The speeds of 50 cars were measured by a radar
device on a Presidio city street with a posted limit
of 30 mph as follows:

27	23	22	38	43	24	35	26	28	25
52	31	30	41	45	29	27	43	29	28
29	36	28	37	28	29	28	26	33	25
34	32	22	32	21	23	24	18	48	23
21	23	23	22	27	25	27	25	16	26

(a) Classify these data into a grouped frequency
distribution.

(b) Construct a histogram of these data with the same number of classes as in the frequency distribution.

(c) Construct a stem-and-leaf display of these data.

11. Refer to problem 17 in Practice Set 7-2 and construct a graph that is appropriate for these data.

Then discuss the "spread" of this graph as it pertains to the average age of a student in the class.

12. Survey the members of your class and find out each person's favorite sport to watch on TV. Construct an appropriate graph for your data. Justify your choice of graph type.

Section 7-4   VARIATION

Averages do not tell all that one might like to know about a set of numbers. For example, consider the set of statistics derived from the sets of numbers shown in Table 7-1. Looking at this table, you could easily assume that the sets of numbers were identical and not really three different sets at all. However, if you look at the actual sets of numbers shown in Table 7-2, it is obvious that there are differences.

■ **TABLE 7-1**

Averages

Number Set	Mean Average	Median
A	5	5
B	5	5
C	5	5

■ **Table 7-2   Numbers for the Averages in Table 7-1**

Number Set	Numbers				
A	5	5	5	5	5
B	6	5	5	5	4
C	7	6	5	4	3

Averages (measures of central tendency) try to tell us about numbers near the middle of a set. If more information is needed, then other statistics must be calculated based on some other criteria.

Suppose we had a question about how similar the numbers in a group are to each other (or how different they are). An average would not tell us anything about that question. In statistics, the difference between and among numbers in a set of data is called **variation**. Measures of variation (or **dispersion**) tell us about similarities and dissimilarities between numbers within a set of observations. There are two commonly used measures of variation, the **range** and the **standard deviation** of the set of data.

Definition

Range
The range of a set of data is the difference between the highest and the lowest number in the data set.

$$R = (\text{highest number}) - (\text{lowest number})$$

EXAMPLE 17   Finding the Range of Data Sets

Referring to Table 7-2, what is the range of each set of data?

$$\text{For set } A: \quad R = 5 - 5 = 0$$

$$\text{For set } B: \quad R = 6 - 4 = 2$$

$$\text{For set } C: \quad R = 7 - 3 = 4$$

It can be seen from the calculations in this example that all three sets of numbers are *not* the same. All three have different ranges. When the value of the range is reported along with the measures of central tendency, it is easy to see that there are differences in the sets of numbers.

The range of a set of data is easy to calculate and gives us some sense of the variability of our data. However, one problem with range is that it only uses two data items — the highest and the lowest — to give an answer. An extreme value, either high or low, can create a large range value even if the majority of the numbers are relatively consistent. Consider the set of grades consisting of 80, 82, 20, and 86. Although the range is 66 points, three of the four grades are fairly close together. Because of this problem with range, another method of variability, called standard deviation, is more commonly used in describing the dispersion of a set of data.

Definition

Standard Deviation
A rough measure of the average amount by which the observations in a set of data deviate from the mean average value of the group. This deviation may be either above or below the value of the mean.

The standard deviation measures how much the data differ from the mean. It is symbolized by either the Greek letter σ (sigma) or the letter s. The σ is used when the standard deviation of a population of data is being calculated. The letter s is used for the standard deviation when the data being analyzed represent a sample taken from a population. For purposes of this book, we will assume that the data we are analyzing represent sample data.

When the standard deviation of a set of data is small, most of the data items are close to the mean. As the spread of the data around the mean becomes larger, the standard deviation number becomes larger. Look at these two sets of data.

$$8, 8, 9, 10, 10 \qquad 6, 7, 9, 11, 12$$

The mean of both sets of data is 9. However, the numbers in the first set of data are all closer to 9; therefore, the first set of numbers will have a smaller standard deviation value.

The desirability of having a large or small standard deviation number in a set of data varies according to the problem being assessed. In IQ scores, for example, a relatively large standard deviation would be expected. However, a small standard deviation is important in quality control procedures used by many industries. If a company manufactures bags of potato chips, it strives to have consistency in its product. For example, although each individual bag of potato chips might have a slightly different weight, all products should be extremely close in weight to the value stated on the bag. This requires a small standard deviation in the weights of the bags.

The calculation of the standard deviation can be complicated, especially with a larger data set. However, to completely understand the definition of standard deviation as an average deviation from the mean, we will illustrate the step-by-step process of finding the standard deviation.

Steps for Calculating a Standard Deviation

To Find the Sample Standard Deviation of a Set of Data

1. Find the mean $\bar{x}$ of the data.
2. Make a chart having three columns:

    Data: x Data − Mean: $x - \bar{x}$ (Data − Mean)^2: $(x - \bar{x})^2$

3. List the data vertically under the column marked "Data."
4. Complete the "Data − Mean" column for each piece of data.
5. Square the values obtained in the "Data − Mean" column and record these values in the "(Data − Mean)^2" column.
6. Find the sum of the "(Data − Mean)^2" column.
7. Divide the sum in step 6 by $n - 1$ (the number of data items minus 1).
8. Find the square root of the quotient in step 7. This is the standard deviation number.

These steps are summarized by the standard deviation formula. (*Note:* Σ is the mathematical symbol for summation — "add 'em all up.")

$$s = \sqrt{\frac{\Sigma(x - \bar{x})^2}{n - 1}}$$

EXAMPLE 18   **Calculating the Standard Deviation of a Data Set**

Find the standard deviation of the following set of data:

$$8, 6, 0, 2, 9$$

(a) Find the mean:

$$\bar{x} = \frac{8 + 6 + 0 + 2 + 9}{5} = 5$$

(b) Chart the data:

Data ($\bar{x}$)	Data − Mean ($x - \bar{x}$)	(Data − Mean)^2 [$(x - \bar{x})^2$]
8	$8 - 5 = 3$	$(3)^2 = 9$
6	$6 - 5 = 1$	$(1)^2 = 1$
0	$0 - 5 = -5$	$(-5)^2 = 25$
2	$2 - 5 = -3$	$(-3)^2 = 9$
9	$9 - 5 = 4$	$(4)^2 = 16$
Total	0	$\sum(x - \bar{x})^2 = 60$

$$s = \sqrt{\frac{\sum(x - \bar{x})^2}{n - 1}} = \sqrt{\frac{60}{4}} = \sqrt{15} = 3.87$$

Calculating the standard deviation by hand involves a lot of manipulation. Now is a good time to use the capabilities of our calculators to do some complicated calculating.

Calculator Mini-Lesson

Finding a Standard Deviation on a Calculator

A *standard scientific calculator* can do the job, but there are many different ways of entering the initial data. It would be best to consider your calculator's instruction booklet to learn how your version works.

A *graphing calculator* (TI-83 Plus) will do the job efficiently as follows: Press STAT . Select EDIT . You should now be looking at a screen that will allow you to enter lists of numbers. Enter each number, then press the ENTER key. After entering the last number, press STAT . Use the arrow key to move over to CALC . Choose 1-Var Stats by pressing ENTER . Press ENTER a second time. You should now see a list of calculated statistical values. $\bar{x}$ = the mean average, S_x = the sample standard deviation, σ_x = the population standard deviation, n = the number of items in the list, Med = the median, and min X and max X are the smallest and largest numbers that you entered.

EXAMPLE 19   **Using a Calculator to Compute a Standard Deviation**

Use your calculator to obtain the standard deviation for the following numbers.

$$8, 6, 0, 2, 9$$

With a regular scientific calculator, use the $\sum +$ or the M+ button to enter the data. You may need to put your calculator into statistics mode. (See your instructions for specific information.)

The function labeled s or σ_{n-1} is the sample standard deviation number. It should be $3.8729833\ldots$, which rounds to the same answer obtained in Example 18.

When you have finished a problem, you must remember to clear the data from your calculator to start a new problem. This is usually done with SHIFT CE/C or using a button labeled CSR.

If you are using a TI-83 Plus calculator to do your calculations, use the button labeled STAT to access a menu that will let you enter data EDIT and clear old data CLRLST. The CALC function at the top of the screen is used to calculate statistical values of the data. The 1-Var Stats menu option is the one used to find the standard deviation of the list you have entered. You must tell the calculator to calculate for L_1, L_2, or whichever list you have used for the problem.

Problem Set 7-4

1. What does it mean if the standard deviation of a set of data is 0?

2. Without actually calculating the standard deviation, can you tell which of the following sets of data has the greater standard deviation? Explain.

   $$3, 6, 9, 12, 15 \qquad 213, 216, 219, 222, 225$$

Using your calculator, find the mean, range, and standard deviation of each of the following data sets.

3. 0, 1, 2, 3, 4, 5, 6, 7, 8, 9

4. 2, 4, 6, 8, 10, 12, 14, 16, 18, 20

5. 0, 0, 2, 5, 6, 9, 11, 15, 18, 18

6. 2, 2, 2, 2, 2, 2, 2, 2, 2, 2

7. 6, 6, 10, 12, 3, 5

8. 120, 121, 122, 123, 124, 125, 126

9. 4, 0, 3, 6, 9, 12, 2, 3, 4, 7

10. Find the mean average, range, and standard deviation of each of the following sets of numbers. What are the similarities and differences between the data sets? Explain these.

Data set A:	10, 10, 10, 10
Data set B:	1, 6, 13, 20
Data set C:	1, 1, 18, 20
Data set D:	2, 2, 20, 20

11. Two different sections of a math class take the same quiz and the scores are recorded in the following table. Find the range and standard deviation for each section. What do the range values lead you to conclude about the variation in the two sections? Why is the range misleading in this case? What do the standard deviation values lead you to conclude about the variation in the two sections?

    Section 1: 10 90 90 90 90 90 90 90 90 90   90
    Section 2: 20 35 40 40 45 70 75 80 85 95 100

12. The same biology test is given to two different sections of the class. The scores are recorded in the following table. Find the range and standard deviation of each section. What do the range values tell you about the variation in the two sections? Why is the range misleading in this case? What do the standard deviations lead you to conclude about the variation in the two sections?

    Section 1: 15 95 95 85 80 91 72 78 95 73 64 82   97
    Section 2: 20 35 40 40 47 70 78 80 80 88 92 95 100

13. The Forever and Enduring brands of D-cell batteries are both labeled as lasting 150 hours. In reality, they both have a mean life of 155 hours, but the Forever batteries have a standard deviation of 5 hours, whereas the Enduring batteries have a standard deviation of 20 hours. Which brand is the better choice? Why?

14. The Texas Department of Transportation is trying to decide whether to install high-pressure sodium vapor lights or low-pressure sodium vapor lights at various points along the interstate highway through Alamance County. High-pressure bulbs have a mean lifetime of 7000 hours with a standard deviation of 200 hours. Low-pressure sodium bulbs have a mean lifetime of 6400 hours with a standard deviation of 50 hours. Which bulbs should it choose? Why?

15. If you manufacture potato chips that are sold by weight, not by volume, would you want a small standard deviation or a large standard deviation in your quality control measurements? Give a reason for your answer.

16. Assume that the duration of a normal human pregnancy can be described by a mean of nine months (270 days) and a standard deviation of one-half month (15 days).
    (a) Most but not all babies will arrive within two standard deviations of the mean. Therefore, a mother would not expect a baby to arrive sooner than _____ days or later than _____ days.
    (b) In a paternity suit, the suspected father claims that because he was overseas during the entire 10 months before the baby's birth, he could not possibly be the father. Any comments?

17. The annual salaries of three employees at Maxton Office Resources are $20,000, $25,000, and $30,000.

(a) If each of these employees receives a $1000 raise, how does that affect the mean of these salaries? How does it affect the standard deviation?
(b) If each of these employees receives a 3% raise, how does that affect the mean of these salaries? How does it affect the standard deviation?

18. Carole has taken three tests in her civics class. She now has a mean average score of 80 and a median grade of 79. If the range of her scores is 13 points, what are her three test grades?

19. If you add the same amount to each piece of data in a data set, what happens to the value of the mean, range, and standard deviation of the set?

20. Without actually doing the calculations, decide which of the following two sets of data will have the greater standard deviation. Explain.

    5, 8, 9, 10, 12, 16   8, 9, 9, 10, 10, 11

21. Refer to problem 22 in Practice Set 7-2 and answer this question, "If each employee were to receive a $2000 raise, how would this affect the standard deviation of these salaries?"

22. Refer to problem 23 in Practice Set 7-2 and answer this question: "How does the 4% raise affect the standard deviation of the salaries?"

Section 7-5   NORMAL CURVE

Figure 7-6
A normal curve.

In this section, we will demonstrate some applications of the statistics that we have learned to calculate. When data sets are collected and then analyzed, histograms or other types of graphs of the data are often constructed. Many types of data will form a graph that is shaped like a **normal curve** (or **bell curve**). The normal curve has applications in many areas of business and science. A sample graph is shown in Figure 7-6.

Distributions of data that are collected can differ in many ways. As shown in Figure 7-7, data may differ in the location of the average value, in the overall spread of the data, and in shape. In this section, only data that are normally distributed will be considered. Distributions that are not normal require a more extensive study of statistics than is possible in this textbook.

What types of data might be "normally distributed"? Suppose that you were to ask a large number of men how tall they were. You would expect to find a few very tall men and a few very short men. However, you would expect to find that the

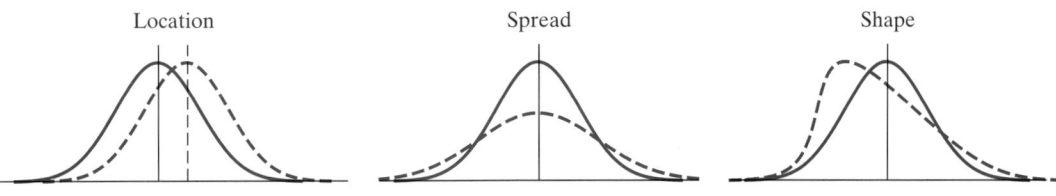

Figure 7-7
Normal curve variations.

vast majority of men were of approximately the same height. If you were to build a graph of this data set, you would plot each height onto the graph. The shape of the graph would slowly emerge as more and more data were added. Eventually, there would be enough data plotted to see the true "shape" of the data. (Refer to Figure 7-8.)

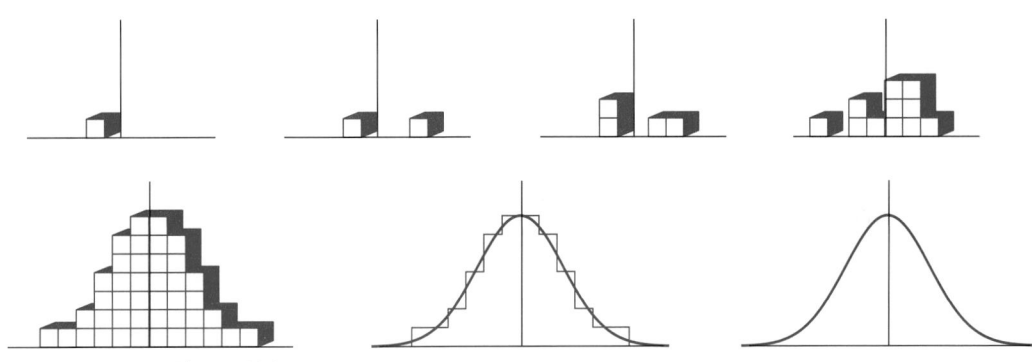

Figure 7-8
Building a normal curve.

If we are sure that the data that have been collected are approximately **normally distributed** (i.e., a graph of the data would be shaped like the normal or bell curve), then we can use some characteristics of the normal curve to analyze the data.

To set up a normal curve for a particular set of data, first calculate the measures of central tendency and dispersion (mean average, median, mode, range, and standard deviation) as described in the preceding sections of this chapter. Because each data set will probably have a different mean average and standard deviation, the normal curve for each will be slightly different.

Figure 7-9 shows a family of normal curves with the same standard deviation number but different mean averages. Figure 7-10 shows a series of normal curves

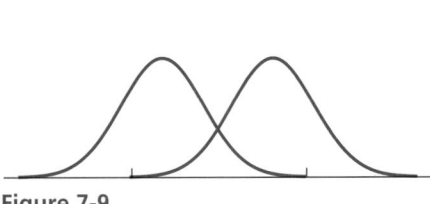

Figure 7-9
Normal curve family.

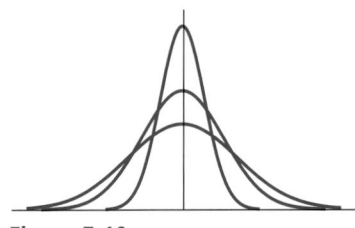

Figure 7-10
Another normal curve family.

with the same mean average but different standard deviations. (*Note:* The larger the standard deviation number, the broader the normal curve will be.)

Once a set of data has been collected and is known to be approximately normally distributed, then the **empirical rule** can be applied to the analysis of the data.

Theorem

The Empirical Rule

For a distribution that is symmetrical and normally distributed:

1. Approximately 68.2% of all data values will lie within one standard deviation on either side of the mean.
2. Approximately 95.4% of all data values will lie within two standard deviations on either side of the mean.
3. Approximately 99.7% of all data values will lie within three standard deviations on either side of the mean.

These percentages are based on the amount of **area under the normal curve** between the locations specified in the empirical rule. In theory, the curve extends infinitely in both directions, and the total area under the whole curve is 1 (100%). Because the curve is **symmetrical**, these percentages will be split evenly on either side of the mean. Figure 7-11 shows these areas and values.

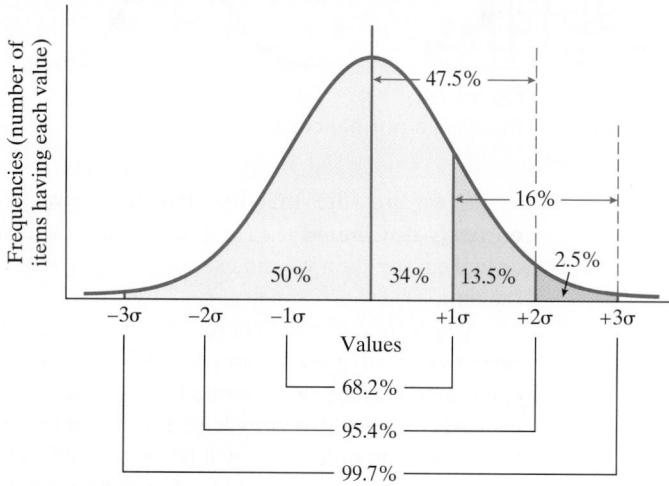

Figure 7-11
Standard normal curve.

As you may have already surmised, the use of the normal curve assumptions (the empirical rule) and the percentages is really just estimation. In fact, the proper word is **probability**, not percentage. A more detailed method of analysis is needed for most studies of data.

At the end of this section, you will find a **table of areas** (Table 7-3) based on the normal curve and **standard scores**, commonly called *z*-scores. To use the table, you must first calculate the mean average and standard deviation for your data as before. Once this has been done, calculating a z-score is simple. The z-score will be used to locate a position on the table of areas.

Definition

z-Score (Standard Score)

A z-score is the number of standard deviations (s) that a particular piece of data (x) is from the mean average ($\overline{x}$) for the set of data. If a z-score is positive, then the piece of data in question is above the mean average, and if the z-score is negative, then it is below the mean average. A z-score is calculated as follows:

$$z = \frac{x - \overline{x}}{s}$$

(See Figure 7-12.)

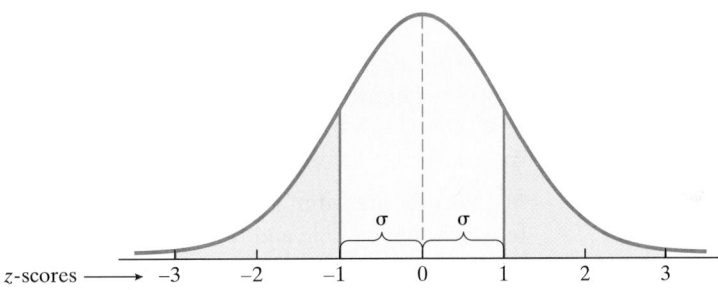

z-scores $\longrightarrow$ -3 -2 -1 0 1 2 3

Figure 7-12
Normal curve and z-scores.

EXAMPLE 20   Calculating z-Scores

Given a mean test score of 80 with a standard deviation of 5, calculate the following z-scores.

(a) What would your z-score be if you scored 85 on the test?
(b) What would your z-score be if you scored 70 on the test?
(c) What would your z-score be if you scored 93 on the test?
(d) What about for a test score of 90?
(e) If you had a z-score of -1.5 on this test, what numerical grade did you have?

(a)
$$z = \frac{x - \overline{x}}{s} = \frac{85 - 80}{5} = \frac{5}{5} = 1$$

A z-score of 1 means that a score of 85 on this test is one standard deviation above the mean average for all students who took this test.

(b)
$$z = \frac{x - \overline{x}}{s} = \frac{70 - 80}{5} = \frac{-10}{5} = -2$$

A z-score of -2 means that a test score of 70 is two standard deviations below average on this test.

(c) $z = \dfrac{x - \overline{x}}{s} = \dfrac{93 - 80}{5} = \dfrac{13}{5} = 2.6$, or 2.6 standard deviations above average

(d) $z = \dfrac{x - \overline{x}}{s} = \dfrac{90 - 80}{5} = \dfrac{10}{5} = 2$, or 2 standard deviations above average

(e) Here we will be solving the z-score formula for the value of "x," the data value corresponding to your test grade.

$$z = \dfrac{x - \overline{x}}{s}$$

$$-1.5 = \dfrac{x - 80}{5}$$

$$-7.5 = x - 80$$

$$72.5 = x$$

Therefore, your score was 72.5 on the test.

z-scores are often used to compare individual data points to the whole group to which they belong and to compare different groups with each other. Consider the following examples.

EXAMPLE 21 **Comparing Heights by Using z-Scores**

Assume that the average height of a male in the United States is 70 in., with a standard deviation of 2.0 in., and that the average height of a female is 67 in., with a standard deviation of 2.0 in. If one of your male classmates is measured to be 75 in. tall and a female in your class is also measured to be 75 in. tall, who is the "tallest" compared to the group to which they belong?

To make a valid comparison between males and females, it is important to realize that the two groups do not have the same mean average height. There is a true difference in the average heights of males and females. So the correct answer to who is "tallest" would be the one that is the most above average for his or her particular group.

$$z_{\text{male}} = \dfrac{75 - 70}{2.0} = 2.5 \text{ standard deviations above average}$$

$$z_{\text{female}} = \dfrac{75 - 67}{2.0} = 4.0 \text{ standard deviations above average}$$

The female is much further above average height for a female than is the male student. Therefore, the female is the "tallest."

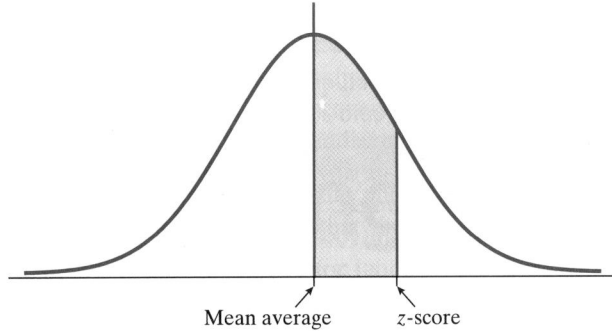

Mean average   z-score

Figure 7-13
Area under the normal curve.

Once you know how to calculate a z-score, then you are ready to use the table of areas under the standard normal curve at the end of this section (Table 7-3). This table will be used to determine the **probability of events** based on data collected; it will also show you the origin of the percentages given in the empirical rule.

Table 7-3 gives the proportion of the area under the normal curve between the mean of the data and the chosen z-score. This is pictured in Figure 7-13.

The absolute value of the z-score is used so that areas to the left and right of the center of the normal curve are all given based on positive z-scores. The table is only for half of the curve. Remember that in a theoretical normal curve, 50% of the area is below the mean and 50% is above the mean.

EXAMPLE 22   **Areas Applied to Grade Point Averages**

Admission to a state university depends in part on the applicant's high school grade point average (GPA) at graduation. Suppose that the mean average GPA of all applicants to this university is 3.20, with a standard deviation of 0.30, and the GPAs of applicants are approximately normally distributed.

(a) If all applicants who have a GPA of 3.50 or higher are automatically admitted, what proportion of applicants will be automatically admitted?

(b) Applicants with GPAs below 2.50 will be automatically denied admission. What proportion will be automatically denied?

(c) Applicants with GPAs of 3.75 or higher may apply for special scholarships. What proportion of applicants will be eligible for these scholarships?

(d) What proportion of applicants have GPAs between 3.00 and 3.50?

(e) What is the probability that you would randomly select an applicant to the university who has a GPA between 3.00 and 3.50?

(a) To solve these types of problems, you should sketch a normal curve with the given mean and standard deviation. Next, locate the value of special interest on your sketch and shade the area of interest.

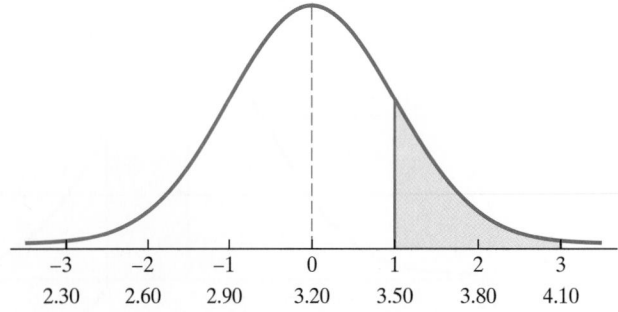

Calculate the z-score for a GPA of 3.50.

$$z_{3.50} = \frac{x - \overline{x}}{s} = \frac{3.50 - 3.20}{0.30} = 1.00$$

Now find $z = 1.00$ on the area table. For $z = 1.00$, the proportion of area under the curve between the mean and 1.00 is 0.341. Because we are interested in the proportion of students with GPAs *higher* than this, we will subtract this number from 0.50, resulting in 0.159 (or approximately 16% of the total area under the curve).

(b) As in part (a), locate the area specified. This area will begin at a GPA of 2.50 and extend into the left-hand tail of the normal curve.

$$z_{2.50} = \frac{2.50 - 3.20}{0.30} = \frac{-0.70}{0.30} = -2.33$$

Now find $|z| = 2.33$ on the area table. The number from the table is 0.490. Again, we will need to subtract this proportion from 0.50 to find the proportion lower than this value. Calculating this tells us that fewer than 1% of applicants will be automatically rejected.

(c)
$$z_{3.75} = \frac{3.75 - 3.20}{0.30} = 1.83$$

The proportion of the area under the curve between the mean and $z = 1.83$ is 0.466 or (46.6%). Subtracting from 50%, we find that slightly more than 3% of applicants will be eligible for these special scholarships.

(d) The area between GPAs of 3.00 and 3.50 is not a tail-end area. It overlaps the center line (mean) of the normal curve. We will need to find two z-scores, one above the mean and one below the mean. The proportions corresponding to these two z-scores will then be added to answer the question.

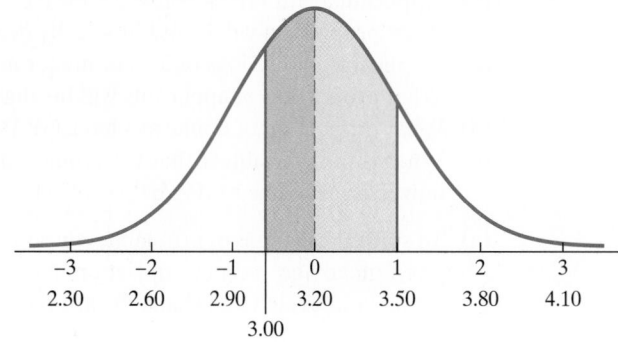

$$z_{3.00} = \frac{3.00 - 3.20}{0.30} = -0.67 \qquad \text{(proportion from table: 0.249)}$$

$$z_{3.50} = \frac{3.50 - 3.20}{0.30} = 1.00 \qquad \text{(proportion from table: 0.341)}$$

Adding the two proportions will give the total proportion of the area shown in our sketch: $0.249 + 0.341 = 0.590$ (or about 59%) of applicants.

(e) This is the same area as specified in part (d) of this problem. Thus, the probability that you would randomly pick an applicant with a GPA between 3.00 and $3.50 = 0.590$ (or a 59% chance).

Often, in testing such as achievement tests given in elementary school and related areas, it is useful to measure the position of an individual score relative to all other scores in the whole distribution. Ranking scores or values or data points is also useful when comparing differing groups (refer to Example 21 on comparing heights). One common way of doing this is to calculate the **percentile rank** for the score. A *percentile rank* indicates the *percentage of scores falling below* the given score. This can be done fairly easily using z-scores and finding the total area to the left of the given score.

EXAMPLE 23   Calculating a Percentile Rank

Refer to Example 22, part (c).

(a) What must the percentile rank of an applicant's GPA be to get one of the special scholarships?

(b) What is the percentile rank of the median GPA of 3.20?

(a) The GPA must be at least 3.75 to be eligible for these scholarships, and the z-score was calculated to be 0.466 in Example 22(c). This is the proportion of the area under the normal curve between the mean and the required minimum GPA of 3.75 ($z = 1.83$). To find the total area to the *left* of $z = 1.83$, we must add 0.466 and 0.500. So, $0.446 + 0.500 = .966$ or about 97% of all GPAs are less than 3.75.

Thus, the percentile rank for a GPA of 3.75 would be 97—in other words, the 97th percentile.

(b)
$$z_{3.20} = \frac{3.20 - 3.20}{0.30} = 0.00$$

This is the location of the peak of the normal curve and, by definition, exactly 50% of the data are located to the left of this point. Thus, a GPA of 3.20 is at the 50th percentile. In fact, *the median score is always at the 50th percentile rank*.

Practice Set 7-5

Value Watt lightbulbs have an average lifetime of 750 hr of use before burning out, with a standard deviation of 80 hr, according to the quality control department. Assume these times are normally distributed.

1. What percent of bulbs will last between 750 and 830 hr?

2. What percent of bulbs will last longer than 910 hr?

3. What percent of bulbs will burn out before being used 670 hr?

4. If a company were to buy 1500 of these lightbulbs, how many may burn out before burning for 830 hr?

Suppose that men's shirts have an average neck size of $15\frac{1}{2}$ in., with a standard deviation of $\frac{1}{2}$ in. Assume that neck sizes are normally distributed.

5. What percent of men have a neck size of 15 in. or larger?

6. What percent of men's neck sizes are between $14\frac{1}{2}$ and $16\frac{1}{2}$ in.?

7. If a company is going to manufacture 75,000 men's shirts, how many should have a neck size between $14\frac{1}{2}$ and $16\frac{1}{2}$ in?

Scores on the mathematics portion of the Scholastic Aptitude Test (SAT) are normally distributed, with a mean average math score of 500 and a standard deviation of 100. Use this information to answer the following questions.

8. What proportion of high school students taking the math portion of the SAT test will score 675 or higher?

9. What proportion will score less than 350?

10. What proportion will score between 350 and 675?

The average burning times of American Standard lightbulbs (made in China) are normally distributed, with a mean of 1200 hr and a standard deviation of 120 hr, according to quality control studies. A company installs a large number of these bulbs at the same time.

11. After what amount of time should we expect 1% of them to burn out? (*Hint:* This will split the total

area under the normal curve into an area of 0.0100 on the left-hand tail and 0.9900 on the other.)

12. After what amount of time should we expect 10% of them to fail?

13. After what amount of time should we expect 95% of them to fail?

14. If the company installed 2000 lightbulbs, about how many would they have to replace after 1500 hr of use?

A researcher in the town of Killeen did a survey with children. He discovered that they watched TV an average of 20 hr per week (standard deviation = 2.0 hr, and the data are normally distributed).

15. If a child is chosen at random in the town of Killeen, what is the probability that he or she watches TV for more than 22 hr per week?

16. If a child is chosen at random in the town of Killeen, what is the probability that he or she watches TV for less than 14 hr per week?

17. If a child is chosen at random in the town of Killeen, what is the probability that he or she watches TV for between 15 and 25 hr per week?

Beech Mountain Ski Resort has measured the depth of the snowpack (in inches) each February for the past 20 years. The results are given in the following table.

37	52	25	48	26	41	22	15	52	40
50	16	58	59	51	26	39	12	37	20

18. Find the mean average and standard deviation of the snow depths.

19. Assuming that the snowpack depths are approximately normally distributed, what are the maximum and minimum snow depths that define the 68% area under the normal curve? (In other words, what range of snowpack depths will occur 68% of the time at Beech Mountain?) Below what amount will the snowpack depth be 95% of the time?

Assume that the mean average height of a male in the United States is about 72 in., with a standard deviation of 5 in., and that the height of males in the United

States matches a normal distribution very well. Identify the location of the area under the standard normal curve for each of the following. (For example, for males taller than 72 in., the area would be the area under the curve to the right of 72 in. on the baseline.)

20. Males taller than 65 in.

21. Males shorter than 63 in.

22. Males between the heights of 74 and 64 in.

23. Suppose that you took a mathematics achievement test to try and skip some basic math courses when you enrolled in a college. If you scored at the 85th percentile, what percentage of persons who have taken the same test scored below your level?

24. On most tests, scores can range from 0 to 100. If you got a grade of 90 on such a test, would this mean that your score was at the 90th percentile? Why or why not?

25. Ray and Susan are in different sections of Algebra II at East High School. Ray scored 82 on the first test in his class. In his class, the mean average was 65, with a standard deviation of 12. Susan scored a 78 on the first test in her section of the class. In her section, the mean was 65, with a standard deviation of 10. Whose grade was better if they were graded on a curve referenced to the normal curve?

26. A banker studying customer needs finds that the number of times people use automated teller machines (ATMs) in a year are normally distributed, with a mean of 40.0 and a standard deviation of 11.4 (based on data from McCook Marketing Research, Inc.). Find the percentage of customers who use ATMs between 30 and 50 times. Among 5000 customers, how many are expected to have between 30 and 50 uses in a year?

27. Given a mean test score of 78, with a standard deviation of 5, calculate the z-score for a test score of 82.

28. Given a mean test score of 84 and a standard deviation of 7, calculate the z-score for a grade of 90 on the test.

29. Suppose that your z-score for the test in problem 27 was a negative number. What does that mean about your actual test score? Suppose your z-score was -1.6; what grade did you make on the test?

30. If your z-score on the test in problem 28 was 0.4, what was your actual test score?

Problems 31 to 36 refer to a normal distribution of IQ scores that have a mean average of 100 and a standard deviation of 15. You may round your answers to the nearest whole number or whole percentage.

31. What percent of IQs are below 110?

32. What percent of IQs are above 115?

33. What IQ score corresponds to the 5th percentile?

34. What percent of IQs fall between 130 and 145?

35. What pair of IQs separate the middle 95% from the remainder of the distribution?

36. If the z-score for your IQ is 1.3, what is your IQ?

37. The average Internet connection time for customers of connectme.com is 75 seconds with a standard deviation of 10 seconds. What percent of customers are able to connect between 63 and 83 seconds?

38. The Beanstalk Club has a minimum height requirement of 5 ft 10 in. for women to join the club. If women in the general population have a mean height of 5 ft 5.5 in. and $s = 2.0$ in., approximately what percentage of women would be eligible for membership?

Table of *z*-Scores: Proportion of Area under the
Standard Normal Curve for Values of *z*

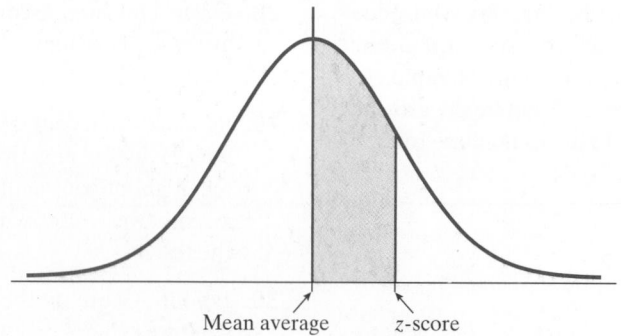

Mean average   *z*-score

Values are for areas beginning at the mean and going out to the *z*-score of choice.

z	A	z	A	z	A	z	A	z	A	z	A	z	A	z	A
0.00	0.000	0.37	0.144	0.74	0.270	1.11	0.367	1.48	0.431	1.85	0.468	2.22	0.487	2.59	0.495	2.96	0.499
0.01	0.004	0.38	0.148	0.75	0.273	1.12	0.369	1.49	0.432	1.86	0.469	2.23	0.487	2.60	0.495	2.97	0.499
0.02	0.008	0.39	0.152	0.76	0.276	1.13	0.371	1.50	0.433	1.87	0.469	2.24	0.488	2.61	0.496	2.98	0.499
0.03	0.012	0.40	0.155	0.77	0.279	1.14	0.373	1.51	0.435	1.88	0.470	2.25	0.488	2.62	0.496	2.99	0.499
0.04	0.016	0.41	0.159	0.78	0.282	1.15	0.375	1.52	0.436	1.89	0.471	2.26	0.488	2.63	0.496	3.00	0.499
0.05	0.020	0.42	0.163	0.79	0.285	1.16	0.377	1.53	0.437	1.90	0.471	2.27	0.488	2.64	0.496	3.01	0.499
0.06	0.024	0.43	0.166	0.80	0.288	1.17	0.379	1.54	0.438	1.91	0.472	2.28	0.489	2.65	0.496	3.02	0.499
0.07	0.028	0.44	0.170	0.81	0.291	1.18	0.381	1.55	0.439	1.92	0.473	2.29	0.489	2.66	0.496	3.03	0.499
0.08	0.032	0.45	0.174	0.82	0.294	1.19	0.383	1.56	0.441	1.93	0.473	2.30	0.489	2.67	0.496	3.04	0.499
0.09	0.036	0.46	0.177	0.83	0.297	1.20	0.385	1.57	0.442	1.94	0.474	2.31	0.490	2.68	0.496	3.05	0.499
0.10	0.040	0.47	0.181	0.84	0.300	1.21	0.387	1.58	0.443	1.95	0.474	2.32	0.490	2.69	0.496	3.06	0.499
0.11	0.044	0.48	0.184	0.85	0.302	1.22	0.389	1.59	0.444	1.96	0.475	2.33	0.490	2.70	0.497	3.07	0.499
0.12	0.048	0.49	0.188	0.86	0.305	1.23	0.391	1.60	0.445	1.97	0.476	2.34	0.490	2.71	0.497	3.08	0.499
0.13	0.052	0.50	0.192	0.87	0.308	1.24	0.393	1.61	0.446	1.98	0.476	2.35	0.491	2.72	0.497	3.09	0.499
0.14	0.056	0.51	0.195	0.88	0.311	1.25	0.394	1.62	0.447	1.99	0.477	2.36	0.491	2.73	0.497	3.10	0.499
0.15	0.060	0.52	0.199	0.89	0.313	1.26	0.396	1.63	0.449	2.00	0.477	2.37	0.491	2.74	0.497	3.11	0.499
0.16	0.064	0.53	0.202	0.90	0.316	1.27	0.398	1.64	0.450	2.01	0.478	2.38	0.491	2.75	0.497	3.12	0.499
0.17	0.068	0.54	0.205	0.91	0.319	1.28	0.400	1.65	0.451	2.02	0.478	2.39	0.492	2.76	0.497	3.13	0.499
0.18	0.071	0.55	0.209	0.92	0.321	1.29	0.402	1.66	0.452	2.03	0.479	2.40	0.492	2.77	0.497	3.14	0.499
0.19	0.075	0.56	0.212	0.93	0.324	1.30	0.403	1.67	0.453	2.04	0.479	2.41	0.492	2.78	0.497	3.15	0.499
0.20	0.079	0.57	0.216	0.94	0.326	1.31	0.405	1.68	0.454	2.05	0.480	2.42	0.492	2.79	0.497	3.16	0.499
0.21	0.083	0.58	0.219	0.95	0.329	1.32	0.407	1.69	0.455	2.06	0.480	2.43	0.493	2.80	0.497	3.17	0.499
0.22	0.087	0.59	0.222	0.96	0.332	1.33	0.408	1.70	0.455	2.07	0.481	2.44	0.493	2.81	0.498	3.18	0.499
0.23	0.091	0.60	0.226	0.97	0.334	1.34	0.410	1.71	0.456	2.08	0.481	2.45	0.493	2.82	0.498	3.19	0.499
0.24	0.095	0.61	0.229	0.98	0.337	1.35	0.412	1.72	0.457	2.09	0.482	2.46	0.493	2.83	0.498	3.20	0.499
0.25	0.099	0.62	0.232	0.99	0.339	1.36	0.413	1.73	0.458	2.10	0.482	2.47	0.493	2.84	0.498	3.21	0.499
0.26	0.103	0.63	0.236	1.00	0.341	1.37	0.415	1.74	0.459	2.11	0.483	2.48	0.493	2.85	0.498	3.22	0.499
0.27	0.106	0.64	0.239	1.01	0.344	1.38	0.416	1.75	0.460	2.12	0.483	2.49	0.494	2.86	0.498	3.23	0.499
0.28	0.110	0.65	0.242	1.02	0.346	1.39	0.418	1.76	0.461	2.13	0.483	2.50	0.494	2.87	0.498	3.24	0.499
0.29	0.114	0.66	0.245	1.03	0.349	1.40	0.419	1.77	0.462	2.14	0.484	2.51	0.494	2.88	0.498	3.25	0.499
0.30	0.118	0.67	0.249	1.04	0.351	1.41	0.421	1.78	0.463	2.15	0.484	2.52	0.494	2.89	0.498	3.26	0.499
0.31	0.122	0.68	0.252	1.05	0.353	1.42	0.422	1.79	0.463	2.16	0.485	2.53	0.494	2.90	0.498	3.27	0.500
0.32	0.126	0.69	0.255	1.06	0.355	1.43	0.424	1.80	0.464	2.17	0.485	2.54	0.495	2.91	0.498	3.28	0.500
0.33	0.129	0.70	0.258	1.07	0.358	1.44	0.425	1.81	0.465	2.18	0.485	2.55	0.495	2.92	0.498	3.29	0.500
0.34	0.133	0.71	0.261	1.08	0.360	1.45	0.427	1.82	0.466	2.19	0.486	2.56	0.495	2.93	0.498	3.30	0.500
0.35	0.137	0.72	0.264	1.09	0.362	1.46	0.428	1.83	0.466	2.20	0.486	2.57	0.495	2.94	0.498	3.31	0.500
0.36	0.141	0.73	0.267	1.10	0.364	1.47	0.429	1.84	0.467	2.21	0.487	2.58	0.495	2.95	0.498	3.32	0.500

Section 7-6   SCATTER DIAGRAMS AND LINEAR REGRESSION

In statistical analysis, there are many problems that require a comparison of two variables. We often want to know, "Are these two variables related?" or "Is there a strong correlation between these two factors?" We are not examining cause and effect but looking at mathematical relationships that will allow us to predict the behavior of one variable based on knowledge about another variable. For example, is a voter's opinion of a president's defense policy related to his or her political party affiliation? In this section, we will introduce one method of examining these relationships.

One way to see quickly if two variables are closely related is to use a graph called a **scatter diagram**. The data being analyzed are written in the form of ordered pairs, (x, y), where x is the independent variable and y is the dependent variable. For example, if we were interested in examining the relationship between a person's height and weight, x would be a person's height and the corresponding y would be that person's weight. In drawing a scatter diagram, the independent variable (x) is plotted on the horizontal axis, and the dependent variable (y) is plotted on the vertical axis (as explained in Chapter 3).

EXAMPLE 24

Drawing a Scatter Diagram: Do Heavier Cars Get Poorer Gas Mileage?

Weight of Car (lb)	Gas Mileage (mpg)
1600	46
4100	15
2100	31
2300	20
3400	15
3300	20
2700	25
1800	31
2100	20
2050	36
3800	15
3500	20

Draw a scatter diagram that relates the weight of various cars with their gas mileage for city driving.

We will let the weight of the cars be the x (independent) variable and gas mileage (miles per gallon of gas, mpg) the y (dependent) variable. We make this choice of variables because we suspect that the gas mileage may *depend* on the weight of the car. A plot of these ordered pairs is shown in Figure 7-14.

We can now look at the plot of the data to determine whether there appears to be a relationship between the weight of a car and its gas mileage in the city.

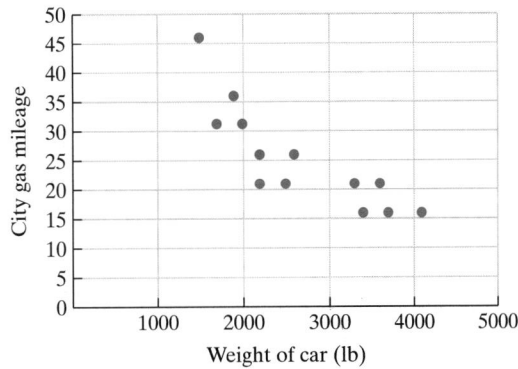

Figure 7-14
Weight versus mileage for selected cars.

Generally, it looks as though gas mileage decreases as the weight of a car increases. Because the points trend downward from left to right, we might say that there appears to be a **negative correlation** between the weight of a car and the gas mileage that it gets. (Remember from Chapter 2 that a line that slopes downward from left to right has a negative slope.)

In generalizing about the relationship between two variables, you can use a scatter diagram to help you draw some preliminary conclusions about your data. For example, you might try to answer the following questions about the data after you have drawn a scatter diagram.

(a) Does the pattern of the scatter diagram roughly follow a straight line (or other shape such as a parabola)?

(b) If it is somewhat linear, do the points slope upward (positive slope) or downward (negative slope)?

(c) Is the pattern of dots on the scatter diagram fairly tightly grouped or widely scattered?

(d) Are there any points that look significantly out of place (a significant deviation)?

Look at the scatter diagrams in Figure 7-15. Notice that the points in both scatter diagrams line up very well. They may not lie in a perfectly straight line but they are very close. Such a pattern indicates a strong relationship between the two variables. In scatter diagram 1, the line of points is "uphill," from left to right (a positive slope). Thus, there is a *positive relationship* (sometimes called a *positive correlation*) between the x and y variables. This can also be called a *direct variation*. See Chapter 3 to review this kind of relationship.

In scatter diagram 2, the slope is "downhill," from left to right (a negative slope). Thus, there is a *negative relationship* (sometimes called a *negative correlation*) between x and y. This can also be called an *inverse variation*. See Chapter 3 to review this kind of relationship.

If a scatter diagram shows that a set of data is fairly linear, then the next logical step is to set up a model for the data. The usual model would be to determine

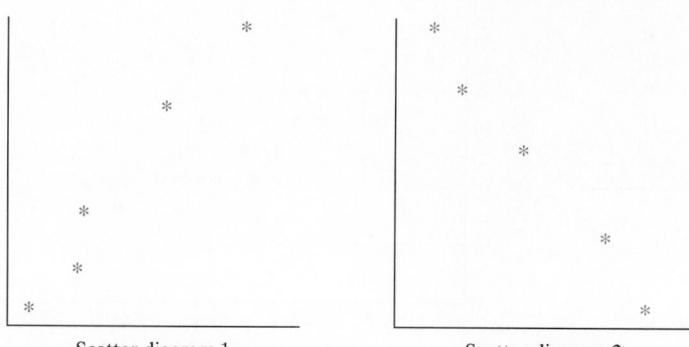

Scatter diagram 1   Scatter diagram 2

Figure 7-15
Scatter diagram comparison.

the equation of the line that best fits the data points that you have. The idea is to choose a line through the data points that by visual inspection seems to best fit the data.

This **best-fit line** can be calculated based on the data that you have. There is an area of statistics that deals with this process of determining the best-fit line. It is called **linear regression analysis**. The name is intimidating and so are the necessary formulas. We will not go into the formulas in this book, but a graphing calculator can be used to do the job for us, as we will see later. The line that best fits the data as determined by linear regression techniques is called the **least-squares line**. The regression equation is in the form $y = ax + b$. This equation should remind you of the slope-intercept form of a linear equation, which you studied previously. The equations determined by this method are models of the data that can be used as **prediction equations**. Given the regression equation for a situation involving two variables, one can predict the value of the dependent variable based on chosen values of the independent variable.

An important note needs to be made before we go too far with this topic. A high degree of correlation (either positive or negative) between two quantities does *not* imply (or prove) that one is the cause of the other (causation). As an example, the size of children's shoes and their measured reading ability will show a fairly high degree of correlation. That does not mean that having big feet causes a child to read well. Having larger feet and reading better are both a consequence of growing older, but neither *causes* the other.

In Figure 7-16 are the same two scatter diagrams that were shown previously, but these include the least-squares lines for the data. Notice that the lines do not go through all the points.

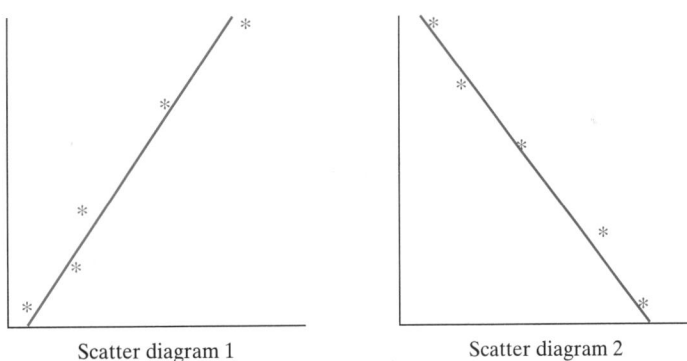

Scatter diagram 1   Scatter diagram 2

Figure 7-16
Scatter diagrams with least-squares lines.

■ EXAMPLE 25   **An Application of a Prediction Equation**

A study was done of the heights and weights of a sample of women ages 20–30. Use the resulting prediction equation (least-squares line) to predict the weight of a 26-year-old woman who is 65 in. (5 ft 5 in.) tall.

Prediction equation: $y = 4.71x - 186.5$

where y is weight and x is height in inches.

Solution: $y = 4.71(65) - 186.5 = 119.65$ or about 120 lb

As previously mentioned, deriving a prediction equation is a complicated process and beyond the scope of this textbook. However, we can use a graphing calculator to help us derive prediction equations. General directions are given in the following example, but you will need to refer to your calculator manual for specific instructions.

EXAMPLE 26   **Using a Calculator to Derive a Prediction Equation**

The following table gives the cooking time for a turkey based on its weight. Use this table to find a prediction equation for cooking time based on weight.

Weight (lb)	Cooking Time (hr)
5	3.5
7	4.0
10	4.5
14	5.5
18	6.75
22	8.5

If you are using a TI-83 Plus graphing calculator, enter the data into the calculator. STAT , EDIT , L$_1$ (weight), L$_2$ (cooking time). Then go to the STAT , CALC menu and find the LinReg (ax + b) $(ax + b)$ option. When you press ENTER for this option, the values of a and b will be displayed. Use these in the form $y = ax + b$ and write the prediction equation for this problem.

$$a = 0.2840557276 \approx 0.28$$
$$b = 1.860294118 \approx 1.86$$
$$y = 0.28x + 1.86$$

Now predict the cooking time for a 20-lb turkey.

$$y = 0.28x + 1.86 = 0.28(20) + 1.86 = 7.46$$

or about 7.5 hr. (If you are following along with this example in your calculator, do not erase the numbers you have listed until you finish reading this section. We are going to refer back to this example shortly.)

Once the regression line is calculated, another piece of information is needed to determine just how good the model (equation) will be at making predictions

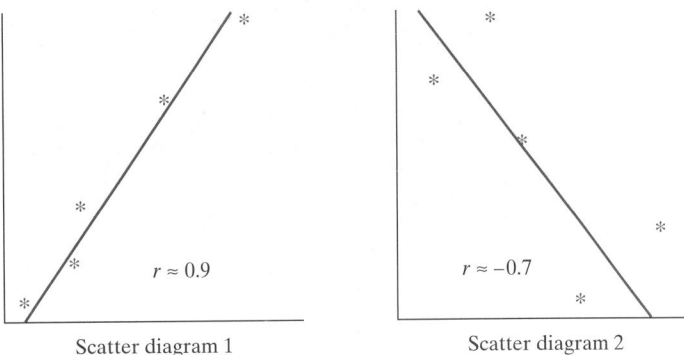

Scatter diagram 1   Scatter diagram 2

Figure 7-17
Scatter diagrams with least-squares lines and correlation coefficients.

about potential data. Look at the two scatter diagrams in Figure 7-17 and their associated best-fit lines. You will note that one of the sets of data is much closer to fitting the line than the other. In other words, scatter diagram 1 is nearer to actually being a line than scatter diagram 2. There is a number that can be calculated to indicate the degree to which a particular regression line fits the actual data. This number is the **correlation coefficient (r)** and is sometimes called the Pearson correlation coefficient, after Karl Pearson who developed this method in the 1890s. The value of r is a number between 1 and -1 ($-1 \leq r \leq 1$). If $r = 1$ or $r = -1$, then the data are perfectly linear in nature. The sign of the number for r indicates whether the correlation is positive or negative, as has already been discussed. A value for r that is not equal to 1 or -1 indicates that the data are not exactly linear. The closer the value is to 0, the less linear the data. The following list gives the most commonly used degrees of correlation based on the value of r.

$0 < |r| < 0.33$ shows a *weak correlation* (or none at all when r is near 0)

$0.34 < |r| < 0.67$ shows a *moderate correlation*

$0.68 < |r| < 1.00$ shows a *strong correlation*

Refer back to the data you entered into your calculator in Example 26. In addition to calculating the coefficients for the least-squares line, the calculator will also calculate a value for the correlation coefficient, r. On the screen with the values for a and b ($\boxed{\text{STAT}}$, $\boxed{\text{CALC}}$, $\boxed{\text{LinReg (ax + b)}}$), you will find the value of r. (If the value for r is not visible, use the $\boxed{\text{CATALOG}}$ function and select the option $\boxed{\text{Diagnostic On}}$). For the data in Example 26, the value of $r = 0.9879245263$. This value is very close to 1 and indicates that there is a high positive correlation between the weight of a turkey and the time it takes to cook it.

Practice Set 7-6

1. In general, is the correlation between the age of a secondhand car and its price positive or negative? Why?

2. In general, is the correlation between current age and years of life expectancy positive or negative? Why?

3. In general, is the correlation between the weight of a car and its gas mileage positive or negative? Why?

4. In general, is the correlation between people's height and weight positive or negative? Why?

5. The correlation coefficient r of the relationship between years of education and personal income is 0.75.
   (a) What are the independent and dependent variables in this problem?
   (b) How would you describe the strength of this relationship?
   (c) What does the positive sign of the correlation coefficient indicate in this problem?

6. The correlation between the number of police officers patrolling a public park and the number of muggings is calculated as $r = -0.97$.
   (a) What are the independent and dependent variables in this problem?
   (b) How would you describe the strength of this relationship?
   (c) What does the negative sign of the correlation coefficient indicate in this problem?

7. The following least-squares prediction equation is based on college GPAs (y) and SAT scores (x) in English:

$$y = 0.005x + 0.40$$

   If a student scores 600 on the SAT, predict the student's GPA.

8. A scientist developed a prediction equation to predict the number of seed pods that would develop on a plant based on the number of branches on the plant. The equation is

$$y = 18x - 208$$

   Predict the number of seed pods that would be produced by a plant with
   (a) 16 branches
   (b) 20 branches

9. Using a sample of 50 college graduates, a regression equation for estimating the final college GPA (y') based on a student's SAT source (x) was derived. Use the equation $y' = 0.002x + 0.667$ to estimate the final college GPA of a student with an SAT score of 1060.

10. Using a sample of 15 houses in one neighborhood, a salesperson studied the relationship between the size of a house (in square feet) and the selling price of the property (in thousands of dollars). She developed a prediction equation, $y' = 0.0728x - 25.0$, to assist in the prediction of the selling price of a house based on its square footage. Use this equation to predict the selling price of a 1500-square-foot house in this neighborhood.

11. The following data were recently collected. We will use these data to determine if there is a relationship between age and the length of hospital stay for surgical patients.

Age	Days in Hospital
40	11
36	9
30	10
27	5
24	12

   (a) Draw a scatter diagram. (*Note:* Let x = age and y = days in hospital.)
   (b) Does there appear to be a correlation between age and number of days in the hospital?

12. Is there a correlation between a man's height and his shoe size? Can a man's shoe size be predicted from his height? How reliable is this prediction? Use the data in the table collected from adult males to answer the following questions.

Height (in inches)	68	73	67	74	65	70	75
Shoe Size	10	11	10	13	8	9	13

Height (in inches)	70	67	72	64	68	74	69
Shoe Size	10	9	12	8	9	12	10

   (a) Draw a scatter diagram using this data set. Be sure to label it properly.
   (b) What is the correlation coefficient for these data? Is there a strong, weak, or moderate correlation?
   (c) What is the regression equation for the data?

(d) Predict the shoe size of an adult male whose height is measured at 5 ft $7\frac{1}{2}$ in.

13. Medical research indicates that there is a positive correlation between the weight (x) of a 1-year-old baby and the weight (y) of that baby as a mature adult (30 years old). A random sample of medical files produced the following information for 11 females:

x (lb)	21	25	23	24	20	15
y (lb)	125	125	120	125	130	120

x (lb)	25	21	17	24	26
y (lb)	145	130	115	130	140

(a) Draw a scatter diagram of these data.
(b) Is there a strong, weak, or moderate correlation?
(c) What is the prediction equation?
(d) What is the correlation coefficient of these data?
(e) Predict the weight of a 1-year-old 20-lb baby at age 30.

14. Sociologists are interested in the correlation between years of education and yearly income. The following data were collected from eight men with full-time jobs who had been employed for 10 years.

Years of Education	12	13	10	14	11	14	16	16
Yearly Income (in thousands)	34	45	36	47	43	35	50	42

(a) Use these data to find a prediction equation for income (y) based on years of education (x).
(b) Predict the income after 10 years of a man with 15 years of education.
(c) What is the degree of correlation?

15. Ten students in a physics class have each taken two brief quizzes. Each quiz has a maximum score of 10. The scores of all 10 students for tests 1 and 2 are listed next. (*Note:* The scores are given in the same order by student in both lists so that the first score in both lists is for student 1, the second in both for student 2, etc.)

Quiz 1 scores: 6, 5, 8, 8, 6, 7, 7, 9, 10, 4
Quiz 2 scores: 8, 7, 7, 10, 8, 5, 6, 8, 10, 6

(a) Construct a scatter diagram of the scores, letting quiz 1 scores be the xs.
(b) Does there appear to be any correlation between the scores on the quizzes? If so, what kind of correlation is it?

16. Find a prediction equation for the data in problem 15. Let x = quiz 1 scores and y = quiz 2 scores. Use this equation to predict the quiz 2 score of a student who scored 8 on the first quiz.

Chapter Summary

Key Terms, Properties, and Formulas

area under the normal curve	empirical rule	mode
average	frequency distribution	negative correlation
bell curve	inferential statistics	normal curve
best-fit line	least-squares line	normally distributed
bias	linear regression analysis	percentile rank
cluster sampling	mean average	pie graph
convenience sampling	measures of central	population
correlation coefficient (r)	tendency	prediction equation
data	median	probability
descriptive statistics	midpoint of the class	probability of events
dispersion	modal class	qualitative data

quantitative data	standard scores	systematic sample
random sampling	statistics	table of areas
range	stem-and-leaf display	variation
sample	strata	weighted mean
scatter diagram	stratified sampling	z-scores
standard deviation	symmetrical	

Formulas to Remember

Mean average: $\bar{x} = \dfrac{\text{total of all numbers in the data set}}{\text{number of items in the data set}} = \dfrac{\Sigma x}{n}$

Range: $R = (\text{highest number}) - (\text{lowest number}) = x_{max} - x_{min}$

Standard deviation: $s = \sqrt{\dfrac{\Sigma(x - \bar{x})^2}{n - 1}}$

z-score: $z = \dfrac{x - \bar{x}}{s}$

Chapter Review Problems

1. Discuss the differences between descriptive and inferential statistics.

2. Discuss the differences between quantitative and qualitative data.

For each of the following situations, state which type of sampling plan (simple random, stratified, cluster, systematic, convenience) was used. Explain whether or not you think the sampling plan would result in a biased sample.

3. To survey the opinions of its customers, an airline company made a list of all of its flights and randomly selected 25 flights. All the passengers on those flights were asked to fill out a survey.

4. A large department store wanted to know if consumers would use an ATM machine if it were installed inside the store. An interviewer was posted at the door and told to collect a sample of 100 opinions by asking the next person who came in the door each time she had finished an interview.

5. To find out how its employees felt about higher student fees imposed by the legislature, a community college divided employees into three categories: staff, faculty, and student employees. A random sample was selected from each group and they were telephoned and asked for their opinions.

Find the mean average, median, mode, range, and standard deviation of each of the following sets of data.

6. 10, 11, 12, 13, 14, 15, 16, 17, 18

7. 2, 4, 6, 8, 8, 9, 22, 25, 32, 57

8. Looking back at the sets of numbers in problems 6 and 7, which group has the most variation? Explain how you know this.

9. Looking back at the sets of numbers in problems 6 and 7, what is the "best" average for each set? Explain why you chose the value that you did.

The troubleshooter at a local computer center has recorded the number of calls to technical support from January 1 to February 19.

Number of Calls Daily, January 1 to February 19

6	5	3	7	4	8	10	3	4	5
9	8	3	5	7	4	7	6	7	10
7	3	4	5	5	6	6	8	6	3
3	8	10	5	12	9	6	11	3	8
11	12	14	7	13	14	7	8	11	14

10. Construct a frequency table of the preceding data (use six classes).

11. Construct a histogram. Describe the distribution shape.

A survey is conducted, and it is discovered that the average adult male's waist size is 35 in., with a standard deviation of 2 in.

12. What percent of men have a waist size greater than 37 in.?

13. What percent of men have a waist size less than 35 in.?

14. What percent of men have a waist size between 31 and 37 in.?

15. You took two tests yesterday. On the math test, you scored 88. The class average for this test was 80, with a standard deviation of 5. You also took a history test and scored 88. The class average for the history test was 85, with a standard deviation of 3. Compared to the other students in these classes, on which test did you do the best?

Tough Tread Tire Company manufactures tires for automobiles. The company quality control department has determined that its best tire has a tread life of 45,000 miles, with a standard deviation of 8200 miles, and the data are normally distributed.

16. If the company guarantees these tires for 30,000 miles, what proportion can it expect to replace under this guarantee?

17. What if the company guarantees the tires for 40,000 miles?

A student of criminology, interested in predicting the age at incarceration (y) using the age at first police contact (x), collected the following data.

Age at First Contact	Age at Incarceration
11	21
17	20
13	20
12	19
15	18
10	23
12	20

18. Construct a scatter diagram of these data. Does there appear to be a strong correlation?

19. Find the regression equation for this set of data.

20. Predict the age at incarceration for an individual who at age 14 had his first contact with police.

21. What is the linear coefficient of correlation for these data?

22. Interpret the meaning of the coefficient of correlation in this situation.

Chapter Test

If you were to collect the following data, would it be quantitative or qualitative data?

1. The bacteria count in your house drinking water

2. The occupation of your parents' friends

3. The favorite TV show of members of your immediate family

4. The number of students in math classes at your high school

Consider the following sets of data:

Data set A: 2, 4, 6, 8, 10

Data set B: 1, 3, 5, 7, 19

Without calculating any numerical values, answer the following questions.

5. Which group will have the largest variation?

6. What measure of central tendency would be the "best" for each group?

Calculate the mean average, median, mode, range, and standard deviation of each of the following sets of data.

7. 32, 33, 33, 35, 35, 36, 36, 36, 40, 42, 44

8. H, M, L (High, Medium, Low)

Many airline passengers seem weighted down with their carry-on luggage. Just how much weight are they carrying? The carry-on luggage weights for a random sample of 40 passengers returning from a vacation to Hawaii were recorded in pounds.

Weight of Carry-on Luggage (lb)

30	27	12	42	35	47	38	36	27	35
22	17	29	3	21	10	38	32	41	33
26	45	18	43	18	32	31	32	19	21
33	31	28	29	51	12	32	18	21	26

9. Construct a stem-and-leaf display of these data.

10. Does this display approximate any of the shapes we have discussed?

11. A certain community college gives a numerical-skills placement test to all incoming students each year. The average score made by students on this test is 41, with a standard deviation of 4. If a score of 37 is needed to place out of the first required math course, what percent of incoming students must take this course?

A recent statistics test had a class average score of 80, with a standard deviation of 5, and the grades are normally distributed.

12. If a student scored 65 on this test, what would that student's z-score be?

13. If your z-score was 1.75, what was your grade on the test?

14. If 70 is the minimum passing grade, what proportion of students passed?

15. If a grade of B is earned by scoring between 80 and 89, what proportion of students made a B?

16. If your height were two standard deviations above that of the average person of your sex, what would the z-score for your height be?

17. A company manufactures automobile batteries and wants to guarantee them for 60 months (5 years). Quality control testing determines that its average battery has a life of 64 months, with a standard deviation of 3 months. What proportion of batteries is the company likely to be replacing under this guarantee?

18. A regression equation for predicting weight in pounds (y) from height in inches (x) is

$$y = 4x - 130$$

Predict the weight of a person who is 69 in. tall.

19. Following is a list of the ages of 10 employees at a local company and their current salaries. Determine the linear coefficient of correlation of this set of data and then interpret its meaning in this situation.

Age	Salary ($)
25	22,500
55	46,000
27	41,500
30	31,500
35	36,000
58	71,500
19	17,500
33	51,000
40	37,000
42	38,500

The following table lists the number of Burger King restaurants that were in operation worldwide in the year indicated. (Source: www.burgerking.com.)

1991	1992	1993	1994	1995
6385	6648	7121	7547	8030

1996	1997	1998	1999	2000
8696	9400	9835	10,526	11,150

20. Draw a scatter diagram of these data.

21. What is the prediction equation for the number of restaurants that Burger King has in operation?

22. Based on these data and your equation in problem 21, predict the number of restaurants that will be in operation in 2006.

Suggested Laboratory Exercises

LAB EXERCISE 1

A Statistical Analysis of M&Ms

As a class, buy a number of small packages (all of the same weight) of plain chocolate M&Ms. Open each package and weigh the contents of each separately. Also, count the number of M&Ms of each color in each package. Keep a complete record for each package separately.

The M&M/Mars company mixes colors in a certain percentage that it has found to be pleasing to its customers. The current (2004) mix is approximately 13% brown, 14% yellow, 13% red, 24% blue, 20% orange, and 16% green.

Calculate the average package weight and standard deviation. Using your class standard deviation, and assuming that the package weights are normally distributed, determine the proportion that meet the package claims of weight. Discuss your results.

Is the color mix that you measured approximately what was intended by the manufacturer? Discuss your results.

Assuming you washed your hands and used clean holders for weighing your candy, eat all of 'em.

LAB EXERCISE 2

SAT Statistics

Gather information from your guidance office about the SAT scores of students at your high school last year. Determine the average test score on the mathematics, writing, and critical reading section for students at your school. According to information from www.collegeboard.com, the average scores in 2005 for college-bound seniors were Critical Reading 508 and Math 520. (No data was available for the writing portion.) How does your school compare?

LAB EXERCISE 3

Radio Advertisements

Contact a local radio station and find out the amount of advertising time per hour of broadcast it claims to follow. Get the average and standard deviation if at all possible. Listen to that station for 1 hour and, with a stopwatch in hand, measure the amount of time devoted to advertising. Does the time you measured match the station claims?

LAB EXERCISE 4

Predicting Sales at Burger King

The following table gives the worldwide sales for Burger King Restaurants in billions of dollars per year. These data may be used to determine a linear equation that models the sales amounts. This is done by using a statistical process called linear regression analysis. The equation obtained using pairs of numbers such as $(x, y) = $ (year number, sales) is $y = 0.1429x - 275.7$.

1. Complete the following table. It lists the sales per year and the sales for the year as estimated by the previous model.

Year	Actual Sales	Model Sales	Actual Sales – Model Sales	Dollars Difference
1998	10.3	9.81	0.49	$490,000,000
1999	10.9			
2000	11.4			
2001	11.2			
2002	11.3			
2003	11.1			

2. What do the negative numbers in the "Actual Sales – Model Sales" column mean?

3. By what percent does the model over- or underestimate the sales for 2001?

4. Here are two more possible models for these data. Are any of these better than the model originally given? (*Note:* The instructor may wish to assign each group an equation to study and then present the results to the class.)

    (a) $y = 0.1429x + 1055$, where the pairs are numbers such as $(1, 10.3)$ instead of $(1998, 10.3)$, where the years are numbered as $1, 2, \ldots$.

    (b) $y = -0.0067x + 11.3$, where the pairs are numbers such as $(98, 10.3)$.

5. What does the best model predict for sales in 2006? For what purposes might a company like to model various aspects of its business over a period of time?

LAB EXERCISE 5   ## Calculating Your GPA in College

When you go to a college or university, your grade point average (GPA) is dependent on two things: the grades you earn and the number of credit hours of each course. The college assigns a number of *grade points* (or quality points) to each letter grade. For example, a grade of A usually earns 4 grade points per credit hour, a B earns 3 grade points, a C earns 2, a D earns 1, and an F earns 0 points.

Suppose you and four friends all took a history course that was a 3-credit-hour course and you each made a different grade. The one who made the

A would receive (3 credit hours)(4 points per credit hour for an A) = 12 grade points

B would receive (3 credit hours)(3 points per credit hour for a B) = 9 grade points

C would receive (3 credit hours)(2 points per credit hour for a C) = 6 grade points

D would receive (3 credit hours)(1 point per credit hour for a D) = 3 grade points

F would receive (3 credit hours)(0 points per credit hour for an F) = 0 grade points

The number of grade points for every credit class that you take is calculated this way and then the total number of grade points earned is divided by the total number of credit hours of all the classes involved. This is a cumulative operation semester after semester.

Assume that John and Maria take biology (4 credit hours), English (3 credit hours), psychology (3 credit hours), golf (1 credit hour), and history (3 credit hours). Calculate the GPA for each, given these grades:

John: biology, A; English, B; psychology, B; golf, A; history, C.
Maria: biology, C; English, A; psychology, A; golf, B; history, B.

LAB EXERCISE 6

Cookie Monster

This activity is essentially a brief look at product testing and comparisons. The guidelines given here are brief and not nearly as detailed or rigorous (statistically or procedurally) as the "real thing" would be, if it were done by a manufacturer. The good part is that you get to eat chocolate chip cookies and call it a math lab.

Are all chocolate chip cookies equal? Do they all taste good? Are they all the same size and texture? Do they all cost the same? Do the more expensive ones really taste better (by whatever standard you wish to measure "better")? Let's do some investigating to find out. What follows are some basic guidelines for performing this investigation. You may wish to modify these questions for your particular class.

1. What cookies to buy? Buy as many different brands of chocolate chip cookies as the class budget will allow. Purchase only "hard" chocolate chip cookies or only "soft" chocolate chip cookies and not a mixture. A mixture will impact the results of questions involving the texture of the cookies. Be sure to record the brand name, actual price (no tax), and weight of each package. From this, you can determine the cost per ounce of cookies for each brand.

2. Next, open each package and have someone who will not actually participate in the testing (perhaps your instructor) label some plain brown lunch bags with letters A–enough to match up with the number of different brands purchased. Then have this person place cookies of one brand in each bag. This is the only person who should know which brand is in which bag. Make a list for future reference.

3. Now the taste-testers get to eat some cookies. (Got milk?) Remember, we're after opinions here, not skipping lunch. What opinions do we want? Well, let's rate the cookies as to their taste, texture, and appearance and give an overall rating of the brand. Perhaps a rating sheet patterned as follows would be helpful.

Rating Chocolate Chip Cookies

Name of tester: _____.
My favorite brand of chocolate chip cookie before this test was: _____.
("no preference" is a valid response here)
I am Male   Female   (please circle one)

Rating Scale:
P = poor, F = fair, G = good, V = very good, and E = excellent
Using this scale, please rate each brand of cookie (A–?) by circling your opinion in each of the following categories:

Brand	Taste	Texture	Appearance	Overall
A	P F G V E	P F G V E	P F G V E	P F G V E
B	P F G V E	P F G V E	P F G V E	P F G V E
etc.	P F G V E	P F G V E	P F G V E	P F G V E

4. Now for the mathematical fun. Let's use a 5-point scale, with P = 1 and E = 5, and convert the entire class data set into number ratings.

5. Using the numbers for taste and the cost per ounce numbers, is there a relationship between the two? What kind?

6. Make any other comparisons that your instructor may choose. For example, compare the overall ratings with cost.

7. Have a general discussion of this testing procedure. What is good and what is bad about it? If you had it to do over again, what would you change? And so forth.

LAB EXERCISE 7 Histograms

Your TI-83 Plus or TI-84 calculator will fairly easily give you a histogram of data that you enter in a list. Just for practice, let's try one.

Start by entering your data in list 1 (L_1): Press STAT, then ENTER (Edit) to get to L_1. Enter the following data set (20 numbers):

$$2, 2, 3, 4, 4, 5, 5, 5, 5, 6, 6, 7, 7, 7, 7, 8, 8, 9, 10, 10$$

Now go to STAT PLOT by pressing 2nd Y=. First, be sure that only Plot 1 is on. If Plot 2, 3, or 4 is on, arrow down to that plot, ENTER, and arrow over to **Off**. Arrow up to Plot 1 and ENTER, highlight **On**, arrow down to type and over to the **histogram symbol**.

Now press ZOOM 9 (zoom stat) and your histogram will appear, automatically scaled to fit the screen.

Press TRACE and the calculator will tell you how many pieces of your data are represented by the first bar and then press the ► to shift from bar to bar.

If the scale of the graph doesn't suit you, you can change it manually by pressing WINDOW and changing the values shown.

This is just a brief look at the process. Your instructor may want you to try and reproduce some of the graphs in this chapter on your calculator.

LAB EXERCISE 8 Deriving an Exponential Function from a Data Set

We have looked at linear regression models in this chapter. However, not all data will fit the linear model. Some data are best modeled with an exponential function of the form $y = ab^x$. (Recall your work with these functions in Chapter 3.) In this problem we will look at the per capita income in the state of Texas for years 1970–2000 to create a function that models the growth in per capita income.

The table lists the per capita (per person) income in the state of Texas for the last four census reports: 1970, 1980, 1990, and 2000. The data source is the U.S. Bureau of Economic Analysis.

Per Capita Income (in dollars) for the State of Texas

Years Since 1970	Income
0	$ 3646
10	$ 9957
20	$17,446
30	$28,035

1. Enter the data points into your graphing calculator. Put the years in L_1 and the income in L_2.

2. To fit an exponential function to the data, press $\boxed{\text{STAT}}$ and choose the $\boxed{\text{CALC}}$ option. Now select option $\boxed{0}$ ExpReg. Next, press $\boxed{\text{VARS}}$, choose the $\boxed{\text{Y-VARS}}$ option, then choose option $\boxed{1}$, Function, and then choose option $\boxed{1}$, $\boxed{Y_1}$. When you press $\boxed{\text{ENTER}}$, you will see the values of a and b in the equation $y = ab^x$. By doing these keystrokes, you have also copied the regression equation into the Equation Editor® screen as $\boxed{Y_1}$. What is the regression equation for this data? Round your values to one decimal place.

3. Now use the calculator to make a scatterplot of this data set. Go to the $\boxed{\text{STATPLOT}}$ function, choose option $\boxed{1}$, and turn on the first plot. Arrow down to choose the picture of a scatterplot (the first graph shown), and be sure that the screen shows that the data will be taken from L_1 and L_2. Now press the $\boxed{\text{ZOOM}}$ button and select option 9, $\boxed{\text{ZOOMSTAT}}$. The graph should be displayed on your screen. Sketch it below. Is this a linear function?

4. Use the equation to predict the per capita income in Texas in the year 2001 ($x = 31$). What amount did you get? The reported per capita income in 2001 was $28,581. How close was your prediction? Now predict the per capita income in the year 2010. How accurate do you believe this prediction to be?

chapter eight

Additional Applications of Algebraic Modeling

"There is no excellent beauty that hath not some strangeness in the proportion."
— Sir Francis Bacon

This chapter will give you a brief taste of many areas where mathematical modeling is used every day. Several of the areas, such as music, may surprise you at first. Don't let the fact that mathematics is involved ruin your enjoyment of music and the arts.

333

Section 8-1 MODELS AND PATTERNS IN PLANE GEOMETRY

Formulas are mathematical models that have been developed over the course of hundreds of years by mathematicians who noticed constant relationships among variables in similar problems. Many geometric formulas were developed by the Greeks and ancient Egyptians after much trial and error. Euclid, one of the most prominent mathematicians of antiquity, wrote a treatise called *The Elements,* which was a compilation of the geometric knowledge of the time (365–300 BC). This book was used as the core of geometry textbooks for the next 2000 years. The use of geometric formulas has made the design of buildings and construction projects much simpler. If there were no formula to calculate the area of a rectangle, for example, a person wanting to carpet a floor shaped like a rectangle would need to roll out a large sheet of paper to cover the floor, trace the outline of the floor, cut it out, take it to the store, trace it onto a piece of carpet, and cut out a suitable piece to finish the job. How much simpler it is to measure the length and width of the room and use the formula to calculate the square footage required for the job!

Perimeter and area are two basic geometric concepts that have many real-life applications. The **perimeter** of any plane geometric figure is the distance around that figure, or the sum of the lengths of its sides. Perimeter is measured in linear units, such as inches, feet, yard, meters, or kilometers. Calculating the length of a wallpaper border needed for all four kitchen walls in a house would require finding the perimeter of the room. Buying the correct amount of fencing needed to enclose a dog lot would also require the calculation of the perimeter of the lot to be surrounded.

A rectangle is a geometric figure with right angles and opposite sides the same length. Because perimeter is the sum of the lengths of the sides of any figure, the perimeter of a rectangle such as the one in Figure 8-1 would be $l + w + l + w$ or $P = 2l + 2w$. There are other formulas for the perimeter of geometric figures, such as the square ($P = 4s$) and triangle ($P = a + b + c$), but many real-life shapes are not perfectly geometric. Therefore, it is usually best to think of the "formula" for perimeter as "add all the sides together."

Figure 8-1

EXAMPLE 1 Finding the Perimeter of a Rectangle

Christopher is building a 7 1/2-ft × 13-ft rectangular dog pen in his back yard. If fencing costs $4.37 per ft, find the cost of enclosing the dog pen.

Since the dog pen is rectangular, we can use the formula $P = 2l + 2w$ to find the perimeter and, therefore, the amount of fencing he needs to buy.

$$P = 2l + 2w$$

$$P = 2(13 \text{ ft}) + 2\left(7\frac{1}{2}\text{ ft}\right)$$

$$P = 26 \text{ ft} + 15 \text{ ft}$$

$$P = 41 \text{ ft}$$

Christopher needs 41 ft of fencing to enclose the lot, and the cost is $4.37 per foot. To find his total cost we multiply these numbers.

$$\text{Cost} = (41 \text{ ft})(\$4.37/\text{ft}) = \$179.17$$

The total cost for the dog pen will be $179.17.

The distance around the outside of a circle is called its **circumference.** The formulas that are used to calculate the area and circumference of circles involve the use of the irrational number *pi* (π), which is derived from the ratio of the circumference of a circle to its diameter. The value of **pi** is approximately 3.14. The symbol π appears on your calculator and will display a value for pi that contains more than two decimal places. To calculate the distance around any circle, use the formula $C = \pi d$ or $C = 2\pi r.$ The two formulas are equivalent, since the length of the diameter is twice that of the radius of the circle. (See Figure 8-2.)

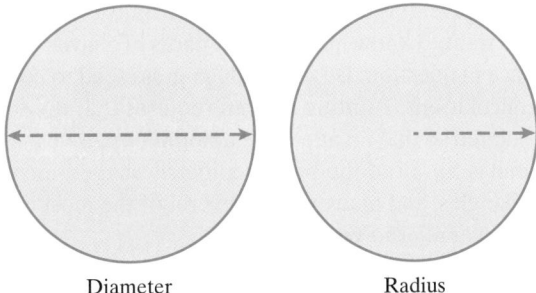

Diameter   Radius

Diameter = 2(radii) or $d = 2r$ Figure 8-2

EXAMPLE 2   Finding the Circumference of a Circle

── 60 cm ──

Figure 8-3

The diameter of a bicycle tire is 60 cm (see Figure 8-3). Through what distance does the tire go when it makes one turn? Give the answer to the nearest centimeter.

Because the diameter of the tire is given, we will use the formula $C = \pi d$ and the rounded value 3.14 for π.

$$C = \pi d$$

$$C = (3.14)(60 \text{ cm})$$

$$C = 188.4 \text{ cm}$$

$$C \approx 188 \text{ cm}$$

EXAMPLE 3   Window Molding

Figure 8-4

At \$0.30 per foot, how much will it cost to put molding around the window pictured in Figure 8-4?

We need to calculate the distance around the outside of the window. The window is 5 ft tall and 4 ft 6 in. wide.

(a) Adding the three straight sides together gives a total of 14 ft and 6 in., or 14.5 ft.

(b) To calculate the length of the curved part of the window, we need to use the circumference formula ($C = \pi d$). Because the curve is only half a circle, we will halve the circumference after it is calculated. To make our calculations easier, we will convert 4 ft 6 in. to 4.5 ft.

$$C = \pi d$$

$$C = \pi(4.5 \text{ ft}) = 14.14 \text{ ft.}$$

$$\text{Length of arc} = 14.14 \text{ ft} \div 2 = 7.07 \text{ ft.}$$

(c) Total distance around the window would be:

$$14.5 \text{ ft} + 7.07 \text{ ft} = 21.57 \text{ ft}$$

(d) Cost of molding is (21.57ft)(\$0.30 per foot) = \$6.47

The **area** of any flat surface is the amount of surface enclosed by the sides of the figure. It is measured in square units (square feet, square meters, etc.) because we want to know how many squares of a given size will be needed to cover the surface in question. Buying enough grass seed to cover a lawn involves the use of area calculations. Painting a room requires that the square footage of the walls be calculated so that an adequate amount of paint can be purchased. There are area formulas for all of the basic geometric shapes, including squares, rectangles, circles, triangles, and many more. Several of the most commonly used formulas are probably familiar to you.

Important Equations

Common Area Formulas

Circle
$A = \pi r^2$

Square
$A = s^2$

Rectangle
$A = lw$

Triangle
$A = 0.5bh$

In calculating the area of a triangle using the formula given previously, the base b and the height h of the triangle must be known in order to use this formula. Height is measured from one vertex of the triangle perpendicularly to the opposite side. In many real-life applications, this distance may not be known. Another formula, called Hero's formula, can also be used to find the area of a triangle using only the lengths of the sides of the triangle.

Important Equations

Hero's Formula for the Area of a Triangle

$$A = \sqrt{s(s - a)(s - b)(s - c)}$$

where

$$s = \frac{a + b + c}{2} \qquad \text{(called the semi-perimeter)}$$

and a, b, and c are the lengths of the sides of the triangle.

Hero's formula avoids the problem of trying to measure or calculate the height of a particular triangle.

When trying to find the answer to a word problem involving perimeter or area, first decide on the formulas needed for the problem. Then organize the data, apply the formula, and calculate the answer. Be sure the answer makes sense for your problem. Look at the following examples.

■ EXAMPLE 4   **Wallpapering a Bedroom**

Juan needs to purchase wallpaper to cover the four walls of his rectangular bedroom and a border to use at the top of his walls as a decorative accent. The dimensions of the room are 12 ft 6 in. by 15 ft 3 in., and his ceilings are 10 ft high. Calculate the amount of wallpaper needed and the length of the border he needs to buy. (For this problem, do not subtract the area of windows or doors that may be in the walls.)

(a) *Wallpaper:* This calculation will require the use of the area formula for rectangles:

$$A = lw$$

First, note that 15 ft 3 in. = 15.25 ft, and 12 ft 6 in. = 12.5 ft. Using these forms of the measurements will make the calculation easier. (See Table 8-1.)

Therefore, Juan will need 555 ft^2 of wallpaper to cover the bedroom walls.

■ **Table 8-1**

	Length × Width = Area		
	(ft)	**(ft)**	**(ft^2)**
Front wall	15.25	10	152.5
Back wall	15.25	10	152.5
Side wall	12.5	10	125
Side wall	12.5	10	125
		Total area	555

(b) *Wallpaper border:* Calculation of the perimeter will be required in this instance. We need to add the lengths of the walls to calculate the total length of border that Juan needs to purchase.

$$15.25 \text{ ft} + 12.5 \text{ ft} + 15.25 \text{ ft} + 12.5 \text{ ft} = 55.5 \text{ ft of border}$$

Or, using the perimeter formula for a rectangle:

$$2l + 2w = 2(15.25 \text{ ft}) + 2(12.5 \text{ ft}) = 55.5 \text{ ft of border}$$

■ EXAMPLE 5   Making Pennants

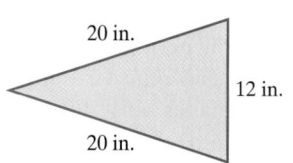

20 in.

12 in.

20 in.

Figure 8-5

Calculate the amount of material that will be needed to make 10 pennants in the shape of a triangle if the sides of each triangle measure 12 in., 20 in., and 20 in. (See figure 8-5.)

Because we know only the lengths of the sides of the triangle, we can use Hero's formula to calculate the area of each flag.

Step 1   Step 2

$$s = \frac{a + b + c}{2} \qquad\qquad A = \sqrt{s(s - a)(s - b)(s - c)}$$

$$s = \frac{12 + 20 + 20}{2} \qquad\qquad A = \sqrt{26(26 - 12)(26 - 20)(26 - 20)}$$

$$s = 26 \text{ in.} \qquad\qquad A = \sqrt{26(14)(6)(6)} = \sqrt{13104} = 114.5 \text{ in.}^2$$

Because 10 pennants are to be made, at least $10 \times 114.5 \text{ in.}^2 = 1145 \text{ in.}^2$ of material will be needed.

We can convert this answer to square feet by dividing the total number of square inches by 144 in.^{2} (because 1 ft^2 = 144 in.^{2}).

$$\frac{1145 \text{ in.}^2}{144 \text{ in.}^2/\text{ft}^2} = 7.95 \text{ ft}^2 \quad \begin{array}{l} \text{(or approximately 8 ft}^2 \text{ of material} \\ \text{will be needed for these pennants)} \end{array}$$

Figure 8-6

Many shapes are not standard shapes. A window, for example, might be a combination of a rectangle and a half-circle (or semicircle). (See Figure 8-6.) A roller rink is a rectangle with a half-circle on each end. Problems involving the area of a figure that is a combination of several shapes must be worked in parts. The areas of all the parts are then totaled to get the final answer.

■ EXAMPLE 6   Area of the Floor at the Roller Rink

The hardwood floor needs to be replaced at the local roller rink. The measurements are given in the diagram found in Figure 8-7. Calculate the amount of flooring needed for this project.

Figure 8-7

(a) Calculate the area of the center rectangle.

$$A = lw = (150\text{ ft})(35\text{ ft}) = 5250\text{ ft}^2$$

(b) Calculate the area of the circle (two half circles). Because the diameter of the circle is given as 35 ft, we must divide it by 2 to determine the radius needed for the area formula.

$$r = 35\text{ ft} \div 2 = 17.5\text{ ft}$$

$$A = \pi r^2 = \pi(17.5)^2 = 962.113\text{ ft}^2$$

(c) Find the total area.

$$5250 + 962.113 = 6212.113 \approx 6212\text{ ft}^2$$

Practice Set 8-1

1. A square has a perimeter of 54 in. What is the area of this square?

2. A rectangle has an area of 65 cm^2 and a length of 13 cm. Find the perimeter of this rectangle.

3. Julianne is planting a ground cover in one area of her yard. The area she wants to cover is rectangular shaped and measures 8.75 ft by 4.5 ft. The manager of the garden shop tells her that she will need to purchase four plants for every square foot of area she wishes to cover. How many plants will she need to buy to complete this project?

4. Mike is buying a rectangular building lot measuring 220 ft by 158 ft in a new golfing community. He plans to sow new grass on this lot, and each 40-lb. bag of turf grass blend will cover 1000 ft^2 of lawn. How many bags does he need to buy?

5. A builder is completing the flooring in the living room shown in the drawing. He needs to purchase an adequate amount of baseboard molding and enough carpet to cover the floor. The openings for the two doors are 3 ft wide. Calculate the number of feet of molding he must purchase. Then calculate the number of *square yards* of carpet needed

to complete the job. (*Remember:* 1 yd = 3 ft, so 1 yd^2 = 9 ft^2)

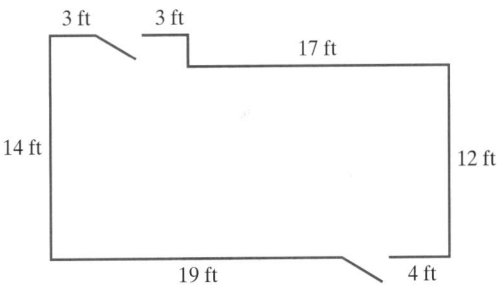

6. The Dodsons are planning to paint the outside of their house this spring. The paint can states that 1 gallon of paint will cover 350 ft^2 of surface. Using the dimensions of the house shown in the drawing on the next page, calculate the number of gallons of paint (rounded to the nearest gallon) they will need to buy to complete the project. (Don't include paint for the doors or windows!)

7. A sailor wishes to make a new sail for his boat. The sail is triangular shaped and measures 18 ft by 11 ft by 25 ft. Calculate the number of square feet of material that will be needed for this sail.

Square windows are 2.5 ft by 2.5 ft
Rectangular windows are 2.5 ft by 6 ft

Doors are 3 ft by 6.5 ft

8. Tameka's back yard has three trees that form a small triangle. She is planning to plant a flower garden in this triangular area and must calculate the area in order to buy the correct amount of fertilizer and mulch. She measures the following distances for the three sides of the triangle: 10.5 ft, 8.25 ft, and 5.25 ft. Calculate the area of this garden.

9. How many plants spaced every 6 in. are needed to surround a circular walkway with a 25-ft radius?

10. Maria is finalizing the set for the school play and needs to buy fringe to sew onto the edges of the three tablecloths needed for the final scene. Each tablecloth is 6 ft in diameter. How much fringe will she need for the three tablecloths?

11. A soup can is in the shape of a cylinder. If it is cut and flattened into geometric shapes, it consists of two circles and a rectangle. If a can is 4.5 in. tall and measures 7.9 in. around, how many square inches of paper will be needed for the label on the can?

12. If the soup can in Problem 11 has a diameter of 2.5 in., how many square inches of metal will be needed to make the can? (Ignore the overlap of metal needed when actually producing the can.)

13. Will a rectangular piece of wrapping paper that is 20 in. by 15 in. cover a shirt box that is 12 in. long, 8 in. wide, and 3 in. deep?

14. The poster you are giving your friend is in a cardboard tube with a 2-in. diameter and 26-in. length. Will a rectangular piece of wrapping paper that is 8 in. by 28 in. completely cover the tube?

15. PIZZAZZ Pizza Parlor sells an 8-in. pepperoni pizza for $6.99. The price of its 16-in. pizza is $15.95. Which pizza is the better buy per square inch?

16. A 12-in. by 24-in. rectangular pizza is the same price as a pizza with a 10-in. diameter. Which shape will give you more pizza?

17. Find the area of the shaded parts of the following figure.

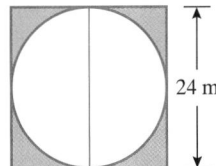

24 m

18. Find the area of the shaded parts of the following figure.

74 cm

48 cm

37 cm

19. A rectangular lot with a 50-ft frontage and a 230-ft depth sold for $8625. Find the following:
  (a) the cost of the lot per square foot
  (b) the cost of the lot per front foot
  (c) the cost of the lot per acre (1 acre $= 43,560\,\text{ft}^2$)

20. A cement walk 3 ft wide is placed around the outside of a rectangular garden plot that is 20 ft by 30 ft. Find the cost of the walk at $12.25 a square yard.

21. What effect would each of the following have on the area and perimeter of a square?
  (a) doubling the length of the sides
  (b) halving the length of the sides
  (c) tripling the length of the sides
  (d) doubling the length of the diagonal distance between opposite corners

22. What effect would each of the following have on the area and circumference of a circle?
  (a) doubling the diameter
  (b) halving the diameter
  (c) doubling the radius

23. Eight circles of equal size are inscribed in a rectangle so that four are in each row. The circles touch each other and the sides of the rectangle. What percent of the area of the rectangle is covered by the circles?

24. Can two geometric figures have the same perimeter and area and yet not be identical? Explain how you arrived at your answer.

25. Let us revisit the window in Example 3. To determine the amount of molding (L) needed to go around the outside of this shape of window, you need to add one width (w), two heights (h), and the distance around the semicircular top (half of the circumference of a circle whose radius is half of the width: $C = 2\pi r$). So, a formula for calculating the perimeter would be written as:

$$w + 2(h) + \pi\left(\frac{w}{2}\right) = \text{amount of molding needed}$$

$$w + 2h + \pi \cdot \frac{w}{2} = L$$

Assume that you have 20 ft ($L = 20$ ft) of molding that you may use.

$$w + 2h + \pi \cdot \frac{w}{2} = 20 \text{ ft}$$

  (a) Solve this equation for h.
  (b) Construct a graph of height versus width.
  (c) Make a table of values by choosing various widths in whole feet and calculating the value that the height would need to be to keep a constant perimeter of 20 ft.
  (d) How many of such windows of different widths and heights can be constructed with a perimeter of 20 ft?

Section 8-2   **MODELS AND PATTERNS IN RIGHT TRIANGLES**

The triangle is structurally the strongest of the polygons. Triangles are evident in the construction of tall towers and bridges. **Right triangles** are especially useful in building projects. The framing of a house requires that the studs be braced with boards that form right triangles. Tall towers are often braced with guy wires to give support to the tower. The tower, the ground, and the guy wire form a right triangle.

In a right triangle, the sides of the triangle have lengths that demonstrate certain relationships. One of these relationships is stated by the **Pythagorean theorem.**

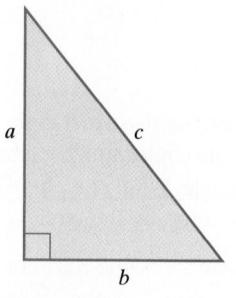

Figure 8-8

Theorem

Pythagorean Theorem
In a right triangle, the sum of the squares of the legs of the triangle equals the square of the hypotenuse, or as illustrated in Figure 8-8:

$$a^2 + b^2 = c^2$$

This theorem is only true for right triangles. It allows us to calculate the length of the third side of a right triangle if the lengths of the other two sides are known. Remember that the **hypotenuse** (c) is always the longest side of the triangle and is directly opposite the right angle. The other two sides of the triangle (a and b) are called the **legs.**

EXAMPLE 7   Using the Pythagorean Theorem

Find the length a in the right triangle shown in Figure 8-9.

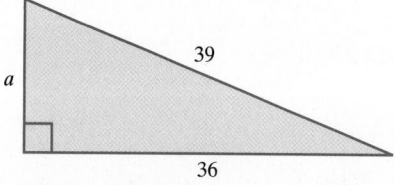

Figure 8-9

The base b is 36, and the hypotenuse c is 39. Substitute these values into the Pythagorean theorem.

$$a^2 + b^2 = c^2$$
$$a^2 + 36^2 = 39^2 \qquad \text{(substitute the given values)}$$
$$a^2 + 1296 = 1521 \qquad \text{(simplify by squaring)}$$
$$a^2 + 1296 - 1296 = 1521 - 1296 \qquad \text{(subtract 1296 from both sides)}$$
$$a^2 = 225$$
$$a = \sqrt{225} = 15 \qquad \text{(take the square root of 225)}$$

EXAMPLE 8   Guy Wires for the Communications Company

A 40-foot tower will be constructed for a cellular communications company. Guy wires will be needed for stability and will be attached 5 feet below the top of the tower. The wires will be anchored to the ground at a distance of 50 feet from the base of the tower. (Assume the tower makes a right angle with level ground.) What length of wire will be needed if the tower is to be stabilized with four guy wires? (See Figure 8-10.)

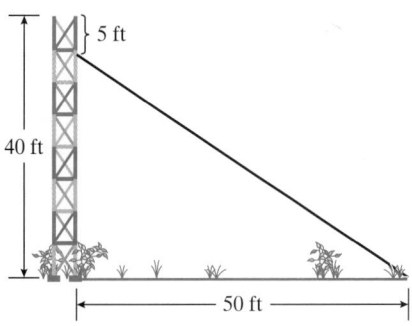

Figure 8-10

Let side a = 40 ft − 5 ft = 35 ft

side b = 50 ft

side c = ?

$$a^2 + b^2 = c^2$$

$$(35)^2 + (50)^2 = c^2$$

$$1225 + 2500 = c^2$$

$$3725 = c^2$$

$$\sqrt{3725} = c$$

$$61.03 = c$$

Because we need to have four guy wires, the total amount of wire needed will be:

$$4 \times 61.03 \text{ ft} = 244.12 \text{ ft},$$

or approximately 245 ft to complete the job.

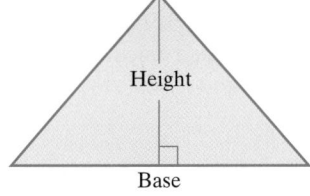

Figure 8-11

In trying to solve some geometry problems, figures can be subdivided into right triangles in order to calculate certain lengths. An isosceles triangle, for example, can be divided into two congruent right triangles by drawing in a perpendicular segment called the height from the vertex angle of the triangle to the base. (See Figure 8-11.)

EXAMPLE 9   **Pitch of the Roof**

Calculate the pitch (or slope) of the roof shown in Figure 8-12.

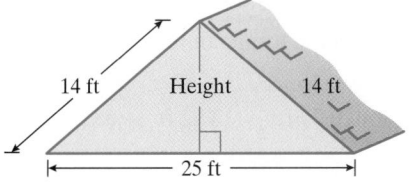

Figure 8-12

If a perpendicular line is drawn from the peak of the roof to a horizontal line connecting the ends of the house, two right triangles are formed. In Chapter 2, slope was defined as the ratio of the *rise* to the *run* of a line, so for this roof line the slope will be $\frac{h}{12.5}$. (Remember that the height of an isosceles triangle will bisect the base.)

Using the Pythagorean theorem, we can calculate the length of h.

$$a^2 + b^2 = c^2$$

$$12.5^2 + h^2 = 14^2$$

$$h = \sqrt{14^2 - 12.5^2} = 6.3 \text{ ft.}$$

Therefore, the slope of this roof line will be

$$\frac{6.3 \text{ ft}}{12.5 \text{ ft}} = 0.504 \approx \frac{1}{2}.$$

EXAMPLE 10   The Area of a Composite Figure Using the Pythagorean Theorem

Find the area of the end of the house pictured in Figure 8-13. Do not use Hero's formula to find this area.

To find the area of the end of the house, we divide it into a rectangular portion and a triangle. We calculate the area of the rectangular portion using the formula $A = lw$ and then subtract the area of the two windows as calculated with the same formula.

$$\text{Area} = (18)(24) = 432 \text{ ft}^2 \quad \text{(total rectangular area)}$$

$$\text{Area} = (2.5)(2.5) = 6.25 \text{ ft}^2 \quad \text{(area of the small window)}$$

$$\text{Area} = (2.5)(6) = 15 \text{ ft}^2 \quad \text{(area of the rectangular window)}$$

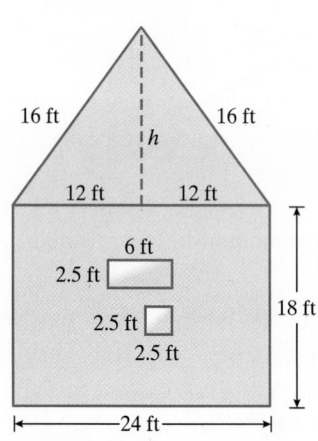

Figure 8-13

Therefore, $432 - 6.25 - 15 = 410.75 \text{ ft}^2$ is the painted area of the rectangular portion of the house.

Next, we need to calculate the area of the triangular portion of the end of the house. The easiest area formula for a triangle is $A = 0.5bh$. In this problem, the base is 24 ft. We do not know the height, but we can calculate the height using the Pythagorean theorem.

$$a^2 + b^2 = c^2$$

$$h^2 + 12^2 = 16^2$$

$$h = \sqrt{16^2 - 12^2} = \sqrt{112} = 10.6 \text{ ft}$$

Therefore,

$$\text{Area of the triangular portion} = 0.5bh$$

$$\text{Area of the triangular portion} = 0.5(24)(10.6)$$

$$\text{Area of the triangular portion} = 127.2 \text{ ft}^2$$

Finally, to find the total painted area of the end of the house, we add our two results.

$$410.75 \text{ ft}^2 + 127.2 \text{ ft}^2 = 537.95 \text{ ft}^2 \text{ of painted surface}$$

Practice Set 8-2

1. What information must you have about a triangle *before* you know that you can use the Pythagorean theorem?

2. Does a triangle with sides of lengths 1.5 ft, 2.5 ft, and 2 ft form a right triangle? How do you know?

Use the Pythagorean theorem to find the missing side of the following right triangles. (*Note:* Round to the nearest tenth,)

3. $a = 9$, $b = 12$

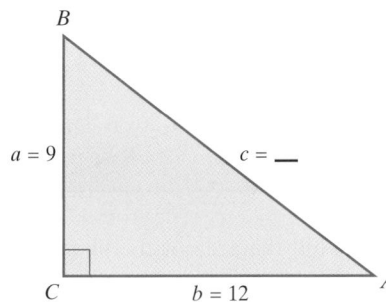

4. $b = 25$, $c = 35$

5. $b = 6, c = 12$

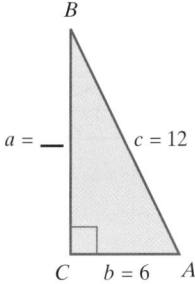

6. $a = 45$, $b = 45$

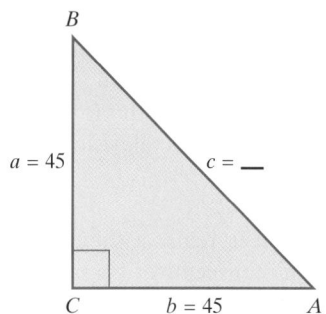

7. $a = 10$, $c = 26$

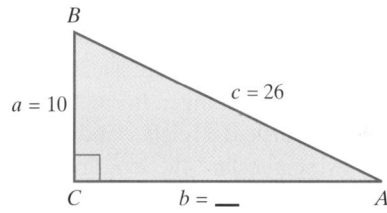

8. $a = 7$, $c = 25$

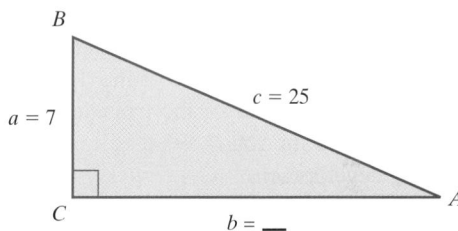

Complete the following word problems. Draw a sketch to help you solve each problem.

9. The bottom of a 25-ft ladder leaning against a house is 7 ft from the house. If the ground is level, how high on the house does the ladder reach?

10. A 6-ft ladder is placed against a wall with its base 2.5 ft from the wall. How high above the ground is the top of the ladder?

11. A rope 13 m long from the top of a flagpole will just reach a point on the ground 9 m from the foot of the pole. Find the height of the flagpole.

12. Clint wants to keep a young tree from blowing over during a high wind. He decides that he should

tie a rope around the tree at a height of 180 cm and then tie the rope to a stake 200 cm from the base. Allowing 30 cm of rope for doing the tying, will the 270-cm rope he has be long enough to do the job?

13. A television screen measures approximately 15.5 in. high and 19.5 in. wide. A television is advertised by giving the approximate length of the diagonal of its screen. How should this television be advertised?

14. A baseball diamond is really a square, and the distance between consecutive bases is 90 ft. How far does a catcher have to throw the ball to get it to second base if a runner tries to steal second?

15. Jackson is 64 miles east of Lazy Day Resort. Fairfield Heights is 25 miles south of Jackson. A land developer proposes building a shortcut road to directly connect Fairfield Heights and Lazy Day. Sketch a drawing and find the length of this new road.

16. A new housing development extends 4 miles in one direction, makes a right turn, and then continues for 3 miles. A new road runs between the beginning and ending points of the development. What is the perimeter of the triangle formed by the homes and the road? What is the area of the housing development?

17. An isosceles triangle has a base of 28 in. and two congruent sides of 25 in. each. Find the height of the triangle. (Round to the nearest tenth.)

18. For a "shed" roof, the height h is half the width w of the building. Find the length of the rafter r if a building is 42 ft wide.

19. The slope, or pitch, of the roof on a new house should be in the ratio 11:20. If it is 30 ft from the

front of the house to the back of the house, how far is it from the edge of the roof to its peak?

20. A yardstick held vertically on level ground casts a shadow 16 in. long. What would be the distance from the top of the yardstick to the edge of its shadow?

21. Find the area and perimeter of the triangle shown in the following figure.

22. Find the area of the figure shown. $\angle C$ is a right angle.

23. Find the distance from A to B on the graph.

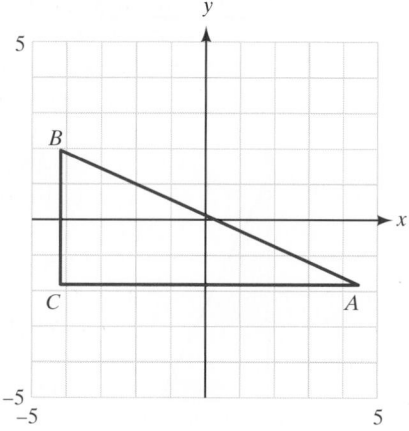

24. Find the distance from *R* to *S* on the graph.

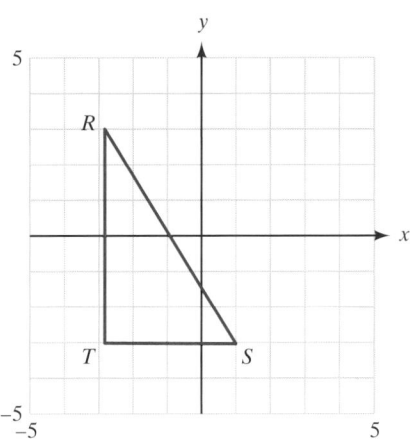

25. A rectangular doorway's inside dimensions are 200 cm by 75 cm. Could a circular mirror measuring 220 cm in diameter pass through the doorway?

26. A carpenter is building a floor for a rectangular room. To avoid problems with the walls and flooring, the corners of the room must be right angles. If he builds an 8-ft by 12-ft room and measures the diagonal from one corner to the other as 14 ft 8 in., is the floor "squared off" properly?

27. Find the length of a side of a square whose diagonal is 10 in. long.

Section 8-3   **MODELS AND PATTERNS IN ART AND ARCHITECTURE: PERSPECTIVE AND SYMMETRY**

The visual arts, such as sculpture, painting, drawing, and architecture, are directly related to mathematics. The mathematical terms *perspective*, *proportion*, and *symmetry* are important parts and parcel of art and architecture. In fact, architects, industrial designers, illustrators of all kinds, and engineers will all, at one time or another, be involved in producing a pictorial representation of the objects they are building or designing.

In order to paint or draw with realism, an understanding of **perspective** is essential. Perspective is a geometric way of thinking that allows an artist or architect to give the sense of depth or three dimensions to a flat painting or drawing. (The original form of the word *perspective* means "to see through.") The process of producing a flat drawing that "looks" three-dimensional is based on the laws of optics. Because this section is part of a math book and not an art or architecture book, we will limit our presentation of topics to straight-line drawings only. Of course, no painting, drawing, or photograph (photographs are perspective "drawings") can really duplicate our visual perception of a scene or object.

The basis of perspective drawing is a principle that roughly says that all lines that are parallel in a real scene are not parallel on the perspective drawing but actually converge at a single point called the **principal vanishing point.** This vanishing point is located on a horizontal line called the **horizon line** or **eye level** in the drawing. The horizon line is at the level of the observer's eye when looking at the drawing. A simple example of this is shown in Figure 8-14. Imagine that you are standing near a long, straight road with a fence running down the left-hand side. The fence and the road appear to vanish in the distance. You could also imagine standing in the middle of a railroad track that goes straight away from you into the far distance.

Drawings done for the purpose of producing a painting or an architectural drawing often have more than one vanishing point located on the horizon line. Drawings with one, two, and three vanishing points are common. In Figure 8-15 you will see two blocks. The real blocks are of equal size, but one is closer to you

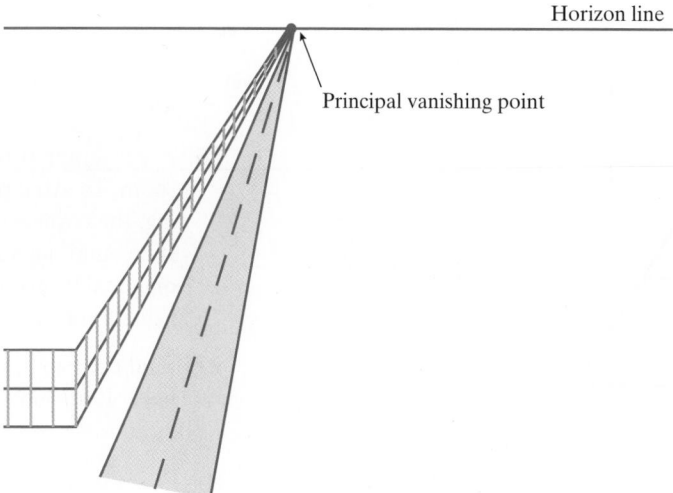

Figure 8-14

than the other in the drawing. Block A has a single vanishing point. Block B has two vanishing points. Set two such blocks on a table in the same location as shown in the drawing and position your eye so that you are looking just slightly over the top of Block A. Does your perception match the drawing?

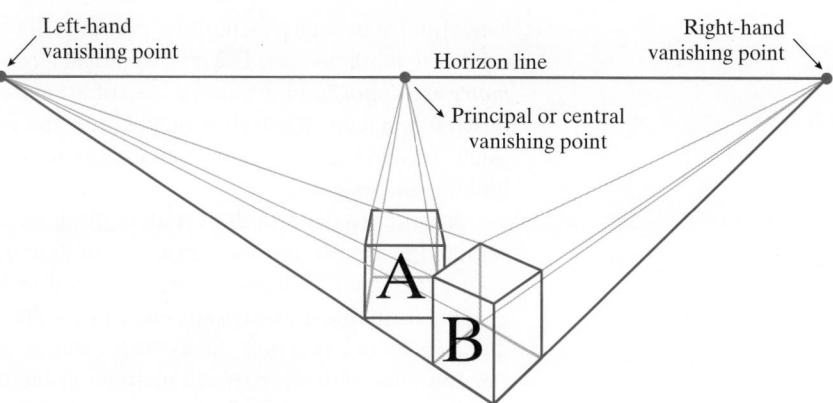

Figure 8-15
One and two vanishing point perspectives.

Figure 8-16 shows a person looking down a street lined with equally spaced telephone poles on both sides. Figure 8-17 shows a perspective drawing done from the point of view of that person.

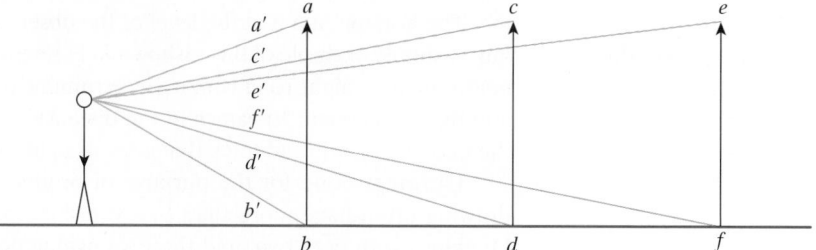

Figure 8-16
Looking down a double row of telephone poles.

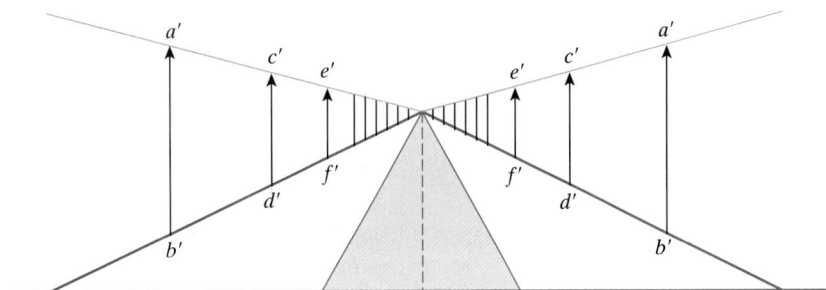

Figure 8-17
A perspective drawing of Figure 8-16.

Another aspect of perspective is that of one's point of view of an object or set of objects. Looking at a structure such as a house or building can yield different pictures depending on which side you look at.

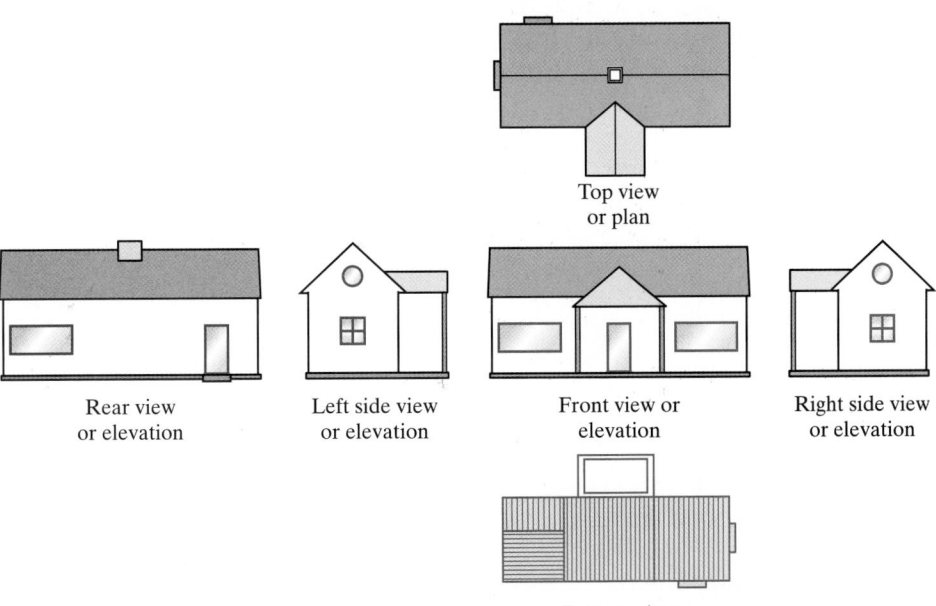

Figure 8-18
Six views of a house.

EXAMPLE 11   Your Point of View

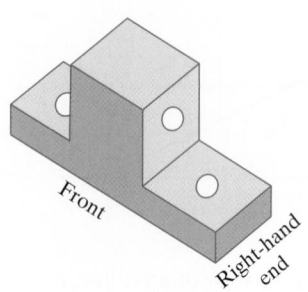

Look at the following structure. It is some kind of machine part with three holes in it.

Create line drawings to show what this machine part would look like if you viewed it:

(a) directly from the top
(b) directly from the front
(c) directly from the bottom
(d) directly from the right-hand end

(a)

(b)

(c)

(d)

The term **symmetry** has several meanings. Symmetry implies some kind of balance. If you were to draw a vertical line from your head to your toes, a line that goes through your nose and your navel, your body is then divided into two *symmetrical* halves. They aren't identical but they are balanced. Repetitive patterns are also said to be symmetrical. For an example of this, look at the brick walkway shown in Figure 8-19.

To the mathematician, an object has symmetry if it remains unchanged after some "operation" is performed on it. Though there are many *symmetries* possible, we will only look at two that are easy to identify: reflection symmetry and rotational symmetry.

If an object has **reflection symmetry,** then the object and its mirror image are identical. For example, the capital letter H and its reflection in a mirror are identical. In addition to this, the letter H exhibits reflection (or mirror) symmetry when reflected across (cut by) a vertical line or a horizontal line as shown in Figure 8-20. Note that if you fold the letter H along the dotted lines, the two halves will exactly coincide with each other.

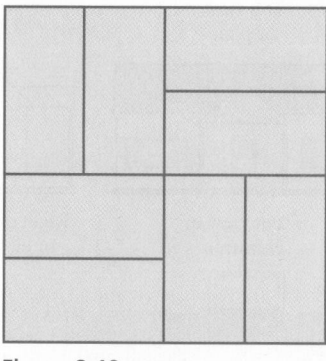

Figure 8-19
Brick walkway pattern.

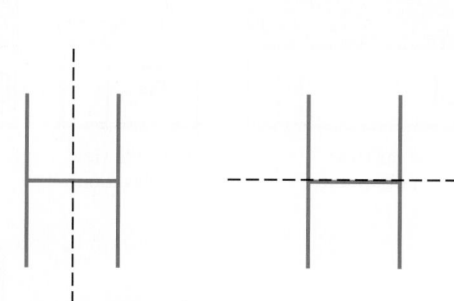

Figure 8-20

EXAMPLE 12   **Reflection Symmetry for a Rectangle**

A rectangle is pictured here with three possible lines of reflection symmetry. Does the rectangle exhibit reflection symmetry in all the cases shown? If not, which pictures do and why?

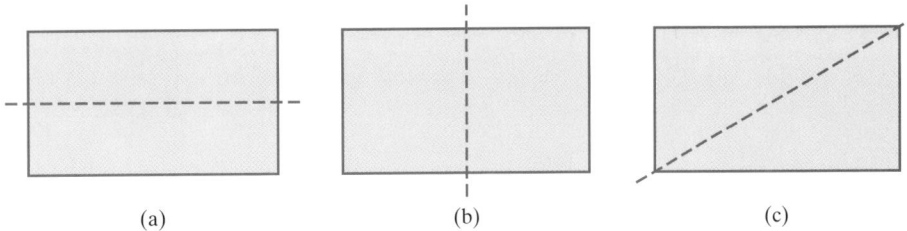

(a)   (b)   (c)

If you were to fold rectangles (a) and (b) along the dotted line of symmetry, the two halves would exactly coincide with each other. So, rectangles (a) and (b) both have reflection symmetry along the line drawn. However, in rectangle (c) the two halves would not coincide. Thus, rectangle (c) does not have reflection symmetry along the diagonal line.

If an object exhibits **rotation symmetry,** then when it is rotated a specified amount around some chosen point, it will coincide with the original object. For example, the letter H exhibits rotation symmetry if it is rotated 180° around its center.

EXAMPLE 13   **Rotation Symmetry**

Which of the following objects exhibits rotation symmetry if rotated 180° around the point or line shown?

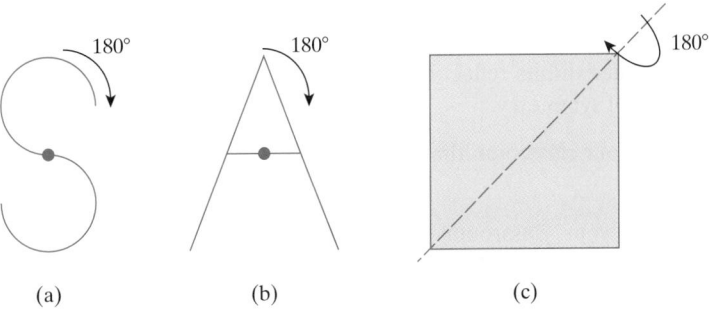

(a)   (b)   (c)

The following figures show the results of each 180° rotation. As you can see, the letter S and the square exhibit rotation symmetry under these conditions but the letter A does not.

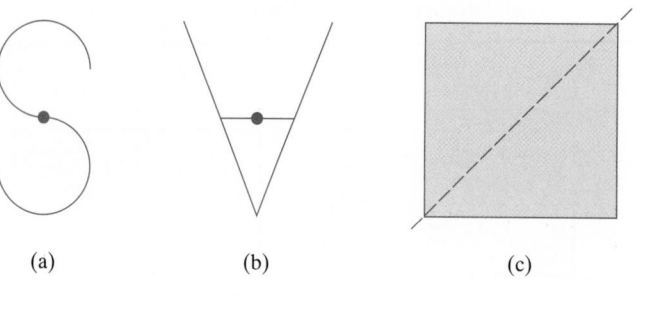

(a)   (b)   (c)

Practice Set 8-3

1. What is the basic idea behind the use of perspective in drawings?

2. Are all drawings perspective drawings? Why or why not?

3. What is a horizon line?

4. What is a central or primary vanishing point in a perspective drawing?

5. What is symmetry?

6. Describe both rotation symmetry and reflection symmetry. Find four examples of symmetry in your classroom.

7. Draw an object that exhibits rotation symmetry and show the line of symmetry.

8. Find an object in your classroom that exhibits rotation symmetry.

9. Draw an object that exhibits reflection symmetry and show the line of symmetry.

10. Find an object in your classroom that exhibits reflection symmetry.

11. Find an object in your classroom that exhibits both rotation symmetry and reflection symmetry. Sketch the object and show the lines of symmetry.

12. Describe at least three ways in which visual perspective affects your everyday life.

13. Explore your school and find as many examples of symmetry as you can. (This would be a good group project.) Are the examples you found uses of symmetry for artistic purposes or practical purposes?

14. Explore your school and find examples of the use of perspective.

15. Sketch a long, straight highway with a row of telephone poles down one side using perspective. Label the principal vanishing point in your sketch.

16. Sketch a pattern of rectangular bricks or some other shape that exhibits symmetry.

These letters are for use in answering Problems 17–20:

A B C D E F G H I J K L M N O P Q R S T U V W X Y Z

17. Find letters of the alphabet that exhibit reflection symmetry about a vertical or horizontal line through their centers, and show the line of symmetry for each one. Which letters do not exhibit reflection symmetry?

18. If you rotate all the letters 90°, which ones exhibit rotation symmetry?

19. If you rotate all the letters 180°, which ones exhibit rotation symmetry?

20. Without rotating the letters 360°, which letters do not exhibit rotation symmetry for any amount of rotation?

Use these three geometric figures for Problems 21–24.

      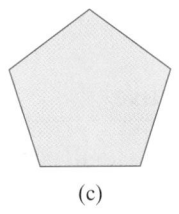

(a)   (b)   (c)

(a) An equilateral triangle (3 equal side lengths)
(b) A square (4 equal side lengths)
(c) A regular pentagon (5 equal side lengths)

21. What is the least number of degrees that you could rotate Figure (a) around its center so that it appears to be unchanged?

22. What is the least number of degrees that you could rotate Figure (b) around its center so that it appears to be unchanged?

23. What is the least number of degrees that you could rotate Figure (c) around its center so that it appears to be unchanged?

24. All of the figures, (a), (b), and (c), are figures in which all the sides of the figure are of equal length. There is a pattern between the number of sides and the number of degrees that they may be rotated and yet remain unchanged in appearance. What is that pattern? Use the pattern to write a formula for rotating any closed figure with any number of equal sides.

25. Draw a geometric figure with eight equal sides (an octagon or a stop sign) and show that your formula from Problem 24 works.

26. Draw sketches of the following figure as it would look viewed from the front, one end, and looking directly down on it.

27. Draw sketches of this machine part from the front, top, and right-hand end.

Front

Right-hand
end

28. A block building is shown in the following figure. To its right is a drawing of the "footprint" of the building. Place the number of blocks that are in each portion of the building in the appropriate block in the "footprint."

Block building   Building "footprint"

Section 8-4   MODELS AND PATTERNS IN ART, ARCHITECTURE, AND NATURE: SCALE AND PROPORTION

One of the most important rules in doing realistic looking drawings or art is to keep objects in the sketch in **proportion.** If the proportions in a drawing are bad, then the sketch will generally be of little use. Of course, artists can bend the rule to the breaking point and do paintings that are badly out of proportion for comic or other useful effects. In many areas, **scale drawings** are used. One good example of a scale drawing is a map of a state or a country. Near the bottom of the map you will see the *scale factor* that was used, perhaps 1 in. = 5 mi or something similar.

EXAMPLE 14   A Scale Drawing of a House

An architect is going to draw a house so that his picture is $\frac{1}{24}$ the size of the actual house. If the highest point on the house is 14 ft 6 in. and a tree in the yard is 24 ft tall, how large will each of these be in the architect's drawing? Give all your answers in inches.

Since the drawing will be drawn to scale in inches, the two measurements given need to be converted to inches.

$$14 \text{ ft } 6 \text{ in.} = (14 \text{ ft})(12 \text{ in./ft}) + 6 \text{ in.} = 180 \text{ in.}$$

$$24 \text{ ft} = (24 \text{ ft})(12 \text{ in./ft}) = 288 \text{ in.}$$

Now we will find the size to be used in the scale drawing by multiplying by the scale factor, $\frac{1}{24}$.

$$\left(\frac{1}{24}\right)(180) = 7.5 \text{ in.} \quad \text{and} \quad \left(\frac{1}{24}\right)(288) = 12 \text{ in.}$$

Thus on the scale drawing, the tallest point on the house will be 7.5 in. and the tree will be 12 in. tall.

EXAMPLE 15   Scaling a Rectangle Down in Size

A rectangle is 45 in. long and 25 in. wide. If a scale factor of $\frac{1}{5}$ is used to redraw the rectangle, what size will it be then?

Each side of the rectangle will be reduced to one-fifth of its original size.

$$\left(\frac{1}{5}\right)(45 \text{ in.}) = 9 \text{ in.} \quad \text{and} \quad \left(\frac{1}{5}\right)(25 \text{ in.}) = 5 \text{ in.}$$

Thus, the scale drawing of the rectangle will be 9 in. long and 5 in. wide.

The next example involves *similar triangles.* If two shapes are similar, then one is an enlargement or reduction of the other. This means that the two triangles will have the same angles and their corresponding sides will be in the same proportion. For example, the sides of a large triangle may have sides that are five times the corresponding sides of the other similar triangle.

■ **EXAMPLE 16**   **Scaling Triangles**

The two triangles pictured here are similar triangles and $m\angle A = m\angle D, m\angle B = m\angle E$, and $m\angle C = m\angle F$.

(a) What scale factor was used to transform $\triangle ABC$ into $\triangle DEF$?
(b) How long is side $\overline{AB}$?
(c) How long is side $\overline{EF}$?

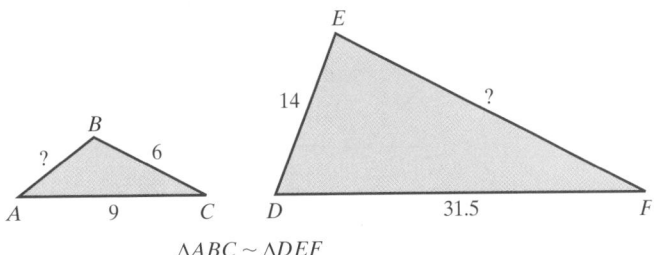

$$\triangle ABC \sim \triangle DEF$$

(a) Because the triangles are *similar,* the ratio of the corresponding sides of the two triangles is a constant. Thus, we will compare side $\overline{AC}$ with the corresponding side, $\overline{DF}$, in the other triangle as follows:

$$\frac{9}{31.5} = \frac{90}{315} = \frac{2}{7}$$

This means that all of the sides of the smaller triangle are $\frac{2}{7}$ the length of the sides in the larger triangle.

(b) Using our scale factor:

$$\frac{2}{7} = \frac{\overline{AB}}{14}$$
$$(2)(14) = 7(\overline{AB})$$
$$\frac{28}{7} = \overline{AB}$$
$$\overline{AB} = 4$$

Thus, side $\overline{AB}$ is 4 units long.

(c)
$$\frac{2}{7} = \frac{6}{\overline{EF}}$$
$$2(\overline{EF}) = (7)(6)$$
$$\overline{EF} = \frac{42}{2}$$
$$\overline{EF} = 21$$

Thus, side $\overline{EF}$ is 21 units long.

As we have said before, a mathematical basis underlies all of art, music, and architecture. Even in ancient times this was apparent. Ancient artists and architects used ratios or lengths to position objects and scale drawings, paintings, and buildings. One famous such ratio can be found in many ancient art works and buildings. It goes by several names: *the golden mean, the golden ratio, the golden section,* and even *the divine proportion.* This ratio dates back to about 500 BC, the time of Pythagoras, when Greek scholars were asking how to break a line segment into two pieces that would have the most visual appeal or balance to the eye. This is a question of *beauty* being asked by mathematicians, and oddly enough, there was good agreement on the answer.

Stated in mathematical terms, the Greeks said that the most visually pleasing division of the line was into two pieces of unequal length, such that the ratio of the longer piece to the shorter piece is the same as the ratio of the entire length to that of the longer piece. In the early 20th century, the Greek letter *phi,* ϕ (pronounced fi), was chosen to represent this ratio.

In case this isn't clear, here it is in pictorial and algebraic form.

$$\text{The Golden Ratio} = \phi = \frac{a}{b} = \frac{a+b}{a}$$

By cross-multiplying and generating a quadratic equation, the numerical value of the Golden Mean can be easily calculated.

$$\frac{a}{b} = \frac{a+b}{a}$$

$$(a)(a) = (b)(a+b)$$

$$a^2 = ba + b^2$$

$$a^2 - ba - b^2 = 0$$

Now we can use the quadratic formula to solve for *a.*

$$a = \frac{b \pm \sqrt{b^2 - 4b^2}}{2}$$

Remember that only a positive answer is possible for lengths.

$$a = \frac{b + b\sqrt{5}}{2}$$

Next substitute this result into the original ratio.

$$\frac{a}{b} = \frac{\dfrac{b + b\sqrt{5}}{2}}{b} = \frac{b + b\sqrt{5}}{2}\left(\frac{1}{b}\right)$$

$$\phi = \frac{1 + \sqrt{5}}{2} = 1.618033988\ldots$$

Thus, the value of the **Golden Ratio** turns out to be an irrational number (a nonending, nonrepeating decimal because of $\sqrt{5}$) with a value of about 1.62.

Well, I'm sure that you have found all of this to be fascinating so far, but what good is the Golden Ratio? As you will see, it has had many uses and turns up in one form or another in a lot of art work, architecture, and in natural objects, both living and nonliving.

The Greeks and others applied this idea of "pleasing lengths" to the construction of geometric figures of many kinds. A simple example is a "golden rectangle," where the ratio of the length and width is the Golden Ratio.

EXAMPLE 17   Constructing a Golden Rectangle

Suppose the following rectangle has a length of 5 cm, and you wish to find the width so that the ratio of the length to the width, $\frac{l}{w} = \phi$.

Here we will round off the value of the Golden Ratio to 1.62 to make the calculation more reasonable to do.

$$\phi = \frac{l}{w}$$

$$1.62 = \frac{5 \text{ cm}}{w}$$

$$w = \frac{5 \text{ cm}}{1.62} = 3.086419753\ldots \text{ cm}$$

So the width should be about 3.1 cm.

Many artists over the centuries have scaled sculptures using the Golden Ratio and placed objects in paintings so that they will fit within a golden rectangle. Even the front of the famous Greek Parthenon is very close to a golden rectangle.

Width = height × φ

Figure 8-21

Many say that the "perfect" or most pleasing human faces exhibit many Golden Ratios relating to the placement of facial features and their relative sizes. Here are just a few:

$$\phi = \frac{\text{height of face}}{\text{width of face}} = \frac{\text{eye to chin}}{\text{nose to chin}} = \frac{\text{eye to mouth}}{\text{eye to nose}} = \frac{\text{nose to chin}}{\text{mouth to chin}} = \frac{\text{width of face}}{\text{distance between eyes}}$$

The Golden Mean turns up in the "art" of nature in many forms. One common example of this is based on golden rectangles. If you start with a golden rectangle, then divide the rectangle into a square and a rectangle, the new small rectangle will also be a golden rectangle. If you continue breaking each new rectangle down and then connect the corners of all the squares with a smooth curve, you will create a *logarithmic spiral*. This is shown in Figure 8-22. These spirals are called *Hambridge's whirling squares*. If you were to accurately measure the length of any section of this spiral, you would find that it is about 0.618 as large as the remainder of the spiral.

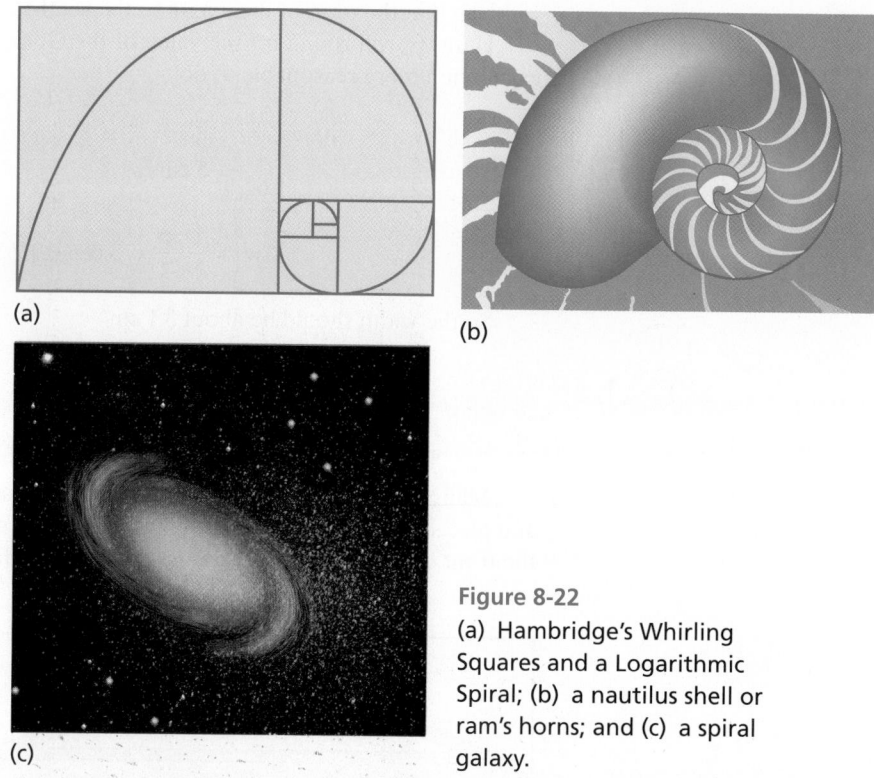

(a)

(b)

(c)

Figure 8-22
(a) Hambridge's Whirling Squares and a Logarithmic Spiral; (b) a nautilus shell or ram's horns; and (c) a spiral galaxy.

This logarithmic spiral can be seen in a chambered nautilus shell, the curve of ram's horns, comet tails, the curl of the surf, a parrot's beak, the roots of human teeth, a spider web, bacterial growth curves, and the list just goes on and on. The hexagonal-shaped scales on a pineapple, the "leaves" on a pinecone or an artichoke, and the seeds in a sunflower all spiral around in several directions if you look carefully. All of these spirals match this same logarithmic spiral.

Look at this set of members: {1, 1, 2, 3, 5, 8, 13, 21, . . .} What is the next number in this list and how did you find it? Note that 2 = 1 + 1, 3 = 2 + 1, and 5 = 3 + 2. This shows that the next number in the list is equal to the sum of the previous two,

13 + 21 = 34. This particular sequence is called the *Fibonacci sequence,* or they are collectively called **Fibonacci numbers.** Here is a longer listing of them:

$$1, 1, 2, 3, 5, 8, 13, 21, 34, 55, 89, 144, 233, 377, 610, 987, \ldots$$

"That's nice," you say, "but, so what?" If you start dividing successive Fibonacci numbers, the answer you get eventually produces the Golden Ratio as a result.

EXAMPLE 18   **Fibonacci Numbers and the Golden Mean**

$$1/1 = 1, 2/1 = 2, 3/2 = 1.5, 5/3 = 1.6667, 8/5 = 1.6$$

$$13/8 = 1.625, 21/13 = 1.6154, 34/21 = 1.619, 55/34 = 1.6176$$

As you go farther down the list of Fibonacci numbers, the answers all begin to be numbers that round off to about 1.61803, which is almost precisely the Golden Ratio.

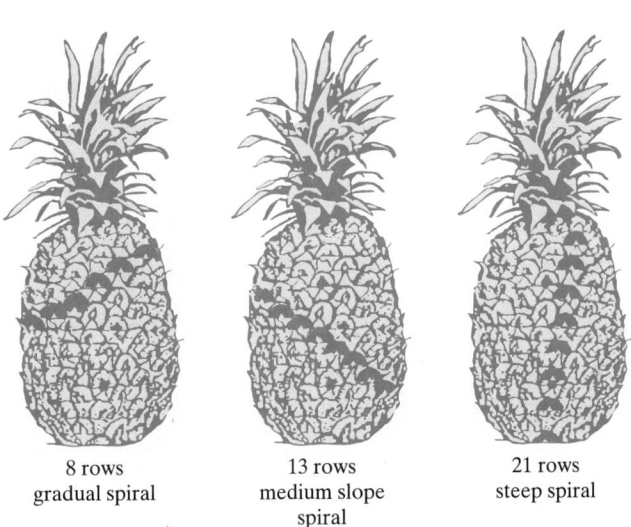

8 rows	13 rows	21 rows
gradual spiral	medium slope spiral	steep spiral

Figure 8-23
The spirals of a pineapple.

As with the logarithmic spiral that was discussed earlier, the Fibonacci numbers turn up in many places in nature. No one really knows why this is so. Here is a short list of places that you will find the Fibonacci numbers: There are 8 spirals right and 13 spirals left of the "leaves" on a pinecone. A large sunflower will have 55 seed spirals in one direction and 89 in the other. A pineapple will exhibit 8 spirals right, 13 left, and 21 vertically. (See Figure 8-23.) Daisy petals are 21, 34, 55, or 89 petals per bloom. Petal counts of other common flowers are as follows: iris or lily = 3, butter cup or wild rose or columbine = 5, cosmos or delphiniums or bloodroot = 8, ragwort or double delphiniums = 13, black-eyed Susans or chicory or astor = 21, field daisies or plantain = 34, African daisies or heleniums or Michaelmas daisies = 55. All of these petal counts are Fibonacci numbers.

Buds, branches, and leaves on branches occur at regular intervals but not directly in line on the branch. For example, if the leaves grew in line with each other, they would all end up on one side of the branch and shade each other from necessary sunlight. Rather, leaves grow at fractions of a full circle around a branch. Generally these fractions are 2/5 (poplar, plum, live oak, holly, apple, and cherry trees), 3/5, 3/8 (weeping willow, pear, and locust trees), or 5/13 (bottle brush, almond, and pussy willow) of a full circle. Curiously, the numbers in these ratios are all Fibonacci numbers. These are called *phyllotactic ratios* by botanists.

Practice Set 8-4

1. A $\frac{1}{16}$ scale model (1 in. = 16 ft) of an airplane has a wingspan of 21 in. What is the wingspan of the actual airplane in feet?

2. If a model of an airplane is be $\frac{1}{16}$ scale (1 in. = 16 ft), how many inches long would the model be if a certain airplane were 48 ft long?

3. The larger of two similar polygons has a perimeter of 175 cm. If the scale factor between the two polygons is $\frac{3}{4}$, what is the perimeter of the smaller polygon?

4. Two similar triangles have perimeters of 45 cm and 75 cm respectively. What scale factor would relate these two triangles?

5. A $\frac{1}{800}$ scale model (1 cm = 800 cm) of the aircraft carrier USS *Eisenhower* (CVN-69) is 42.2 cm long and 8.2 cm wide at the widest point of the deck. What is the actual length and width of this ship in meters?

6. You want to do a scale drawing of a Boeing 747 passenger plane. The actual length of the plane is 225 ft, and the wingspan is 204 ft. If you did a $\frac{1}{144}$ (1 in. = 144 in.) scale drawing, what would the length and wingspan be, in inches, on your drawing?

7. A particular map shows a scale of 1:5000. If a distance measures 8 cm on the map, what is the actual distance in cm and m?

8. A particular map shows a scale of 1 cm:5 km. What would the map distance be (in cm) if the actual distance to be represented is 14 km?

9. The following is the silhouette of the battleship USS *Texas* as she appeared in 1942. The USS *Texas* is 573 ft long. Measure the length of this

picture and determine the scale of the drawing (? in. = ? ft).

10. The following is the silhouette of the battleship USS *North Carolina* as she appeared in 1942. The USS *North Carolina* is actually 728 ft. Determine the scale of this drawing (? in. = ? ft).

11. A road map of the state of Texas has a scale of 0.5 in = 50 mi. If the distance between two points in the state is 600 mi, what would the equivalent distance be on the state map?

12. A building is 250 ft by 120 ft. If you were to draw this building using a scale of 1 in. = 20 ft, what would the dimensions of your drawing be?

13. Describe at least three ways in which you have made use of scale drawings in your life.

14. Describe at least three ways in which visual proportion affects your life.

15. What is the twentieth Fibonacci number?

16. What is the ratio of the twentieth and nineteenth Fibonacci numbers?

17. Use your calculator and find the value of the Golden Ratio, $\phi = \frac{1 + \sqrt{5}}{2}$. Now square the answer. What unusual thing do you observe?

18. Use your calculator and find the value of the Golden Ratio, $\phi = \frac{1 + \sqrt{5}}{2}$. Now find the reciprocal of the answer. What unusual thing do you observe?

19. A golden rectangle is to be constructed such that the shortest side is 23 ft long. How long is the other side?

20. If a golden rectangle has a width of 9 cm, what is its length?

21. If one dimension of a golden rectangle is 45.5 cm, what *two* values are possible for the length of the other side?

22. If one dimension of a golden rectangle is 36 in., what *two* values are possible for the length of the other side?

A *golden box* is a rectangular box whose dimensions match the Golden Ratio as follows:

$$\frac{w}{h} = \frac{l}{w} \approx 1.62.$$

23. If a golden box has a height of 5 in., what would its length and width be?

24. If a golden box has a length of 9 cm, what would its height and width be?

Section 8-5   **MODELS AND PATTERNS IN MUSIC**

We hate to ruin your day but it's true: Mathematics and music are linked together. Gottfried Wilhelm von Leibniz (1646–1716), who along with Sir Isaac Newton gets credit for developing modern calculus, said, roughly translated, "Music is the pleasure the human soul experiences from counting without being aware that it is counting." In medieval times, schools linked arithmetic, astronomy, geometry, and music together in what was called the *quadrivium*. Today, computers are often used to produce music, and thus the link between math and music is being perpetuated.

Symbols used to denote musical notes are really indicators of the duration (time) of a note in a musical composition. Table 8-2 shows some of the symbols used for notes of various times and for rests where no note is played for a time.

Tempos can be 3/4 time (three quarter notes per measure), 4/4 time (four quarter notes per measure), or 3/8 time (three eighth notes per measure), for example. In a 4/4 measure, each whole note counts four beats, each half note counts two beats, each quarter note counts one beat, each eighth note counts ½ beat, and each sixteenth note counts ¼ beat.

In addition to notes, there are also *rests* where no notes are played for a period of time. Rests can be for the same length of time as any of the notes listed. This means that a rest can last the length of a whole note, half note, quarter note, and so forth. A musician has to count beats per measure and then deal with whole notes, half notes, quarter notes, eighth notes, sixteenth notes, and rests. Music is written so that there are a fixed number of beats per measure. All those half notes and quarter notes must add up to the same number of beats for each measure of

■ **Table 8-2   Symbols and Names of Common Musical Notes**

Note	Rest	American name	British name
o	▬	whole note	semibreve
♩	▬	half note	minim
♩	≀	quarter note	crotchet
♪	╕	eighth note	quaver
♫	╕	sixteenth note	semiquaver
♫	╕	thirty-second note	demisemiquaver
♫	╕	sixty-fourth note	hemidemisemiquaver
♫	╕	hundred-twenty-eighth note	quasihemidemisemiquaver

music. For example, all of the notes in each measure of music written in 4/4 time must add up to 4 beats. It is the same as finding common denominators for fractions so that you may add them. Look deeply enough at music and you will find such topics as ratios, periodic functions, and exponential curves.

EXAMPLE 19   **Adding Notes**

A measure of music written in 4/4 tempo must have four beats in the measure. One way to achieve this is to use four quarter notes as shown here.

$$\text{♩} + \text{♩} + \text{♩} + \text{♩} = \frac{1}{4} + \frac{1}{4} + \frac{1}{4} + \frac{1}{4} = \frac{4}{4}$$

Fill in the missing note or notes so that each of the following totals four beats.

(a) ♩ + ♩ + ____   **(b)** ♩ + ♩ + ♪ + ____   **(c)** ♩ + ♩ + ♩ + ♪ + ____ + ____

If you write each note as a fraction and then add them, the total must equal 4/4 as shown in the first set of notes.

(a) Translating into fractions:

$$1/4 + 1/2 + ? = 4/4$$

$$1/4 + 2/4 + ? = 4/4$$

$$3/4 + ? = 4/4$$

$$4/4 - 3/4 = 1/4$$

Thus, one quarter note is needed.

(b) Translating into fractions:

$$1/2 + 1/4 + 1/8 + ? = 4/4$$

$$4/8 + 2/8 + 1/8 + ? = 8/8$$

$$7/8 + ? = 8/8$$

$$8/8 - 7/8 = 1/8$$

Thus, one eighth note is needed.

(c) Translating into fractions:

$$1/4 + 1/4 + 1/4 + 1/8 + ? + ? = 4/4$$

$$2/8 + 2/8 + 2/8 + 1/8 + ? + ? = 8/8$$

$$7/8 + ? + ? = 8/8$$

$$8/8 - 7/8 = 1/8$$

So, one eighth note is needed, but there are two missing notes. Let each note be half of an eighth note. Half of 1/8 is 1/16. The two missing notes are both sixteenth notes.

The Pythagoreans in Greece are the first ones known to have related music and math. They discovered that the sound (note) produced by a string when it is plucked varies with the length of the string. With a little experimentation, they found that equally tight strings would give "harmonious" notes if their lengths were in whole-number ratios to each other.

Vibrations produce waves that propagate through the surrounding medium. For example, a vibrating string on a violin produces sound waves that propagate (move through) the medium (air) that surrounds the violin. The **frequency** of the string's vibration is the number of times the string vibrates up and down in one second. A frequency of 200 vibrations per second is said to have a frequency of 200 **Hertz,** or 200 Hz.

Suppose that you have a string that will generate a sound with a frequency of 200 Hz when the whole string vibrates as one piece. This is called the *fundamental frequency* of the string. If you then hold this string down at its mid point and pluck it, the new wave will be half as long as the original wave, but its frequency will be 400 Hz, twice that of the whole-string vibration. This is called the *first harmonic* or *first overtone.* If you hold the string down so that only one-fourth of its original length is plucked, the wave will be one-fourth the original wavelength, and the frequency will double again to 800 Hz. This is called the *second harmonic* or *second overtone.*

To our ear, these different frequencies have different **pitch.** The higher the frequency, then the higher the pitch of the sound to your ear. Also, when the frequency of a note is doubled, the pitch is said to have been raised an **octave.** For example, A above middle-C on a piano has a frequency of 440 Hz. The next higher-pitched A on the keyboard will have a frequency of 880 Hz and is one octave higher in pitch. The next-lower pitched A below middle-C will have a frequency of 220 Hz

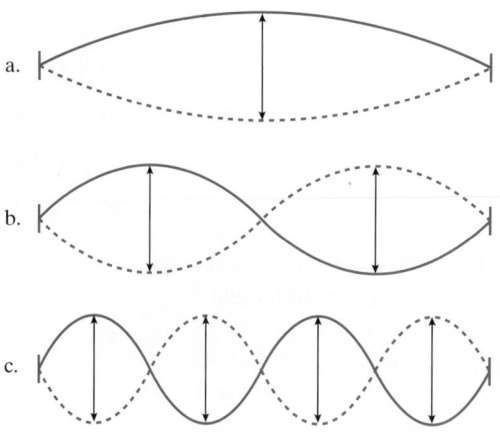

Figure 8-23
The fundamental frequency of a string (a) and its first (b) and second (c) harmonics.

and be one octave lower in pitch. To the Greeks and to people today, the most pleasing combination of notes are those that are the same note but an octave apart in pitch.

Figure 8-24 shows part of a piano keyboard. The white keys are the notes called C, D, E, F, G, A, B. The black keys are either called sharps, if they are to the right of the white key and thus a higher pitch; or flats, if they are to the left of a white key and thus lower in pitch. This means that all of the black keys are both sharps and flats. The symbol for D-sharp is D$^\#$ and the symbol for D-flat is D$^\flat$.

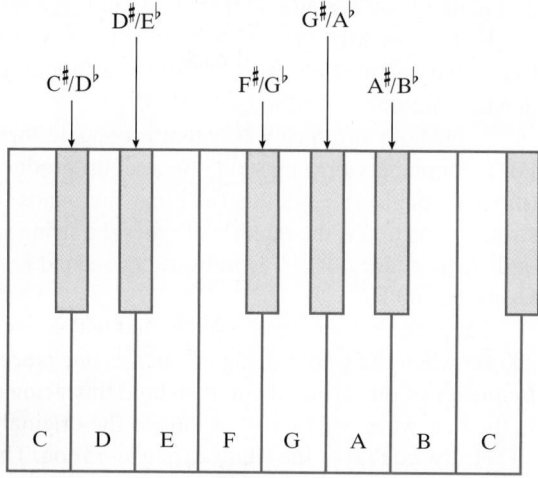

Figure 8-24
An octave on a piano keyboard.

If you count the keys from C to the next C on the keyboard pictured in Figure 8-24, you will count 12 keys (C$^\#$/D$^\flat$, D, D$^\#$/E$^\flat$, E, F, F$^\#$/G$^\flat$, G, G$^\#$/A$^\flat$, A, A$^\#$/B$^\flat$, B, C). These 12 keys produce 12 *semitones* between the two C's that are an octave apart. To change a frequency by an octave, the frequency is multiplied by 2 as mentioned before. This leads to the most common method of tuning pianos. Each key is tuned so that it is $\sqrt[12]{2}$ (the twelfth-root of two) different from the key next to it. This means to multiply or divide by $\sqrt[12]{2} = 1.0594630943593\ldots$, or about 1.05946. Stated mathematically, the ratio between the frequencies of any two successive pitches is 1.05946. . . . Thus, if middle-C has a frequency of 261.626 Hz, C-sharp has a frequency of C$^\#$ = (261.626)(1.05946) = 277.182 Hz. If you continue to multiply by $\sqrt[12]{2}$, the C an octave above middle-C will have a frequency of 523.251, or twice that of middle-C. Complete lists of frequencies of the modern chromatic scale may be obtained from many sources, including local music stores or the Internet at sites like answers.com.

If you play the same note of a violin and a flute, they sound entirely different in many respects. The reason for this has to do with *harmonics,* which were mentioned in relation to the length of plucked strings. When a note is played on a flute, only one note is heard. When a note is played on a violin or other acoustic instrument, not only the fundamental frequency is produced but many harmonics as well. For example, an A at 440 Hz played on a violin with full harmonics will produce not only the A at 440 Hz but also an A at 880 Hz with approximately half the volume of the primary A; an A at 1320 Hz and about a third of the volume of the primary A; and so forth until either the frequency gets too high for the human ear to respond or the volume gets too low to be heard.

Our discussion of music and math would not be complete without mentioning *digital* recordings. Sound is a wave and, in the past, recordings were made that actually reproduced the shape of the wave in the grooves of a vinyl record. If you are too young to remember phonograph records, ask some "old person" what a 33⅓- or 45-RPM is. This method of recording music is called the *analog* method.

To produce a modern digital recording, a computer takes the analog style of a piece of music and chops it up into very small pieces, each only a fraction of a second long; measures the frequencies present in each piece; and then records them *numerically.* This method of transforming music or sound into a list of numbers (digits) is called *digitizing.* A CD player is really a small computer that reverses the digitizing process and converts the stored numbers back into sound waves that you can hear. This process leaves a very short blank space between each set of numbers on the CD, but when played back at a normal speed, these gaps are small enough that the music sounds continuous to the human ear. A similar process is used with light waves to produce DVDs.

Many modern bands produce music using *synthesizers* that can imitate many instruments, such as pianos, drums, and horns, at the push of a key. This all goes under the heading of *digital signal processing.* Here is where music and mathematics merge with each other.

For some interesting connections between music and the Golden Ratio that you learned about in Section 8-4, refer to the suggested lab at the end of this chapter regarding sonatas written by Mozart.

Practice Set 8-5

1. How are frequency and pitch related?

2. In what fundamental way does one musical note differ from another?

3. What is an analog recording of music?

4. How does an analog recording differ from a digital recording of music?

5. What does it mean to digitize sound?

6. What kinds of waves are digitized on a DVD?

7. If you start with a note with a frequency of 261.626 Hz, what frequencies are one octave higher and one octave lower than this frequency?

8. If you start with a note with a frequency of 110 Hz, what frequencies are one octave higher and one octave lower than this frequency?

9. The note that is G above middle-C has a frequency of approximately 392 Hz. What is the frequency of the next highest semitone?

10. The note that is G above middle-C has a frequency of approximately 392 Hz. What is the frequency of the next lowest semitone?

11. If a certain piece of music is written in 4/4 time, how many half notes are required for one measure of music?

12. If a certain piece of music is written in 3/4 time, how many eighth notes are required per measure of music?

13. If a certain piece of music is written in 3/2 time, how many half notes are required per measure of music?

14. If a certain piece of music is written in 3/8 time, how many sixteenth notes are required per measure of music?

Find the missing note(s) in each of the following so that the proper tempo is maintained.

15. Tempo = 3/4   ♩ + ♩ + ___

16. Tempo = 3/4   ♩ + ___

17. Tempo = 3/8   ♪ + ♪ + ___

18. Tempo = 3/8   ♩ + ___

19. Tempo = 2/4   ♩ + ___

20. Tempo = 2/4   ♪ + ♩ + ___

Section 8-6   **MODELS AND PATTERNS IN SCIENCE AND TECHNOLOGY**

Many mathematical relationships exist in the world of science. In biology, formulas can help predict the number of bacteria that will be in a culture after a certain period of time. In physics, the velocity of a ball dropped from the top of a building can be calculated using a mathematical model. The relationship between voltage and current can be expressed using formulas or mathematical models. We will examine a few of the simpler scientific and technical formulas in this section.

Mathematical models can be used to predict numbers in growth situations or decay situations. This includes the growth of bacteria in a culture, growth in demand for electricity, growth of a population, or the decay of radioactive elements or a declining population. If the rate of growth, $r > 0$, then the population is growing, and if $r < 0$, then the population is declining. The model used for growth situations is called an **exponential function.** The number represented by the symbol e is discussed following the next equation box.

Important Equations

Exponential Growth

$$y = Ae^{rn}$$

where r = rate of change, A = initial amount, n = time interval, and y = new amount.

Calculator Mini-Lesson

e^x

Any *standard scientific calculator* has a second function that can be used for problems that contain a factor with a base e. The $\boxed{e^x}$ function is located over the $\boxed{\ln}$ button on your calculator. In order to calculate the value of e^2, you should enter 2 followed by the $\boxed{2\text{nd}}$ button and then the $\boxed{\ln}$ key (allowing you access to the $\boxed{e^x}$ function). The value 7.389056099 will be displayed without using the $\boxed{=}$ key.

A *graphing calculator (TI-83 Plus)* also has the $\boxed{e^x}$ function above the $\boxed{\ln}$ key. However, you must access the $\boxed{e^x}$ function before you enter the exponent in order to calculate the correct value. After entering the exponent, you must press $\boxed{\text{ENTER}}$ in order to see the correct answer.

The symbol e is an irrational number and is approximately equal to 2.71828. This number has its origin and definition in calculus, so don't worry too much about where it comes from. Suffice it to say that just as the number π occurs as part of the very nature of circles, e occurs as part of the very nature of things that grow or decay exponentially. The formula for exponential growth shown previously can be used to predict bacterial growth rates or the rate of population growth of cities and states. This formula can also calculate rates of decay or decline in growth. If the formula is used for calculating a "growth," then the exponent used will be a positive number ($r > 0$), as in the example that follows. Whenever the formula is used for calculating "declining growth," or "decay," the exponent will be a negative number ($r < 0$). This is shown in an example as well.

EXAMPLE 20   Bacteria Growth

A bacteria culture contains 120,000 bacteria. It grows at the rate of 15% per hour. How many bacteria will be present in 12 hours?

Use $y = Ae^{rn}$, where $A = 120{,}000$, $r = 0.15$, and $n = 12$.

$$y = 120{,}000e^{(0.15)(12)}$$

$$y = 120{,}000e^{1.8}$$

$$y = 725{,}957.6957$$

$$y \approx 726{,}000 \text{ bacteria}$$

The graph of this equation shown in Figure 8-25 makes it evident that the growth rate of bacteria is very rapid after a time. This is called **exponential growth** and is true for the rate of increase of many living things, even the population of humans on the earth.

Figure 8-25

EXAMPLE 21   **Population Decline**

According to government estimates (from www.census.gov), the population of persons aged 5–17 years in the state of West Virginia is declining at an average rate of 0.62% per year. If there were 300,000 persons in this age range in West Virginia in the year 2000, what would be the estimate of the number of persons in this age range in the year 2010?

Use $y = Ae^{rn}$, where $A = 300{,}000$, $r = -0.0062$, and $n = 10$.

$$y = 300{,}000e^{(-0.0062)(10)}$$

$$y = 300{,}000e^{-0.062}$$

$$y = 281{,}965$$

This shows a decline in this age group of about 20,000 over 10 years.

Many technical application problems involve the use of *quadratic equations.* Quadratic equations generally have two valid solutions and can be solved in a number of ways, including factoring, completing the square, and using the quadratic formula. The following examples show the use of this common type of equation.

▪ EXAMPLE 22   Electrical Currents

A variable voltage in a given electrical current is given by the formula $V = t^2 - 12t + 40$. At what values of t (in seconds) is the voltage V equal to 8.00V?

$$8 = t^2 - 12t + 40$$

$$0 = t^2 - 12t + 32$$

$$0 = (t - 4)(t - 8)$$

$$t - 4 = 0 \qquad \text{or} \qquad t - 8 = 0$$

$$t = 4 \text{ sec} \qquad \text{or} \qquad t = 8 \text{ sec}$$

▪ EXAMPLE 23   Shooting Projectiles

A projectile is shot vertically upward at an initial velocity of 96 ft/sec. Its height h in feet after t seconds may be expressed by the formula $h = 96t - 16t^2$.

(a) Find the height of the projectile at 7 sec.

$$h = 96t - 16t^2$$

$$h = 96(7) - 16(7)^2$$

$$h = 672 - 784 = -112 \text{ ft}$$

Because we have a negative height, the projectile must have landed on the ground before 7 seconds had passed. (See Figure 8-26.)

(b) Find t when $h = 0$.

$$0 = 96t - 16t^2$$

$$0 = 16t(6 - t)$$

$$16t = 0 \qquad \text{or} \qquad 6 - t = 0$$

$$t = 0 \text{ sec} \qquad \text{or} \qquad t = 6 \text{ sec}$$

The projectile was on the ground at the initial take-off ($t = 0$) and back on the ground 6 seconds later.

(c) Figure 8-26 shows the height of the projectile from $t = 0$ to $t = 6$ sec. Note that it is back to an altitude of zero before 7 seconds have passed [see Part (a) of this example].

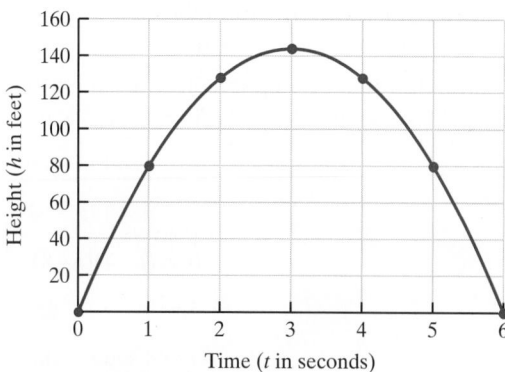

Figure 8-26

Not all quadratic equations can be factored. If an equation is not factorable (or even if it is!) you can find the solutions of the equation using the quadratic formula.

Important Equations

Quadratic Formula

If $ax^2 + bx + c = 0$, $a \neq 0$, then

$$x = \frac{-b \pm \sqrt{b^2 - 4ac}}{2a}$$

When using the quadratic formula to solve a problem, remember that the equation must be set equal to zero (0) before designating the values of a, b, and c. The signs of each term must also be used in order for the formula to give correct solutions. If the value of the expression under the radical is negative, this indicates a nonreal (imaginary) solution. The basic use of the quadratic formula is reviewed in Example 24 and it is applied in Example 25.

EXAMPLE 24   Solving a Quadratic Equation Using the Quadratic Formula

Solve the following equation using the quadratic formula:

$$3x^2 - 5x - 4 = 2$$

The first step in using the quadratic formula is to set the equation equal to 0 on one side. This is the same as if you were going to try to *factor* the equation in order to solve it.

$$3x^2 - 5x - 6 = 0$$

For use in the quadratic formula, once the equation is set equal to 0, the coefficient of the square term is a, the coefficient of the first power term is b, and any number that has no variable is c. (Please refer to the Important Equations box containing the quadratic formula.) Therefore, we will match up the numbers in our equation to the letters used:

$$a = 3, \quad b = -5, \quad \text{and} \quad c = -6$$

Now we will fill in the quadratic formula:

$$x = \frac{-b \pm \sqrt{b^2 - 4ac}}{2a}$$

$$x = \frac{-(-5) \pm \sqrt{(-5)^2 - 4(3)(-6)}}{2(3)}$$

$$x = \frac{5 \pm \sqrt{25 + 72}}{6}$$

We can find the two possible solutions as follows:

$$x = \frac{5 + \sqrt{97}}{6} \quad \text{or} \quad x = \frac{5 - \sqrt{97}}{6}$$

$$x = 2.4748 \ldots \quad \text{or} \quad x = -0.8081 \ldots$$

Answers in real applied problems will often be long decimal numbers. You will need to round the answers appropriately to match the scale of the problem and the type of answer required.

EXAMPLE 25   Electrical Current (An Application of the Quadratic Formula)

The following equation models the relationship among the electrical current i measured in amperes, voltage E measured in volts, and resistance R measured in ohms for a particular circuit.

$$i^2R + iE = 4000$$

If the resistance in the circuit is 20 Ω and the voltage is 50V, what is the current flowing in the circuit?

First, substitute the known values:

$$i^2(20) + i(50) = 4000$$

This is a quadratic equation, so we will rearrange it and set it equal to 0.

$$20i^2 + 50i - 4000 = 0$$

Because of the large value of 4000 compared with the other coefficients, this equation is not factorable. Thus, we will use the *quadratic formula* to solve it. In using the quadratic formula, first set the equation equal to zero as if you were going to factor it. We have already done this.

Next assign values to *a*, *b*, and *c* in the quadratic formula. In this application, $a = 20$, $b = 50$, and $c = -4000$. Now, plug these values into the quadratic formula.

$$x = \frac{-b \pm \sqrt{b^2 - 4ac}}{2a}$$

Here we are solving for the value of the current, *i*.

$$i = \frac{-50 \pm \sqrt{50^2 - 4(20)(-4000)}}{2(20)}$$

$$i = \frac{-50 \pm \sqrt{2500 - (-32000)}}{40}$$

There are two solutions as follows:

$$i = \frac{-50 + \sqrt{34500}}{40} \quad \text{or} \quad \frac{-50 - \sqrt{34500}}{40}$$

$$i = 3.3935\ldots \text{ amperes} \quad \text{or} \quad i = -5.8935\ldots \text{ amperes}$$

Because there is no such thing as a negative current value, we choose the positive answer of about 3.4 amperes for the current.

Practice Set 8-6

For each problem, write a mathematical model and use it to find the correct answer.

1. The population in Loving County is 15,000 people. The growth rate of the area is estimated to be 6.5% per year. Predict the population in 10 years.

2. The population of deer in rural Culberson County, Texas, is declining at an estimated rate of 0.8% per year. If this year's deer population is an estimated 12,500 deer, what will the deer population be in 7 years?

3. Due to the HIV/AIDS pandemic in Zimbabwe, Africa, over 3500 people per week are dying from AIDS. The situation is so bad that the overall population of the country is actually declining at a rate of about 0.75% per year when deaths due to all causes (AIDS, other diseases, internal warfare, starvation, etc.) are taken into account. If the population of Zimbabwe was about 12,576,800 in January of 2004, what will be the population of the country in 10 years? In 50 years?

4. The population of a city is 95,000. Assuming a growth rate of 2.5%, what will its population be in 15 years? Use a graphing calculator to help you sketch the graph of this function.

5. The public school enrollment of a city is 13,500. Enrollment is declining at a rate of 4.5%. Predict the enrollment in 5 years. (Hint: use $r = -0.045$.) Use a graphing calculator to draw the graph of this function and sketch it.

6. The amount of decay of a certain radioactive element is given by

$$y = y_o e^{-0.04t}$$

where *t* equals time in seconds, -0.04 is the decay rate per second, y_o is the initial amount, and *y* is the amount remaining. If a given sample has a mass of 155 g, how many grams remain undecayed after 30 seconds? After 2 minutes?

7. A variable voltage is given by the formula $V = t^2 - 14t + 48$. At what time after the circuit begins to function will the voltage be 3 V?

8. Using the formula in Problem 7, at what time will the voltage be 35 V?

9. Using the formula in Problem 7, at what time will the voltage be 0 V?

10. If you stand on top of a building 240 ft high and throw a rock upward with a speed of 32 feet per second, by the laws of physics, the equation

$$h = 240 + 32t - 16t^2$$

gives the height of the rock above the ground t seconds after it is thrown. How many seconds does it take the rock to reach the ground? Use your graphing calculator to sketch this graph and verify your solution.

Use the quadratic formula to solve the following equations. (Round to two decimal places.)

11. $x^2 - 2x - 15 = 0$ 12. $2x^2 + 3x - 4 = 0$

13. $3x^2 + 1 = 7x$ 14. $x^2 - 18 = 0$

15. $2x^2 - 3x = 9$ 16. $7x = 2x^2$

The formula $h = rt - 16t^2$ gives a good approximation of the height h in feet that an object will reach in t seconds, when it is projected upward with an initial speed of r feet per second. Write a model for each of the following situations in Problems 17–19. Solve each equation and then use your graphing calculator to sketch the function and verify your answer.

17. If a ball is thrown vertically upward with an initial velocity of 112 ft/sec, at what times will it be 160 feet above the ground?

18. A rifle bullet is fired upward with an initial velocity of 3200 ft/sec. After how many minutes does it hit the ground?

19. A toy rocket is fired upward with an initial velocity of 560 ft/sec. A person in a hot air balloon 1056 ft high sees it pass him on the way up. How long will it be before it passes him again on the way down?

20. In business, the cost of producing a product may by represented by an equation that is quadratic in nature. This is called a *cost equation*. A cost for manufacturing a certain item is defined by the equation $C = x^2 + 16x + 114$, where x represents the units manufactured per week. Determine the number of units that can be manufactured with a weekly cost of $6450.

21. Rock & Roll Chair Company has determined that the cost, $C(x)$, of producing a given number, x, of one model of its chairs can be accurately estimated by the following equation: $C(x) = 2400 - 40x + 2x^2$. If the company has $53,400 to invest in manufacturing these chairs, how many will it be able to manufacture with the money that is available?

22. An appliance manufacturer has determined that the profit, $P(x)$, that it makes in manufacturing and selling x number of washing machines can be determined from the following equation: $P(x) = 3x^2 + 240x - 1800$. How many machines must the company manufacture and sell in order to make a profit of $70,200?

23. Any good physics text will explain that as you dive deeper and deeper under water, the pressure increases and, as you climb higher and higher above the earth's surface, the air pressure decreases. Table 8-3 gives some data about depth, altitude, and pressure. These numbers have been rounded for convenience but are realistic.

■ **Table 8-3**

Depth below Surface of Water		Altitude above the Earth's Surface	
Depth below Surface (ft)	Pressure (atm)	Altitude (thousands ft)	Pressure (atm)
0	1	0	1.00
66	3	20	0.70
167	5	30	0.30
300	10	50	0.11
500	16	60	0.07

(a) Are either (or both) sets of data approximately linear? How did you decide this?

(b) If you decided that there is a linear relationship for one (or both) sets of data, determine what the slope would be for the line. Do this several times using different pairs of points each time. Are all of the slopes the same? If they are not exactly equal, then explain why.

Chapter Summary

Key Terms, Properties, and Formulas

area	Golden Ratio	proportion
circumference	hypotenuse	Pythagorean theorem
scale drawing	perimeter	symmetry
exponential growth	perspective	vanishing point

Formulas to Remember

Circumference of a Circle:

$$C = 2\pi r = \pi d$$

Area Formulas:

Square $A = s^2$

Rectangle $A = lw$

Triangle $A = 0.5bh$

Circle $A = \pi r^2$

Hero's Formula for the Area of a Triangle:

$$A = \sqrt{s(s - a)(s - b)(s - c)} \qquad s = \frac{a + b + c}{2}$$

Pythagorean Theorem:

$$a^2 + b^2 = c^2$$

The Golden Ratio:

$$\phi = \frac{a}{b} = \frac{a + b}{a}$$

Exponential Growth:

$$y = Ae^{rn}$$

Quadratic Formula:

$$x = \frac{-b \pm \sqrt{b^2 - 4ac}}{2a}$$

Chapter Review Problems

1. The lengths of the sides of a triangle are 6 in., 8 in., and 12 in. Find the area of the triangle. (Round to the nearest tenth.)

2. Find the perimeter and area of the figure shown in this diagram.

3. At $0.55/ft, how much will it cost to put molding around the window pictured?

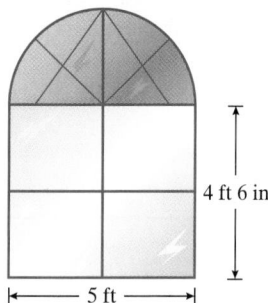

4. How many square feet of concrete surface are there in a circular walkway 8 ft wide surrounding a tree if the tree has a diameter of 3 ft? (Round to the tenths place.)

5. The siding on one side of a house was damaged in a storm and needs to be replaced. The drawing gives the dimensions of the end of the house and the windows in that end.
   (a) Find the area that needs to be covered with new siding.
   (b) If siding costs $22.25/yd², what will the cost of the siding be for this side of the house? (Note that you cannot buy a fractional part of a square yard.)

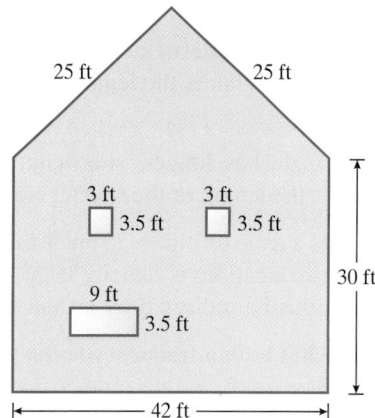

6. How long must a piece of board be to reach from the top of a building 15 ft high to a point on the ground 8 ft from the building?

7. A slow-pitch softball diamond is a square with sides that are each 60 ft long. What is the distance from first base to third base? (Round to the nearest tenth.)

8. Does a triangle with side lengths of 7.5 ft, 12.5 ft, and 10 ft form a right triangle? How do you know?

9. An isosceles triangle has a base 24 in. long and a height from the vertex angle to the base of 18 in. How long is each of the other sides of the isosceles triangle?

10. Give an example of the use of a perspective drawing of a building or house.

11. Give an example of something that has either horizontal or vertical reflection symmetry.

12. Give an example of something that has rotational symmetry.

13. Which type of symmetry, horizontal and/or vertical reflection symmetry, does each of the following exhibit?
    (a) The letter W
    (b) The number 3
    (c) An isosceles triangle sitting on its unequal side
    (d) The number 9

14. The corresponding sides of two similar triangles have lengths of 50 cm and 75 cm. What scale factor would relate the lengths of the sides of these two similar triangles?

15. A $\frac{1}{32}$ (1 in./32 in.) scale model of an automobile has a length of 4.125 in. What is the length of the actual car?

16. A golden rectangle has longest side lengths of 32.4 cm. What is the length of the shorter sides?

17. A road map uses a scale of 1 in. = 20 mi. If the distance between two locations is actually 35 mi, what distance would this be indicated by on the map?

18. A musical note has both a frequency and a pitch. Explain what they are.

19. What frequency is two octaves below 110 Hz?

20. If only quarter notes are used, how many are required for one measure of music written in 3/2 time?

21. A bacteria culture contains 25,000 bacteria and grows at the rate of 7.5% per hour. How many bacteria will be present in 24 hours?

22. A bacteria culture contains 500,000 bacteria and is dying off at the rate of 5% per hour. How many bacteria will be left after 48 hours?

23. A city has a population of 850,000, and the city loses population at a rate of 2% per year. Find its population in 5 years.

24. Solve this equation using the quadratic formula: $x^2 - 10x - 4 = 0$

25. An object is thrown downward with an initial velocity of 5 ft/sec. The relation between the distance s it travels and time t is given by $s = 5t + 16t^2$. How long does it take the object to fall 74 feet? Use a graphing calculator to draw a sketch of this problem and verify your answer.

26. The weekly profit p (in thousands of dollars) obtained from manufacturing telephones is given by the equation $p = -x^2 + 16x - 24$, where x is the number of telephones produced weekly. How many telephones should be produced to generate a weekly profit of $40,000?

Chapter Test

1. The lengths of the sides of a triangle are 2.6 ft, 3.4 ft, and 4.1 ft. Find the area of the triangle.

2. (a) Find the area and perimeter of the room shown in the figure.
   (b) If carpet costs $24.95 per square yard, how much will it cost to carpet the room? (Remember: 1 yd^2 = 9 ft^2)

3. A 26-ft ladder is leaning against a wall, and the foot of the ladder is 4.5 ft from the foot of the wall. If the ground is level, what is the height of the point at which the top of the ladder is resting on the wall?

4. Find the width of a rectangle having a diagonal of 6.5 cm and a length of 5.8 cm.

5. A car tire stands 21 in. tall.
   (a) How far will the tire move if it completes one revolution?
   (b) There are 5280 ft in a mile. How many times will this tire turn each mile it travels?

6. In a perspective drawing, where is the primary vanishing point located?

7. What letter(s) of the alphabet exhibit(s) rotational symmetry if rotated 45°? (Consider capital letters only.)

8. What letters of the alphabet exhibit rotational symmetry if rotated 270°? (Consider capital letters only.)

9. A map has a scale that says 1 cm = 2500 m. What distance on the map would indicate an actual distance of 6.25 km?

10. An HO-scale model train is a 1/87 scale. This means that each inch (or foot) of model size is equivalent to 87 in. (or 87 ft) in real life. If a model of a steam engine that is actually 75 ft long is to be made, how long will the model be in inches?

11. Does the ratio of the lengths of the sides of a rectangle that is 48 in. by 64 in. match the Golden Ratio?

12. If you wished to construct a golden rectangle with one side 48 in. long, what are the two possible lengths of the other sides that could be used?

13. Which is closer to being a golden rectangle, an 8.5-in. by 11-in. sheet of notebook paper or an 8.5-in. by 14-in. sheet of paper from a legal pad?

14. What is the difference between an analog sound recording and a digital sound recording?

15. What frequency is three octaves above a note of 440 Hz?

16. What two kinds of waves are digitized on a DVD recording of a movie?

17. What is the difference between 3/4 time and 4/4 time in music?

18. Suppose the population of a certain city is 125,000 with a growth rate of 3%. Estimate the population in 5 years.

19. Use the quadratic formula to calculate the solutions for the equation: $3x^2 - 11x = 7$. (Round to hundredths place.)

20. A toy rocket is launched from a deck. The function $h = -16t^2 + 96t + 28$ (where h = feet above the ground and t is time in seconds) defines the path of the rocket.
    (a) Use a graphing calculator to draw the sketch of this model.
    (b) Determine the height of the rocket at 2 seconds.
    (c) How many seconds will it take the rocket to hit the ground?

Suggested Laboratory Exercises

LAB EXERCISE 1   Room Areas

Refer back to Chapter 4, Lab Exercise 4, and assume that the floor plan pictured there has a scale of 1 in. = 8 ft. What is the size of the two bedrooms, the living/dining area, and the kitchen? What is the approximate square footage for the entire house? How many square yards of carpet would be needed to carpet the two bedrooms, including the closets and the living/dining area?

LAB EXERCISE 2   A Comparison of Calculated and Measured Volumes

In this exercise you will compare a measured quantity with a calculated value for the same quantity (i.e., comparing a ruler measure with a model or formula value).

Obtain four cans of differing sizes, a liquid measuring cup or similar item from the chemistry department with SI (metric) volume units (ml), a ruler with SI markings (mm, cm), and a source of water. You will also need your calculator.

First measure the height and radius of each can in centimeters (cm). Use these values to calculate the volume of each can. $V_{cylinder} = \pi r^2 h$ is the formula that "models" the volume of cylinders with circular, parallel ends. These volumes will be in cubic centimeters (cm^3). Record all of your data in a table like the one below.

Now use the measuring cup and fill each can with water, recording the number of milliliters (ml) of water that it takes to fill each one.

The volume in ml can easily be converted to the equivalent volume in cm³ because:

$$1 \text{ ml} = 1 \text{ cm}^3. \text{ Do this for each of the cans.}$$

Now compare the calculated volumes with the measured volumes as follows:

$$\frac{measured\ value - calculated\ value}{calculated\ value} \times 100\%$$

This calculation will give you the percent difference between the two volume measures for each can.

Table 8-4

Can	Measured Height (cm)	Measured Radius (cm)	Calculated Volume (cm³)	Measured Volume (cm³)	Difference	Percentage Difference
1						
2						
3						
4						

1. Were your calculated and measured volumes exactly the same in any/all cases? If not, what might be some reasons for the difference observed?
2. If an error of difference of ±5% is acceptable, did your values fall below this level? What changes might be made in the procedure that you use so as to minimize differences?

LAB EXERCISE 3   Musicians and Mathematics

If you do a little research on the Internet about the connection of music to math, you will find that many musicians, both modern and classical, used mathematics as a basis for some of their compositions. Research one of these persons and write a 2-page essay on how they used mathematics.

LAB EXERCISE 4   Are Golden Rectangles Really Cute?

Draw a series of four or five rectangles, only one of which is a golden rectangle. Then do a survey around your school asking which rectangle is most "pleasing" in appearance. Is the one that is the golden rectangle chosen most often?

LAB EXERCISE 5   The Golden Belly Button Project

It has been theorized that, on the average, a person's total height and the height of that person's belly button from the floor approximates the Golden Ratio. Collect lots of belly button data and test this theory. What is your conclusion?

LAB EXERCISE 6   Fibonacci Flowers

Bring in some flowers and count petals to see how many really do have a Fibonacci number of petals on the average. You will need to count petals on several blooms of each type of flower. Be careful to pick flowers with no obvious missing petals.

LAB EXERCISE 7

Mozart Sonatas and the Golden Ratio

Table 8-5 lists the number of measures of music in the first and second parts of several of Mozart's piano sonatas. Fill in the third column by calculating the ratio of the total number of measures in Parts 1 and 2 all together to the number of measures in the longest part. Write a discussion of your results and whether or not you think that Mozart had the Golden Ratio in mind when he wrote these sonatas.

■ Table 8-5

Measures in Part 1	Measures in Part 2	Ratio
77	113	$(77 + 113)/113 = 1.681$
24	36	
39	63	
53	67	
38	62	
28	46	
15	18	
40	69	
56	102	
46	60	

LAB EXERCISE 8

Examining Exponential Decay

When drugs are administered to a patient, the amount of medication in the bloodstream decreases continuously at a constant rate. This type of situation can be modeled with the function used for continuous exponential growth: $y = Ae^{rn}$, where r = rate of change, A = the initial amount of medication (in mg) injected into the bloodstream, and n = time periods. A particular medication is known to decrease at a rate of 6.5% per hour (-6.5% per hour). The common dose of this medication for adult patients is 5 mg per injection.

1. Use these numbers to write an exponential function that describes the decrease of this medication in a patient's bloodstream over time.

2. Now, use this function equation to fill in the missing values in the table.

Hours after Injection	Amount of Medication (in mg)
0	
1	
2	
3	
4	

3. Using these ordered pairs, sketch a graph of this function. What does the *x*-intercept of this function represent?

4. If a patient is given 5 mg of medication at 9 a.m., how much medication is still in his bloodstream at 11:30 a.m.?

5. Using your exponential equation and a graphing calculator, define Y_1 by entering it into the calculator. If another dose is to be administered when there is approximately 1 mg of the drug present in the bloodstream, at approximately what time should you give the patient another injection? Use your TABLE function to help you answer this question.

Appendix 1
Commonly Used Calculator Keys

KEY	FUNCTION*
SHIFT or 2nd	Allows access to the calculator functions printed above the keys
+/−	Used to change the sign of a number or enter a negative number into the calculator
$\sqrt{x}$	Used to take the square root of a number
x^2	Used to raise a number to the second power (square a number); enter 10^2 as: 10 x^2
y^x or x^y	Used to raise a number to an exponential power; enter 5^3 as: 5 y^x 3 =
EXP or EE	Used to enter a number written in scientific notation into the calculator; enter 3×10^2 as: 3 EE 2
a%	Used to enter a fraction into the calculator; enter $\frac{1}{2}$ as: 1 a% 2
x^{-1} or $\frac{1}{x}$	Used to find the reciprocal of a number
π	Gives the value of pi to nine decimal places
$\bar{x}$	Gives the arithmetic mean of a set of data when the calculator is in the statistics mode
σ or σ_n	Gives the population standard deviation for a set of data when the calculator is in the statistics mode
σ_{n-1} or s	Gives the sample standard deviation for a set of data when the calculator is in the statistics mode

Calculator Practice

Purpose: To familiarize students with the functions found on a scientific calculator

Apparatus: Scientific calculator, pencil

Introduction: Scientific calculators are used frequently in our study of mathematics to facilitate the arithmetic calculations required by our problems. Though different manufacturers include varying functions, many of the same functions are found on all scientific calculators. This exercise will allow you to explore your own

*The keystrokes and keys on individual calculators vary according to brands. This list is a general resource to help you quickly find an explanation of certain keys. For complete information, consult the manual that accompanied your particular calculator.

calculator and become familiar with its operation. For instructions specific to your brand of calculator, see your instruction manual.

Procedure:

SHIFT or 2nd

1. This key allows you to access the functions written above each key.

− +/−

2. This key is used to change the sign of the number that appears on your screen. To enter a negative number, many calculators require that you enter the number first, followed by the +/− button. Direct entry calculators allow you to enter the sign first − followed by the number.

Activity: (a) Enter the number 5 and then push the +/− key. A negative sign should appear in front of the 5. To add two negative numbers in the calculator, look at the following example. Calculate $-5 + (-3)$ by entering 5 +/− + 3 +/− =. The answer on your screen should be -8.

(b) Try these problems in your calculator.

   1. $-6 + (-3) =$ 2. $-8 - (-5) =$
   3. $5 \times (-4) =$ 4. $(-10) \div (-2) =$

a%

3. This key is used when entering a fraction into the calculator.

Activity: (a) To enter the fraction $\frac{2}{3}$, use this sequence: 2 a% 3. The screen display will look like 2 ⌋ 3. To reduce a fraction such as $\frac{5}{10}$, enter 5 a% 10 =. To enter a mixed fraction such as $1\frac{1}{4}$, enter 1 a% 1 a% 4. The screen display reads 1 _ 1 ⌋ 4.

(b) Use the fraction key to solve the following problems.

   1. $\frac{1}{4} + 2\frac{1}{2} =$ 2. $(-\frac{1}{2})(1\frac{3}{4}) =$
   3. $-\frac{3}{4} + 1\frac{1}{2} - (-\frac{1}{4}) =$ 4. $(3\frac{1}{4}) \div 5 =$

x²   yˣ

4. These keys are exponent keys.

Activity: (a) The x^2 key is used specifically for squaring numbers. To solve the problem 5^2, enter 5 x^2. The answer appears on the screen immediately. The y^x key allows you to raise any base to any given exponent. To calculate the problem $(-5)^3$, enter 5 +/− y^x 3 =. The screen should display the answer -125.

(b) Use the appropriate exponent key to solve the following problems.

   1. $0.8^2 =$ 2. $2^5 =$ 3. $(\frac{3}{4})^2 =$ 4. $(-3)^4 =$

√x

5. This key is a square root key. This key allows you to reverse the process of squaring done by the x^2 key.

Activity: (a) If you are asked to find $\sqrt{16}$, you need to find the number that was originally squared to get 16. To do this on the calculator, enter 16 √x and the answer 4 will appear on the screen. On a direct entry calculator, enter √x 16.

(b) Calculate the following values. (Round to the nearest tenth, if necessary.)

   1. $\sqrt{1.25} =$ 2. $\sqrt{8} =$ 3. $\sqrt{12,100} =$ 4. $\sqrt{4000} =$

( )   **6.** Parentheses keys are used for calculating problems containing grouping symbols.

Activity: **(a)** If a problem contains grouping symbols, they can be entered into the calculator as you enter the numbers. If a problem has a number immediately preceding the parentheses indicating the operation of multiplication, you will probably need to include the $\times$ button in your entry. For example, to solve 3(5 + 2), enter 3 $\times$ (5 + 2) $=$ and the display should show 21 as the correct answer.

(b) Calculate the answers to each of the following problems.

1. $2(15 - 6) =$ **2.** $(-4 + 3) - (6 - 4) =$
3. $5(8 - 3) + 6 =$ **4.** $-2(4 + 7) - 3^2 =$

EXP or EE   **7.** Your calculator will have one (but not both) of these keys. This key is used to enter values into the calculator that are given in scientific notation form.

Activity: **(a)** A number written in the form 5×10^3 is said to be written in scientific notation. To enter this number into the calculator, enter 5 EE 3. The display shows 5^{03}. If you now press $=$, the number will be changed to the decimal equivalent 5000. The $\times$ and the 10 are not displayed on most screens when a number is entered in scientific notation form.

(b) Use the scientific notation key to solve the following problems.

1. $2.5 \times 10^{-2} =$ **2.** $(6 \times 10^{-4}) \times (2.1 \times 10^2) =$ **3.** $5.14 \times 10^4 =$

Appendix 2

Formulas Used in This Text

GEOMETRY FORMULAS

Circumference of a circle: $C = 2\pi r = \pi d$

Area formulas: square $A = s^2$

             rectangle $A = lw$

             triangle $A = 0.5bh$

             circle $A = \pi r^2$

Hero's formula for the area of a triangle:

$$A = \sqrt{s(s - a)(s - b)(s - c)} \qquad s = \frac{a + b + c}{2}$$

Pythagorean theorem: In a right triangle, $a^2 + b^2 = c^2$, where a and b are the lengths of the legs and c is the length of the hypotenuse.

BUSINESS FORMULAS

$$\text{Percent increase/decrease} = \frac{\text{new value} - \text{original value}}{\text{original value}} \times 100$$

Simple interest: $I = Prt$

Maturity value: $M = P + I$

Interest compounded quarterly: $M = P\left(1 + \dfrac{r}{4}\right)^{4t}$, where r = annual rate, t = number of years

Interest compounded monthly: $M = P\left(1 + \dfrac{r}{12}\right)^{12t}$, where r = annual rate, t = number of years

Interest compounded daily: $M = P\left(1 + \dfrac{r}{365}\right)^{365t}$, where r = annual rate, t = number of years

Straight-line depreciation: $\dfrac{\text{original value} - \text{residual value}}{\text{number of years}}$

Fixed-rate mortgage monthly payment formula: $P = A\left[\dfrac{\dfrac{r}{12}\left(1 + \dfrac{r}{12}\right)^{12t}}{\left(1 + \dfrac{r}{12}\right)^{12t} - 1}\right]$
where A = amount borrowed
         t = number of years
         r = annual rate

ALGEBRA FORMULAS

Direct variation: $y = kx$

Inverse variation: $y = \dfrac{k}{x}$

Joint variation: $y = kxz$

Slope of a line: $m = \dfrac{y_2 - y_1}{x_2 - x_1}$

Linear equation: $Ax + By = C$

Slope-intercept form: $y = mx + b$

Point-slope form: $y - y_1 = m(x - x_1)$

Quadratic formula: If $ax^2 + bx + c = 0, a \neq 0$, then

$$x = \frac{-b \pm \sqrt{b^2 - 4ac}}{2a}$$

Exponential growth: $y = Ae^{rn}$

Cramer's rule: To find the solution of a system of equations $ax + by = c$, $dx + ey = f$:

$$x = \frac{\begin{vmatrix} c & b \\ f & e \end{vmatrix}}{\begin{vmatrix} a & b \\ d & e \end{vmatrix}} \qquad y = \frac{\begin{vmatrix} a & c \\ d & f \end{vmatrix}}{\begin{vmatrix} a & b \\ d & e \end{vmatrix}}$$

PROBABILITY FORMULAS

$$P(E) = \frac{\text{number of successes}}{\text{number of possible outcomes}}$$

$$n! = n(n - 1)(n - 2)(n - 3) \ldots (2)(1)$$

$$_nP_r = \frac{n!}{(n - r)!}$$

$$_nC_r = \frac{n!}{r!(n - r)!}$$

odds in favor: success:failure

odds against: failure:success

STATISTICS FORMULAS

Mean average: $\bar{x} = \dfrac{\Sigma x}{n}$

Range: $R = $ highest number $-$ lowest number

Sample standard deviation: $s = \sqrt{\dfrac{\Sigma (x - \bar{x})^2}{n - 1}}$

z-scores: $z = \dfrac{x - \bar{x}}{s}$

Appendix 3
Levels of Data in Statistics

In addition to being classified as either quantitative or qualitative, data may also be classified based on how much real information they provide. There are four levels of data (or measurement): nominal, ordinal, interval, and ratio. As the level of the data collected increases from the lowest level (nominal) to the highest (ratio), so does the amount of information that is available from the data. We will now look at each level separately, starting with the lowest level.

Nominal-level data consist of *names only*. The data may be sorted into named groups or categories but no other comparisons are possible with this low level of data. No calculation or other mathematical manipulation may be done with nominal-level data. The "names" do not contain any inherent or implied order. Nominal-level data are *qualitative* in nature.

Ordinal-level data do contain more information than nominal-level data. Data of this level may be sorted into categories like nominal-level data but, in addition, these categories may be placed into a *meaningful order*. Generally speaking, ordinal-level data are qualitative in nature.

EXAMPLE 1   CLASSIFYING QUALITATIVE DATA

If you were to ask someone what color his or her eyes were, you would get data such as blue, brown, green, and hazel. There is no way to place eye color in a meaningful order that has to do with eye color. (Alphabetical order has to do with the alphabet, not eye color. In fact, translating these colors into another language could change their alphabetical order. For example, in Portuguese these colors are *azul*, *maroon*, *verde*, and *avela*. Placing these color names in alphabetical order would place *avela*, which is hazel, first in the list.) This means that eye color is nominal-level data. If you were to ask someone what their level of anxiety was in regard to taking a test on this chapter, you would get answers like high, medium, and low. These answers do have a meaningful order and thus are ordinal-level data.

Interval-level data can be placed in a meaningful order like ordinal-level data but also have the distinction of having equal intervals. Interval measurements allow us to make meaningful claims about measurable differences in amount between observations. Most measurement scales, such as for measuring temperature, are clearly interval-level data. Because interval measurements are numerical, this level of data is quantitative in nature. Also, "zeros" here are not "real zeros" in the sense of meaning "nothing" or "none of."

Ratio level is the highest level of data. Ratio-level data allow us to introduce the idea of one measurement exceeding another, not by just a certain amount as in interval-level data, but by a certain ratio such as "twice as much." Zeros here are "real," and this level of data is quantitative in nature.

EXAMPLE 2   CLASSIFYING QUANTITATIVE DATA

Consider measuring a temperature (we will use the Celsius scale) and measuring a height (we will use meters). First, look at the "zeros." There is a zero in both measurements but only one is a "real" zero. A temperature of 0°C is not a real zero in that it does not mean that there is no temperature at all or that there is no temperature below it. A measurement of 0 m is a real zero. It means no height and there is no measurement shorter than 0 m. A temperature of 40°C is not twice as hot as a temperature of 20°C but a height of 40 m is twice a height of 20 m. Thus, the Celsius temperature scale is interval level and heights in meters are ratio level.

The following table is a brief summary of the four levels of measurement that have been discussed.

Levels of Measurement

Level	Properties	Items Show	Examples	Type of Data
Nominal	Classifications	Differences in kinds	Sex Political party Colors	Qualitative
Ordinal	Classification order	Differences in degree	Letter grades Graded attitudes S, M, L H, M, L Scale of 1–10	Qualitative
Interval	Classification order Equal intervals	Measurable differences in amount	Celsius and Fahrenheit temperature scales GPAs	Quantitative
Ratio	Classification order Equal intervals True zero	Measurable differences in total amount	Income Weights Lengths Times	Quantitative

Now decide the proper level of data for each of the following:

(a) years of education that you have had
(b) your favorite TV show
(c) your daily caloric intake
(d) your place of birth
(e) your blood type

Answer Key

Answer Key to Problems in the Textbook

Chapter 1

Practice Set 1-2

1. $-2.6, -\sqrt{5}, -1, 0, \frac{7}{13}, 3\frac{1}{2}, 4$
2. $-3.5, -1.625, -1, \frac{1}{2}, 1\frac{3}{8}, |-2|, \sqrt{5}$
3. (a) $<$ (b) $>$ (c) $>$
4. (a) $<$ (b) $>$ (c) $>$
5. 2
6. -11
7. Undefined
8. Undefined
9. 2
10. -12
11. $-\frac{11}{24}$
12. $-2\frac{1}{20}$
13. 12
14. 15
15. $-\frac{14}{3}$
16. -1
17. -5
18. 1
19. -3
20. -9
21. -10
22. 30
23. 0

24. 0
25. 13
26. -14
27. $\frac{5}{4} = 1.25$
28. $\frac{22}{13}$
29. $-\frac{1}{4}$
30. 5
31. 0
32. $\frac{1}{3}$
33. 14.3125
34. 27.75
35. $\frac{19}{8} = 2.375$
36. -7
37. 76
38. 102
39. 0
40. -38

Practice Set 1-3

1. $x = -10$
2. $x = 3$
3. $x = -3.5$
4. $x = 1$
5. $x = 10$
6. $x = -7$
7. $x = 10$
8. $x = -16$

9. $x = 4.5$

10. $x = 3$

11. $x = -2.5$

12. $x = \frac{7}{6}$

13. $x = 11$

14. $x = 5$

15. $x = -1$

16. $x = \frac{1}{5}$

17. $x = 5$

18. $x = 1$

19. $x = -1.5$

20. $x = 2$

21. $x = 1.25$

22. $x = -\frac{35}{16}$

23. $x = 95$

24. $f = \frac{5}{3}$

25. $w = -\frac{1}{8} = -0.125$

26. $x = -\frac{11}{30}$

27. $x = -\frac{45}{4} = -11.25$

28. $x = 7.2$

29. $x = -\frac{13}{3}$

30. $x = -\frac{56}{9}$

31. $x = 0$

32. $x = 4.8$

33. $k = 120.54$

34. $m = -34.78$

35. $x = 24$

36. $x = 2$

37. $x = -1.9$

38. $x = \frac{7}{11}$

39. No solution

40. No solution

41. $a = -2.5$

42. $s = \frac{7}{8}$

43. $x = -6$

44. $x = -\frac{1}{3}$

45. $x = -4.5$

46. $p = 11$

47. $x = 12$

48. $x = -2$

49. $x = -\frac{2}{5} = -0.4$

50. $x = \frac{19}{6}$

Practice Set 1-4

1. $t = 2.5$ hours

2. $r = 68$ mph

3. $500

4. $r = 0.055 = 5.5\%$

5. 28.26 in.^{2}

6. $r = 2$ ft

7. $b = 9$ in.

8. $b = 7.5$ cm

9. 30 in.^{2}

10. 6 in.^{2}

11. 20°

12. −20°

13. 14°

14. 212°

15. $m = -\frac{1}{3}$

16. $m = 1$

17. $7834.96

18. $14,114.28

19. $x = -6$ or 1

20. $5, -\frac{1}{2}$

21. 2,204,421 bacteria

22. 52,283 people

23. $r = \dfrac{I}{pt}$

24. $L = \dfrac{P - 2W}{2}$

25. $b = \dfrac{2A}{h}$

26. $m = \dfrac{F}{a}$

27. $2A - y = x$

28. $y = -\frac{2}{3}x + 2$

29. $w = \dfrac{V}{lh}$

30. $B = \dfrac{2A - bh}{h}$

31. $h = \dfrac{S - 2\pi r^2}{2\pi r}$

32. $C = \frac{5}{9}(F - 32)$

33. $b = \dfrac{3V}{h}$

34. $t = \dfrac{\sqrt{d}}{4}$

Practice Set 1-5

1. 3:8
2. 12:7
3. 1:12
4. 3:5
5. 2:3
6. 1:2
7. 7:2
8. 5:7
9. 1:40
10. 6:5
11. 32 mpg
12. 22.5 mpg
13. $0.35/min

14. $0.12/kWh
15. $170/day
16. $6.75/hr
17. 1.6 lb/person
18. 0.4583 lb/person
19. $x = 3.75$
20. $x = 3$
21. $x = 7$
22. $x = 2$
23. $x = 12$
24. $x = 5$
25. $x = 6$
26. $x = 11$
27. $x = 3$
28. $x = 8$
29. $5.85
30. $4.76
31. 2700 km
32. 13.75 hr
33. 6 dozen or 72 muffins
34. $4\frac{1}{6}$ cup
35. 112 in. or 9 ft 4 in.
36. 121.9 in. or approx 10 ft
37. 54V
38. 125V
39. 20 lb
40. 6.25 lb
41. $300
42. 1.8 hr
43. 700 L
44. 50 gal
45. 2650 women

Practice Set 1-6

1. $\frac{2}{25}$

2. $\frac{3}{20}$

3. $\frac{180}{100} = \frac{9}{5}$

4. $\frac{3}{2}$

5. $\frac{1}{3}$

6. $\frac{129}{200}$

7. 0.05

8. 0.08

9. 0.0005

10. 0.00125

11. 0.015

12. 0.049

13. 1.25

14. 2.00

15. 0.5%

16. 25%

17. $66\frac{2}{3}\%$

18. 350%

19. 150%

20. 255%

21. 11.25

22. 67.5

23. 1340

24. 60

25. 68%

26. $22\frac{1}{3}\%$

27. 7.65 or 8 games

28. 7.8 = 8 freethrows

29. $1.96

30. $8.06/hr

31. About 8.5%

32. 2.5%

33. 5%

34. 2.5%

35. 1,709,541

36. 24,612

37. 11.8%

38. 5.6%

39. 1.50 kg

40. 2.684 m

Practice Set 1-7

1. $2x + 6$

2. $2x - 3$

3. $7x - 2$

4. $3 + 4x$

5. $3(4 + x)$

6. $2(x - 6)$

7. $\frac{1}{3}x - 5$

8. $x - \frac{3}{4}x$

9. Ann = $x + 5000$; Bill = x

10. Friday = $3 + 0.5x$; Monday = x

11. Width = x; length = $2x + 5$

12. Short = x; middle-sized = $x + 1$; long = $x + 2$

13. 20 m, 40 m

14. Joshua 14; Mario 32

15. 86

16. 101; no

17. About 470 kWh

18. 75 min

19. 20 points

20. Jim 215; Gaylord 314

21. 28, 29, 30

22. No

23. $-89, -91, -93$

24. 499, 501, 503

25. Brand Z is the better buy.

26. Five for $4.95

27. Lot = $23,333; house = $151,667

28. $20,500

29. $6.50

30. $118.40

31. Bush: 271 votes; Gore: 266 votes

32. Dem: 48; Rep: 51

33. 27 in., 9 in., 4 in.

34. 4 cm, 20 cm, 32 cm

35. 3 hrs 12 min

36. 6.7 hrs

37. Palmisano: $7 million; Dell: $3.44 million

38. Ford: 8,896,000; GM: 8,913,000

39. Panthers: 71,501; Redskins: 80,493

40. Hemric: 2556; Dawkins: 2587

Chapter 1 Review Problems

1. $-\frac{2}{3}$

2. 9

3. -2

4. $-7^2 + 9 = -49 + 9 = -40$

5. 8.25

6. About -6.865

7. 9

8. $x = \frac{16}{7}$

9. $x = -3$

10. $x = -\frac{4}{3}$

11. $n = 2$

12. $x = 18$

13. $x = 6$

14. $x = -6$

15. $x = 0$

16. $t = \dfrac{I}{pr}$

17. $y = -\frac{2}{3}x + 3$

18. $d = \dfrac{C}{\pi}$

19. $c = P - a - b$

20. 3:20

21. 4:3

22. 1:10

23. $12/hr

24. 5.5 bushels/tree

25. $8.25/hr

26. $x = \frac{12}{7}$

27. $x = 6$

28. $x = 9$

29. $x = -1$

30. 18.75

31. 12.5%

32. 1600

33. $320

34. 6 in.^{2}

35. $300

36. 1440 liters

37. 69 dentists

38. 48%

39. $1827 new monthly salary

40. 1.6 kg

41. 1.5742 m

42. 7.8%

43. About 3.87% increase

44. 13 min

45. 138 min

46. 2.5 hrs

47. $-15°$ Fahrenheit

48. −3° Celsius

49. 15 in., 18 in.

50. 13 cm, 27 cm, 39 cm

51. $34.00

52. 18 nickels and 34 dimes

53. $N = 950$ units produced

54. First remove the parentheses by use of the distributive property, then add 2:

$$2 + 3(2x + 4) = 2 + 6x + 12 = 6x + 14$$

55. 3.5 hrs

Chapter 1 Test

1. Its distance from zero on the number line and distances are always positive.

2. The "same" number with the opposite sign

3. −16

4. 7

5. −31

6. $y = -26$

7. $x = 6$

8. $x = 1.8$

9. $y = -25$

10. $x = 1$

11. $w = \dfrac{V}{lh}$

12. $v = \dfrac{h + 16t^2}{t}$

13. 1:6

14. 3:4

15. $103.30 per day

16. 1.25 lbs/person

17. 5 eggs per chicken

18. $x = \frac{35}{18}$

19. $x = -\frac{60}{7}$

20. 12.75

21. Approximately 22.3%

22. 650

23. $1.80

24. $6.87

25. 18

26. 675

27. 64 ft

28. Let x = the number of miles driven. $20.00 + $0.10/mile$(x)$ = $10.00 + $0.30/mile$(x)$; $x = 50$ mi

29. 56.67% decrease

30. 750 passengers

31. Sarah is 9 and Michelle is 35

32. $30.25

33. Approximately 113 volts

34. Max = 0.454 cm; min = 0.452 cm

35. 5 ft, 16 ft

Chapter 2

Practice Set 2-1

1–12.

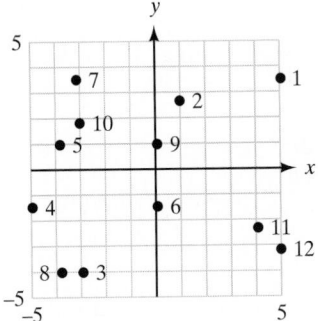

13. $(0, 0)$ origin

14. $(2, 1)$ I

15. $(-3, 4)$ II

16. $(1, -1)$ IV

17. $(-3, -3)$ III

18. $(5, 0)$ x axis

19. $(0, -3)$ y axis

20. $(4, -3)$ IV

21. C

22. F, G

23. F, C

24. G

25. B, F

26. B

27. No

28. Yes

29. Yes

30. $(0, -6)$ $(3, -3)$ $(4, -2)$ $(6, 0)$

31. $(0, 8)$ $(3, 5)$ $(10, -2)$ $(8, 0)$

32. $(0, 6)$ $(3, 0)$ $(4, -2)$ $(3, 0)$

33. $(0, -4)$ $(3, -3)$ $(6, -2)$ $(12, 0)$

34. $(0, 2)$ $(3, 0.8)$ $(10, -2)$ $(5, 0)$

35. $(0, 0)$ $(3, -0.75)$ $(8, -2)$ $(0, 0)$

36. $(0, -2)$ $(3, 0.25)$ $(0, -2)$ $(\frac{8}{3}, 0)$

37. $(0, 0)$ $(3, 3)$ $(-2, -2)$ $(0, 0)$

38. $(0, -3)$ $(3, 9)$ $(0.25, -2)$ $(0.75, 0)$

39. $(0, -3)$ $(3, -4.5)$ $(-2, -2)$ $(-6, 0)$

40. $(0, 0)$ $(3, -3)$ $(2, -2)$ $(0, 0)$

Practice Set 2-2

1. Let the y value $= 0$ in the equation and solve for x.

2. Let $x = 0$ and solve for y.

3. Calculate the coordinates of another point on the line by assigning either x or y a nonzero value, and solving for the matching coordinate.

4. b

5. $(6, 0)$ $(0, -6)$ $(4, -2)$

6. $(8, 0)$ $(0, 8)$ $(10, -2)$

7. $(3, 0)$ $(0, 6)$ $(4, -2)$

8. $(12, 0)$ $(0, -4)$ $(6, -2)$

9. $(3, -2)$ $(0, -2)$ (any real number, -2)

10. $(3, 0)$ $(3,$ any number$)$ $(3, -2)$

11. $(5, 0)$ $(0, 2)$ $(10, -2)$

12. $(0, 0)$ $(0, 0)$ $(8, -2)$

13. x-intercept: $(-4, 0)$; y-intercept: $(0, -2)$

14. x-intercept: $(10, 0)$; y-intercept: $(0, -2)$

15. x-intercept: $(-5, 0)$; y-intercept: $(0, -2.5)$

16. x-intercept: $(6, 0)$; y-intercept: $(0, 2)$

17. x-intercept: $(3, 0)$; y-intercept:$(0, 2)$

18. x-intercept: $(-4, 0)$; y-intercept: $(0, -6)$

19. x-intercept: $(5, 0)$; y-intercept: $(0, -3)$

20. x-intercept: $(3, 0)$; y-intercept: $(0, -4)$

21. x-intercept: $(\frac{3}{4}, 0)$; y-intercept: $(0, -3)$

22. x-intercept: $(4, 0)$; y-intercept: $(0, -1.6)$

23. x-intercept: $(0, 0)$; y-intercept: $(0, 0)$

24. x-intercept: $(0, 0)$; y-intercept: $(0, 0)$

25. x-intercept: $(0, 0)$; y-intercept: $(0, 0)$

26. x-intercept: $(0, 0)$; y-intercept: $(0, 0)$

27. x-intercept: $(-4, 0)$; y-intercept: $(0, -2)$

28. x-intercept: $(0.5, 0)$; y-intercept: $(0, -1)$

29. x-intercept: $(2, 0)$; y-intercept: $(0, -1)$

30. x-intercept: $(2, 0)$; y-intercept: $(0, 6)$

31. x-intercept: $(20, 0)$; y-intercept: $(0, -4)$

32. x-intercept: $(12, 0)$; y-intercept: $(0, 3)$

33. x-intercept: $(3, 0)$; y-intercept: $(0, 6)$

34. x-intercept: $(-\frac{8}{3}, 0)$; y-intercept: $(0, -2)$

35. x-intercept: $(-3, 0)$; y-intercept: none

36. x-intercept: $(0.6, 0)$; y-intercept: none

37. x-intercept: none; y-intercept: $(0, \frac{2}{3})$

38. x-intercept: none; y-intercept: $(0, 6)$

39. x-intercept: $(4, 0)$; y-intercept: $(0, \frac{4}{3})$

40. x-intercept: $(-8, 0)$; y-intercept: $(0, 1.6)$

Practice Set 2-3

1. slope $= -\frac{5}{2}$

2. slope $= 13$

3. slope $= \frac{2}{11}$

4. slope $= \frac{2}{5}$

5. slope $= \frac{5}{2}$

6. Undefined

7. slope $= 8$

8. slope $= -\frac{2}{3}$

9. $x = 5$

10. $y = 15$

11. $y = 22$

12. $x = -\frac{41}{7}$

13. $y = -4x + 1$
    $m = -4$
    y-intercept $= (0, 1)$

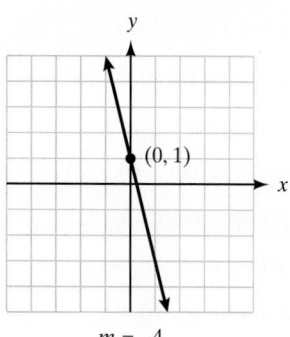

$m = -4$

14. $y = -4$
    $m = 0$
    y-intercept $= (0, -4)$

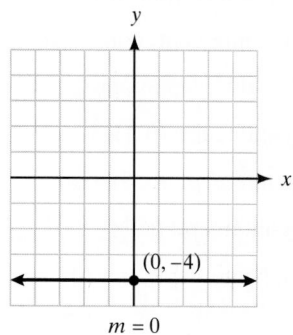

$m = 0$

15. $3x + 2y = 6$
    $m = -\frac{3}{2}$
    y-intercept $= (0, 3)$

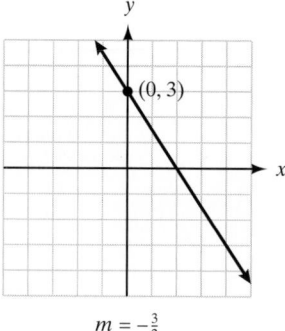

$m = -\frac{3}{2}$

16. $x + 3y = 12$
    $m = -\frac{1}{3}$
    y-intercept $= (0, 4)$

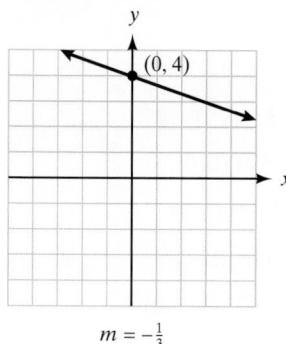

$m = -\frac{1}{3}$

17. $2x - 3y = 4$
    $m = \frac{2}{3}$
    y-intercept $= (0, -1.33)$

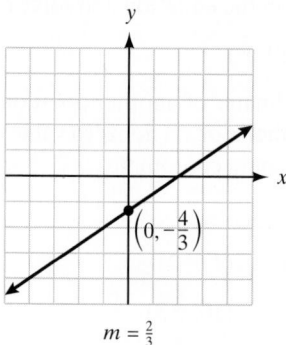

$m = \frac{2}{3}$

18. $4x = 11$
$x = \frac{11}{4} = 2.75$

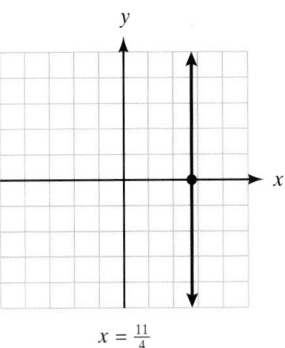

$x = \frac{11}{4}$

19. $4y - x = 10$
$m = \frac{1}{4}$
y-intercept $= (0, 2.5)$

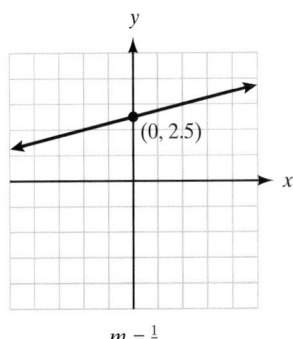

$m = \frac{1}{4}$

20. $2x - y = 2$
$m = 2$
y-intercept $= (0, -2)$

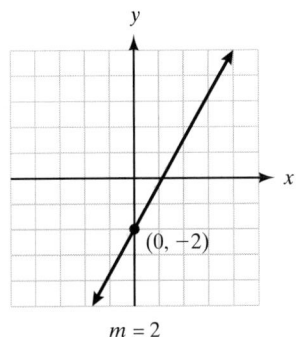

$m = 2$

21. $\frac{3}{4}x - \frac{1}{2}y = \frac{5}{8}$
$m = \frac{3}{2}$
y-intercept $= (0, -1.25)$

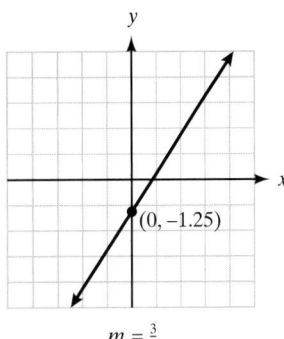

$m = \frac{3}{2}$

22. $\frac{2}{3}x + 2y = 2$
$m = -\frac{1}{3}$
y-intercept $= (0, 1)$

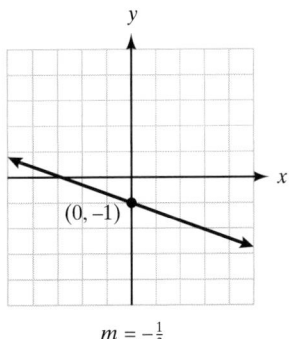

$m = -\frac{1}{3}$

23. $y = -x$
$m = -1$
y-intercept $= (0, 0)$

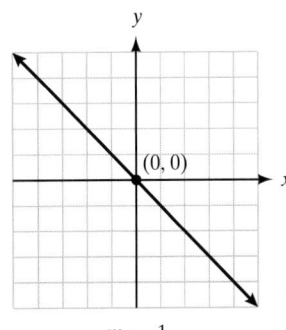

$m = -1$

24. $3x - 2y = 7$
$m = \frac{3}{2}$
y-intercept $= (0, -3.5)$

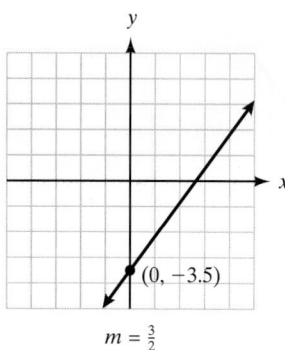

$m = \frac{3}{2}$

25. $4y = 12 + x$
$m = \frac{1}{4}$
y-intercept $= (0, 3)$

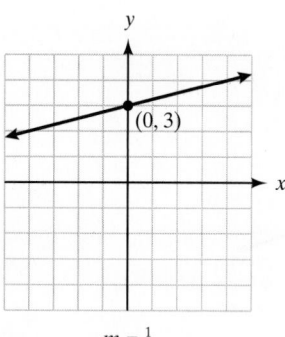

$m = \frac{1}{4}$

26. $m = -4$

27. $m = \frac{3}{8}$

28. Undefined

29. $m = \frac{1}{6}$

30. $m = 0$

31. $m = 1$

32. $m = -\frac{2}{3}$

33. $m = 0$

34. $m = -\frac{5}{2}$

35. Undefined

36. Parallel

37. Perpendicular

38. Perpendicular

39. Neither

40. Perpendicular

Practice Set 2-4

1. $y = -2x + 8$

2. $y = 5x - 3$

3. $y = \frac{1}{2}x - 5$

4. $y = -\frac{3}{4}x + 7$

5. $y = -2x - 25$

6. $y = -x + 7$

7. $y = \frac{5}{2}x + \frac{13}{2}$

8. $y = -\frac{1}{3}x$

9. $y = -\frac{1}{3}x + \frac{5}{3}$

10. $y = -\frac{2}{5}x - 2$

11. $y = 2x - 5$

12. $y = \frac{7}{5}x + \frac{8}{5}$

13. $y = -2$

14. $y = 1$

15. $y = -x + 3$

16. $y = -3x + 15$

17. $y = \frac{1}{2}x - \frac{13}{6}$

18. $y = 3x - 12$

19. $y = -2.5x - 7$

20. $y = -1.75x + 6.75$

21. $x = 3$

22. $x = 5$

23. $x = 1$

24. $x = -3$

25. $y = -2x - 5$

26. $y = 0.5x + 8$

27. $y = -3x + 19$

28. $y = -0.5x + 5$

29. $y = -x - 7$

30. $y = -\frac{2}{5}x - \frac{22}{5}$

31. $y = -\frac{5}{2}x - \frac{21}{2}$

32. $y = \frac{1}{3}x + 5$

33. $x = 3$

34. $y = 1$

35. $y = 3$

36. $x = -2$

37. $y = \frac{1}{3}x - 1$

38. $y = -\frac{6}{5}x - 6$

39. $y = -x$

40. $y = \frac{2}{3}x$

Practice Set 2-5

1. $y \leq x + 4$

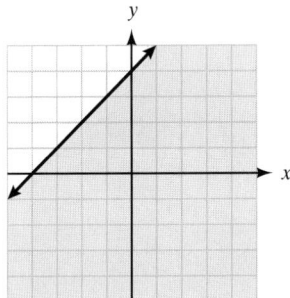

2. $y \leq x - 2$

3. $y > x - 3$

4. $y > x + 1$

5. $y \geq 2x$

6. $y \geq -3x$

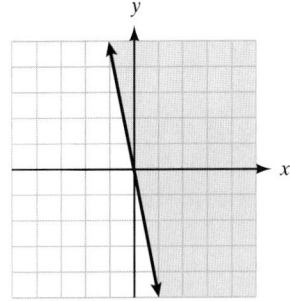

7. $x + y \geq 2$

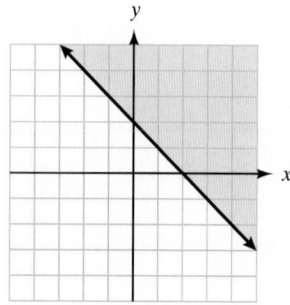

8. $x + y \geq 1$

9. $x - y < -1$

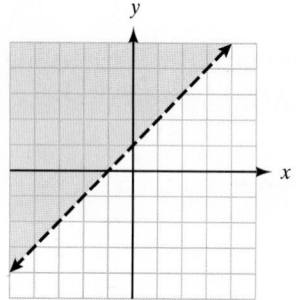

10. $x - y < -5$

11. $y \geq -3$

12. $y \geq 2$

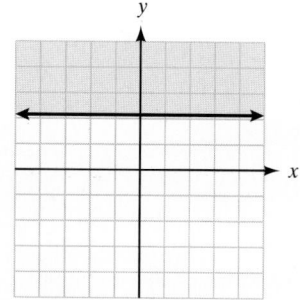

13. $2x + 5y \leq -10$

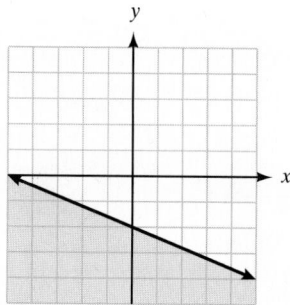

14. $3x + 4y \leq -12$

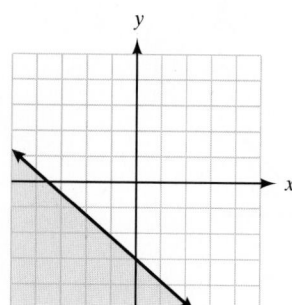

15. $3x - 2y \leq 5$

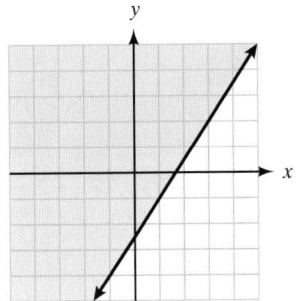

16. $5x - 2y \leq 8$

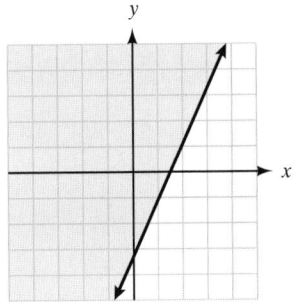

17. $4 - 3y > 2x$

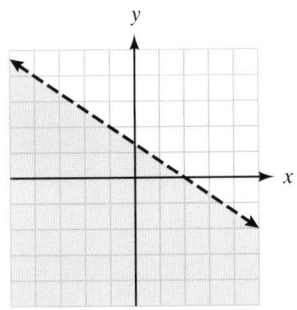

18. $6 - 2y > 4x$

19. $y < x - 1$

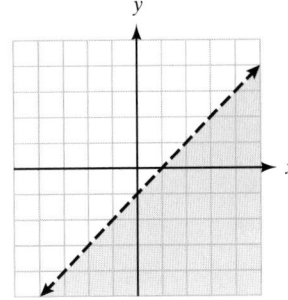

20. $y < 2x + 1$

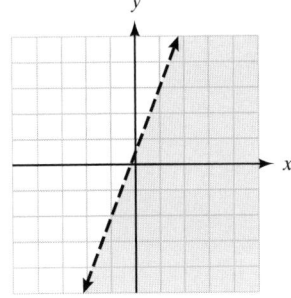

21. $x < 2y + 4$

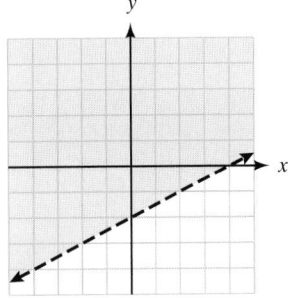

22. $x < 3y + 2$

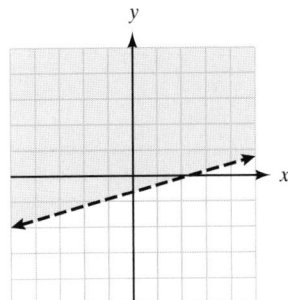

23. $5x + 4y > 20$

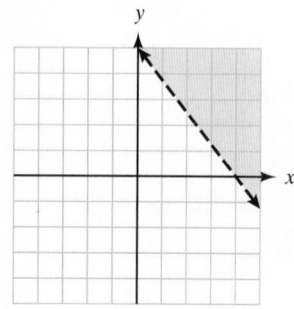

24. $5x - 2y < -10$

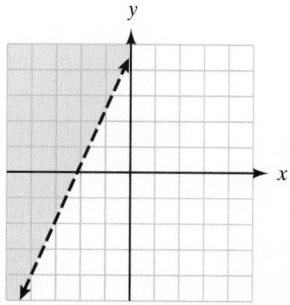

25. $x + 2 \leq -3$

26. $x < 3$

27. $y > x$

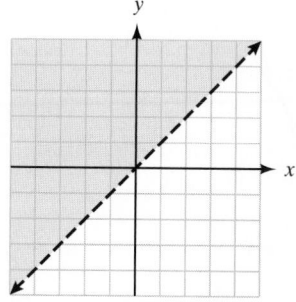

28. $-2x - 0.5y > -1$

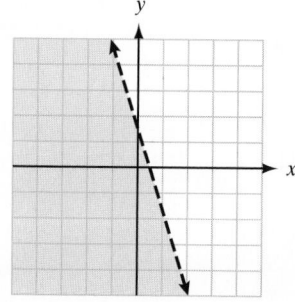

29. $x - 2y > 4$

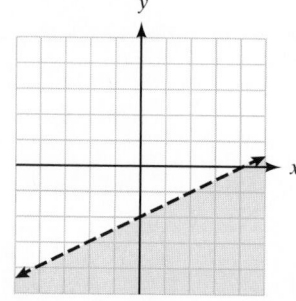

30. $3x + 4y < 1$

Chapter 2 Review

1–4.

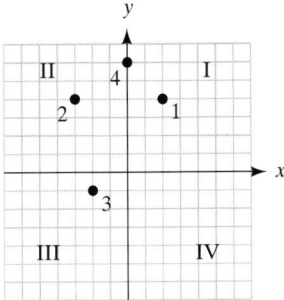

5. Yes

6. $(-2, -12)$

7. $(6, -40)$

8. $(0, 4)$

9. (any real number, 7)

10. $(0, -\frac{11}{3})$

11. $m = \frac{1}{3}$

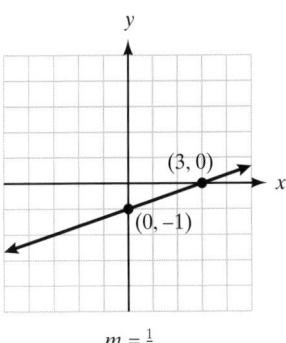

$$m = \frac{1}{3}$$

12. $m =$ undefined

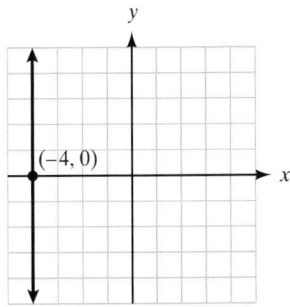

no y-intercept
$m =$ undefined

13. $m = -2$

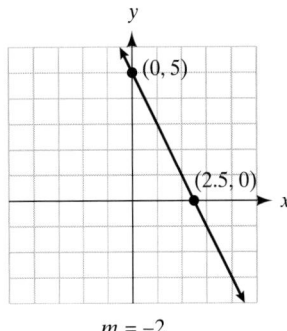

$$m = -2$$

14. $m = \frac{3}{2}$

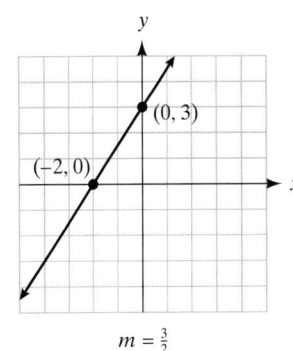

$$m = \frac{3}{2}$$

15. $m = \frac{1}{3}$

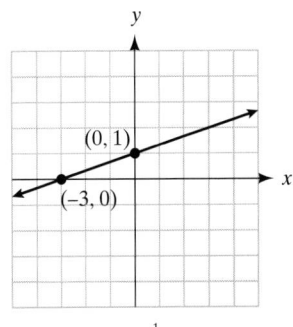

$$m = \frac{1}{3}$$

16. $m = 0$

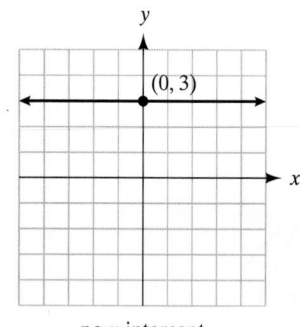

no x-intercept
$m = 0$

17. slope $= 3$

18. slope $= -2$

19. slope $=$ undefined

20. slope $= \frac{7}{2}$

21. $2x - y = 3$

22. $10x - y = -26$

23. $2x + y = 10$

24. $x + 2y = 8$

25. $3x - 4y = -16$

26. $y > -2x + 3$

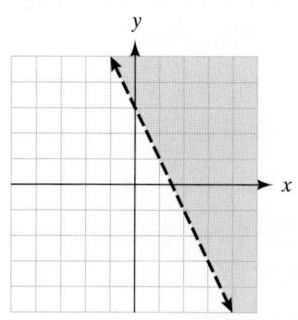

27. $2x - 2y \leq 6$

28. $-y < -x$

29. $x \leq 5$

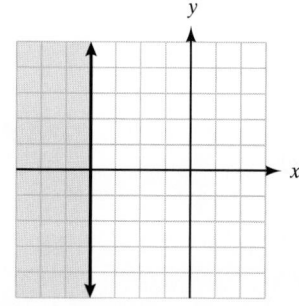

30. $4x + 3y \geq 6$

Chapter 2 Test

1–3.

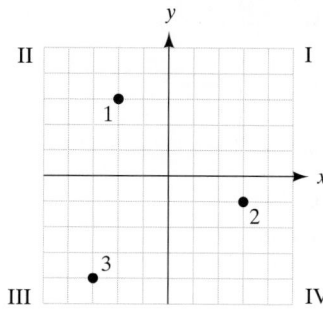

4. No

5. $m = 4$

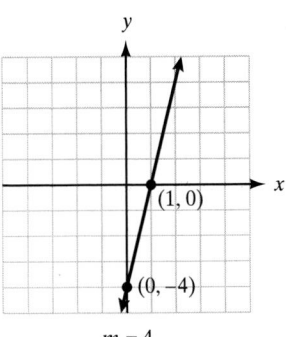

$m = 4$

6. $m = -2$

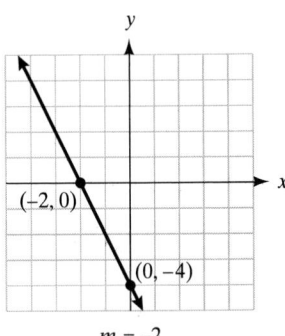

$m = -2$

7. $m = $ undefined

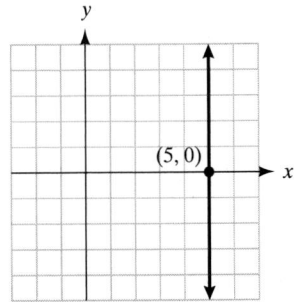

no y-intercept
$m = $ undefined

8. $m = -1$

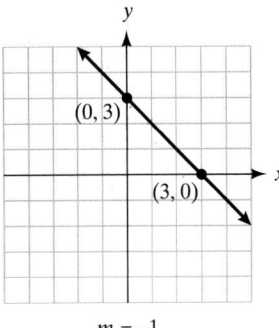

$m = -1$

9. $m = 0$

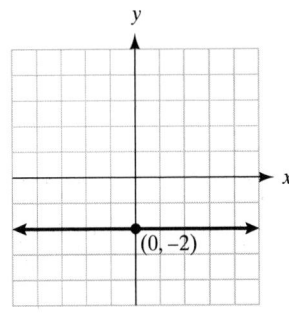

no x-intercept
$m = 0$

10. $m = \frac{1}{5}$

11. $m = \frac{1}{3}$

12. Slope is undefined

13. $m = 1$

14. $y = -3x + 3$ or $3x + y = 3$

15. $y = \frac{1}{2}x + 4$ or $x - 2y = -8$

16. $y = 6x - 4$ or $6x - y = 4$

17. $y = -\frac{1}{2}x + 4$ or $x + 2y = 8$

18. $x = 2$

19. $y < -2x - 3$

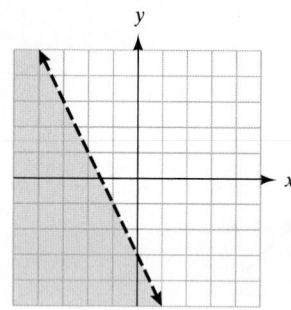

20. $2x - 3y \leq -6$

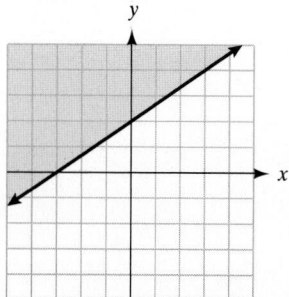

Chapter 3

Practice Set 3-1

1. A function is a relation or rule in which for each input value there is exactly one output value. The independent variable is the input and is the variable that we control. The dependent variable is the output, and its value is a result of the original choice of the value of the independent variable.

2. The domain is the set of all possible values for the independent variable, and the range is the set of all possible values for the dependent variable.

3. (a) 68°
   (b) The high temperature is a function of the date.

4. (a) $90
   (b) Fine is a function of the speed.

5. (a) The independent variable is the year, and the dependent variable is the world population.

(b) The domain includes the years 1975–2005, and the range is 4.3 billion–6.5 billion.

6. (a) The independent variable is the year, and the dependent variable is the value of the account.
   (b) The domain is 1995–2007, and the range is $1000–$1625.

7. Grades are a function of student ID.

8. Monthly premium is a function of a person's age.

9. As the weight of a bag increases, the price of the bag increases, so price is dependent on weight.

10. As demand for a product increases, the price of the product increases.

11. As the slope of a hill increases, the speed of the scooter going uphill decreases, so the speed is dependent on the steepness of the hill.

12. As the distance from earth increases, the strength of gravity decreases.

13. As a person's age increases, his target heart rate when exercising decreases, so the target heart rate when exercising is dependent on a person's age.

14. As time passes, the distance an object falls from the top of a building increases until it hits the ground.

15. 10:00 p.m.

16. 4:00 p.m.

17. January 2 and December 30

18. May 15, August 1

19. 10:15 p.m. is the latest; 2:50 p.m. is the earliest

20. 1:45 p.m.–10:15 p.m.

21.

22.

23.

24.

25.

26.

27. $D = 315$ ft; graph is not linear. The faster the speed, the longer the stopping distance.

28.

h	68	69	70	71	72	73
w	150	155	160	165	170	175

Graph is linear

29.

rate	5.5	5.75	6.0	6.25
payment	709.74	729.47	749.44	769.65

rate	6.5	6.75	7
Payment	790.09	810.75	831.63

30. Answers will vary.

Practice Set 3-2

1. $g(0) = -5$

2. $g(-4) = -17$

3. $g(10) = 25$

4. $g(-0.5) = -6.5$

5. $f(x) = 2x + 1; f(-2) = -3$

6. $f(x) = 2x - 4; f(-2) = -8$

7. $f(x) = 3x^2 - 1; f(-2) = 11$

8. $f(x) = 2x^2 - 1; f(-2) = 7$

9. $f(x) = \frac{5}{2}x - 4; f(-2) = -9$

10. $f(x) = \frac{2}{3}x - 3; f(-2) = -4\frac{1}{3}$

11. $f(2) = 576$; 2 sec after the ball is thrown, it is 576 ft above the ground.

12. 44.1 m

13. 173.41 cm

14. 166.485 cm

15. 50.63 cm

16. 40.85 cm

17. (a) 2^{30} = 1,073,741,824 (b) $10,737,418.24

18. $116,328 is value of house after 8 years.

19. (a) $960 (b) $M(n) = \$7.50n$ (c) domain = 0 – 200 people; range = $0–$1500

20. (a) $224.25 (b) $F(x) = 1.95x$ (c) independent variable = miles; dependent variable = earnings

21. $f(20) = 170$ and $f(60) = 136$; as a person gets older, his target heart rate decreases.

22. $P(10) = 165$; predicted population of town in 10 years is 165,000.

23. $f(3) = \$26,580$; a person with three teaching years of experience will make an annual salary of $26,580; the independent variable is the number of years of experience, and the dependent variable is the salary.

24. $f(6) = \$3480$; monthly salary of a teacher with a Master's degree; independent variable is years of experience; dependent variable = monthly salary

25. $f(4) = 0721$, which means that the sun rises at 7:21 a.m. on Jan 4; $g(10) = 1655$, which means that the sun sets on Jan 10 at 1655 hours or 4:55 p.m.; the independent variable is the date; the dependent variables are the sunrise and sunset times.

26. $f(02) = 4.1$; average monthly snowfall in February; independent variable is month, dependent variable is snowfall amount.

27. (a) 75 mi (b) approx. 130 mi from the graph (127.5 mi using the formula)

28. (a) $f(0) = 0$ (b) $f(-2) = 1$ (c) $f(4) = 2$ (d) $f(-4) = 2$

29. $f(100) = \$30$, which means that it cost $30 to rent this car and drive 100 miles; the domain is numbers ≥ 0, and the range is numbers $\geq \$25$.

30. $f(50,000) = \$6500$; car with 50,000 miles has a value of $6500; range = $0–$14,000

Practice Set 3-3

1. (a)

x	f(x)
1	$ 1.75
3	$ 5.25
5	$ 8.75
7	$12.25
9	$15.75

(b) initial value is 0; rate of change is $1.75
(c) $f(x) = \$1.75x$ where x = miles
(d) $f(8) = 14$, which means that an 8-mile taxi ride will cost $14.

2. (a)

x	0	15	30	45	60
f(x)	4.95	5.25	5.55	5.85	6.15

(b) initial value: $4.95; rate of change: $0.02/min
(c) $f(x) = 4.95 + 0.02x$
(d) $f(110) = \$7.15$; cost of 110 min of calls

3. (a) 5.5 million   (b) 2% per year
(c) 5.6 million

4. (a) $50   (b) $20/hr
(c) $C(0) = 50$; cost of house call

5. (a) $C(x) = \$525 + \$17.50x$ where x = number of guests
(b) $4025   (c) 150 people

6. (a) Business A charges $200 plus $1.75 per invitation; Business B charges $150 plus $2.00 per invitation
(b) Business A

7. (a) −$340/year
(b) $V(x) = 1800 - 340x$ where x = years
(c) $V(4) = 440$; after 4 years, the value is $440

8. (a) −$340/year
(b) $V(x) = 3650 - 340x$ where x = years
(c) $V(8) = \$930$; after 8 years, the value is $930

9. $f(x) = -\frac{1}{5}x$

10. $f(x) = \frac{3}{4}x - 1$

11. $f(x) = 5$

12. $f(x) = -\frac{1}{2}x - 5$

13. (a) rate of change = +20/year
(b) $f(x) = 450 + 20x$ where x = years

(c) $f(15) = 750$; in the year 2010, the predicted population is 750 people.

14. (a) $11 million
(b) $f(x) = 11x + 150$
(c) $f(10) = 260$; in 2009, deposits should be about $260 million.

15. (a) $80,000/year
(b) $f(x) = \$600,000 + \$80,000x$ where $x =$ number of years after 1998
(c) in 11.25 years or during the year 2010

16. (a) $4/unit
(b) $f(x) = \$8000 + \$4x$ where $x =$ units
(c) 500 units

17. (a) $579/year
(b) $f(x) = \$3536 + \$579x$ where $x =$ number of years after 2001
(c) tuition

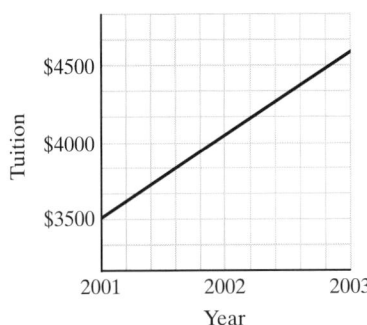

(d) $4822

18. (a) 3(thousand)/year
(b) $f(x) = 124 + 3x$
(c) income

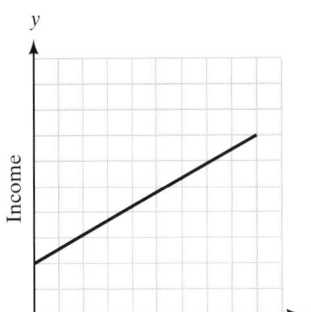

(d) $f(9) = 151$ or 151,000

19. (a) $f(x) = 100 + 5x$ where $x =$ inches > 60 in.
(b) $f(67) = 135$ lbs

20. (a) $f(x) = 3910 + 0.25(x - 28{,}400)$
(b) $5672.50

Practice Set 3-4

1. direct
2. direct
3. inverse
4. inverse
5. direct
6. inverse
7. $y = kz$
8. $p = \dfrac{k}{q}$
9. $a = kbc$
10. $m = kn^2$
11. $d = kef^3$
12. $f = \dfrac{kgh}{j^2}$
13. $m = \dfrac{k\sqrt{n}}{p^3}$
14. $v = \dfrac{k}{\sqrt{g}}$
15. $y = kx$ $k = \frac{1}{3}$ $y = 12$
16. $p = kq$ $k = 0.05$ $p = 5$
17. $y = \dfrac{k}{x}$ $k = 54$ $y = 1.5$
18. $r = \dfrac{k}{t}$ $k = 12$ $r = 1.5$
19. $y = k\sqrt{x}$ $k = 6$ $y = 36$
20. $y = \dfrac{k}{\sqrt{x}}$ $k = 60$ $y = 5$
21. $y = kxz^2$ $k = 2$ $y = 1536$
22. $y = kx\sqrt{z}$ $k = 4$ $y = 60$
23. $p = \dfrac{kq}{r^2}$ $k = 32$ $p = 12$
24. $y = \dfrac{kr}{xt}$ $k = 2$ $y = 4\frac{2}{3}$
25. 153.86 cm^2

26. 20 lb

27. 12 ft

28. 294 ft

29. 36 in.

30. $45.60

31. 4 in.

32. 2.5 ft^3

33. 142 lb

34. 2.8 hrs

35. 480 W

36. 172.8 kg

37. 0.72 in.

38. 8 tons

39. (a) direct variation (b) $\frac{4}{3}\pi$ (c) 972π in.^{3}

40. (a) direct (b) π (c) 28.3 in.^{2}

Practice Set 3-5

1. minimum = −4   roots = −1, −5

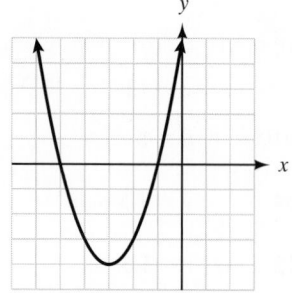

2. minimum = −4   roots = 1, 5

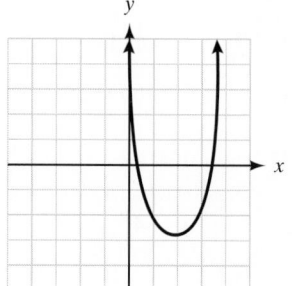

3. minimum = −2.3   roots = −1, −4

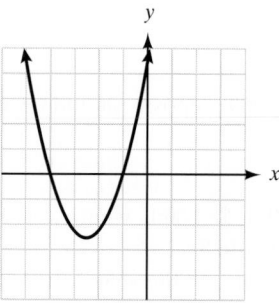

4. maximum = −4   roots = no real roots

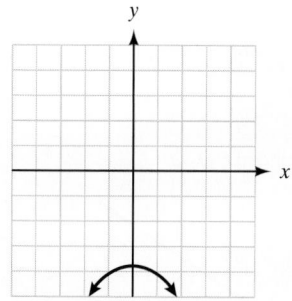

5. maximum = 5.3   roots = 1.7, −1

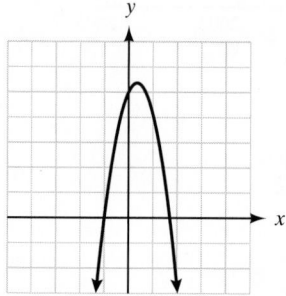

6. maximum = −2.875   roots = no real roots

7. $f(x) = 3x^2$

8. $f(x) = -4x^2$

9. $f(x) = \frac{1}{3}x^3$

10. $f(x) = 2x^4$

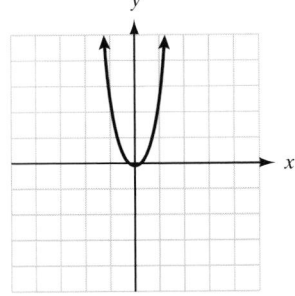

11. $f(x) = 2^x$ $f(2) = 4$

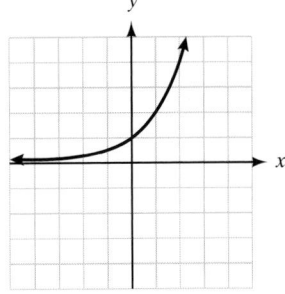

12. $f(x) = 3^x - 2$ $f(2) = 7$

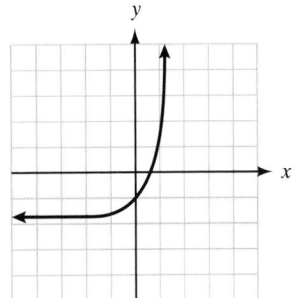

13. $f(x) = -3^x$ $f(2) = -9$

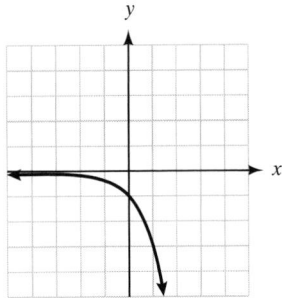

14. $f(x) = -\left(\frac{1}{4}\right)^x$ $f(2) = -\frac{1}{16}$

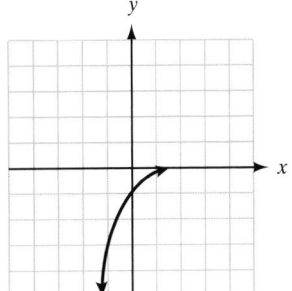

15. $f(x) = \left(\frac{1}{2}\right)^x$ $\qquad f(2) = \frac{1}{4}$

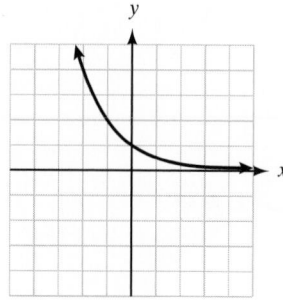

16. $f(x) = 2^x - 1$ $\qquad f(2) = 3$

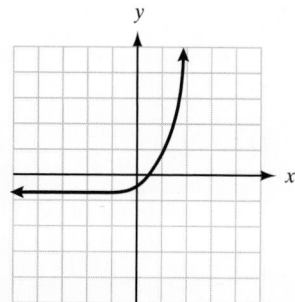

17. 0.2 sec, 4.6 feet

18. 174 ft

19. (a) 389 ft (b) 405 ft (c) 10.03 sec

20. (a) 426 ft (b) 431.6 ft (c) 6.6 sec

21. $p(1.5) = \$2070$

22. 55.3 ft

23. $f(10) = 15{,}767$ people

24. \$6744.25

Chapter 3 Review

1. You will pay \$0.72 tax on a \$12 purchase.

2. Answers will vary.

3. Both the domain and the range must be greater than or equal to 0.

4. As the age of a person increases, his height increases up to a certain age. Then it remains steady, with some shrinkage in later years.

5. As time passes, the number of bacteria in a culture increases.

6. The faster the speed of a car, the less time it takes to drive from home to school.

7. independent variable: number of minutes; dependent variable: cost

8. domain: 0–65 minutes; range: \$5.00–\$11.50

9. $f(20) = 40$ ft; $f(40) = 120$ ft; $f(60) = 240$ ft; $f(80) = 400$ ft; the graph is nonlinear with stopping distances increasing exponentially.

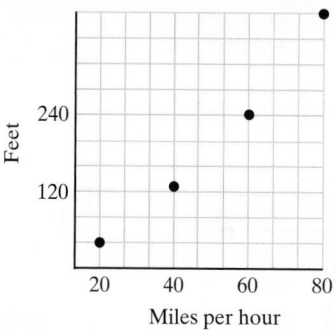

10. (a) -10 (b) -6 (c) 2 (d) -5

11. $f(x) = -3x + 2$

12. $f(x) = -\frac{2}{3}x - 2$

13. $f(x) = x - 8$

14. $f(x) = -\frac{3}{2}x + 3$

15. $f(x) = -4x + 1$

16. $7, 1, -1, 1, 7$

17. (a) -3 (b) 3 (c) 0

18. $C(120) = \$36.20$, the cost of renting a car and driving 120 miles

19. (a) $C(x) = 75 + 30x$ (b) \$435

20. (a) $f(x) = 1000 + 5.50x$ where x = number of books printed
 (b) domain is natural numbers
 (c) $f(375) = \$3062.50$

21. (a) $f(x) = 1400 + 0.15(x - 14{,}000)$ where x is taxable income
 (b) $f(32{,}355) = \$4153.25$

22. (a) $f(s) = \$1000 + 0.25s$ (b) \$1625

23. $f(x) = 2x - 3$

24. $f(x) = 0.5x + 4$

25. independent variable: time; dependent variable: growth of fingernails; direct variation

26. independent variable: time; dependent variable: depth of pool; inverse variation

27. $s = kt$

28. $z = \dfrac{k}{p}$

29. $m = krs$

30. $x = \dfrac{k\sqrt[3]{z}}{y^2}$

31. $u = kv^3$ $k = 8$ $u = 64$

32. $x = \dfrac{k}{y^2}$ $k = 18$ $x = 0.72$

33. $s = ktg$ $k = 1.33$ $s = 56$

34. $N = \dfrac{kL^2}{M^3}$ $k = 2.25$ $N = 4.5$

35. $d = kt^2$ $k = 16.1$ $d = 144.9$ ft

36. $f = \dfrac{k}{d^2}$ $k = 7200$ $f = 18$ units

37. (a) minimum $= -8$; roots $= -1, 3$

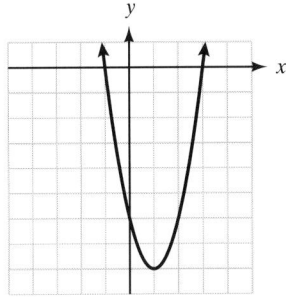

(b) maximum $= 9$; roots $= -4, 2$

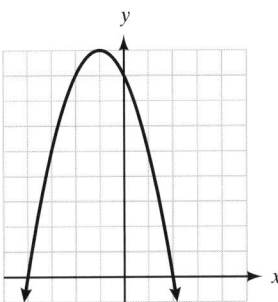

38. (a) $f(-3) = 40.5$

(b) $g(-3) = 54$

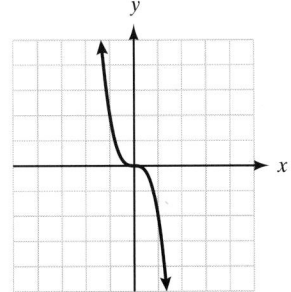

39. (a) $f(-2) = \frac{1}{9}$

(b) $g(-2) = 4$

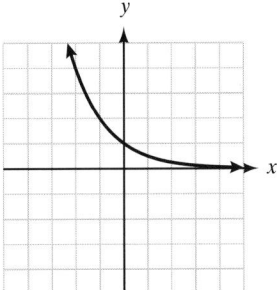

40. 116.8 million

Chapter 3 Test

1. A linear function has a constant rate of change.

2. $25,000 initial value; −$1500 in value per year

3. The cost of a house is a function of its square footage. The larger the amount of square footage, the more a house usually costs; independent variable: the square footage, dependent variable: cost

4. (a) independent variable is time; dependent variable is the number of widgets produced
   (b) initial value is 0; the function is not perfectly linear

5. $f(x) = 2x − 4$ $f(−4) = −12$

6. $f(x) = 5$ $f(−4) = 5$

7. $f(x) = −3x^2 − 2$ $f(−4) = −50$

8. $V(t) = \$22,500 − \$2200t$

9. $C(12) = \$10.50$; a cab ride of 12 mi is $10.50

10. (a) $f(x) = \$21 + \$28x$ where x is number of credit hours taken
    (b) domain: set of whole numbers 12–15; range: {$357, $385, $413, $441}
    (c) $f(14) = \$413$; cost of 14 credit hours

11. $f(x) = −3x + 2$

12. independent variable: time; dependent variable: height of candle; inverse variation

13. independent variable: time; dependent variable: diameter of tree; direct variation

14. $t = \dfrac{kB}{P^2}$ $k = 5$ $t = 35$

15. $y = kx^2z^3$ $k = 1.25$ $y = 2.5$

16. $1139.69

17. 158.4 grams

18. maximum = 9; roots = 3, −3

19. $f(4) = −16$

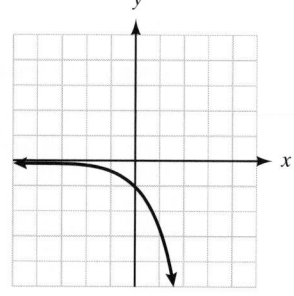

20. $11,484.09

Chapter 4

Practice Set 4-1

1. (a) $1.92   (b) $11.68   (c) $19.21

2. sales tax = $87; total bill = $1537

3. state = $1600.94, county = $512.30

4. $100.75

5. $25,120 in merchandise; $2009.60 in taxes

6. $8235 in merchandise; $164.70 in taxes

7. $199.95

8. $65

9. $330 per year

10. $462.50

11. $1207.14

12. $3000

13. 12%

14. 28%

15. loss of $53,000

16. loss of $8500

17. profit of $6500

18. 178,333.33 pens

19. loss of $8000

20. profit of $449,500

21. profit of $602,000

22. 2623 games

23. profit of $340

24. profit of $1077.50

25. (a) $C(x) = 0.01x + 3500$
(b) $3705   (c) loss of $1245

26. (a) $C(x) = 0.05x + 150$
(b) $375   (c) profit of $1875

27. $54.25

28. $1925

29. 80% markup

30. 200% markup

Practice Set 4-2

1. $1488.65

2. $1606.18

3. $3520

4. $35,857.15

5. $2297

6. No; $14,666.67 worth of equipment

7. $3125

8. $285

9. $9.75

10. $3.38

11. $5400

12. $3000

13. 8.5%

14. 4.5%

15. (a) $3199.65 (b) $3284.65

16. $19,632.50

17. He will owe $49 less using the 4.5% rate.

18. Owes more as married filing separately

19. $27,000 gross salary; $1045 tax

20. gross income: $59,280; taxes owed: $2661.42

21. (a) Pay = 800 + 0.095(sales)
(b) 0.095
(c) makes $9.50 for every $100 of sales
(d) yes
(e) commission because it is dependent on sales
(f) $18,157.89

22. (a) 3% of $55,000 in sales plus 2% of $20,000 plus 1% of the remaining balance
(b) yes   (c) $1440   (d) $2580

23. total expenses = $1450; $1855 − $1450 = $405; 7%(1855) = $129.85, so he can save 7%

24. No, expenses are more than the take-home pay.

25. $296.70

26. $330.90

27. Answers will vary.

28. Answers will vary.

Practice Set 4-3

1. $I = $45; M = 545

2. $I = $22.50; M = 522.50

3. $I = $216; M = 1416

4. $I = $1771; M = 4571

5. 12%

6. 8.5%

7. $11.25

8. $108

9. $212

10. $176.67

11. $162.50

12. $244.27

13. (a) $420   (b) $2020   (c) 14%

14. (a) $22.40   (b) $287.80

15. interest = $85; rate = 10.2%

16. $r = 14\%$

17. $2148.85

18. $24,824.11

19. $33,671.38

20. $4025.93

21. (a) $M = \$1210.40$; $I = \$310.40$
    (b) $M = \$1213.36$; $I = \$313.36$

22. (a) $M = \$1152.92$ (b) $I = \$152.92$

23. Yes, the account will contain $6744.25.

24. $M = \$23,457.76$

25. $53.79 more if compounded monthly

26. The savings account will return $202.24 more than the CD.

27. $31,308.07

28. $5741.74

29. $170,006.39

30. $1.78

Practice Set 4-4

1. $5.26

2. $22.15

3. $10.82

4. $9.46

5. June: $5.25 finance charge; $342.10 unpaid balance
   July: $342.10 beg. of month; $5.13 finance charge; $297.63 unpaid balance
   August: $297.63 beg. of month; $4.46 finance charge; $416.24 unpaid balance

6. January: $46.07 finance charge; $2642.17 unpaid balance
   February: $2642.17 beg. of month; $39.63 finance charge; $2470.65 unpaid balance
   March: $2470.65 beg. of month; $37.06 finance charge; $2195.48 unpaid balance

7. October: $0.90 finance charge; $371.51 unpaid balance
   November: $371.51 beg. of month; $5.57 finance charge; $581.74 unpaid balance
   December: $581.74 beg. of month; $8.73 finance charge; $926.89 unpaid balance

8. April: $4.69 finance charge; $226.72 unpaid balance
   May: $226.72 beg. of month; $3.40 finance charge; $316.77 unpaid balance
   June: $316.77 beg. of month; $4.75 finance charge; $321.96 unpaid balance

9. June: $19.43 finance charge; $1259.43 unpaid balance
   July: $1259.43 beg. of month; $18.89 finance charge, $2407.17 unpaid balance
   August: $2407.17 beg. of month; $36.11 finance charge; $2349.35 unpaid balance

10. March: $0 finance charge; $695 unpaid balance
    April: $695 beg. of month; $10.43 finance charge; $1669.28 unpaid balance
    May: $1669.28 beg. of month; $25.04 finance charge; $6602.14 unpaid balance

11. average daily balance: $177.28; finance charge: $2.66

12. average daily balance: $224.82; finance charge: $3.37

13. average daily balance: $356.74; finance charge: $5.35

14. average daily balance: $531.49; finance charge: $7.97

15. average daily balance: $694.49; finance charge: $10.42

16. average daily balance: $729.24; finance charge: $10.94

17. 12.5% APR

18. 8.5% APR

19. 11% APR

20. 9% APR

21. 9% APR

22. 10.5% APR

23. finance charge: $113.68; 8.5% APR

24. finance charge: $579.20; 9% APR

25. total interest: $323.60

26. $203.80

27. $257.76

28. $112.94

29. $132.55

30. $134.35

Practice Set 4-5

1. Answers will vary.

2. Calculate the interest owed, add it to the balance due, and divide by the number of months the car is financed.

3. Lower monthly payments, repairs under warranty (answers will vary)

4. Limited mileage, never actually own a car (answers will vary)

5. Customize the car, sell the car at any time (answers will vary)

6. May have high payments, large depreciation in the value of the car first few years (answers will vary)

7. $48,394.50

8. $17,561.91

9. $31,227.60

10. $24,147.90

11. $60,887.28

12. $36,416.10

13. interest = $5493.18; monthly payment = $722.95

14. interest = $2315.38; monthly payment = $383.22

15. interest = $2362.05; monthly payment = $503.03

16. interest = $6926.20; monthly payment = $692.62

17. interest = $5721.32; monthly payment = $766.50

18. interest = $9896.72; monthly payment = $812.60

19. Total paid: $11,430.00; finance charge: $2430

20. Total paid: $5098.32; finance charge: $1098.20

21. Total paid: $19,608.56; finance charge: $3158.56

22. Total paid: $8886.48; finance charge: $2088.48

23. 9%

24. 9.2%

25. 4.8%

26. 7.7%

27. finance charge = $579.20; APR = 8%

28. $257.76

29. $262.56

30. $479.72

31. $21,803.79

32. $1260

33. amount to finance = $22,500; payments = $523.13; total cost = $27,610

34. $31,076.55

35. $936

36. amount to finance = $28,000; payments = $409.89: total cost = $36,512

Practice Set 4-6

1. Interest rate, type of loan, fees, points (answers may vary)

2. Amount of down payment, interest rate

3. Subtract your monthly bills and multiply by 36%.

4. Use the monthly payment formula and the amortization table.

5. Use the maximum amount of loan formula and the amortization table.

6. down payment = $7435; amount financed = $141,265

7. down payment = $15,325; amount financed = $137,925

8. down payment = $39,000; amount financed = $156,000

9. down payment = $44,975; amount financed = $134,925

10. down payment = $41,017.50; amount financed = $232,432.50

11. down payment = $94,650; amount financed = $220,850

12. $347.40

13. $306.05

14. $788.40

15. $594.00

16. $417.60

17. $1098.00

18. $890.33

19. $1337.19

20. $3476.30

21. $680.37

22. $939.44

23. $804.42

24. $2077.46

25. $573.75

26. $1168.91

27. $1006.88

28. $1050

29. $1674.80

30. $173,927.04

31. $118,670.89

32. $112,679.43

33. $261,669.02

34. $151,162.79

35. $82,574.77

36. down payment = $18,000; monthly payment = $475.20

37. monthly payment = $1094.20

38. (a) down payment = $20,800; monthly payment = $614.85
(b) $205,255

39. (a) down payment = $17,775; monthly payment = $620.18
(b) $241,039.80

40. Answers will vary.

41. Answers will vary.

Practice Set 4-7

1. Insurance is an economical way of helping an individual deal with a severe financial loss by pooling the risk over a large number of people.

2. The payment made to purchase insurance coverage is called the premium.

3. The amount of insurance specified by the policy is called the face value of the policy.

4. The insurance company is the insurer.

5. The payment that the insurance company makes to reimburse the policyholder is called an indemnity.

6. It pays for bodily injury, property damage, and some additional expenses of the other drivers, their passengers, and your passengers when you or a driver covered by your policy causes an accident.

7. 20/40/15

8. Comprehensive insurance covers damage to the car resulting from fire, theft, vandalism, acts of nature, falling objects, and so on.

9. Collision insurance pays for repairs to the vehicle of the insured when the policyholder is responsible for an accident.

10. $185.90

11. $300

12. $500.95

13. $204.60

14. $243.60

15. $631.80

16. $129

17. $211.40

18. $406

19. $175

20. $321.90

21. $264.60

22. $251.90

23. $581.40

24. (a) $105,000 (b) $15,000

25. (a) $8000 (b) $0

Practice Set 4-8

1. (a) $85,725   (b) $1714.50
2. (a) $15,255   (b) $381.38
3. (a) $1366.50   (b) $25.50
4. (a) $3123   (b) $64.03
5. (a) $41,580   (b) $873.18
6. (a) $17,801   (b) $445.03
7. (a) $989.60   (b) $29.74
8. (a) $7118.75   (b) $202.14
9. (a) $200   (b) 178,606,000 shares
   (c) $29.90   (d) $30.27   (e) 1.22%
10. (a) $1680   (b) 120,468,000 shares
    (c) $36.70   (d) $36.90   (e) 0.5%
11. (a) $16   (b) 68,540,000 shares
    (c) $22.72   (d) $22.68   (e) 0.18%
12. (a) $375   (b) 110,227,000 shares
    (c) $24.20   (d) $24.08   (e) 0.5%
13. 250 shares
14. 400 shares
15. 350 shares
16. 500 shares
17. Bonds are issued by companies or governments who are trying to raise money for projects. Bonds are generally safer investments than stocks. If a company goes bankrupt, the bondholders are paid before the stockholders receive any money (answers may vary).
18. A mutual fund is a group of stocks managed by a professional who invests your money into a portfolio of various investments. It may be safer since your portfolio is not as easily affected by large changes in value of a single stock because there are many investments included in a mutual fund.
19. Invest more of your money in stocks and mutual funds because over long periods of time, these investments usually grow at a better rate than bonds or savings accounts.
20. As an older investor closer to retirement, you should invest the majority of your money in safer investments such as bonds or savings accounts.

Chapter 4 Review Problems

1. state tax: $564.66; county tax: $313.70
2. $3950
3. $2.23
4. 20%
5. $2350
6. $10,000
7. $1425
8. Both plans would yield the same amount.
9. 6.5%
10. $712
11. Tax = $1275 + 0.07(x − $21,250)
12. $1362.50
13. $357.90
14. 6.5%
15. maturity value: $18,900; payment: $787.50
16. $360
17. $8976.49
18. $708.40
19. $49,530.32
20. $56.71
21. avg daily bal.: $1355.33; interest: $20.33
22. $57.97
23. $28,347.90
24. interest: $1254.83; payment: $485.66
25. Total paid = $7084.80; interest: $584.80; interest rate: 3%
26. $20,232.91
27. $322.20
28. $491.67
29. $1615.57
30. $714.23
31. $843.48
32. $235.20

33. $331.80

34. $20,000

35. $5491.99

36. (a) $12,276   (b) $306.90

37. 2500 shares

Chapter 4 Test

1. $857.50

2. $27.90

3. $1550

4. $16,435

5. $353

6. $9945

7. $4891.61

8. 5%

9. $10,432.26

10. $65.63

11. average daily balance: $189.50; interest: $2.84

12. $58.70

13. monthly payment: $847.37; interest owed: $3125.79

14. $32,200

15. $550.81

16. $1597.50

17. $306

18. $0

19. $16,152.48

20. (a) $2225   (b) $40.88

Chapter 5

Practice Set 5-1

1. $(3, -2)$

2. $(2, 4)$

3. $(-3, -1)$

4. $(3, 0)$

5. $(\frac{1}{2}, 1)$

6. $(\frac{3}{2}, \frac{2}{3})$

7. $(1, 2)$

8. $(-1, 1)$

9. $(2, 0)$

10. No solution (parallel lines)

11. $(4, 1)$

12. $(4, 5)$

13. $(0, 1)$

14. $(4, 4)$

15. Infinite solutions or $\{(x, y)/1x + 6y = 27\}$

16. $(5, 4)$

17. No solution (parallel lines)

18. $(2, 3)$

19. $(-2, -4)$

20. Infinite solutions or $\{(x, y)/6x - 4y = 10\}$

21. $(-3, -1)$

22. $(8, 5)$

23. Infinite solutions or $\{(x, y)/x + y = 4\}$

24. No solution (parallel lines)

25. No solution

26. $(4, 5)$

27. $(2, 0)$

28. No solution (parallel lines)

29. $(2, -1)$

30. $(3, -2)$

31. Infinite solutions or $\{(x, y)/2x - 3y = 1\}$

32. Infinite solutions or $\{(x, y)/1x + 1y = -2\}$

Practice Set 5-2

1. $(12, 6)$

2. $(0, 0)$

3. $(2.5, -0.5)$

4. $(-2, 3)$

5. $(5, 11)$

6. Infinite solutions or $\{(x, y)/x - 2y = 5\}$

7. $(2, -1)$

8. $(-1, 1)$

9. $(5, 1)$

10. $(1, 1)$

11. $(5.5, 2.5)$

12. No solution (parallel lines)

13. Infinite solutions or $\{(x, y)/3x - 2y = 6\}$

14. $\left(\frac{26}{9}, -\frac{5}{9}\right)$

15. $(3, 4)$

16. No solution (parallel lines)

17. $(2, 3)$

18. $(8, 4)$

19. $(4, 3)$

20. $(2, -2.5)$

21. $(13, 5)$

22. $(2, 0)$

23. Infinite solutions or $\{(x, y)/7x + y = 3\}$

24. $(-1, 2)$

25. $(-5, 9)$

26. $(-6, -6)$

27. No

28. No

29. $(11, 9)$

30. $(41, 22)$

31. $(12, 18)$

32. $(9, -9)$

33. $(16, 48)$

34. $(13, 11)$

35. $\left(26\frac{2}{7}, 19\frac{5}{7}\right)$

36. $(10, 5)$

Practice Set 5-3

1. 1

2. -2

3. 0

4. -16

5. 22

6. 1

7. $(5, 1)$

8. $(-1, 5)$

9. $(7, 3)$

10. $\left(-\frac{2}{3}, \frac{5}{6}\right)$

11. $(0, -4)$

12. No solution (parallel lines)

13. $(-2, 6)$

14. $(5, -1)$

15. Infinite number of solutions or $\{(x, y)/3x - 2y = 13\}$

16. $\left(-\frac{1}{4}, \frac{1}{2}\right)$

17. $(-2, -6)$

18. No solution (parallel lines)

19. $(3.5, -1)$

20. $(-1, -24)$

21. $(4, -1)$

22. $\left(\frac{6}{7}, \frac{11}{7}\right)$

23. $(-6, -8)$

24. $(-3, 1)$

25. No solution (parallel lines)

26. $\left(-\frac{23}{3}, -\frac{40}{9}\right)$

27. $\left(\frac{4}{5}, -\frac{1}{5}\right)$

28. $\left(\frac{1}{3}, \frac{1}{3}\right)$

29. No solution (parallel lines)

30. $(2, 1)$

Practice Set 5-4

1. 14 ml of 10%; 16 ml of 25%
2. 13 qt of 10%; 16 qt of 20%
3. 12 units @$650; 8 units @$825
4. 600 people
5. Equilibrium price is $5
6. $11
7. 32.5 years; Model A
8. tights = $12.50; leotards = $45
9. 12 g of 60%; 8 g of 40%
10. 12 L of 17%; 14 L of 30%
11. 160 miles; John's Rent A Car
12. lettuce = $0.69/head; tomatoes = $0.99/lb
13. $2000; $200 plus 5% commission
14. $66.67
15. pizza: $15; soda: $4
16. $L = 5$ ft, $W = 2$ ft
17. 10 cm by 90 cm
18. 5 lb of each
19. Coca-Cola: $41.40; Pepsi: $43.50
20. 1500 backpacks
21. 275 widgets
22. 37 ft wide; 111 ft long
23. 12 in. by 18 in.
24. 53 double; 27 single
25. notebook paper: $0.80 each; pens: $0.20 each
26. 20 ml of 10%; 30 ml of 60%
27. 20 oz of 16%; 12 oz of pure water
28. 10 m wide, 17 m long
29. 4 yd by 10 yd
30. 2 sides are 17 in.; base is 14 in.

Practice Set 5-5

1. $\{(2, 4), (-5, 25)\}$
2. No solution
3. $\{(-1, -1), (0.5, 0.5)\}$
4. $\{(1, 3), (-1, 3)\}$
5. $\{(6, 12), (1, 2)\}$
6. $\{(-1, -1), (3, 7)\}$
7. $\{(3, 5), (-1, -3)\}$
8. $\{(-2, 5), (1, 2)\}$
9. $\{(1, 0), (\frac{1}{3}, -\frac{2}{3})\}$
10. $\{(5, -\frac{6}{5})\}$
11. $\{(3, 2), (3, -2), (-3, 2), (-3, -2)\}$
12. $\{(\frac{11}{5}, \frac{2}{5}), (-1, 2)\}$
13. The numbers are 3 and 4.
14. The numbers are 8 and 11.
15. 3 and -7, or 7 and -3
16. The numbers are 5 and 7.
17. 13 ft by 11 ft
18. 40 in. long; 25 in. wide
19. 12 and 5
20. The numbers are 2 and 2.
21. 15,000 pairs of sunglasses @ $37.50
22. The time is about 7.56 years, or near the end of July 1987

Chapter 5 Review Problems

1. Yes
2. Yes
3. No
4. Yes
5. (7, 1)
6. No solution
7. (3, 2)

8. $(1, 3)$

9. $(0, 2)$

10. $(2, -1)$

11. $(3, -1.6)$

12. $(1, -3)$

13. $(3, 12)$

14. Infinite number of solutions or $\{(x, y)/6x + 3y = 0\}$

15. $(\frac{1}{3}, -\frac{1}{2})$

16. No solution

17. $(6, 4)$

18. $(-4, 1)$

19. $(5, 6)$

20. $(-1, 3)$

21. No solution

22. $(1, -6)$

23. $(1, 5)$

24. $(0, 8)$

25. $\{(-3, -9), (1, -1)\}$

26. $\{(2.5, 13.5), (-1, 3)\}$

27. 34 boxes of donuts; 28 stadium cushions

28. 80 ml of 40% acid; 40 ml of 70% acid

29. 200 clocks

30. $45

31. 5 nickels; 55 dimes

32. potatoes: $0.34/lb; bananas: $0.69/lb

33. 1200 packages

34. Premium = $1.54/gal.

35. Answers will vary.

Chapter 5 Test

1. Yes

2. 7

3. $(4, 1)$

4. $(2, -1)$

5. No solution

6. No solution

7. $(2, -1)$

8. $(3, 1)$

9. $(\frac{1}{2}, 1\frac{1}{2})$

10. $(2, -1)$

11. $(3, 1)$

12. $\{(-\frac{1}{2}, \frac{1}{2}), (2, 8)\}$

13. $(0, 2), (-3.5, 3.75)$

14. 500 calculators

15. 60 double rooms

16. 3.75 gal of 7%; 6.25 gal of 3%

17. $4000 @ 10.5%: $8000 @ 12%

18. length = 27; width = 11

19. $6

20. 4250 leotards

Chapter 6

Practice Set 6-1

1. Empirical probability is the relative frequency of the occurrence of an event. It is determined by actual observations of an experiment.

2. An experiment is something that you do in order to gain information (data); outcomes are all the possible results of a given experiment; and events are the individual possible outcomes that occur when the experiment is done.

3. The law of large numbers states that the more times an experiment is performed, the more accurately we can predict the probability.

4. No. It means that is the die is rolled a large number of times, not just six times; the number 5 will turn up about one time in six.

5. No. It means that the average person with traits similar to those of Mr. Timmons will live another 23.25 years.

6. You would roll the die a large number of times and find out how many times a 3 turns up compared with the total number of times the die is rolled.

7. Roll a die many times and find the relative frequency of odd numbers to the total number of rolls; $\frac{1}{2}$; answers may vary.

8. $\frac{155}{60,000} = 0.26\%$

9. $\frac{2350}{4000} = 58.75\%$ $\frac{1650}{4000} = 41.25\%$

10. cardinal: $\frac{5}{30}$; robin: $\frac{2}{3}$

11. (a) $\frac{64,528}{81,800} = 79\%$ (b) $\frac{71,862}{81,800} = 88\%$

12. $\frac{5}{70} = 7.1\%$

13. $\frac{12}{70} = 17.14\%$

14. $\frac{41}{672} = 6.1\%$

15. $\frac{265}{672} = 39.43\%$

16. $\frac{8}{72} = 11.1\%$

17. $\frac{35}{72} = 48.61\%$

18. $\frac{13}{26} = 50\%$

19. $\frac{13}{26} = \frac{1}{2} = 50\%$

20. $\frac{1}{2}$

21. $\frac{1}{2}$

22. (a) $\frac{55}{91} = 60.4\%$ (b) $\frac{62}{91} = 68.1\%$

    (c) $\frac{35}{91} = 38.5\%$ (d) $\frac{27}{62} = 43.5\%$

23. (a) $\frac{95}{145} = 0.66 = 66\%$ (b) $\frac{50}{65} = 0.769 = 77\%$

    (c) $\frac{35}{80} = 0.44 = 44\%$ (d) $\frac{15}{65} = 0.526 = 52.6\%$

24. (a) $\frac{215}{300} = 71.7\%$ (b) $\frac{130}{180} = 72.2\%$

    (c) $\frac{35}{120} = 29.2\%$

25. (a) $\frac{120}{230} = 0.522 = 52\%$ (b) $\frac{50}{95} = 0.526 = 53\%$

    (c) $\frac{60}{135} = 0.44 = 44\%$ (d) $\frac{75}{95} = 0.789 = 79\%$

Practice Set 6-2

1. Outcomes that have the same chance of occurring in an experiment

2. Empirical probabilities are based on actual experimental results, whereas theoretical probabilities are not.

3. No. A theoretical probability of 1 means that the event is certain to occur.

4. It is a list of all possible outcomes to a given experiment.

5. (11 letters, 4 s's; $P(s)) = \frac{4}{11}$

6. $P(p) = \frac{2}{11}$

7. No a's; $P(a) = 0$

8. $P(m \text{ or } i) = \frac{5}{11}$

9. $\frac{10}{20} = \frac{1}{2}$

10. $\frac{4}{20} = \frac{1}{5}$

11. $\frac{1}{20}$

12. (a) 2%   (b) about 8

13. $1 - 0.375 = 0.625$ or $\frac{625}{1000} = \frac{5}{8}$

14. $\frac{4}{52} = \frac{1}{13}$

15. $\frac{12}{13}$

16. $\frac{13}{52} = \frac{1}{4}$

17. $\frac{1}{2}$

18. 0

19. $\frac{6}{52} = \frac{3}{26}$

20. $\frac{12}{52} = \frac{3}{13}$

21. $\frac{3}{13}$

22. $\frac{3}{12} = \frac{1}{4}$

23. $\frac{7}{12}$

24. $\frac{7}{12}$

25. $\frac{1}{2}$

26. $\frac{2}{6} = \frac{1}{3}$

27. 0

28. $13\% = \frac{13}{100}$

29. $16\% = \frac{4}{25}$

30. 0

31. $\frac{1}{6}$

32. $\frac{1}{2}$

33. $\frac{1}{3}$

34. $\frac{1}{6}$

35. $\frac{2}{3}$

36. 0

37. $\frac{1}{13}$

38. $\frac{2}{52} = \frac{1}{26}$

39. $\frac{2}{52} = \frac{1}{26}$

40. $\frac{1}{10}$

41. $\frac{1}{2}$

42. $\frac{8}{10}$

43. $\frac{1}{6}$

44. $\frac{1}{4}$

45. $\frac{35}{90} = 0.3888 = 38.9\%$

46. $\frac{10}{90} = 0.111 = 11.1\%$

47. $\frac{55}{90} = 0.611 = 61.1\%$

48. $\frac{45}{90} = \frac{1}{2}$

49. $\frac{24}{100} = 0.24 = 24\%$

50. $\frac{64}{100} = 0.64 = 64\%$

51. $\frac{84}{100} = 0.84 = 84\%$

52. 0

Practice Set 6-3

1. 17:3

2. 2:5

3. 3:17

4. (a) $\frac{1}{6}$ (b) 1:5   (c) $\frac{5}{6}$ (d) 5:1

5. 1:1

6. 2:3

7. 1:2

8. (a) $\frac{1}{4}$ (b) 1:3

9. 1:12

10. 1:3

11. 10:3

12. 12:1

13. (a) 19:13   (b) 13:19

14. 5:3

15. 3:7

16. 999,999:1

17. 999,990:10 = 99,999:1

18. $\frac{1}{6}$

19. $\frac{5}{14}$

20. $\frac{2}{11}$

21. $\frac{9}{11}$

22. $\frac{9}{14}$

23. $\frac{5}{14}$

24. $\frac{7}{12}$

25. $\frac{5}{12}$

26. $\frac{1}{7}$

27. $\frac{6}{7}$

28. $\frac{2}{7}$

29. $\frac{5}{7}$

Practice Set 6-4

1. 4000

2. 2016

3. 125

4. 60

5. 20

6. 25

7. 8

8. HHH, HHT, HTH, HTT, THH, THT, TTH, TTT

9. $\frac{3}{8}$

10. $\frac{1}{2}$

11. 12

12.

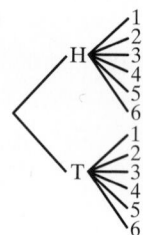

13. $\frac{1}{12}$

14. $\frac{1}{4}$

15. (a) 36   (b) $\frac{1}{6}$ (c) 0   (d) $\frac{1}{36}$

16. 24

17. HH1, HH2, HH3, HH4, HH5, HH6, HT1, HT2, HT3, HT4, HT5, HT6, TH1, TH2, TH3, TH4, TH5, TH6, TT1, TT2, TT3, TT4, TT5, TT6

18. $\frac{1}{24}$

19. $\frac{1}{12}$

20. $\frac{1}{8}$

21.

AA, AQ, AJ, QA, QQ, QJ, JA, JQ, JJ

22. $\frac{1}{9}$

23. $\frac{1}{9}$

24. $\frac{5}{9}$

25.

bb, bg, gb, gg

26. $\frac{1}{4}$

27. $\frac{3}{4}$

28. $\frac{1}{4}$

29. 1,757,600

30. $\frac{1}{1,757,600}$

31. 6

32. $\frac{1}{6}$ (oak)

Practice Set 6-5

1. $\frac{8}{52} = \frac{2}{13}$ Yes; it is impossible to pick one card and get a king and a queen at the same time.

2. $\frac{16}{52} = \frac{4}{13}$ No, because one ace is also a club.

3. $\frac{26}{52} = \frac{1}{2}$ No; it is possible to pick one card and get a black spade because all spades are black!

4. 1   Yes, because you can't draw one card that is both red and black.

5. $\frac{32}{52} = \frac{8}{13}$ No; it is possible to pick one card and get a black face card (jack of spades and clubs, queen of spades and clubs, king of spades and clubs).

6. $\frac{8}{52} = \frac{2}{13}$ Yes, because you can't draw one card and have it be a 2 and a 5.

7. $\frac{7}{8}$

8. $\frac{3}{4}$

9. $\frac{5}{6}$

10. $\frac{1}{2}$

11. $\frac{11}{221}$

12. $\frac{9}{169}$

13. $\frac{5}{46}$

14. $\frac{35}{3036}$

15. $\frac{85}{253} = 0.336$

16. $\frac{35}{1012} = 0.0346$

17. $\frac{108}{3125} = 0.03456$

18. $\frac{32}{3125} = 0.01024$

19. $\frac{243}{3125} = 0.07776$

20. (a) $\frac{21}{99} = 0.212$ (b) $\frac{14}{165} = 0.0848$

21. (a) $\frac{343}{1331} = 0.258$ (b) $\frac{112}{1331} = 0.084$

22. $\frac{1}{8}$

23. $\frac{1}{8}$

24. $\frac{1}{8}$

25. $\frac{1}{8}$

Practice Set 6-6

1. 21

2. 3003

3. 42

4. 51,891,840

5. 362,880

6. $6.042373705 \times 10^{15}$

7. Only positive whole numbers have a factorial value; thus, no value here.

8. Only positive whole numbers have a factorial value; thus, no value here.

9. In a combination, order is unimportant so that 1, 2 and 2, 1 are the same combination of the numbers 1 and 2. In a permutation, order is important so that 1, 2 and 2, 1 are different permutations (orderings) of the numbers 1 and 2.

10. $_5C_4 = 120$

11. If Jane must be on the committee, then the other three members will be chosen from the nine remaining students, and order doesn't matter here. $_9C_3 = 84$

12. 2,598,960

13. $9! = 362,880$ or $_9P_9 = 362,880$

14. 5,040

15. A person may choose no toppings, or 1 or 2 or . . . no toppings + 1 topping + 2 toppings + 3 toppings + 4 toppings + 5 toppings

$1 + _5C_1 + _5C_2 + _5C_3 + _5C_4 + _5C_5$
$1 + 5 + 10 + 10 + 5 + 1 = 32$

16. $2/25,827,165 = 0.000000077$

17. 24

18. 20,160

19. (a) 362,880   (b) 3024

20. 72

21. (a) 40,320   (b) 336   (c) 1680

22. 131,040

23. 72

24. 95,040

25. 1,000,000,000

26. 26,970

27. 210

28. $_{10}C_4 \times _{14}C_4 = 210,210$

29. 84

30. 65,780

Practice Set 6-7

1. $\frac{5}{42}$

2. $\frac{125}{729}$

3. $\frac{1}{5}$

4. $\frac{1}{4}$

5. $\frac{1}{14}$

6. $\frac{1}{8}$

7. $\frac{3}{14}$

8. $\frac{1}{4}$

9. (a) 720 (b) 360

10. (a) pn, pd, pq, nd, nq, dq

    (b) $\frac{1}{2}$ (c) $\frac{5}{6}$

11. $\frac{1}{14}$

12. $\frac{3}{800}$

13. (a) $0.940606 = 94.1\%$ (b) Answers will vary.

14. $\frac{1}{2}$

15. $\frac{1}{5}$

16. $\frac{253}{9996}$

17. $\frac{2}{39}$

18. $\frac{5}{28}$

19. $\frac{1}{12}$

20. $\frac{1}{8}$

21. 1000

22. 8,000,000

23. Answers will vary.

24. 10 billion in number are possible, and so long as the total population alive at any one time does not exceed this number, then it is possible.

Chapter 6 Review Problems

1. A probability is a mathematical calculation of the likelihood of a given event occurring in preference to all other possible events that could occur in a given situation (or experiment). In other words, it is the proportion (or fraction) of times that a particular outcome will occur.

2. In problems where several outcomes are possible, use the addition rule if the word *or* is used to connect the events and use the multiplication rule if the word *and* is used.

3. A probability is the proportion of outcomes considered favorable compared to the total number of possible results. The odds of an event compares outcomes considered favorable to the number of outcomes considered unfavorable.

4. $\frac{5}{36}$

5. 0

6. $\frac{5}{12}$

7. $\frac{7}{20}$

8. $\frac{13}{20}$

9. $\frac{1}{114}$

10. $\frac{63}{200}$

11. $\frac{6}{25}$

12. $\frac{63}{113}$

13. $\frac{24}{49}$

14. There are three face cards (K, Q, J) per suit (4 suits); thus, there are 12 face cards. This means that there are 40 nonface cards in the deck: $s = 12$, $f = 40$. Odds in favor of drawing a face card $= 12:40 = 3:10$.

15. $10^9 = 1$ billion

16. Yes, because by 2050 AD the population will be well over one billion.

17. $\frac{73}{75}$ or about a 97% chance

18. $\frac{92}{365}$ or about a 25% chance

19. $\frac{22}{43}$

20. $\frac{26}{43}$

21. $\frac{5}{23}$

22. 210

23. 294,000

24. 455

25. 2:373

26. 24

27. undefined

28. undefined

29. 35

30. 2520

31. 1771

Chapter 6 Test

1. $S = \{H1, H2, H3, H4, H5, H6, T1, T2, T3, T4, T5, T6\}$

2. $\frac{1}{12}$

3. $\frac{1}{4}$

4. $\frac{17}{30}$

5. $\frac{29}{60}$

6. $\frac{17}{45}$

7. 8,985,600

8. 1:1

9. $\frac{1}{2}$

10. 0.41

11. 6

12. 1

13. $\frac{1}{6}$

14. Only nine plates out of all possible plates will have all four numbers the same; $9 \times 9 \times 9 \times 9 = 6561$ different possible plates

$$\frac{9}{6561} = \frac{1}{729}$$

15. $\frac{1}{2}$

16. $\frac{1}{13}$

17. $\frac{1}{2704}$

18. $\frac{11}{26}$

19. $P(\text{Ringo wins}) = \frac{1}{4}$ $P(\text{Bonnie wins}) = \frac{1}{16}$

    $P(\text{Clyde wins}) = \frac{5}{13}$ $P(\text{Zero wins}) = \frac{2}{5}$

20. There are only two choices for children, boy or girl, each time, so for four births, $2 \times 2 \times 2 \times 2 = 16$ possible combination of boys and girls. But because order is not specified, many of the groupings are the same. If you list all possible combinations, 6 of the 16 will contain BBGG, $\frac{6}{16} = \frac{3}{8}$.

21. 720

22. 0

23. $\frac{1}{1024}$

24. $\frac{2}{5}$

25. $\frac{3}{4}$

26. $\frac{3}{20}$

Chapter 7

Practice Set 7-1

1. inferential
2. descriptive
3. descriptive
4. inferential
5. descriptive
6. descriptive
7. descriptive
8. inferential
9. descriptive
10. inferential
11. quantitative
12. qualitative
13. quantitative
14. qualitative
15. qualitative
16. qualitative
17. qualitative
18. quantitative
19. quantitative
20. qualitative
21. cluster sample
22. systematic sample
23. simple random sample
24. stratified sample
25. convenience sample
26. cluster sample
27. stratified sample
28. stratified sample
29. random sample
30. convenience sample

Practice Set 7-2

1. {answers will vary}
2. {should match the definitions}
3. mean = 4.6; median = 3.5; mode = 2; best avg. is the mean
4. mean = 4.7; median = 4.5; mode = none; best avg. is the mean
5. mean = 12.6; median = 6; mode = 9; best is the median
6. mean = 242.5; median = 245; mode = 245; best avg. is the mean
7. mean = 3.65; median = 2.865; mode = none; best is the median
8. mean = 23.9; median = 24.15; mode = none; best avg. is the mean
9. A relatively few individuals with huge incomes (like Michael Jordan and Bill Gates) "drag" the mean average off center. The median income is the best for most comparisons for persons and families of "normal" incomes.
10. (a) $39.20   (b) $38.30   (c) $38   (d) $45
11. (a) mode   (b) mean   (c) median
    (d) mean
12. (a) median   (b) mean   (c) mode
    (d) mean   (e) mode
13. (a) mean = 4.57; median = 4; mode = 4
    (b) The mean becomes 5 and the others remain unchanged.
14. GPA = 3.4
15. 38.6 mph
16. 110
17. The median is best here, $\tilde{x} = 22$.
18. mean = 0.125°C; median = 0.5°C; mode = 0°C
19. {answers will vary}
20. 5
21. No, because doctors earn much more than a receptionist or any others on the staff, so the mean is skewed toward their salaries.

22. The mean would increase by $2000.

23. It will raise the mean average by 4%.

24. {answers will vary based on survey results}

25. {answers will vary}

26. {answers will vary, but one or two numbers need to be very large compared to the others}

Practice Set 7-3

1.
```
0 | 6 5 4 8 9 3 8 4
1 | 5 2 6 2 2 1 0 4 3 0 2 6 5 2 1
2 | 5 1 5 2 9
3 | 1 6
```

2. (a)

Classes	Frequency
50–54	1
45–49	2
40–44	3
35–39	4
30–34	6
25–29	21
20–24	11
15–19	2

(b)

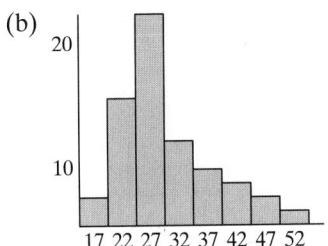

(c) skewed left; relatively few higher speeds

3. (a)

Classes	Frequency
50–54	2
45–49	0
40–44	2
35–39	2
30–34	3
25–29	11
20–24	5
15–19	13
10–14	7

(b)

Bimodal distribution

4.

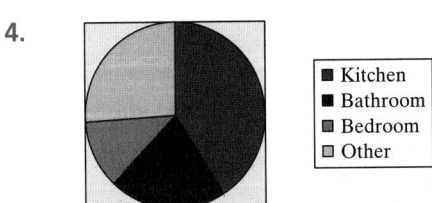

5. (a) 3%   (b) yes (37% > 33.3%)
(c) 3,675,000   (d) Oceania

6. (a)

Classes	Frequency
500–549	1
450–499	0
400–449	3
350–399	3
300–349	4
250–299	2
200–249	8
150–199	7
100–149	10
50–99	10
0–49	6

(b)

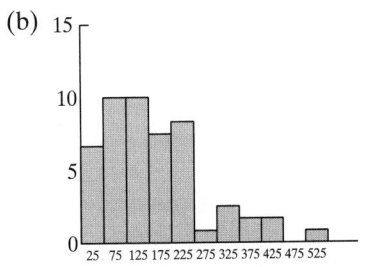

7. (a)

Classes	Frequency
1–5	8
6–10	11
11–15	13
16–20	11
21–25	4
26–30	4
31–35	2
36–40	3
41–45	2
46–50	2

(b)

Skewed left

8. (a)

```
1 | 9899
2 | 078729299
3 | 1023951
4 | 1536
5 | 311584663
6 | 533
```

(b)

Classes	Frequency
61–67	3
54–60	5
47–53	3
40–46	4
32–39	4
25–31	8
18–24	5

(c)

9. (a)

Classes	Frequency
70–74	8
75–79	15
80–84	8

(b)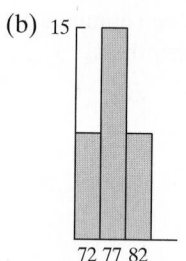

10. (a)

Classes	Frequency
52–57	1
46–51	1
40–45	4
34–39	5
28–33	14
22–27	21
16–21	4

(b)

```
5 | 2
4 | 13138
3 | 4612087253
2 | 279133282328174993578476658958536
1 | 86
```

11. {various graphs are possible; this is a stem-and-leaf plot}

```
1 | 8,8,9,9,9
2 | 0,0,2,2,2,3,3,5,7
3 |
4 | 2,3
5 | 7
```

12. {answers will vary depending on survey results}

Practice Set 7-4

1. All data items are identical.

2. The first set; larger differences

3. mean $= 4.5$; $R = 9$; $s = 3$

4. mean $= 11$; $R = 18$; $s = 6.1$

5. mean $= 8.4$; $R = 18$; $s = 6.9$

6. mean $= 2$; $R = 0$; $s = 0$

7. mean $= 7$; $R = 9$; $s = 3.3$

8. mean $= 123$; $R = 6$; $s = 2.2$

9. mean $= 5$; $R = 12$; $s = 3.6$

10.

	mean	R	s
A	10	0	0
B	10	19	8.3
C	10	19	10.4
D	11	18	10.4

11. For Sec. 1: $R = 80$, $s = 24$; for Sec. 2: $R = 80$, $s = 27$; equal R's might lead you to conclude that the sets were identical but the standard deviation numbers tell you that the sets are really different.

12. S#1: $R = 82$, $s = 21.8$
    S#2: $R = 80$, $s = 26.6$

13. Forever batteries because they have the smallest standard deviation.

14. Prices being equal, high-pressure sodium lamps; higher s is offset by much longer life.

15. Small standard deviation; indicates a consistent packing process

16. (a) 240 days; 300 days
    (b) He is likely correct as it is unlikely that a pregnancy will last longer than 10 months (300 days).

17. (a) The mean increases by the amount added to all numbers, but the standard deviation does not change.
    (b) Since 3% of each amount is different, different amounts are being added to each number; thus, both the mean and standard deviation will change.

18. 74, 79, 87

19. The mean will increase by the amount added. The range and standard deviation will not change.

20. The first set, greater differences between numbers

21. The standard deviation would not change.

22. It would rise by 4%.

Practice Set 7-5

1. 34.1%

2. 2.3%

3. 15.9%

4. about 1260 hours

5. 84.1%

6. 95.4%

7. 71,550

8. 0.04 (or about 4%)

9. 0.067 (or about 7%)

10. about 89%

11. 922 hours

12. 1046 hours

13. 1397 hours

14. 1988

15. 0.159 (or about a 16% chance)

16. 0.001 (or about 0.1%)

17. 0.988 (or about a 99% chance)

18. mean $= 36.3$ in.; $s = 15.1$ in.

19. From 21.2 in. to 51.4 in. 95% of the time it will be below 61 in.

20. The area under the curve to the right of 65 in. ($z = -1.4$) on the baseline

21. The area under the curve to the left of 63 in. ($z = -1.8$) on the baseline

22. The area under the curve between 74 in. ($z = 0.4$) and 64 in. ($z = -1.6$) on the baseline

23. 85%

24. No, because a percentile rank compares scores with other scores, not with the maximum score it may be possible to make.

25. Ray, because his *z*-score (1.4) is larger than Susan's (1.3)

26. about 3110 customers (62.2%)

27. $z = 0.8$

28. $z = 0.86$

29. It would mean that your test score was below the class average of 78; 70

30. 86.8

31. 75%

32. about 16%

33. 75

34. about 2.2%

35. 70 and 130

36. 119.5 or about 120

37. 67%

38. about 1.2%

Practice Set 7-6

1. Negative; as age increases, price decreases.

2. Negative; as age increases, life expectancy decreases (unfortunately).

3. Negative; as weight increases, mileage decreases.

4. Positive; as height increases, weight increases (in general).

5. (a) independent variable: education; dependent variable: personal income
   (b) strong positive correlation
   (c) As the years of education increase, personal income increases.

6. (a) independent variable: number of officers; dependent variable: number of muggings
   (b) strong negative correlation
   (c) As the number of officers increases, the number of muggings decreases.

7. 3.4

8. (a) 80   (b) 152

9. 2,787

10. $84,200

11. (a)

(b) no

12. (a)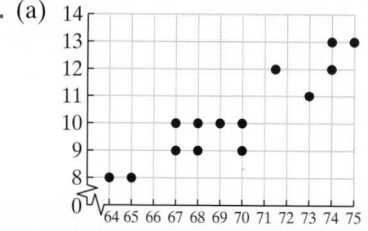

(b) $r = 0.92$, a strong correlation
(c) $y' = 0.45x - 21$
(d) size 9

13. (a)

(b) a weak correlation
(c) $y' = 1.6x + 92.5$
(d) $r = 0.64$ (e) 124.5 lb

14. (a) $y' = 1.4x + 22.9$
(b) $43,900
(c) $r = 0.52$ (weak)

15. (a)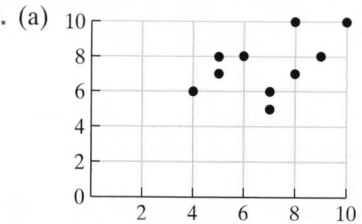

(b) somewhat linear

16. $y' = 0.5x + 4$, $r = 0.55$, score = 8

Chapter 7 Review Problems:

1. Descriptive statistics makes no predictions or guesses. It summarizes a population of data. Inferential statistics takes descriptive data and uses it to help make "educated guesses" about the data or about the group from which the data were gathered.

2. Quantitative data is data that can be "quantified" (i.e., it has amounts or numbers associated with it). Qualitative data is generally nonnumerical in nature.

3. cluster sample

4. convenience sample

5. stratified sample

6. mean = 14; median = 14; mode = none; $R = 8$; $s = 2.7$

7. mean = 17.3; median = 8.5; mode = 8; $R = 55$; $s = 17.2$

8. The data in #7 has the most variability. The larger value of the standard deviation tells us this.

9. For the data in #6, the mean average is best. The numbers are all relatively in the same size category. For data in #7, the median is the best average because the relatively large value of 57 drags the mean average off center for the group.

10.

Classes	Frequency
13–14	4
11–12	5
9–10	5
7–8	13
5–6	12
3–4	11

11.

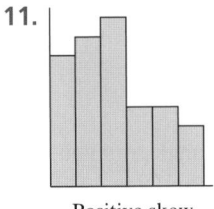

Positive skew

12. 16%

13. 50%

14. 81.8%

15. $z_{88 \text{ on math}} = 1.6$ and $z_{88 \text{ on history}} = 1.0$. The z-scores indicate that you would be farther above average for the math group than for the history group.

16. 0.034 (or about 3%)

17. 0.271 (or about 27%)

18.

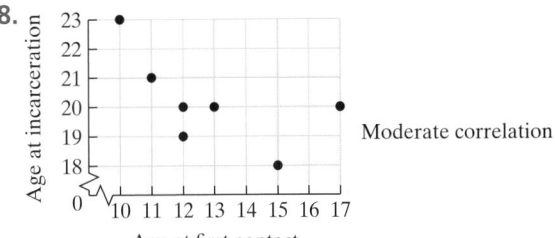

Moderate correlation

19. $y' = 25.3 - 0.40x$

20. 19.7 yrs

21. $r = -0.61$

22. a weak negative correlation

Chapter 7 Test

1. quantitative

2. qualitative

3. qualitative

4. quantitative

5. data set B

6. For data set A, the mean average; for data set B, the median

7. mean = 36.5; median = 36; mode = 36; $R = 12$; $s = 3.9$

8. median = M; $R = H$ to L

9.
```
0 | 3
1 | 2 7 0 8 8 9 2 8
2 | 7 7 2 9 1 6 1 8 9 1 6
3 | 0 5 8 6 5 8 2 3 2 1 2 3 1 2
4 | 2 7 1 5 3
5 | 1
```

10. normal distribution

11. about 16%

12. $z = -3$

13. grade $= 88.75$

14. 0.977 (or about 98%)

15. 0.464 (or about 46%)

16. $z = 2$

17. 0.092 (or about 9%)

18. 146 lb

19. $r = 0.8$ (interpretations will vary)

20.
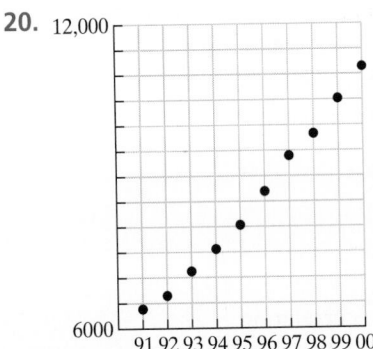

21. $y' = 544x - 1077816$

22. 13,448

Chapter 8

Practice Set 8-1

1. 182.25 in.^{2}

2. 36 cm

3. approx. 158–160 plants

4. 35 bags

5. 74 ft of molding; 37 yd^2 of carpet

6. 7 gal

7. 88.18 ft^2

8. 21.3 ft^2

9. 314 plants

10. 56.5 ft $\approx$ 57 ft

11. 35.55 in.^{2}

12. 45.4 in.^{2}

13. No

14. Yes

15. The 16-inch pizza is a better buy.

16. The rectangular pizza

17. 123.61 m^2

18. 2664 cm^2

19. (a) \$0.75 per ft^2
(b) \$172.50 per front ft
(c) \$32,670 per acre

20. \$457.33

21. (a) four times the area, twice the perimeter
(b) one-fourth the area, one-half the perimeter
(c) nine times the area, three times the perimeter
(d) four times the area, twice the perimeter

22. (a) four times the area, twice the circumference
(b) one-fourth the area, half the circumference
(c) four times the area, twice the circumference

23. 78.5%

24. No

25. (a) $h \approx -1.3w + 10$ ft

(b)
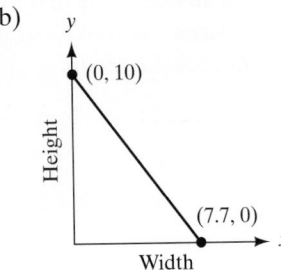

(c)

w	0	1	2	3
h	10	8.7	7.4	6.1

(d) Theoretically, an infinite number

Practice Set 8-2

1. The triangle must be a right triangle and you must know the length of two sides.

2. Yes, because the side lengths correctly solve the Pythagorean Theorem.

3. $c = 15$

4. $a = 24.5$

5. $a = 10.4$

6. $c = 63.6$

7. $b = 24$

8. $b = 24$

9. 24 ft

10. 5.5 ft

11. 9.4 m

12. No

13. 24.9 = 25-in. TV

14. 127.3 ft

15. 68.7 mi

16. $P = 12$ mi; $A = 6$ mi^2

17. 20.7 in.

18. 29.7 ft

19. 17.12 ft

20. 39.4 in.

21. $A = 120$ cm^2; $P = 60$ cm

22. 14 cm^2

23. 8.94 units

24. 7.2 units

25. No

26. No

27. 7.07 in.

Practice Set 8-3

1. To make drawings in two dimensions that are true representations of what we see in three dimensions with our eyes.

2. No, only drawings designed to mimic depth (3-D) are perspective drawings.

3. The line on which the principal vanishing point in a perspective drawing is located

4. The point at which all "parallel" lines of sight appear to converge

5. The term *symmetry* implies that balance or a regular pattern exists.

6. An object that can be rotated less than one complete rotation ($< 360°$) and coincide with itself has rotational symmetry. If an object and its mirror reflection are identical in all respects, then the object has reflection symmetry. (Objects chosen will vary.)

7. Answers will vary.

8. Answers will vary.

9. Answers will vary.

10. Answers will vary.

11. Answers will vary.

12. Answers will vary.

13. Answers will vary.

14. Answers will vary.

15. Answers will vary.

16. Answers will vary.

17. horizontal symmetry: B, C, D, E, H, I, O, X.
    vertical symmetry: A, H, I, M, O, T, U, V, W, X, Y.
    neither horizontal nor vertical symmetry: F, G, J, K, L, N, P, Q, R, S, Z

18. The letter O

19. H, I, O, S, X, Z

20. A, B, C, D, E, F, G, J, K, L, M, N, P, Q, R, T, U, V, W, Y

21. 120°

22. 90°

23. 72°

24. $\dfrac{360°}{\text{number of sides}}$ = the number of degrees of rotation

25.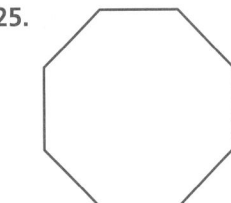

formula: $\dfrac{360°}{\text{number of sides}} = \dfrac{360°}{8} = 45°$

26. a.

b.

c.

27. a.

b.

c.

28.

1	3	4
2	3	
1	2	

Practice Set 8-4

1. $\left(\dfrac{16 \text{ ft}}{1 \text{ in.}}\right)(21 \text{ in}) = 336 \text{ ft}$

2. $\left(\dfrac{1 \text{ in.}}{16 \text{ ft}}\right)48 \text{ ft} = 3 \text{ in.}$

3. $\left(\frac{3}{4}\right)(175 \text{ cm}) = 131.25 \text{ cm}$

4. $\frac{45}{75} = \frac{9}{15}$, so the sides of the smaller triangle are $\frac{9}{15}$ the length of the sides in the larger triangle

5. $\left(\dfrac{800 \text{ cm}}{1 \text{ cm}}\right)(42.2 \text{ cm}) = 33760 \text{ cm} = 337.6 \text{ m}$ long

$\left(\dfrac{800 \text{ cm}}{1 \text{ cm}}\right)(8.2 \text{ cm}) = 6560 \text{ cm} = 65.6 \text{ m}$ wide

6. $(225 \text{ ft})\left(\dfrac{12 \text{ in.}}{\text{ft}}\right)\left(\dfrac{1 \text{ in.}}{144 \text{ in.}}\right) = 18.75 \text{ in. long} =$
17 in. wingspan

7. $\left(\frac{5000}{1}\right)(8) = 40,000 \text{ cm} = 400 \text{ m}$

8. $(14 \text{ km})\left(\dfrac{1 \text{ cm}}{5 \text{ km}}\right) = 2.8 \text{ cm}$

9. 1 in = 232 ft

10. 1 in = 243 ft

11. $\left(\dfrac{0.5 \text{ in.}}{50 \text{ mi}}\right)(600 \text{ mi}) = 6 \text{ in.}$

12. $(250 \text{ ft})\left(\dfrac{1 \text{ in.}}{20 \text{ ft}}\right) = 12.5 \text{ in.;}$

$(120 \text{ ft})\left(\dfrac{1 \text{ in.}}{20 \text{ ft}}\right)6 \text{ in.; } 12.5 \text{ in. by } 6 \text{ in.}$

13. Answers will vary.

14. Answers will vary.

15. $610 + 987 = 1597; 987 + 1597 = 2584; 1597 + 2584$
$= 4181; 2584 + 4181 = 6765$
#15 + #16 = #17; #16 + #17 = #18; #17 + #18 =
#19; #18 + #19 = #20

16. $\frac{6765}{4181} = 0.6180\ldots$

17. The decimal portion of the two numbers is essentially the same.

18. $1.6180; \frac{1}{1.6180} = 0.6108$

19. $(23 \text{ ft})(1.618) = 37.214 \text{ ft} = 37 \text{ ft } 2.6 \text{ in.}$

20. $(9 \text{ cm})(1.6180) = 14.562 \text{ cm} = 14.6 \text{ cm}$

21. $(45.5 \text{ cm})(1.618) = 73.6 \text{ cm; } (45.4 \text{ cm})/(1.618) =$
28.1 cm

22. $(36 \text{ in.})(1.6180) = 58.248 \text{ in.} = 58.2 \text{ in. or}$

$\dfrac{36 \text{ in.}}{1.6180} = 22.2496\ldots \text{ in.} = 22.2 \text{ in.}$

23. $\dfrac{w}{5 \text{ in.}} = 1.62$; $w = (1.62)(5 \text{ in.}) = 8.1$ in. wide

   $\dfrac{l}{8.1 \text{ in.}} = 1.62$; $l = (1.62)(8.1 \text{ in.}) = 13.1$ in. long

24. $\dfrac{9 \text{ cm}}{w} = 1.62$; $w = \dfrac{9 \text{ cm}}{1.62} = 5.56$ cm wide

   $\dfrac{5.56 \text{ cm}}{h} = 1.62$; $h = \dfrac{5.56 \text{ cm}}{1.62} = 3.4$ cm high

Practice Set 8-5

1. Pitch refers to how our ears interpret different frequencies of sound. The higher the frequency of a sound wave, the higher the pitch we would hear.

2. Their frequencies (which are called "pitch" as well) are different.

3. A recording in which the actual wave form is copied as closely as physically possible

4. An analog recording reproduces the wave form itself as nearly as possible. A digital recording records the frequency of the sound as a number.

5. Frequencies are measured numerically and recorded as numbers in short strings.

6. Sound and light

7. $(261.626 \text{ Hz})(2) = 523.252$ Hz is one octave higher
   $(261.626 \text{ Hz})/2 = 130.813$ Hz is one octave lower

8. $(110 \text{ Hz})(2) = 220$ Hz is one octave higher;
   $(110 \text{ Hz})/2 = 55$ Hz is one octave lower

9. $(392 \text{ Hz})(1.05946) = 415.3$ Hz

10. $\dfrac{392 \text{ Hz}}{1.05946} = 369.998 \ldots \text{ Hz} = 370$ Hz

11. 2

12. (3 quarter notes/measure)(2 eighth notes/quarter note) = 6 eighth notes/measure

13. 3

14. (3 eighth notes/measure)(2 sixteenth/eighth notes) = 6 sixteenth notes/measure

15. 1 quarter-note

16. 1 quarter-note

17. 1 eighth-note

18. 1 eighth-note

19. None are required.

20. 1 eighth-note

Practice Set 8-6

1. 28,733 people

2. 11,819 deer

3. In 10 years: 11,668,044; in 50 years; 8,643,900

4. 138,225 persons

5. 10,780 students

6. after 30 sec: 46.7 g; after 2 min: 1.28 g

7. 5 sec, 9 sec

8. 1 sec, 13 sec

9. 6 sec, 8 sec

10. 5 sec

11. $\{5, -3\}$

12. $\{0.851, -2.35\}$

13. $\{2.18, 0.15\}$

14. $\{4.24, -4.24\}$

15. $\{-1.5, 3\}$

16. $\{0, 3.5\}$

17. 2 sec, 5 sec

18. 200 sec = 3.3 min

19. 33 sec

20. 72 units

21. 170 chairs

22. 120 machines

23. (a) P vs. A: nonlinear; P vs. D: linear
    (b) $M = 0.03$ atm/ft; they are not all the same due to rounding.

Chapter 8 Review Problems

1. 21.3 in.^{2}

2. $P = 70$ m; $A = 186$ m^2

3. $12.02

4. 276.5 ft^2

5. (a) 1492.4 ft^2 (b) $3693.50

6. 17 ft

7. 84.9 ft

8. Yes, by the Pythagorean theorem

9. 21.6 in.

10. Answers will vary.

11. Answers will vary.

12. Answers will vary.

13. (a) vertical (b) horizontal (c) vertical (d) neither

14. $\dfrac{50\ cm}{75\ cm} = \dfrac{2}{3}$

15. (32)(4.125 in.) = 132 in. = 11 ft

16. $\dfrac{32.4\ cm}{1.62} = 20$ cm

17. (35 mi)(1 in./20 mi) = 1.75 in.

18. Frequency is a measure of the number of vibrations (waves) per second. Pitch is how high or low a frequency sounds to the human ear.

19. 27.5 Hz

20. 6

21. 151,242

22. 45,359 bacteria

23. 769,112 persons

24. {10.4, −0.39}

25. 2 sec

26. 8

Chapter 8 Test

1. 4.4 ft^2

2. (a) $A = 370.125$ ft^2; $P = 80$ ft   (b) $1026.07

3. 25.6 ft

4. 2.9 cm

5. (a) 65.94 in. = 5.495 ft   (b) approx. 961 times

6. On the horizon line

7. O

8. O, X

9. $(6250\ m)\left(\dfrac{1\ cm}{2500\ m}\right) = 2.5$ cm

10. $(75\ ft)\left(\dfrac{1\ ft}{87\ ft}\right) = 0.862\ldots$ ft = 10.3 in.

11. No

12. 77.8 in. or 29.6 in.

13. The legal pad–size paper

14. Analog recordings are essentially copies of the actual physical wave pattern, whereas digital recordings are simple numbers.

15. 3520 Hz

16. Sound and light waves

17. The number of quarter notes per measure is different, three in 3/4 time and four in 4/4 time.

18. 145,230 persons

19. {4.22, −0.55}

20. (b) 156 ft   (c) 6.3 sec

Index